UNITED STATES NATIONAL MUSEUM

BULLETIN 219

WASHINGTON, D.C.

SMITHSONIAN INSTITUTION

1960

The National Watercraft Collection

by

Howard I. Chapelle

Curator of Transportation

MUSEUM OF HISTORY AND TECHNOLOGY

of the

UNITED STATES NATIONAL MUSEUM

Publications of the United States National Museum

The scientific publications of the United States National Museum include two series, *Proceedings of the United States National Museum* and *United States National Museum Bulletin*.

In these series are published original articles and monographs dealing with the collections and work of the Museum and setting forth newly acquired facts in the fields of Anthropology, Biology, History, Geology, and Technology. Copies of each publication are distributed to libraries and scientific organizations and to specialists and others interested in the different subjects.

The *Proceedings*, begun in 1878, are intended for the publication, in separate form, of shorter papers. These are gathered in volumes, octavo in size, with the publication date of each paper recorded in the table of contents of the volume.

In the *Bulletin* series, the first of which was issued in 1875, appear longer, separate publications consisting of monographs (occasionally in several parts) and volumes in which are collected works on related subjects. *Bulletins* are either octavo or quarto in size, depending on the needs of the presentation. Since 1902 papers relating to the botanical collections of the Museum have been published in the *Bulletin* series under the heading *Contributions from the United States National Herbarium*.

This work forms number 218 of the *Bulletin* series.

REMINGTON KELLOGG
Director, United States National Museum

UNITED STATES GOVERNMENT PRINTING OFFICE, WASHINGTON, 1960
For sale by the Superintendent of Documents, U.S. Government Printing Office
Washington 25, D.C. • Price $3.50 (cloth)

Contents

Contents *(Continued)*

Illustrations

Illustrations (Continued)

Illustrations (*Continued*)

Illustrations (*Continued*)

Illustrations (Continued)

INTRODUCTION

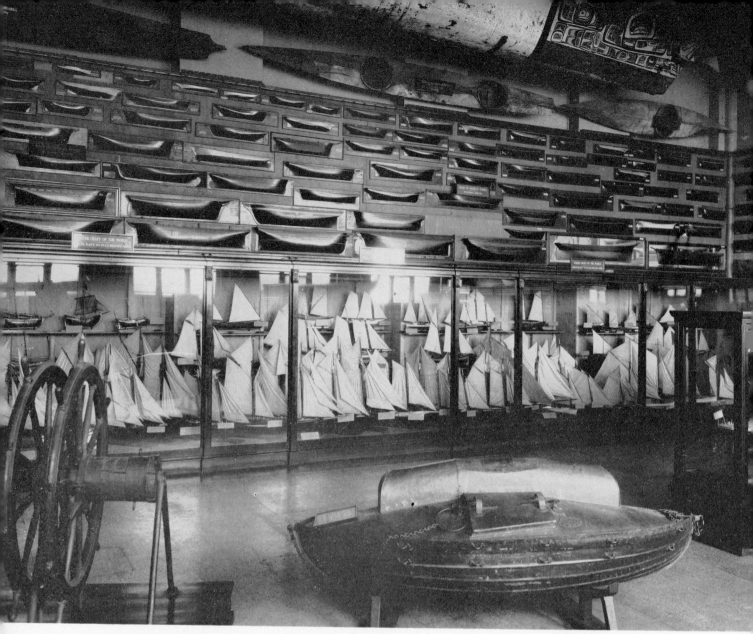

OLD WATERCRAFT HALL IN THE U.S. NATIONAL MUSEUM, showing a portion of the half-model collection and many of the rigged models of fishing boats. The picture was taken before 1930. (*Smithsonian photo 28006–a.*)

THE WATERCRAFT COLLECTION in the United States National Museum, Smithsonian Institution, was established in 1884 as the "Section of American Naval Architecture" by Captain Joseph William Collins, who served as unofficial curator for the first years of its existence. Captain Collins was a former Gloucester fishing-schooner master employed by the U.S. Fish Commission, and he had been responsible in some measure for setting up the American fishery exhibits at two international fisheries expositions, at Berlin in 1880 and London in 1883, and a world's exposition at New Orleans in 1884–85. Later he formed the fisheries exhibits at the World's Columbian Exposition at Chicago in 1892, and the American exhibit at the International Fisheries Exposition at Bergen in 1898.

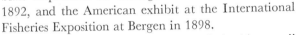

The "Section of American Naval Architecture" served as the repository for the models being used in the American exhibits at these international expositions, and many of the early models became damaged or lost during the years they were being shipped to and from expositions.

The Collection

The basic collection consisted of a large number of builder's half-models used in the construction of vessels, and was almost entirely of New England fishing schooners. Most of the models were identified and were cataloged by the name or names of the vessels built on the individual model. In addition to the half-models were many rigged models of noted fishing schooners and of small American fishing craft from nearly all fishing areas of the United States. Some models of foreign fishing boats were in the collection; many of these were obtained at the Centennial Exposition of 1876 and this collection was later enlarged by models obtained from foreign exhibits at the New Orleans, Chicago, and Bergen expositions.

The fishery models had been collected with three distinct objectives. To show the historical development of the New England fishing schooner, to show all important types of American fishing craft, and to show superior or improved designs of fishing vessels, particularly of fishing schooners, some of which were donated by notable designers. Historical development of the fishing schooner was illustrated by both half-models and rigged models; thus the collection included representations of old vessels as well as those of the then modern types. The rigged models of small craft were typical examples of their individual types, hence there were rarely two models of the same type. A few half-models of small craft were collected, apparently as examples. Improved vessel designs were represented by builder's half-models and by a few rigged models; one of the latter and one of the half-models had received awards at an exposition.

The rigged models of fishing schooners, distinguished by surprising accuracy, were the result of the pride New England fishermen were taking in their schooners at the time the collection was being formed. It had become the fashion, particularly in Gloucester and Boston, for schooner owners and vessel-managing firms to order a scale model of each new vessel built, particularly if she were considered fast and handsome. This interest in scale models was perhaps created by the numerous international fisheries expositions and world's expositions that followed the Centennial Exposition of 1876. Exhibited at one of these expositions, a good model might attract favorable comment or be awarded a medal of excellence and thus bring desirable publicity to the builder and to the owner or managing firm. Models were exhibited in the offices of owners or managers, just as scale models today are exhibited in steamship and airline agencies.

The rigged models of fishing schooners were usually built by a very few skilled ship carpenters, each a master builder, at Gloucester and Rockport, Massachusetts, of whom Thomas Irving and Lawrence Jensen were perhaps the most important. The models were carefully made; the hull form was obtained from the half-model, mould-loft takeoff, or lines plans; the rig was based upon the rigger's draught, or the sailmaker's plan. The deck arrangement was usually obtained by measurement of the finished vessel. Accuracy was necessary, as the completed model had to pass the critical inspection of the owner and skipper and, perhaps of the shipbuilder, none of whom would have much patience with inaccuracies in form, rig, or important detail. Then, of course the model could have been compared with the vessel it represented; now this can be done, and this only in a few instances, by comparing it with a photograph of the full-sized vessel.

However, there is one deficiency in these models; the model makers were not metal workers, and much of the spar ironwork is "faked" or even omitted entirely. Also, among the rigged models are some that were reconstructions of ancient types not in existence at the time the model was made. These are commonly inaccurate; the model builder had no plan or half-model to work from and resorted to imagination. These "historical models," invariably tubby and awkward, are examples of the human vanity that requires anything old to be represented as poor in design, so as to illustrate the greater intellect of the current generation.

The rigged models of small fishing craft were often made to the order of Captain Collins, who in some instances may have been able to furnish plans for them. Some were donated by boatbuilders and fishermen, others were purchased. While the average in workmanship in these models is not quite as high as in the fishing schooner models, on the whole they are reliable representations of their individual types.

After the "Section of American Naval Architecture" was established, Captain Collins, with the same objectives as for the fishing-craft models, made an intensive effort to collect models of commercial craft. In this he was only partly successful. The resulting collection was almost entirely of half-models, as commercial vessel owners did not have scale models built as a rule. Furthermore, such was the state of American shipbuilding at the time he undertook to assemble this collection that only a limited number of vessel types were being built and these were predominantly wooden sailing craft. Shipbuilding was then most active in New England, in the Middle Atlantic States, on the Great Lakes, and on the Pacific Coast, with some steamboat construction on the inland rivers. Hence, the original collection obtained a fine selection of half-models showing the development of the 2-mast coasting schooner, the trading brigantine, and of bark- and ship-rigged ocean freighters. Steamers, however, were rather poorly represented. The great sailing packets and clipper ships were no longer being built, so the collection showed only two models of the clipper ships of the 1850's and no

packet-ship model, although some packet schooners were represented among the half-models. Pilot schooners were quite well represented by half-models, but there were very few river steamers. The boat and shipbuilding of the South Atlantic States, the Gulf Coast, the Great Lakes, and the Pacific Coast were represented mainly by fishing craft.

By the early 1900's the Watercraft Collection, as it came to be called, had become recognized as one of the major collections in the U. S. National Museum. After the first World War the great interest in ship models and the numerous inquiries regarding models in the collection led, in 1923, to the compilation of National Museum Bulletin 127, *Catalogue of the Watercraft Collection*, by Carl W. Mitman, then Curator of Mineral and Mechanical Technology, employing as far as possible the manuscript notes left by Captain Collins. This catalog became a standard reference and remained in print for many years.

In the early 1930's, a Works Progress Administration project was set up under the direction of Eric V. Steinlein to carry out a program of marine historical research. This project, active for nearly 2 years, acquired for the Watercraft Collection many half-models as well as numerous plans, photographs, and drawings, all now part of the Historic American Merchant Marine Survey material. In the period just before the second World War a number of fine steamship models were presented to the collection and after that war the U. S. Maritime Commission donated a large number of models of standard merchant vessel types. Individual donors, of course, have added substantially to the acquisitions over the years.

As the *Catalogue of the Watercraft Collection* has long been out of print and the collection has grown so markedly since 1923, it has now become necessary to prepare a completely new catalog. At the same time, recent progress in marine historical research requires that the older models in the collection be re-examined as to identification, description, and dimensions, and the historical information contained in it re-assessed in the light of this research. In doing this it is necessary to acknowledge the work of the founder of the Watercraft Collection.

Captain Collins

Joseph William Collins was born at Isleboro, Maine, August 8, 1839, the son of David and Eliza B. (Sawyer) Collins. He received only a primary education in country schools, and when ten years old shipped as a

FISHERIES EXHIBIT IN THE U.S. NATIONAL MUSEUM DURING THE 1880's, when Captain J. W. Collins was serving the U.S. Commission of Fish and Fisheries. The Commission was established in 1871 through the efforts of Spencer F. Baird, Secretary of the Smithsonian Institution, and it was headed by him until his death in 1887. (*Smithsonian photo 46597.*)

hand on a fishing vessel. By home study and much reading he succeeded in educating himself; at 23 he became master of a fishing schooner; and in the 1860's he moved to Gloucester, where he was a very successful master of fishing schooners, particularly in the summer mackerel fishery. Among his commands were the schooners *Lizzie F. Choate* and the *Alice G. Wonson*. He married Pauline Coombs in 1861 and after her death, in 1884, he married Sallie Atkinson.

In the 1870's the Gloucester fishing fleet suffered tremendous losses in vessel property and in lives during a number of severe gales. These disasters so horrified Collins that he began to write articles for the newspapers, recommending an improved type of schooner to give greater safety. He also began to study half-model making, obtaining aid from the noted Boston shipbuilder and designer Dennsion J. Lawlor. Collins' newspaper articles attracted wide attention and

5

led indirectly to his being employed by the Commission of Fish and Fisheries, during 1879–80, to prepare a statistical report on the New England fisheries.

The Commission of Fish and Fisheries had been established in 1871 largely through the efforts of Spencer Fullerton Baird, then Secretary of the Smithsonian Institution, who until his death in 1887 held the post of Commissioner. (Popularly known as the U.S. Fish Commission, the Commission of Fish and Fisheries became in 1903 the Bureau of Fisheries, and in 1940 was consolidated with the Bureau of Biological Survey to form the Fish and Wildlife Service, Department of the Interior. During a minor reorganization in 1956 the official name became the U.S. Fish and Wildlife Service.)

Between 1880 and 1892, Captain Collins served the U. S. Fish Commission in numerous capacities, acting as captain of the fisheries research schooner *Grampus* in 1886–87 and holding administrative positions, mostly concerned with actual fishing methods and statistics. He wrote prolifically. In addition to 79 papers in the Fish Commission Reports, he wrote numerous magazine and newspaper articles, all dealing with the fisheries or with fishing craft. He also acted in a responsible position in the preparation of exhibits at the numerous International Fisheries Exposition and the World's Expositions that marked the last quarter of the 19th century. He was soon accepted, in Europe as well as in the United States, as an authority on fishing vessels and boats, and also on fishing gear. In the years 1880–85, when the Commission was considering construction of a fisheries research schooner, Captain Collins made models and designs for a number of proposals; finally the *Grampus* was built from one of his models. After his resignation from the Fish Commission in 1892, he became editor of *The Fishing Gazette* and later, president of the Commercial Fisheries Association. He was appointed U. S. Commissioner for the International Fisheries Exposition at Bergen, Norway, in 1898, and prepared a valuable but little known catalog of that Exposition. He became chairman of the Massachusetts Fish and Game Commission in 1899 and held this appointment at the time of his death in 1904.

The Models

Identification of old models, particularly of the builder's half-models, is often difficult. The donor usually had established the identification when these models were acquired, and normally this identification has proved reliable, but it has become obvious that errors have been made with respect to some models, for these either had the appearance of being of a far different date than that of the assigned vessel, or the Customhouse register dimensions could not be brought into a reasonable comparison with the scaled dimensions of the half-model.

The use of Customhouse register dimensions in the identification of half-models is not very satisfactory, particularly when the vessel in question was built in the United States before 1865. The old tonnage measurement used relatively few precise hull measurements; after 1865 greater precision was required, and a standard method of taking the measurements was employed that apparently had not existed earlier. In addition, improved measuring equipment, such as steel tapes, became available in the 1880's.

In any case, the registered dimensions of a vessel can seldom be made to comply precisely with the true dimensions of the hull as built or as designed. Indeed, it is difficult to establish any fixed proportion in the variation between the two; even in New England coasting and fishing schooners built after 1865 this variation often amounts to as much as 12 inches in each 100 feet of length. The registered length was taken from the stem rabbet to the center of the rudder post at deck level after this date. The registered beam was the greatest width over the plank. The depth was taken from the ceiling alongside the keelson to the underside of the deck plank of the upper, or tonnage, deck. The latter measurement is useless as an aid in identification unless there are very complete structural plans of the vessel available. In vessels built before 1865 identification by use of register dimensions is very difficult, not only because of the variations noted but because there were also some variations in the methods of measurement employed in various sections of the country. As a result, it is particularly difficult to identify the half-model of a clipper ship of the 1850's by the register dimensions, for the scaled dimensions of the half-model not infrequently depart from the register dimensions by 4 or 5 feet of length and by a foot or more in beam. This may be due partly to the indefinite position of the point of measurement at the bow, which under the old measurement law, was, "the forepart of the main stem above deck."

The variations in the real and register dimensions are, and were, due in part to the practical difficulties in taking the external registered length and beam

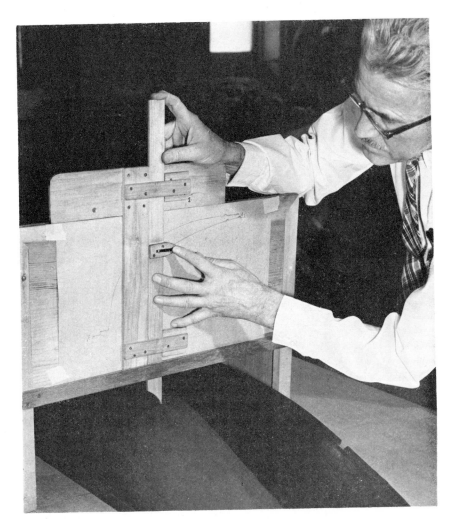

DEVICE FOR TAKING OFF LINES FROM HALF-MODEL. A piece of pencil lead projects through the small, spring-loaded block under the forefinger of the user's left hand. The vertical bar is held against the model by a slight pressure from the forefinger of the user's right hand. As he slides the frame across the top of the rack, the pencil point traces a line on the paper exactly parallel to the vertical sliding bar point resting on the model. The photograph shows one section completed and another being drawn. (*Smithsonian photo 46597–a.*)

when it is necessary to measure with staffs or foot rules over or around deck structures and where measurement points must be plumbed. The difficulty in identification is made greater by the rather common practice of wooden-ship builders of adding frames amidships in order to lengthen a hull over the designed length. This was particularly common among New England builders. In some models the process of adding length by inserting frames required refairing the middle body, with the result that the beam might also be slightly increased in real measurement. Hence one cannot be sure whether the variation between dimensions scaled from the half-model and those of the register require allowance for inserted frames or merely represent inaccuracy in the latter.

A practical example of the difference between real and register dimensions can be shown in the case of the American clipper ship *Challenge*, built at New York in 1951 by William H. Webb. The mould-loft offsets of this vessel exist and also a plan made with great care in England, while the vessel was in drydock. The registered length of the ship, by the old method in force when she was built, was 230 feet 6 inches and the beam 43 feet 2 inches. The loft dimensions and takeoff drawing show that the length of the vessel by the measurement system used at New York in 1857, had it been possible to measure accurately, was actually 227 feet and the beam 42 feet 10 inches.

Note should be made that another method of lengthening hulls under construction was sometimes used; the frame spacing was increased to give the desired increase over the design length. It seems possible that this was used in a few ships, fishing schooners, and coasters.

7

STANDARD LIFT HALF-MODEL WITH FASTENERS REMOVED AND THE LIFTS SLIGHTLY SPREAD. A quarter deck rail lift is shown. This model, in the author's collection, is of a Connecticut schooner, name unknown, of the pilot-boat type, built at Westbrook, Connecticut, about 1825–30. (*Smithsonian photo 45608–t.*).

The identification of rigged models has caused little difficulty for the few in the collection that are in question are usually the result of attempts to "reconstruct" some vessel without plans or precise knowledge of the ship whose name was assigned to the model.

Builder's half-models in the collection represent, in many cases, very useful evidence of the trend of design and the hull-form in certain classes of vessels. Since photographs of such models are of little value, scale drawings have been prepared of the more important of these; the lines have been taken off by a simple pantograph device that gives great accuracy if the half-model is well made, and plans have been prepared in the traditional manner, as though to be used in building. In some cases the existence of rigged models of these vessels has allowed much reconstruction in the plans, in others, paintings or photos have been used for this purpose. Occasionally the deck arrangement is marked on a model.

Half-models were the common means used to design American sailing vessels and boats, and are, in fact, still is use in many boatbuilding centers. There are three basic types of half-model: The lift model, the block model, and the hawk's nest, or crow's nest, model.

LIFT MODELS

The most common model in the Watercraft Collection is the lift model, which was also the last form of builder's model to be developed as a practical aid to boat and vessel design. This form of model is made up of horizontal planks or layers, each known as a "lift"; these are temporarily fastened together to form a solid block. The model was shaped from the block so formed. Two New England cities, Salem and Newburyport, Massachusetts, are claimed as the birthplace of the lift model, which came into use about 1790–95. The Salem claim is based on the half-model made by Enos Briggs, about 1795, for the ketch *Eliza;* that of Newburyport is based on a half-model, supposed to have been made before 1796 by its noted shipbuilder Orlando Merrill, now in the collection of the New York Historical Society. However, it is possible that the lift model was employed much earlier than 1795–96 and it may have been the result of a gradual evolution from a solid block model sawn into vertical sections. Isaac Webb is reputed to have introduced the lift model at New York. In early models the lifts were held together with wooden toggles passed through holes and secured under and on top of the model by small wedges, or the lifts were pegged together with tapered dowels. After about 1820–25 the lifts were secured by iron screws, each lift being fastened in turn to the one below. As a result, to take the lifts apart it is commonly necessary to begin with the uppermost lift.

Various refinements in the lift model were employed; for example thin veneer was sometimes inserted between each pair of lifts and shaped with the block. Another refinement was to use alternate lifts of white

8

pine and walnut, or mahogany, to make sharp contrasts in the change of lines exhibited in the half-model. Most of the half-models in the Watercraft Collection are of white pine, but white cedar and other easily worked woods were sometimes used; in the South yellow pine models were employed, but models of juniper and cypress were perhaps more common.

As a rule the "working" half-model is made without a backboard and without any decoration; after the model has been "taken off" and the lines "laid down" in the mould loft the model might be mounted and decorated to represent the appearance of the finished vessel or boat. Such models were often hung in the shipyard office and some yards had rather large collections. A model might be used by a number of yards in succession and the models in possession of a yard might therefore include some not made in that yard, or by its employees.

The half-model was usually made to the "moulded dimensions" of the vessel or boat; in other words, the model represented the shape of the hull at inside of plank or at the outside of the frames and to the underside of the decking and rail cap. Very few models were made to represent the hull at outside of plank; such models were usually made from a lines drawing and are decorative rather than working models. Exhibition models, highly decorated and well finished, were sometimes made to outside of plank, though a model was not employed in the actual design of a vessel or boat; such models are sometimes seen in yacht designers' offices.

The spacing of the lifts is usually at some single fixed measurement throughout the depth of the model; usually the lifts are of such a thickness that the distance between the seams separating them are of some even measurement at the scale of the model—say 6, 12, 18, or 24 inches. The larger the vessel represented by the model the greater the lift spacing, as a rule, but skilled designers commonly employed closely spaced lift seams, or lines, so as to obtain great precision in taking off for lofting. The upper, or sheer, lift was

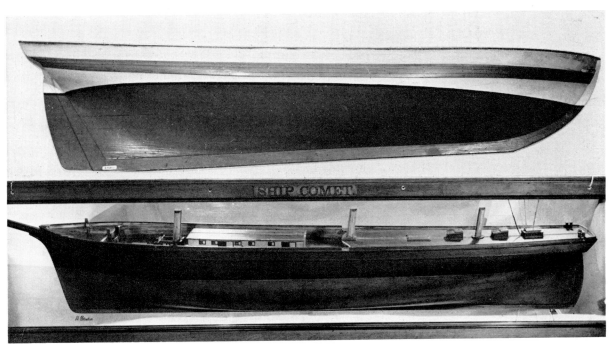

SEMIDECORATIVE LIFT MODEL (TOP) AND MIRROR-MOUNTED HALF-MODEL (BOTTOM). Models exhibited in shipyard offices commonly received the simple decorative treatment illustrated by the top model (USNM 315852; see p. 88). The stem, keel, post and rudder were usually secured to the back board, and masts and bowsprit stubs were sometimes attached. Occasionally a model was mounted on a mirror to give the illusion of a complete deck arrangement, as illustrated (bottom) by the half-model (USNM 76072; see p. 57) of the clipper ship *Comet*. (*Smithsonian photos—top, 45607–d; bottom, 45608.*)

sometimes made of a thick plank cut to the sheer on top and bottom and equal in depth to the height of bulwarks from the deck, or from top of the waterway in large ships. As an alternate, the depth of the bulwarks might be formed of laminated, thin lifts sprung to the sheer of the deck; the upper lift being cut to the deck sheer and made of a thick plank in each case.

The scales used by shipbuilders in making half-models varied with the size of the vessel. Large ships were modeled on ¼-, ⅓-, or ⅜-inch scales. Many of the clipper-ship models that have survived are on ⅛-inch scale. Fishing schooners and coasting vessels were usually on ⅜- or ½-inch scale. Small craft are commonly on ¾- or 1-inch scale. Occasionally some odd scale is encountered—⁵⁄₁₆, ⅝, or ³⁄₁₆ inch to the foot. A ⅛-inch scale was commonly considered too small to give sufficient accuracy; a few models on this scale have been found, but they were not practical so far as precision in taking off was concerned. Bulwark depths are often important in determining scale of a model; fishing schooners as a rule have from 18- to 26-inch bulwarks (moulded depth), those of coasters are from 3 to 4 feet, and of ships, 4 to 6 feet. The depth of the ships' bulwarks is usually to the main sheer; many had "monkey rails" also called "fancy rails," or false hammock rails, above the main sheer, thus higher bulwarks were obtained in fact than the model usually shows.

The half-model was shaped by eye to suit the judgment and artistic skill of its maker. The shipbuilder or his master carpenter, whichever made the model, however, had to satisfy the skipper of the new vessel as well as the owner that the model represented a vessel of the requisite qualities of seaworthiness, capacity, and speed. The tools used in making the model were various sizes of hollow gouges and chisels, a drawknife and spokeshave, small planes, scrapers, and sandpaper. Hollow- and round-sole planes were required.

Model-building practices varied somewhat; in the early development of the lift model, before 1815, it appears that models were usually shaped to the "height of breadth line" (that is, to the heights of the greatest beam at each frame). This was usually below the deck, and only the builder knew what to add to obtain the depth of hold and height of bulwarks. After 1815, models were usually made to the rail line but even as late as the early years of the 20th century schooner models were being made to the deck line, instead of to the rail line. In the 1850's duplicate models were made rather often, one by which to build

the ship and a more elaborate one to decorate the owner's office.

Taking off, or "lifting," the lines of the half-model, the first step in the construction of a ship or boat, required first that a large piece of paper on which to draw the model's lines, or, more commonly, that a smooth pine or spruce board, be prepared. The model was laid on the board or paper and its outline traced, the intersections of the top and bottom of each lift with bow and stern profiles were ticked off, and the model was then removed and the lift lines drawn as straight, horizontal lines on the profile drawing. Perpendicular to the lift lines, the builder then laid off lines representing frames at the scale dimension of their spacing. Sometimes he laid the model back on the drawing and transferred these frame spacings to the top of the model by ticking and then, by means of a trysquare, squared these across the top of the model from the back.

Next, the model was taken apart. The lowest lift was placed topside down on the profile drawing, its back coinciding exactly with its lift line in the profile plan and its ends coinciding exactly with the intersections of the lift line with bow and stern, and its outline was carefully traced. Each lift in turn was treated this way, until the top lift was reached. On this the topside outline was required. It was not feasible to attempt to treat this lift as the others were, since the sheer of the top would make tracing the outline inaccurate, at least amidships. Therefore it was usual to measure on the model with a compass the half breadth of each frame line and to transfer these measurements to the profile plan, using as a centerline either a straight line above the profile and parallel to the lifts below, or a lift line with ends projected enough outboard of the bow and stern to allow the ends of the top, or sheer line of the model to be squared down. Some builders applied the upper lift in the usual way and ticked off the top outline with a square and pencil, and sometimes, if the shape of the lift permitted and if it was thin enough, the top lift was pressed flat over each station in turn.

Now the builder was ready to make the full-size drawing of the hull form; an operation called "lofting," or "laying down." A large, smooth floor, the mould loft, was required or, as an alternate, a "scrieve board," or platform was constructed. If there were a large enough floor, the whole model profile would be drawn full size by scaling it from the drawing of the model. Usually in old yards if the keel was straight, only the frame shapes and the profiles of the

BUILDER'S BLOCK MODEL (USNM 316628) OF THE PRIVATEER *Snap Dragon* (see p. 88). Made before 1812 and the oldest half-model in the collection, it was shaped from a solid block of wood. To raise the deck level and thus alter the depth, a thin plank, or lift, was added to the top. Lines were probably taken off with a lead bar by the builder. (*Smithsonian photo 45608–m.*)

extreme bow and stern were drawn full size, but if the keel was curved this was not a desirable method. If the frames and ends of the hull were laid down, the scrieve board would suffice. The frames were lifted from the model drawing by scaling off in succession, at each frame line, the half breadth of each lift, and by then laying these off full size in the loft or on the scrieve board at the corresponding location, the lift lines, centerline, and profile having first been laid off, of course.

When all the half breadths of a frame had been transferred to the full-size drawing, the frame shape was swept in on the floor or platform by means of a batten (tacked down) and a pencil or chalk. This required a certain "eye," or skill, on the part of the man making the full-size drawings, for often he had to interpret the frame shape between measurement points, so that the frames would fair when being planked. Some yards having a large enough floor space in the mould loft laid off vertical sections through the frame shapes (properly called "buttocks" in the afterbody and "bow lines" in the forebody, but usually called buttocks only) and also added "diagonals" and faired these as long sweeping curves running the length of the hull (see lines plans in this catalog) to "prove" the frame shapes, that is to make sure they were fair and could be planked. Some models in the collection are so carefully made that the lines can be lifted with great precision; others are crudely made and much interpretation is required to reproduce their lines, particularly at the forefoot and at the stern post, where the model was not properly faired to the half breadth of the rabbet or of the keel, post, and stem.

BLOCK MODELS

The oldest form of half model is the block model, made of a single block of wood shaped to represent half the hull of the proposed vessel or boat. This style

HAWK'S NEST, OR CROW'S NEST, HALF-MODEL, WITH KEEL AND DEADWOOD FORM SHOWN. Mould-sections were at alternate frames, and sheer and deck lines were indicated by the use of battens tacked to moulds. The keel detail shown is unusual. One of the older forms of builder's half-models, this one, in the author's collection, is of the 3-masted Baltimore schooner *Flying Fish* of about 1806. (*Smithsonian photo 45607–c.*)

of half model was in use in England and in the colonies at least as early as 1715. The lines were taken off in various ways; the most usual was to trace the profile on a board and then to draw perpendiculars to the keel to represent frames. Next the model was fastened to this board so that its profile coincided with that on the backboard and saw cuts were made at each frame line in the model, care being taken that the saw cuts were vertical to the backboard and coincided exactly with the frame lines at the top and bottom of the model. By inserting note paper or cardboard in each saw cut the frame shape could be traced and, with suitable ordinates drawn, could be measured and transferred to the mould loft. Some builders took off the frame shapes with soft lead bars about $\frac{3}{16}$ inch square, but this required much practice to obtain reasonable accuracy. Others used a laborious template-cutting operation or had a form of pantograph that allowed a pencil point on a drawing board to move exactly parallel to the surface of the model at each station. The solid block model remained in use until the end of the 19th century on some sections of the American coast.

HAWK'S NEST MODELS

The third type of half-model was called the "hawk's nest," or "crow's nest," model and was particularly popular from 1780 to 1820 on the Atlantic seaboard. This model was made up of a plank backboard, or sawn-out profile of the hull, with plank sections mounted on it to represent mould frames. These were usually fastened to the profile, or backboard, by nailing from the back of the latter and were held rigid and vertical to the backboard by battens bent around the plank sections or by a deck or sheer piece. Lines were taken off by removing any battens that would interfere and then tracing the outline of each frame section on cardboard or paper. The earliest use of the hawk's nest model yet established is 1752, in England, but the model type was probably used in the late 17th century, along with the solid block model. This style of model was used in some isolated American areas as late as 1880 but, being quite difficult to shape, it was never as widely used as the block and lift models.

Using the Models

A vessel or boat may be as well shaped, or designed, by use of the half-model as by use of lines drawings, so far as form of hull is concerned. Methods were developed in the early 19th century by which the necessary basic calculations of naval architecture could be made from half-models.[3] Undoubtedly the half-model gives a more complete and precise impression of the hull form than does a lines drawing. The half model produces the same 3-dimensional effect as the finished vessel, something a lines drawing will not do. Hence a lines drawing may produce in the finished hull form an undesirable feature that would be discovered at once in a half-model. In general, the ability to design and judge hull form is more readily acquired by use of the half-model than by use of lines plans and other drawings. Many boatbuilders, ship carpenters, and even fishermen can quickly develop a good judgment of hull form through use of the half-model, whereas some well educated naval architects, using only drawings, never acquire sound judgment of form.

The accuracy with which a designer may convey his ideas to the loft and to the builder is as about as great with the half-model as with plans, if both are equally well made, and, of course, where builders are poorly trained, the half-model conveys more than do plans. The efficiency of the half-model in hull design is the reason why it still survives, in spite of the increased use of plans.

There were many other variations in model construction; one form combining horizontal with vertical lifts; the latter glued; to make what some call the "checkerboard" model, for the lifts were of various natural wood colors. This was a decorative model having no particular practical value, except to show the skill of its maker. In a more common form, the block with every frame, square, and cant was carefully cut, the whole mounted was on a backboard and fitted with planked wales and topsides after the lines had been taken off. This, too, was highly decorative, but it had practical advantages. Hawk's nest models completely planked after the lines were taken off are also sometimes found; these were very popular in England in the last half of the 19th century.

Historical note

The introductions that precede each section of this work cover much ground not illustrated by the models, but which should be known in order to appreciate the value of the collection, as well as its shortcomings. By treating as units in these introductions the important vessel types, a more detailed account of their development is possible.

CLIPPER SHIP *Nightingale*, BUILT AT PORTSMOUTH, NEW HAMPSHIRE, IN 1851. *(Smithsonian photo 44741.)*

MERCHANT SAIL

SURVIVING COLONIAL records in America show that the vessels and boats built in the individual colonies during the 16th and 17th centuries were of the national types of their mother countries. As would be expected, the Spanish were the first to establish extensive shipbuilding operations in the New World. By 1570 they had constructed dockyards in Cuba, Puerto Rico, and Campeche which were already well known for their ability to turn out fast-sailing ships of the *frigata* type; a long, low-waisted, narrow galley-ship fitted to carry her guns on a single deck and to row fast as well as to sail. Drake obtained some of these ships in the 1580's and afterward reported that two of them ran from Cape Florida to the Scilly islands in 23 days. The Spanish also built galleons in the American colonies; these were not all of the lofty sided type that were in the Armada, for the American-built galleons were intended to sail fast and were employed in carrying treasure to Spain. They were larger than the *frigatas* and many carried guns on two decks.

Small craft built in the Spanish colonies included many "brigantines"; this name did not refer to a rig as it did later; the Spanish "brigantines" were small craft of the shallop or pinnace type, often without decks and rigged with two lateen sails. They were fast under sail and oars. A variety of small galleys were also built in the Spanish American colonies to guard the coast; these were of the Mediterranean type, with one or two lateen sails. These reputedly well built Spanish vessels were of cedar, mahogany, and tropical hardwoods. Practically all the ship and boat building in the Spanish colonies was by the government or by government-sponsored expeditions, and no attempt was made to establish private yards and a colonial shipbuilding industry.

Colonial Craft

In the English colonies, ship and boat building did not become particularly active industries until after the middle of the 17th century, when the civil war in England had interrupted trade with the mother country. As a result, the colonies, forced to create a seaboard trade of their own, set about exploiting sea fisheries in order to produce trade goods, and this made boat building necessary as a supporting industry. English colonial ship and boat building were under private ownership; the government made no real attempt to establish naval dockyards. In the 17th and early 18th centuries the boats and ships built in the English colonies were also all of national types, except for canoes and boat-canoes; these were dugouts that could be built by unskilled hands from the large, easily worked timber available.

At the end of the 17th century colonial-built craft included such types as shallop, pinnace, sloop, ketch or catch, pink, galley, and skiff. From English sources it is possible to obtain some idea of what these types were, although type names of vessels and boats were then rather loosely applied.

A shallop thus might be anything from a small open ship's boat fitted to row and perhaps to sail, to a sizable decked coasting craft or fishing boat. Large shallops sometimes had one mast fitted to carry a jib and a gaff or sprit mainsail, but gradually the typical shallop rig became a 2-masted one having two gaff sails, the fore the smaller, and no jib. Most shallops were square sterned; those having sharp sterns were commonly called double shallops. The lateen rig, it is believed, was also used in the shallops, but rarely in boats working in unprotected waters.

The pinnace was either a ship's boat, long and narrow and built to row fast, or a decked craft designed to sail and row and often fitted with the 2-masted shallop rig. The pinnaces were sometimes the English equivalent of the Spanish "brigantine." The name pinnace was also applied to galley-ships in the 16th and early 17th centuries, but by the beginning of the 18th century this application of the name ceased.

At the end of the 17th century colonial shipbuilders were constructing for the North Atlantic run between the New England colonies and England galley-ships and galley-brigantine-rigged vessels both called "gallies" or "galleys." These vessels were required in the unprotected colonial trade, the British Navy then being unable to furnish adequate cruisers for convoy guards. These galleys were flush-decked ships armed for war on one deck and with a rowing deck below; they were sometimes called "runners."

The pink was a sharp-sterned vessel with bulwarks carried abaft the sternpost, rigged as a ship, brigantine, or sloop. It was the forerunner of the later, schooner rigged American pinky.

The ketch was a square-sterned sailing vessel having two masts; the type was used for trading and in the

A DUTCH SHALLOP, AN EARLY SCHOONER-TYPE VESSEL, APPEARS IN THE FOREGROUND of this early view of the capture of Loki, Ceram, by Arnold de Vlamingh van Outshoorn, June 27, 1652. From the *Secret Atlas of the East India Company*, published about 1670, this view appears as plate 118 in *Monumenta Cartographica*, edited by Dr. F. C. Wieder the Hague, M. Nijhoff, 1925–.

Banks fisheries. Colonial records indicate that these vessels had very small crews, so they could not have been very large. It is very doubtful that they ever carried a square rig similar to that of the naval bomb ketch, since their crews would have been inadequate to handle such rigs; probably they were fore-and-aft rigged, with fore and main gaff sails of approximately equal size and with one or more jibs. This supposition is supported by the fact that, early in the 18th century the ketch or "catch," previously very numerous, suddenly disappeared almost completely from colonial records, being replaced by large numbers of "scooners." This suggests that there was merely a change of type name rather than that the "scooner" was a new rig or hull-type. It is noticeable that the "scooner" appeared all along the coast within a very short time.

Sloops were commonly employed in coasting or in the West Indian trade and were usually craft of some size, up to 60 feet length, having one mast, a gaff mainsail, and two or more jibs. The larger sloops were decked and fitted with bulwarks. Large-size sloops, 60 to 65 feet long were being built in the West

Indies by the last half of the 17th century and the fast sailing "Jamaica sloops" produced at Jamaica were popular with the buccaneers and piratical gentry in those waters.

The small craft constructed in the colonies included "boat-canoes," dugouts shaped to resemble ships' boats and usually square sterned, "canoes" being commonly sharp sterned. Except in eastern Maine and in the Canadian Maritime Provinces, the birch-bark Indian canoe was seldom employed on salt water.

"Skiffs" appear to be merely small rowing craft and were not usually fitted to sail.

The rigs of colonial boats in the 17th century were those employed in England and included the leg-of-mutton, a triangular sail fitted with a boom; the shoulder-of-mutton, which was similar but with a very short gaff, or club, at its head; the spritsail; the gaff-sail with a rather short gaff; the hoy sail, which was a gaff-sail with a long gaff, rarely lowered; and the lateen sail. These rigs and sail forms were quite well developed in Britain by the middle of the century when colonial ship and boatbuilding became very active. Large vessels were rigged as ships or brigantines, in the English manner, of course.

The timber employed in colonial ship and boat building offered many problems to the early builders, for while there was apparently suitable timber available, some of it was then unfamiliar to English builders. Gradually the colonial builders found woods that were useful to their purposes. In the northern colonies native oak, cedar, white pine, spruce, elm, maple, and juniper (or hackmatack) were commonly employed. In New England spruce top timbers were used in the framing of many ships to save topside weight; sometimes hackmatack or cedar was used for this purpose. In the Chesapeake Bay region frames were made of mulberry, cedar, laurel, or oak; planking was oak or southern pine. On the Chesapeake and northward to southern New England chestnut was used also for framing and for general structural purposes; farther south cypress and live oak were employed; there, too, long-leaf yellow pine, eventually to become one of the most important American shipbuilding timbers, was found very suitable for both planking and structure. Due to lack of capital, the colonial ship and boat builders were usually unable to maintain a stock of well seasoned timber and this led to many colonial-built vessels having a rather short life, as the green timber often employed rotted very rapidly, particularly if the vessel were sent south to the West Indies in the first few years of her life.

The tools employed by the colonial builders were the common hand tools of the period—the axe, hatchet, hand saw (rip and crosscut), a pit saw for shaping frames and getting out plank, hand planes, adze, maul, hammer, chisels, scrapers, and squares, and measuring devices. Water-powered sawmills of the jigsaw type were established in the northern colonies at an early date, but the location of most shipyards and boatbuilding areas prevented the use of sawmills until other forms of power were available. In fact, steam-powered sawmills were not commonly used in shipyards until after 1840.

The 18th century saw a great increase in American ship and boat building. Increasing wealth and trade created demands for additional types of small boat such as the wherry, whaleboat, barge, cutter, yawl boat, moses boat, longboat (or launch as it was later known), dory, periagua, and cutter. Of these, the moses boat and dory may have been of American design. The moses boat was a square-sterned rowing boat having marked rocker in the keel and great

sheer, used originally in the West Indian trade as a ship's lighter to handle casks. These boats were also used in the Maryland and Virginia tobacco trade. The dory was a flat-bottomed skiff, as it is today, and may have developed from the flat-bottomed skiff or plank canoe of the colonial lumbermen, that later became known as drive boats, or bateaux. The other types were of European origin and most of them were ships' boats.

The name periagua, it is thought, was of West Indian origin and was originally applied to a large dugout canoe with the sides raised by plank and fitted to sail. Later the name became applied to a form of shallop having the foremast raked forward and the mainmast raked aft; these were often craft of some size and were usually decked wholly or in part. In this century the name shallop became less popular and the type, often called a 2-mast boat, gradually developed into the famed Chebacco boat of New England and into large 2-masted, decked, river traders, the last survival of which was probably to be found in the St. John River woodboats in New Brunswick, Canada. Vessels of this class were in use on the Hudson River at least as late as 1845.

Ships built by colonial builders increased in size and naval shipbuilding began; the first Royal Navy ship built in the colonies was the 4th Rate *Falkland*, built by contract at Portsmouth, New Hampshire, in 1690. This ship was followed by three or four others and by numerous sloops, brigs, snows, and schooners intended for service in America, either on the Lakes or on the coast. Merchant ships were all of English types, apparently.

In the early years of the 18th century the construction of fast sailing vessels became profitable. This was largely due to profitable but illegal trades open to colonial traders in the West Indies, as well as to the unstable international conditions that made the seas unsafe for slow-sailing vessels. The American "gallies," first built late in the 17th century, remained popular; and small, swift sloops, schooners and brigantines were also constructed. On the Chesapeake, in particular, the construction of small, fast vessels became common. The type chosen was the old West Indian sloop, or Jamaica sloop which, by this time, had been transplanted to Bermuda and was now commonly called the Bermuda sloop.

This was a keel sloop of some size, up to 65 feet in length, having a straight, rising floor, well rounded bilge, and rather upright topside, giving it a rather "heart-shaped" midsection in extreme cases. The

16

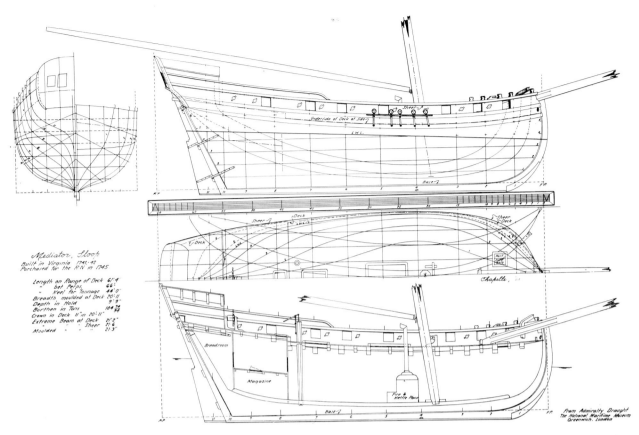

EARLIEST PLANS OF AN AMERICAN-BUILT VESSEL the sloop *Mediator* (see below), built on the Chesapeake, 1741–42. Redrawn from original British Admiralty draught. (*Courtesy of Trustees of the National Maritime Museum, Greenwich, England.*)

stem was usually well rounded in profile and the hull drew much more water aft than forward. The freeboard to the main deck was low, but these vessels usually had high bulwarks pierced for carriage guns and a high, short quarterdeck or a stern cabin with its roof strongly arched athwartships. The main deck of these sloops was commonly heavily crowned, or arched. The mast raked a good deal and the sloops carried two or more headsails, large gaff mainsail fitted with a boom, square course, topsail, and topgallant sail.

Through the early trade to Bermuda, as well as to the colonial West Indies, this type became well known on the Chesapeake. During the first half of the 18th century a great many sloops of this type were built on the Eastern Shore of Maryland and Virginia, in ports on the western side of the Bay, and on the Delaware. The earliest plan of an American built vessel, that has yet been found, is of a sloop of this class, the *Mediator*, purchased for the Royal Navy in 1745 and built in "Virginia" about 1741. This sloop was bought in the West Indies and sailed to England where she was measured and drawings made, shortly before she was lost at Dunkirk.

These large sloops apparently created a problem of manning, particularly when owned in a small village, for the rig in such large hulls required big crews. Hence, it was not long before the more easily managed schooner rig was applied to the type.

In view of a rather old American tradition that the fast-sailing American model was developed from French luggers and vessels that visited America and that had their lines taken off by colonial shipwrights during the Revolution, it should be made clear that no evidence has been found to support such a tradition. On the contrary, there is clear evidence in Maryland records of the construction of the Bermuda sloop type there, as the plan of the *Mediator* bears witness. The hull form of the Bermuda sloop, moreover, was employed to construct a British 24-gun ship in 1739 at London, and this vessel, the *Lyme*, is represented by her building plans in the Admiralty

17

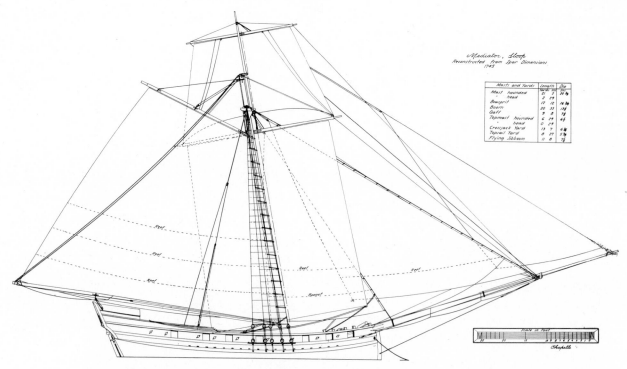

Mediator, Sloop
Reconstructed from Spar Dimensions
1745

Masts and Yards		Length			Dia
		Yards	feet	inch	inch
Mast	hounded	21	1		10 ¾
	head	2	11		
Bowsprit		13	12		14 ¼
Boom		20	33		13¾
Gaff		9	6		7¾
Topmast	hounded	6	29		6¼
	head	0	27		
Crossjack Yard		13	7		6¾
Topsail Yard		8	27		5¾
Flying Jibboom		11	8		7¼

Scale in Feet

Chapelle

SAIL AND RIGGING PLAN, RECONSTRUCTED FROM SPAR DIMENSIONS AND PRINTS of contemporary sloops, of the sloop *Mediator*, built on the Chesapeake, 1741–42 (see p. 17).

Collection of Draughts in The National Maritime Museum, at Greenwich, England. It is obvious, then, that this model for fast-sailing hulls was known in the colonies and in England long before the American Revolution. The plan of the schooners built for the Royal Navy at New York before the Revolution (see p. 163) also shows a fast-sailing hull form.

Other evidence points to the same conclusion. Contracts for building merchant vessels in the colonies during the 18th century have survived and these give very complete descriptions of the vessel in many cases. In addition, just before the Revolution, schooners and ships were purchased into the Royal Navy in America and a few plans of these survive. During the Revolution a number of American-built privateers and American merchant ships were captured; some of these were taken into the Royal Navy and plans, which have also survived, were made. There are, in addition, plans of American Revolutionary Navy ships that were captured by the British. All these plans and building contracts, many of which were for ships built before French intervention in the Revolution, show clearly that there were two basic classes of American vessels: one represented by the usual merchant vessel, similar in burdensome hull-form, size, and appearance to its British counterpart; the second

is represented by the privateer, a rather sharp vessel designed to sail fast.

The development of fast-sailing ships in America during the 18th century did not occur in a single location, but the Chesapeake region probably was the one most active in the building of swift vessels due to its nearness to and interest in the West Indies. In this area two classes of vessels appeared. One was the small pilot-boat schooner having a small-boat hull form with a moderate rise in the floor, rather marked bilges, and flaring topsides; these boats drew markedly more water aft than forward, and the stem profile was well rounded and unadorned by a knee or by mouldings and carvings; they were often flush decked and were low sided; and they had no bulwarks but rather a mere plank-on-edge, or log rail. Their two masts were long and raking, and unsupported by standing rigging, as was a short bowsprit. They set a large jib, a loosefooted and overlapping gaff-foresail, a boomed gaff-mainsail, and a large main-topmast staysail between the masts. Their accommodations were very limited and quite primitive, as they did not cruise far. The type was very numerous at the Virginia Capes and became known in the late 18th century as the "Virginia pilot boat"; the model and rig were gradu-

18

ally adopted at other American colonial ports, particularly at New York and in Delaware waters. At this period pilot boats were rarely over 55 feet long, 35 to 45 feet being the average.

The other was the seagoing schooner produced on the Chesapeake and in the vicinity. This vessel also drew much more water aft than forward and the main deck was but little above the waterline. It had a strongly rising floor, well rounded bilge, and some tumble-home in the topside amidships, giving it a characteristic heart-shaped midsection. These vessels usually had a rounded stem profile, sometimes with a small gammon-knee head and, very rarely, mouldings or carvings. They had high main-deck bulwarks pierced for carriage guns; many of those built before 1780 had high, short quarterdecks. They were relatively sharp ended and, like the small pilot boats, were built to sail very fast and carried a large spread of sail in the square-topsail schooner rig of the period, consisting of two or more headsails, fore and main sails, main-topmast staysail, fore course, square topsail, topgallant and, occasionally square main topsails with light sails in addition. As early as 1757 some of these schooners were 80 feet long, and capable of carrying 14 carriage guns. This class came to be popular during the Revolution; the number of schooners between 75 and 80 feet on deck became very great, and brigs and brigantines were also built on this model at that time, if not before.

In New England this "sharp" vessel was represented by the Marblehead schooner class, a type of fast-sailing Banks fisherman. These had more capacity for their size than the average Chesapeake schooner and commonly had rather upright stems, sometimes with a small gammon head and a little carving. The midsection resembled that of the Chesapeake model and they had short, high quarterdecks fitted with bulwarks. Some had bulwarks on the main deck pierced for guns, but many had no more than a log rail there. The masts had much rake and the schooners carried a rig somewhat similar to the Virginia pilot boat, but with masts supported by standing rigging. At times these schooners were fitted with the rig of a square-topsail schooner, particularly for trading voyages. The first vessels fitted out as cruisers by the American Revolutionary authorities were of this type.

The surviving plans of these three classes of schooners show that the southern seagoing, or pilot-boat, schooners and the Marblehead type retained the basic form of the old Bermuda, or Jamaica, sloop but with different proportions.

It would be natural for the colonial shipbuilders to apply the Bermuda sloop-Chesapeake schooner hull form to large ships, when a fast-sailing merchantman or privateer was required. It is not yet possible to state when this was first done in America, but it has already been shown (p. 17) that the model was applied in England in at least one instance in 1739 and there is, therefore, no sound reason to doubt that the sharp-model full-rigged ship existed in the colonies, as well as in Britain, long before the Revolution. During the Revolution the construction of privateer ships produced such vessels, and plans of a number have been found; these were made after their capture by the British.

One such vessel was the *Rattlesnake* of Salem, Massachusetts, said to have been built at Plymouth and designed by the first American naval architect known, John Peck. This ship was quite sharp ended and had the heart-shaped midsection of a schooner; she was 89 feet 3 inches on deck, 22 feet 4 inches beam, and 8 feet 10½ inches depth in the hold. Another such vessel was bought for the Royal Navy as the *Barbadoes* in 1784; she was also quite sharp in section and had rather fine lines, and was 97 feet 7 inches on deck, 24 feet 11¼ inches beam, and 10 feet 7 inches depth in hold. Her place of building and her original name have not been determined, though she was described in her naval papers as "American built," and her plan is so marked. Comparison of the plans of this vessel with those of the full-model American and British ships of the same period show that the *Barbadoes* was large for her time and the application of the sharp-model to a ship of such size indicates that there was an extensive background of experience with merchant vessels of this form and approximate size.

The sharp-model colonial vessel is likewise represented by plans of the fine American-built 2-master *Swift*, originally a schooner but rerigged as a brig when taken into the British Navy in 1783, having been captured in 1779. She was a sharp model, with short quarterdeck, measuring 75 feet 6 inches on deck, 20 feet 10 inches beam, and 7 feet 9 inches depth. Another example was a large American schooner taken into the Royal Navy in 1780 as the *Berbice*, a very sharp vessel having a short, high quarterdeck and measuring 72 feet 9 inches on deck, and 20 feet 8 inches beam, and 8 feet depth. It will be seen that there are too many plans of American-built vessels of the Revolutionary period in existence to permit acceptance of the tradition of French influence on early American ship design.

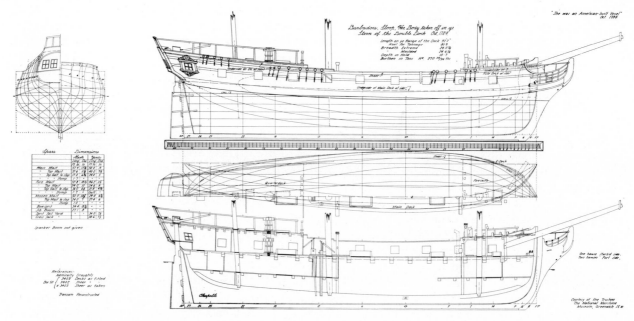

AMERICAN PRIVATEER SHIP OF THE REVOLUTION, ORIGINAL NAME UNKNOWN, taken into the British Navy in 1784 as the *Barbadoes*. This plan, redrawn from original British Admiralty draught, shows an early "sharp-model" vessel built for fast sailing, one of the ancestors of the clipper ship. (*Courtesy of Trustees of the National Maritime Museum, Greenwich, England.*)

A number of vessel types for special service were also developed by Americans during the last half of the 18th century. One of these was the gundalo, a double-ended, shoal-draft hull having a flat bottom fore-and-aft and athwartships, chine (angular) bilges, and vertically curved side timbers. Intended for commercial use in protected waters, on rivers, and on lakes, vessels of this type were also built for naval purposes during the Revolution. The gundalo was sometimes rigged with a single square sail, but more often it was sloop or schooner rigged. Others were the sailing scow, some of which were of large size, the large 2-masted shallop, which was developed into a serviceable river packet and freighter, and the river schooner.

Baltimore Clippers

During the last two decades of the 18th century, the most important development in American ship design was, for a number of reasons, the rise in popularity of the sharp-model, fast-sailing Chesapeake schooner and brig, or brigantine. The type, of course, had become well known on the American coasts during the Revolution and had obtained a great reputation for speed; even the British had come to recognize it as being one of the leading types of seagoing vessel, and

had taken a number of the fast-sailing schooners and brigs into naval service. Then, too, the state of national affairs after the war made the protection of the gradually increasing American merchant marine impossible; for many years there was no naval protection and the states were impotent in foreign diplomacy. As a result, the infant American merchant marine soon became the prey of every freebooter, and of many European naval cruisers as well and it was soon found that speed was the best insurance an American ship could have. The American ports could produce only small cargoes in most cases and this permitted the economic use of small vessels. Hence, it was natural that a great many shipowners turned to the Chesapeake model of schooner or brig.

Furthermore, the widespread use of these vessels by Americans engaged in commerce, particularly in the West Indies, brought the type to the continuous attention of most of the European naval powers. The French, in particular, at the beginning of the War of the French Revolution began purchasing Chesapeake schooners in great number for use as privateers and cruisers. So active were the French purchasers that the British complained and the newly established Federal government was forced to intervene. This interference and the strongly pro-revolutionist sym-

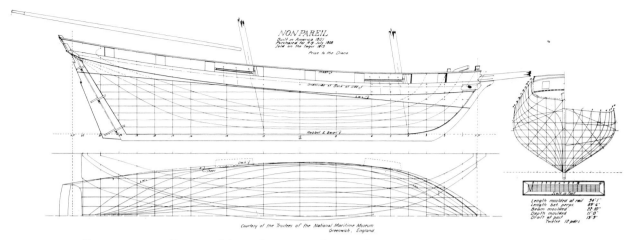

EXAMPLE OF THE EXTREME MODEL BALTIMORE CLIPPER SCHOONER OF THE FIRST DECADE OF THE 19TH CENTURY, the *Nonpareil*, built on the Chesapeake in 1801 and taken into the Royal Navy in 1808. Plan was made from a half-model in the National Maritime Museum, Greenwich, England.

pathy abroad in the Chesapeake region led a few shipbuilders to France, where they took part in the building of French privateers.

The history of this incident is obscure, but British intelligence and naval reports do indicate that some Americans entered into partnership with French builders and constructed privateers on the Chesapeake model in France, and that this activity continued until, late in the 1790's, the deteriorating relations between France and the United States which led to the so-called "quasi-war" put a stop to the cooperation. In this connection it is worthy of notice that soon after 1794 the Royal Navy began to capture from the French large, flush-decked ship-privateers of an entirely new model suspiciously resembling the Chesapeake schooner hull; nothing like these vessels had been taken from the French in previous wars and the new type gradually disappeared after 1800, to be replaced by ships of the usual and distinctive French hull form.

Plans of some of the captured French privateer ships of the new model, taken off by the British, show that there was indeed a very marked similarity between them and the American schooner model. One of the largest of these captured "sharp-model" privateer ships was about 140 feet long, an unusual length for the period. One or two privateer frigates appear to have been built on this model, as well as some large flush-decked ships, and a number of brigs. Most of the schooners used by the French, however, were purchased American-built vessels, as were a few naval brigs. The British also purchased some post-Revolutionary American schooners and took

into service many of those captured from the French or condemned in their courts for illegal trading. Plans of these, made by the British Admiralty, have given the most complete record of the development of the type, prior and during the War of 1812.

An example of a large American-built sharp-model schooner at the beginning of the 19th century is the *Nonpareil*, built in 1801 on the Chesapeake. This vessel was taken by the British in 1807 or 1808, apparently for illegal trading. Some accounts state she was found at Montevideo when that city was captured by the British, but other official records indicate that she was taken at sea. At any rate, she was taken into the Royal Navy in 1808 and remained in naval service until 1813, being sold in the Tagus. The *Nonpareil* was a square-fore-topsail schooner 94 feet 1 inch at the rail, 89 feet 6 inches on deck, 22 feet 10 inches moulded beam, and drawing 13 feet 9 inches aft. The model was sharp in all respects and the vessel was a very fast sailer.

By 1794 the raised quarterdeck of the earlier Chesapeake schooners had gone out of fashion and nearly all schooners and brigs were flush decked fore and aft. It was about 1795 that the 3-masted schooner rig appeared in Chesapeake schooners; some of these were sold to the French. These schooners were not very large and were usually of the Norfolk, or Virginia, pilot boat model; the use of the rig appears to result from an effort to increase sail area on a small hull, rather than from the desire for economy in crew requirements. One such schooner, the *Poisson Volant*, 78 feet 8 inches long on deck, 21 feet 7 inches beam, and 7 feet 10 inches depth of hold, was taken from the

French. She was of the regular pilot boat model but her rails had been raised to form bulwarks and the vessel had been fitted to carry 10 guns. Plans were made of the schooner, and from these six duplicates were built at Bermuda, by contract in 1808, for the British Navy.

Reversing the process that had taken place in colonial times; when the Chesapeake Bay builders had copied the Bermuda sloop; in the last years of the 18th century and early years of the 19th, Bermuda builders copied the American schooners and produced a modification that was called the "Bermudian schooner." It was somewhat like the Chesapeake pilot boat, but was usually fitted with a long, low quarterdeck and without high bulwarks. As a result of the building of the 3-masted schooners in 1808, perhaps, the Bermudians also adopted the 3-masted rig and built schooners of this masting; soon some of these were fitted with three leg-of-mutton sails instead of the gaff sails of the American schooner and the new 3-masted Bermudian schooner type became noted for its speed.

When the U. S. Navy was established in the 1790's, two sharp-model schooners were obtained, the *Enterprise* and *Experiment*. These were followed by a few other schooners, though the rig was never very popular with American naval officers. The U. S. Revenue Service was also equipped with sharp-model schooners, although the vessels, following British usage, were always called "cutters." It may be mentioned in passing that the British Revenue Service employed two American-built sharp-model schooners in the period between 1790 and 1820, and of twelve large schooners in the Royal Navy in 1808, all but three were American-built.

There was only a moderate change in the design of the Chesapeake schooner between 1800 and 1812. The average size of seagoing schooners increased somewhat and the sheer of the vessels gradually became somewhat straighter. Extremes in sharpness had been reached by 1806 and radical designs were quite common in this respect long before the beginning of the War of 1812. When the war began, the Chesapeake Bay builders were soon forced to recognize that small privateers were not wholly effective and they began to build some schooners and brigantines of over 100 feet length on deck; the largest built on the Bay during the war were 115 to 116 feet on deck; perhaps 120 feet at the rail. Although many of these large vessels were built as schooners, most of them were soon rerigged as brigantines or brigs. As was

learned later with regard to New England coasting and fishing schooners, 2-masted schooners above 120 feet in length required a large crew and hence were not economical in trading. The majority of the noted privateer schooners of the War of 1812 ranged from 90 to 100 feet in length. Many of the larger privateers, such as the *General Armstrong* and *Prince de Neufchatel*, were built in New York.

Until shortly after the War of 1812, the Chesapeake model schooner was usually described as being "pilot-boat construction," or "Virginia model," or "pilot-boat model"; during the war "Baltimore built" or "Baltimore model," was sometimes employed. Other names were "sharp model" and "Chesapeake model." The name "Baltimore clipper" became popular in the 1820's and remained in use from then on.

By 1815 the use of the Chesapeake hull form had spread all along the coast, and schooners and brigs of "pilot-boat construction" had been built at New Orleans, Savannah, Charleston, Norfolk, Philadelphia, New York, and in New England from Connecticut to Maine. The New England-built vessels varied from the others, as a rule, in having less rake in the ends. Like the old Marblehead schooners, the New England-built privateers of 1812–15 were more burdensome than their southern sisters. At the end of the war, and for some years after, the fastest sailer in the American Navy was the brig *Spark*, a vessel built at Sag Harbor, on Long Island, New York, as a privateer, on a model brought from the Chesapeake. Pilot boats all along the coast were very similar in form, if not in appearance, to those at Norfolk and Baltimore, and the most common length was 50 to 60 feet on deck.

During the War of 1812 Baltimore shipowners had carried the bulk of the small American seaborne trade simply because they had a large number of small, swift vessels suited to running the blockade and avoiding enemy cruisers. The trade was very profitable, and at the end of the war Maryland shipowners would have liked to retain their advantageous position. Some ex-privateers were put into peacetime trade; the famous ex-schooner-brigantine *Chasseur*, for example, went into the China trade where she almost immediately set a record for the run that stood for many years, being finally broken by a much larger vessel.

It was soon found, however, that the sharp and often very deep ex-privateer was not very profitable in trade. The Chesapeake builders were soon under pressure to produce a good, small, trading vessel.

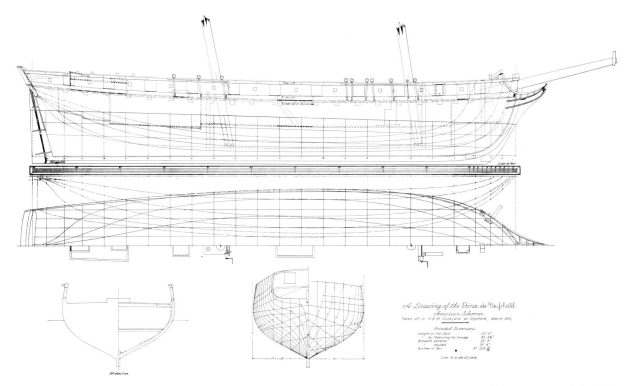

PLAN OF A PRIVATEER BUILT BY ADAM AND NOAH BROWN, NEW YORK, DURING THE WAR OF 1812. The *Prince de Neufchatel*, after a successful career as a privateer, was captured by the British and plans were made of her. She was noted for her speed, and was probably similar to the *General Armstrong*. Redrawn from the original British Admiralty draught.

With their hard-earned reputation for fast sailing so well established, they tried to produce a model that would sail well and carry more with less draft, than the old model. Within a few years of the war an improved trading model had been developed. Compared with the earlier model, the great rake of the ends, particularly at the stem, was somewhat reduced, as was the rise of the floor amidships; the difference in draft fore-and-aft was less marked and the hull was less deep and rather wider than before. The schooner rig of the restless periods before 1815 was no longer needed in ocean trade; the brig and brigantine were now considered more suitable for general trade. A few sharp-model ships were built but, after the war, there was little local demand for these large craft. Most of them were built under contract for Mexico, and the numerous nations being formed of the Spanish colonies in South and Central America, and were intended as men-of-war or privateers.

The use of the heavy spars of the brigantine and brig rigs on the foremast made a basic change necessary in the old schooner model; this consisted not only of reducing the drag and making the draft much deeper at the bow than before, but also of making the entrance somewhat less fine, since the extreme draft was made less than before, to carry the weight forward. As a result the midsection was rather large in area; it had only a slight rise of floor, a low and rather easy bilge, and nearly upright topsides. The entrance was short and fairly sharp; the run was usually quite long and very fine; and the bow sections had marked flare. It is probable that this form had some influence in the design of the large packet ships that were built after 1830, yet it was not greatly different from that of some of the Bay-built ships of 1812.

An example of one of the trading brigantines built in Maryland is one designed and constructed at Baltimore by Flannigan, a builder who had modeled some notable schooners during the War of 1812 and who had been a partner in the firm of Flannigan and Parsons, builders of the U. S. frigate *Java* at Baltimore during that war. This brigantine, built sometime between 1818 and 1828, was a small vessel for her time, of 88 feet 10 inches length on deck, 22 feet 7½ inches moulded beam, and drawing about 9 feet 10 inches, loaded. Vessels of this type were employed

23

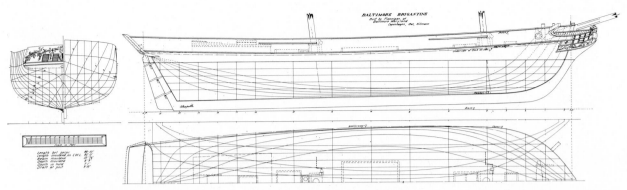

MERCHANT BRIGANTINE OF ABOUT 1818–28, BUILT AT BALTIMORE, MARYLAND, BY FLANNIGAN. Redrawn from a plan, by Hillman, formerly in the Webb Institute of Naval Architecture.

in the coffee trade to Brazil and in the West Indian trade, both of which the Baltimore shipowners were able to retain, in a large measure, during the first half of the 19th century.

Vessels with the old sharp hull form continued to be used, however, as the model proffered to John N. Cushing, Sr., in 1845 by a Baltimore builder, now in the Watercraft Collection (see p. 67), bears witness.

In 1832 the ship *Ann McKim* was built at Baltimore, a vessel on the old sharp schooner model, 143 feet between perpendiculars, 31 feet beam, and 15 feet moulded depth; and she attracted very little attention when launched, the local references to the event showing that she was not viewed as anything particularly unusual. Indeed, she was not, for ship-rigged vessels of even more extreme designs had been built years before, not only at Baltimore but elsewhere. Some 4 years earlier, for example, the very extreme ship *United States* had been built by Eckford at New York for his own account; and of course, sharp-model ships had been built as early as the Revolution. However, because the lines of the builder's model of the *Ann McKim* had been published, and because the vessel had been sold to New York, where she won a reputation for speed, some modern historians, lacking access to the lines of earlier sharp-model ships and basing their argument on the existence of the lines of the ship and her ownership in New York, have been led to assume the *Ann McKim* either to have been the "first clipper ship" or to have influenced the demand for such ships or, at least, to have been an innovation in some respect.

Modifications of the Baltimore clipper models were very popular at Philadelphia, New York, and Boston in the early 19th century. At New York, in particular, there were active shipyards operating, with contracts for small vessels requiring fast sailing. These

yards turned out schooners, brigantines and brigs that, while resembling the Chesapeake Bay vessels, were of a local character. The New York built clippers were admired for their fine workmanship and finish; their hull form was characterized by a very high bilge and rather more depth of keel outside the rabbet than would be average in the southern vessels. The hermaphrodite *Apprentice*, built at New York in 1839, is typical of these New York vessels. Though rather wide she is sharp ended and well formed; by the date of her building the position of the greatest sectional area, the midsection, was being slowly moved aft. She was 80 feet 6 inches at rail, 23 feet 10 inches moulded beam, and drew about 10 feet 5 inches loaded. The first vessel built by William H. Webb, the noted New York clipper ship builder, on his own account was the small brig *Malek-Adhel*, for the Pacific Ocean trade. This brig was a New York clipper model of the size of the *Apprentice* and of somewhat similar proportions; she was a very fast sailer.

It may appear strange that Baltimore and the Chesapeake region, because of the great reputation of the Baltimore clipper, did not become the building center when the great boom in clipper-ship construction began. That it did not was due to the basic structure of the shipbuilding industry there. Baltimore was never the chief building area on the Chesapeake; the industry was carried on along the shores of the Bay, in small towns and villages, particularly on the Eastern Shore of Maryland and Virginia. These country yards were all relatively small, with small crews, a factor that limited the size of vessels they could readily build. The Baltimore yards were larger and could build larger vessels but they often suffered for lack of sufficient labor. The Maryland and Virginia shipwrights preferred to work in their villages, where they could engage in part-time farming, fishing, or hunting,

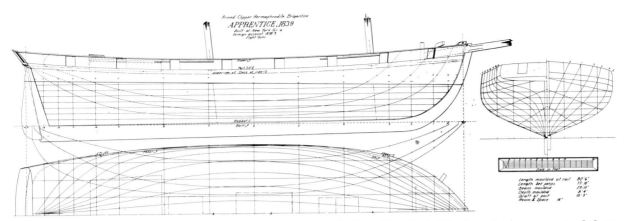

EIGHT-GUN CLIPPER HERMAPHRODITE BRIGANTINE *Apprentice*, built at New York City for a foreign account, 1838–39.

rather than take the risks of industrial, urban employment. During the Revolution, for example, when the frigate *Virginia* was building at Baltimore, there was very great difficulty in getting men to finish the ship. Again, in the War of 1812 the frigate *Java* was delayed by the lack of labor in the city, while the construction of privateer schooners in the country yards gave more attractive employment to workmen. Thus, local conditions limited the Chesapeake Bay shipbuilders to the production of small vessels, and since, at least to 1857, there was a profitable market for these small, fast-sailing vessels, the Bay yards were kept busy, with little surplus labor available for Baltimore. While a few clipper ships and packets were built on the Bay, the whole number was very small compared with the output of Boston, New York, or of the New England States. It may be said, however, that the Chesapeake Bay clipper-ships maintained their great reputation for fast sailing, and in spite of the limited output of clipper ships on the Chesapeake, some very fine small vessels were built for ocean trade, and for coasting.

An example of the small ocean-trading clippers was the topsail schooner *Vaquero*, built at Baltimore, by James M. Foster and Thomas Booz, for Captain Josiah D. Nason of Medford, Massachusetts. This was a large 2-masted schooner intended to carry freight and passengers in the Pacific Ocean trade. Built in 1853 at the height of the clipper-ship boom, her general hull lines were those of an extreme clipper ship. She was about 133 feet 6 inches at rail, 120 feet 9 inches between perpendiculars, 27 feet 2½ inches moulded beam, and drew 13 feet aft, 11 feet 4 inches forward, loaded.

This schooner was as large as many ships and barks in her time. She sailed to California and there gained the reputation of being the fastest vessel out of the port of San Francisco. Described as having very fine passenger accommodations and as being a first-class vessel in all respects, the *Vaquero* was the first vessel to carry passengers from San Francisco to Melbourne, Australia, and for a few years she ran between these ports and Honolulu. This big 2-master held the record between Melbourne and Honolulu; in 1858 she made the run in 36 days, and her previous two runs were 42 and 41 days. The *Vaquero* was lost at sea on June 9, 1859, after 5 years in the trade.

By 1850 the original Baltimore clipper model had nearly gone out of fashion, except in small schooners and in a few brigantines. Most fast vessels built on the Chesapeake, brigs, brigantines, 3-mast schooners, barks and ships, had been on models very similar to those used at New York and in New England, except that the Bay-built vessels commonly had somewhat sharper ends. The last Baltimore clipper type built on the Bay was the "pungy," a shallow-keel schooner used in the Bay trade and in fishing. Some pungies were employed as coastal packets and a few were in the Bahama-Baltimore fruit trade until late in the 19th century. The type finally disappeared about 1940 on the Bay. However, the basic principles of the Baltimore clipper model were sound and, throughout the last half of the 19th century, pilot schooners and some yachts continued to show much resemblance to the old model.

One of the trades in which Baltimore clippers engaged was slaving. A few were actually built for the trade, often very extreme models—brigs, brigantines, and schooners. Few ships, or very large vessels, engaged in slaving, though occasionally one was found with slaves aboard. The slaver was commonly, however, a cheaply built or secondhand vessel and most

25

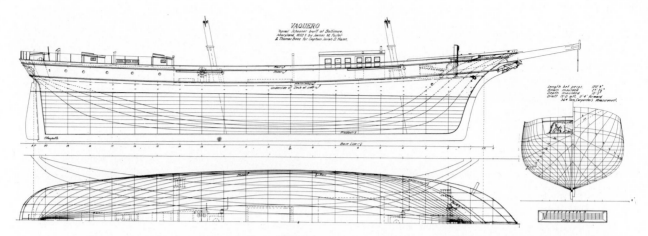

LINES OF THE LARGE 2-MASTED CLIPPER SCHOONER *Vaquero*, built as a packet at Baltimore, Maryland, 1852–53. Until lost at sea, she was employed in the Pacific between San Francisco, Melbourne, and Honolulu.

were not armed, or they were very lightly armed, for they usually depended upon speed to evade capture. Brigs and brigantines were much favored in the trade and any schooners employed in the trade carried large square sails on the foremast, at least, being usually fore-topsail schooner rigged. The slavers were flush decked, with a low trunk on the deck aft in schooners, brigantines, and brigs.

Sometime about 1820–25 a few Chesapeake Bay builders went to Cuba to build slavers that were operated under the Spanish flag. Later many of the South American flags were employed by slavers, since these countries permitted slave trading long after England, United States, and the nations having colonies in the West Indies had forbidden it. From one of the few slavers taken by or purchased for the British Navy, plans of a topsail schooner were made, and the plans of two brigs and two other schooners also survive. Usually captured slavers were hauled up and either burned or broken up by the British, to avoid the slavers purchasing them and putting them back into the trade. The American Navy engaged in suppression of the trade but political and economic factors made it less effective in this than the British Navy. The slave trade gradually declined in the first half of the 19th century, but it did not cease entirely in American waters until the 1860's.

During the period of piracy in the West Indies, that occurred after the peace of 1815, freebooters operated from shore establishments on the Cuban and Florida coasts, from which they made destructive forays upon American commerce in the Gulf and in the Caribbean. They preferred small craft for their operations and had a strong preference for Chesapeake pilot-boat

schooners that they obtained by purchase or capture. These were swift and had the shallow draft required to reach the hideouts the pirates employed. Two such vessels were captured by the British Navy and taken into their service in the 1820's to engage in suppression of West Indian piracy. Copies of the Chesapeake Bay models built in the West Indies were said to be very roughly constructed and inferior to the Chesapeake-built schooners. For many years one of the marks of these West Indian-built schooners was markedly greater rake in the mainmast than the fore; these were known as "Ballahou rigged."

North Atlantic Packets

In early colonial times, passenger transportation between England and her colonies was very irregular, since it depended upon the freighting vessels in the colonial trade. From old accounts it is plain that these ships were very unsatisfactory, for they had very primitive accommodations for passengers; they made very irregular runs as their departures depended upon freight requirements. Government officials preferred to travel by men-of-war when that was possible. In 1755 the British established a mail packet service; the vessels employed were almost entirely fast brigantines of rather small size, and the service was controlled and operated by the Post Office. The Revolution put a stop to this service as far as American ports were concerned, but after the war the service was resumed, to be broken off again just before the War of 1812 and continued after the war until 1828, when it finally ceased due to the competition of the big trans-Atlantic packets. These mail packets carried no freight; this sharply reduced their usefulness as aids in

PACKET SHIP, BUILT IN 1855 AT NEW YORK CITY BY WILLIAM H. WEBB FOR THE BLACK BALL LINE, the *Neptune*. She was wrecked about 1877. Her register dimensions were 191' x 40' x 28', 1,406 tons. From a painting (USNM 310852) in the Watercraft Collection. (*Smithsonian photo 44691.*)

the foreign trade, and limited their value to American merchants.

The coastal packet business which developed in early colonial times was largely carried in sloops and small schooners which made more or less regular runs between Atlantic coastal cities and towns, often in conjunction with stagecoach services. Packet sloops were also employed on the large rivers; those on the Hudson became large and well equipped vessels after the Revolution. On some of the longer runs small brigs were employed, particularly to the Southern ports. At the beginning of the War of 1812 the coastal packets had become well established and some appear to have maintained a fairly regular schedule, at least during the summer months. This coastal packet service, which was really part of the coasting trade, is dealt under coasting vessels (see p. 42).

The coming of peace in 1815 brought a revival in merchantile activity in America to meet the needs that had gathered during the war years. New York merchants saw in this period an opportunity to make their city a great merchantile center. One step in this direction was taken by four well-to-do merchants, who organized a trans-Atlantic packet service with

four ships. One feature of this line of packets was that they were to sail on a fixed schedule; a ship was to leave port at the beginning of each month without regard to weather or the amount of freight on board.

This first venture, the "Old Line," became best known as the Black Ball Line, as the ships carried a flag on which there was a black ball, a mark also carried on their fore-topsail. The Black Ball Line began operation between New York and Liverpool in 1818, and in spite of an economic depression that began in 1819, the Line prospered. This led to the establishment of other packet lines; the second to be organized was the Red Star Line in 1821, and this was followed by the Swallowtail Line, the Le Havre Line, and others. Services thus became established to Liverpool, London, and Le Havre, with two or more lines to each of these European ports.

In order to maintain the schedules proudly advertised by the competing lines, it was necessary to sail the packet ships very hard, and to carry sail as long as possible. Early in the development of the packet lines, ships were racing across the Atlantic and the first arrival obtained a great notoriety which served the line's owners as valuable advertising. Though speed was important, carrying capacity was a basic necessity, due to the type of cargoes accepted. A merely fast ship without high order of cargo-carrying ability would have been a commercial failure in the trans-Atlantic packet trade throughout most of its existence. To resist the strains of hard sailing, which could be destructive to large wooden ships, their structure was necessarily always massive and strong. Thus construction weight as well as cargo capacity made the packet ship a very heavy displacement vessel for her length.

The earliest packet ships were regular traders selected because they sailed well. Such vessels had some rise in the floor amidships, rather firm, rounded bilges, and some tumble-home in the topsides. The bow was very full at the rail, but below the entrance became very fine, though quite short. The run was likewise short but rather easy. The sides were carried well fore-and-aft and almost parallel, so that there was a long, full body. These first ships were relatively small, about 500 tons register or less, approximately 110 to 115 feet along on deck, and 28 to 31 feet beam.

The changes in form necessary to make such ships sail well were known at the time; an increase in the length of run and in the length of the entrance, combined with greater fineness at the ends, would produce more speed but at the cost of a loss in capacity in a short ship. There was also a practical limit to the depth a ship of about 500 tons should have. It was believed that to sail fast, a ship required dead rise in her floors amidships, and the greater the dead rise the faster she would be. Because of these factors and the belief as to the need for dead rise, little change took place in the hull form of packets ships built before 1835, though between 1816 and 1832 the ships increased in overall size.

For reasons of trade, the New York merchants found it necessary in the 1820's to employ ships of some size in the coastal packet trade with Charleston, Savannah, Mobile, and New Orleans (the first line to New Orleans was established in 1821). A necessary hull feature in these coastal packets, a majority of which were ship rigged, was a rather flat bottom in order to keep the loaded draft at a minimum, so that the ship could cross the bar at the mouth of the Mississippi. This change had been accepted as a necessity, as was the supposed loss of speed that was expected to result, but it was noticed that some of these flat-floored coastal packets were very fast ships, of great capacity for their size.

This discovery led to the adoption of the flat-floored hull form in the trans-Atlantic packets, and by 1838 the fashionable packet-ship model had become a vessel with straight sheer, rather straight sided for most of her length, with a very full bow at the rail, sharp and easy in the entrance below the load line, and with a fairly long and fine run. The cutwater was short and deep, naval fashion, a style that had become almost universal in America at the end of the War of 1812; even the Chesapeake Bay builders had given up their simple gammon-knee head and were supplying all their schooners except the small pilot boats with "naval heads." At the same time the rake of stem and post was gradually reduced until, in some of the packets built at Philadelphia for the Cope Line, the stem rabbets and sternposts became upright. The early ships were commonly flush decked, but as the vessels grew in size a long quarterdeck came to be employed and this was utilized for accommodation of the cabin passengers, the steerage passengers being placed in the 'tween decks amidships, or in a deckhouse, and the crew in a forecastle space forward below the main deck. These ships were 2-decked until into the 1840's when 3-decked packets were built. In appearance the packet often resembled a naval frigate, her sheer often being flush, or unbroken, as in the warship. The quarter galleries of the naval ships were omitted in the packets as these ornaments would be damaged in a hard-driven vessel.

Out of the gradual development of the North Atlantic packet-ship hull form came the ship design practices that helped produce the best of the clipper ships of the 1850's: A full midship section and good length of body, combined with fine ends; a strongly built and heavily sparred vessel that could be driven hard without coming apart or losing her spars. As the packets grew in length, improved construction details were introduced until it became possible to build wooden ships of great length without their becoming weak longitudinally. By 1843 packet ships 180 feet long on deck were being built, diagonally strapped (see p. 115).

After the introduction of the clipper ship, in 1850, packets were built that also could be reasonably called true clippers, so fine were they at the ends; the *Racer* and the *Dreadnought*, both built in Massachusetts, were examples. But no ship of really extreme hull design was long employed as a regular North Atlantic packet.

SMITH & DIMON SHIPYARD, NEW YORK, ABOUT 1831, FROM A CONTEMPORARY PAINTING. This firm was then a leading builder of packet ships, and later built *Rainbow, Sea Witch* and other famous clipper ships. A treadmill can be seen at the extreme left and a steam box at the extreme right. (*Smithsonian photo 32914-c.*)

The building of packets centered at New York; out of a total of 185 ocean packets, listed by Albion in *Square-riggers on Schedule,* 160 were New York built; of 116 ship-rigged coastal packets, 78 were New York built. Only one ocean packet was built at the former center of improved shipbuilding, Baltimore. New England's contribution was but 24 ocean and 37 coastal packets.

It was the fierce competition in packet-ship construction among New York builders that had led these shipbuilders to search for scientific information on the design of hulls, and caused them to import English books on the subject and to study and discuss the problem in print. The first American book on naval architecture, published at New York in 1839, was *The Practical Shipbuilder* by L. M'Kay, older brother of Donald McKay, who was to become prominent at Boston in the 1850's as a builder of clipper ships. Later the *Nautical Magazine,* published at New York, and the works on naval architecture and shipbuilding of John Willis Griffiths appeared. The mechanics' societies had lectures on the subject at their athenaeums and the title "mechanic" was proudly claimed by master shipwright and carpenter alike. Consequently, in the latter part of the packet-

ship period, 1820 to 1850, when the great development of the type took place, New York had become a center of advanced merchant ship-design, and although Baltimore retained a reputation for turning out swift sailers, at least in small vessels, the palm for "scientific ship-design" rested in New York.

Not until the 1850's did New England bid for supremacy in this respect. The careful preservation of shipbuilding records in New England and the relative neglect of this in other sections have given a somewhat false concept of the national importance and the actual advance of shipbuilding in New England during the first half of the 19th century. Though shipbuilding was very active in this period throughout the New England States, there was very little evidence of progressive design, particularly in regards to very fast or large ships.

After 1850, steamships gave the sailing packets increasingly strong competition and gradually took over the trans-Atlantic runs and the long coastal runs, the sailing vessels first losing the cabin passengers and then the valuable freight, such as specie and perishable goods. One by one the packet lines ceased operation, and the last sailing packets were reduced to the immigrant trade. The end finally came in the

Clipper Ships

Though of less economic importance than either the packets or the ocean freighters and coasters in the age of sail, the American clipper ships are of very great interest because of their part in the development of American sailing ship design, with its emphasis on speed. The clipper-ship period was very short, so far as building was concerned. The appearance of the clipper ship was brought about by the existence of trades in which high freight rates could be obtained, particularly if fast runs were made. This first developed in the China trade. China cargoes brought good prices and could afford high freight rates. The length of the voyage alone was sufficient to encourage speed, for the individual merchant's investment in a China voyage was large and too long a voyage tied up capital and lost interest. There was yet another factor, the American mania for speed. This had become marked before 1800 in shipping and was, of course, based upon the success of the Baltimore clipper type in this respect. The

LARGE AMERICAN MEDIUM CLIPPER *Queen of Clippers*, from a French print in the Watercraft Collection (USNM 159934). She was built by Robert E. Jackson at East Boston, Massachusetts, in 1853. Her register dimensions were 248'6'' x 45' x 38', an unusually deep ship for her beam. (*Smithsonian photo 44638–a.*)

China trade gave free rein to this desire for speed and the trade conditions permitted the operation of fast sailing vessels of moderate capacity; even extreme Baltimore clippers could be employed in the trade, as they were after 1815. As the value of the China trade gradually increased, the need for fast vessels of greater capacity than that of the privateer models of 1815–1820 attracted attention. Packet ships were tried with some success and their relatively large capacity made them attractive to the China trade merchants in the early 1840's, though their hull design was not otherwise too well suited to the weather and sea conditions of the run.

In 1844, when the merchants were still seeking an improved model of vessel for the China trade, Smith and Dimon, prominent packet-ship designers and builders, laid down the modified packet ship *Rainbow*, designed by John W. Griffiths, a rising shipwright

CLIPPER SHIP *Ocean Herald*, from a French print in the Watercraft Collection (USNM 159928). She was built at Damariscotta, Maine, in 1853, and was sold to France in 1856 and renamed *Malabar*. Said to be a medium-clipper model, her register tonnage was 1658. (*Smithsonian photo 44638–c.*)

in their employ. Historians of the clipper ship have at times considered this as the vessel marking the beginning of the clipper-ship period, although the first ship-rigged clipper in the China trade was probably the *Ann McKim*.

What is a clipper ship? Much space has been given to this question by maritime writers and historians both in the United States and Britain. There are many answers, the fundamental one being that a clipper ship is one that can be sailed at a very high rate of speed. This definition is inherent in the word "clipper," which to Americans of the 19th century meant fast moving. To the naval architect or master shipwright the clipper had to have a hull capable of high speed and a rig to match. In the technical sense, then, a clipper was a very sharp-ended vessel having a hull form that possessed a high potential speed and that could carry a spread of sail sufficient

to drive the vessel at this high potential speed, at least on occasion.

A high potential speed depends on size, particularly length, in ships of sufficient displacement to carry a payload of cargo. Therefore, the numerical expression of high potential speed must vary. For example, the Baltimore clippers of the privateer type are recorded as having sailed at a speed of 13 knots and better on a waterline length of 100 feet, or thereabouts. Naval architects use speed-length ratio to establish the effect of length on maximum speed; this term is the square root of the waterline length divided by the observed maximum speed in nautical miles. Thus, the privateer *Prince de Neufchatel* (see p. 23) was observed to run at a speed of 13½ knots, giving a speed length ratio of about 1.33; the 121-foot waterline schooner-yacht *Sappho*, at a much later date (1869) is credited with 16 knots, giving a speed length ratio of about 1.45; while the clipper ship *James Baines* is credited with a claimed speed of 21 knots on a waterline length of about 240 feet, giving a speed-length ratio of 1.35. On this basis, there was only a slight gain between the *Neufchatel* (built by Adam and Noah Brown of New York in 1813) and the clipper-ship *James Baines* (built by Donald McKay of

31

Boston in 1854). The speed-length ratio of 1.45 may be taken as the highest claimed for a seagoing vessel of sufficient displacement to carry either a small amount of cargo or to give livable accommodations for a sea voyage of much length.

The foregoing criterion of sailing speed gives rather discouraging results as regards progress in sailing ship design between 1812 and 1865; and apparently tarnishes the reputation of the clipper ship. Such a comparison, however, is somewhat unfair, for the privateer was designed to sail under less difficult conditions of sea and weather than the clipper ship and the yacht was designed to sail under the easiest conditions of all.

Marine historians have resorted to the "shortest voyage over a given run" as the criterion of excellence, as, for example, the Baltimore schooner *Vaquero*, noted earlier (p. 25). The use of this criterion to establish the fastest clipper-ship leaves an element to chance; a very fast ship might be on a given run for years, yet, because of weather conditions or because of the way the ship was loaded or because of her commanders and the quality of her crew, none of which are matters of ship design, she might only once make a record or near-record run. Another factor that must be taken into consideration in the lowering of records for given runs is the increase that took place in knowledge of the wind and weather conditions to be expected in any month of the year along the courses sailed between New York and San Francisco, and in the trans-Atlantic and trans-Pacific runs. The meteorological research of Lt. Matthew Fontaine Maury in the 1840's and 1850's at the American Hydrographic Office in Washington established for these runs the sailing courses which, if closely followed, shortened very markedly the time between ports. It is not surprising, therefore, to discover that some of the vessels listed by maritime historians as clipper ships, on the basis of their "record passages," were relatively full-ended vessels having a low maximum speed potential.

Speed under sail is affected by the direction of the wind in relation to the chosen course of a vessel; a ship sailing close-hauled, that is, pointing into the wind to her maximum capability moves through the water much more slowly than when the wind is free, that is, on her beam or abaft that direction. Often a fast ship will sail on all points at higher speed than a slow ship, but when the margin of superiority between ships in this respect is small, the best handled ship will be the fastest. Some fast ships sail better on one course than another. In one case two clipper ships, both notable sailers, were in company and one ship outsailed the other with the wind aft; but when they changed courses, so that the wind came forward of the beam, the position of the ships was soon reversed. When a ship is noted for being fast, then, the question to be asked is: on what course is she fast—close hauled or running free or reaching with the wind abeam?

Wind and sea conditions also affect a ship's performance. The heavy, full-ended packets could be sailed in heavy head winds and seas when the potentially faster Baltimore clipper model brigantine or large schooner or extreme clipper ship had to reduce sail and speed to be safe. In heavy weather the larger vessel always had a basic advantage, for she usually could carry sail when the smaller vessel could not. In an area where the weather was generally poor at a given period, as in the North Atlantic in the late fall and winter or off Cape Horn in winter, large vessels as a rule had the advantage.

Perhaps the simplest test of a ship's being fast is the record of the types and names of vessels she has passed when in company, for this very often shows the inherent speed advantage she had under a specific existing condition. Using the record-run criterion it is necessary to call some full-ended but heavily rigged carriers "clippers" but, if their passing of fast-sailing types of ships or of known clippers is on record, it is usually possible to decide whether or not the vessel in question was truly "fast" in model, for the weather stated, or was merely lucky in her weather.

There are certain "probables" that decide a vessel's qualities when her model is examined. Sharp-model vessels of the Baltimore clipper type were usually quite fast close-hauled and on all other points of sailing if the wind were light or moderate and if the sea were not heavy. Commonly the deeper the draft (in relation to length and beam and therefore the greater the dead rise) in a Baltimore clipper, the faster she might be close-hauled, but she would probably be slower off the wind than some vessel with less draft and dead rise. This was also true at least to some extent in the later clipper ships. A relatively wide and flat-bottomed ship with fine ends would commonly be very stiff under sail and thus be able to carry a heavy press of canvas in strong winds. The North Atlantic packets were of this last description, as were some of the later clipper ships.

It is extremely difficult to draw firm conclusions about the relative speed of vessels of varying date and model. It has been customary to compare indiscriminately, using the criterions of fast passages and high-

32

est recorded speed in surviving ship's logs, the sailing speed of old trading vessels, packets, Baltimore-clipper model schooners and brigs, clipper ships, and the last sailing freighters of the United States, the down-Easters, to show that the design of sailing ships improved steadily during the whole 19th century in North America. As has been suggested (p. 32), the increase in size, or at least in average size, makes such comparisons very misleading; in addition, the question of the conditions of weather and wind under which each passage was made, is not considered. In the packets, for example, the run from New York to Liverpool was commonly made under very favorable conditions with fresh to strong winds abaft the beam; hence conditions on this course are extremely favorable to a ship that could carry a press of sail and maintain a good average speed. On the other hand, the return run to the westward was commonly unfavorable, for head winds could normally be expected; the packet usually had to claw her way to windward at least part way, if not for the whole distance. Thus a weatherly and powerful vessel might make a relatively good passage westward simply because she could sail well close-hauled, though her maximum potential speed might be relatively low. Such conditions, however, would not necessarily favor a powerful ship in all instances, for rig might be a factor. In one case a pilot-boat schooner left New York for Cork, Ireland, at the same time a packet ship sailed from New York for Liverpool. The schooner made the run to Cork under severe winter weather conditions in 26 days; the packet made the Irish coast in 28 days. The advantage of the schooner lay in the easterly winds then faced by both vessels. On the westward run, which packet ships were making in 34 days or more, the schooner came home in 29 days over the longer southern route, for on this run also the schooner rig had the advantage because of the amount of windward sailing required by the prevailing westerlies.

On the long runs to China or California and return to New York or Boston, the average weather encountered played a greater part in determining the length of the passage than the design of the hull of a ship. Since each individual ship had one point of sailing in which she could do her maximum potential speed, her length of passage would often depend upon how much of the time she was in weather conditions that suited this ability. Analysis of clipper-ship passages show numerous cases in which very fast ships, judging by plans, builder's half-models, and previous records, were beaten by potentially slower ships on the long

runs simply because the slower ship had weather conditions that suited her most for much longer periods than had the faster ship.

Another factor that bedevils the marine historian discussing clipper ships is the fashion that developed in the 1850's, in the United States and particularly at Boston and New York, of calling nearly every new and large ship a clipper ship. Since the fashion in design then called for any ship, full or fine ended, to carry a large spread of sail and since the length-of-passage criterion was most commonly used, it is not surprising to find that the "clipper ships" of the contemporary journalists were a mixed lot insofar as form of hull was concerned.

Out of 433 ships listed by Carl C. Cutler in his classic account of the clipper ships, *Greyhounds of the Sea*, and by other clipper-ship historians, the plans or builders' models of 72 have been examined; of these not more than a total of 44 can be considered sharp enough to have a very high potential speed for their length and only 35 could be properly called clippers or extreme clippers. At least 22 of the ships represented were relatively full-ended medium clippers and the rest are by any criterion full-ended ships. It is hardly sound to make any sweeping generalization of the actual number of extreme clippers that were built, with only about 16 percent of the so-called clippers capable of being judged on the basis of their hull form, but one may conclude that ships of very high potential speed were much less numerous among the so-called clipper ships of the 1850's than is indicated by the various listings. Cutler, in particular, makes this point clear in his introductory note.

In truth, the clipper ships introduced no one feature that was entirely new, and the first vessels in this category built for the China trade were really sharp-ended packets like the *Rainbow*, *Helena*, *Montauk*, and others. These were followed by more extreme ships, such as the *Samuel Russell*, *Oriental*, and *Sea Witch;* the latter may be said to have been the first really extreme ship of the new clipper-ship class. In general, then, although the early China clippers had a good deal of rise in the floors amidships, compared to that in the last class of North Atlantic packets, their model in most other respects was nearly that of a good packet.

Nor was the model of the fast packet then in use a recent design, for development of the fast carrier represented in the early China traders had begun at least as early as 1812, and even then the Baltimore builders were producing a medium carrier, having fairly easy lines, suitable for fast-sailing. A plan of one of these, the *Hannibal*, built at Baltimore in 1810 and captured and taken into the Royal Navy during the War of 1812, has been found. This ship, 135 feet 6 inches long on deck, 37 feet 5½ inches beam, and 10 feet 11 inches depth of hold, had rather marked deadrise but her longitudinal lines were rather full. The trend in design illustrated in the *Hannibal* seems to have developed rather slowly, largely in smaller brigs and brigantines; in fact it may be more correct to say the basic design reappeared from time to time, rather than to say that it was developed. By 1838 the Baltimore shipowners and shipbuilders had become very conscious of the shortcomings of the sharp-model vessels as peacetime carriers, recognizing that the old sharp-model vessels could no longer pay as they carried too little cargo in proportion to their dimensions, tonnage taxes, and crew costs. As a result, some attempts were being made to build ships of greater relative capacity with as little loss in speed as possible. This was done by combining the full body of the New England ships of the "Boston model" with the sharper ends of the "Baltimore model." A ship launched about this time was claimed to represent this combination, but her builder's model and drawings have not been found and no report of her performance seems to exist.

It is obvious, then, that the idea of employing a full body with fine entrance and run was nothing new when the *Rainbow* was built, not only because of the Baltimore effort, but also because of the evidence in ship plans dating at least as far back as 1806. Indeed as early as 1800 there had been two schools of thought in American shipbuilding, one considering extreme rise in the floor in the midship section necessary for a fast ship and the other that a large midsection with low dead rise could be used as well if the entrance and run were sharp.

The California gold rush in 1849 had brought the still ubiquitous Baltimore clippers into the new trade, but these small vessels were soon replaced by the new class of ships on the China-trade model; the famed and shortlived California clipper. The demand for fast ships in which speed rather than cargo capacity was paramount produced a boom in shipbuilding, and soon yards from the Chesapeake to the Canadian border were turning them out in numbers. At first the extreme clippers were built at New York (a few were built to the southward), while New England produced only moderately sharp vessels, but soon they were on the stocks in Massachusetts and Maine,

as well as in New Hampshire, Connecticut, and Rhode Island.

Actually there were three types of ships that could be truly called "clipper ships" because of their having higher potential maximum speed than other sailing ships. The most radical type were the extreme clippers, built primarily for speed and with the least regard for cargo capacity. These might be modifications of the old Baltimore clipper model, with marked dead rise and fine ends, as in the *Samuel Russell*, *Nightingale*, *Sea Witch*, *Witch of the Wave*, *Staghound*, and *Gazelle*. Some of these were far more radical in design than others.

Less radical were the clippers, the ships of sharp but more practical model in which there was a definite intent to combine speed with fair cargo capacity. Among these were such noted vessels as McKay's *Flying Cloud*, *Sovereign of the Seas*, and *James Baines*; Webb's *Comet*, *Young America*, and *Invincible*; and Samuel Pook's *Surprise*, *Red Jacket*, and *Belle of the West*. The ships of this class usually had a moderate rise in the floor, and a rather short but very sharp entrance and run, whereas the extreme clipper had a very long entrance and run. The two classes were not sharply divided but shaded gradually from one category to the other. The *Lightning* exemplifies this; with a rather full body she had, to a very marked degree, sharply formed ends, and these were quite long. Hence, even among naval architects and shipbuilders, there could be a valid difference of opinion as to how some ships should be classed.

Least extreme were the medium, or half clippers, vessels in which capacity came first but in which the designer had attempted to produce a reasonably fast vessel. Examples of this class were the *Nor'Wester*, *Andrew Jackson*, and *Golden Fleece*. This class, too, shaded imperceptibly into the next class below, the full-ended ship.

Building of clipper ships reached a maximum in 1853–54, and in these two years many excellent examples of each of the three basic classes of clipper ships came off the ways. A fine example of an extreme clipper was the *Sunny South*, designed and built by George Steers at Williamsburg, New York, in 1854. Steers had won notice as a designer of fast vessels by modeling and building notable pilot boats of the New York fleet and, in 1850–51, he designed the yacht *America* whose success in England brought him, still a young man, to great prominence. In designing the *Sunny South* Steers had followed the basic model he had used so successfully in his fast schooners and

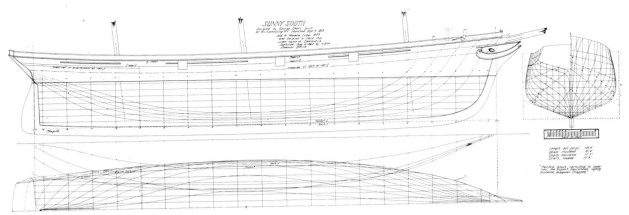

LINES OF THE EXTREME CLIPPER *Sunny South*, built at Williamsburg, New York, in 1854. She became the slaver *Emanuela*. Taken off the half-model in the Mariners' Museum, Newport News, Virginia.

particularly in the *America*. The clipper was relatively small, some 700 tons, and represented perhaps the most extreme design of all the American clipper ships built in the 1840's and 1850's. The vessel was marked by a very long and extremely fine entrance and a fine run, long for a ship-rigged vessel. She also had much dead rise amidships and was beautiful and yachtlike. Her figurehead was a gilded sea serpent carried the length of her curved trails, which were much like those of the yacht *America*, and the head was built up in the same manner as well. Like many of the China clippers and the coastal packets running into the Gulf of Mexico, the *Sunny South* was armed to repel pirates. It is worthy of comment that this beautiful vessel had the reputation of being extremely fast when in company of other ships, yet she made no record passages and she was not a financial success. She was eventually sold in 1858–59 to Havana where, under the name *Emanuela*, she became known as the fastest slaver out of that port. On Aug. 10, 1860, the *Emanuela*, flying the Chilean flag, was captured in the Mozambique Channel by H. M. steamship *Brisk*, when the wind failed the clipper. When taken, the *Emanuela* had 850 slaves aboard. Unlike many slavers taken by the Royal Navy, the *Emanuela* was not immediately destroyed; she appears to have been employed as a storeship for a few years at the Cape of Good Hope, after which she is supposed to have been broken up or burned.

The *Sunny South* was one of the few ships that actually had the feature that clipper ships were popularly supposed to have—a long, sharp, and hollow load line at the bow. She appears to have been the only American clipper ship that had her forefoot much cut away and had curvature for most of the length of her keel. Like some of the ships of her period she had a short, low quarterdeck and deep bulwarks. In appearance she resembled a large schooner hull of an improved Baltimore clipper model.

An example of the less radical clipper model was the Pook-designed *Fearless* built at East Boston, Massachusetts, in 1853 by A. and G. T. Sampson.

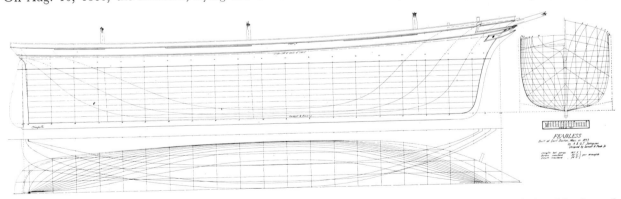

LINES OF THE CLIPPER SHIP *Fearless* built at East Boston, Massachusetts, in 1853. She was designed by Samuel Pook, Jr. Taken off the half-model in the Weld family collection.

MEDIUM CLIPPER *Coeur de Lion*, built at Portsmouth, New Hampshire, in 1854. From a painting in the Water-craft Collection (USNM 309517). Painted by the Chinese artist Chong Qua with great clarity of detail. The picture, as is usual in clipper ship portraits, slightly exaggerates the rake of bow and overhang of stern. (*Smithsonian photo 44635.*)

She was a fine-lined ship having a rather large midsection with little dead rise, a long, sharp and convex entrance, and a rather long and fine run. This ship might well be described as being as typical as any clippers could be in a class having so extensive a variation in design. Though the *Fearless* is said to have been somewhat less heavily sparred than some of her sisters, she was a very fast vessel and also held some notable passage records: Manila to Boston in 86 days in 1855 and San Francisco to Manila in 36 days in 1856.

As an example of a medium, or half, clipper the *Coeur de Lion* will serve; this fine ship was built at Portsmouth, New Hampshire, in 1854 by George Raynes, who designed and built a number of other fine vessels of this class, as well as at least two extreme clippers. The *Coeur de Lion* had a large midsection with some rise in the floor; the entrance was short,

moderately sharp, and convex; and the run was also short but well formed. This ship was heavily sparred and sailed well but held no passage records. Vessels of the class of the *Coeur de Lion* differed very little in model and in potential maximum speed from some of the better down-Easters built after the Civil War, except that the vessels of the clipper-ship period were usually more heavily canvassed and carried a larger crew, even though smaller in size.

The building of extreme clippers and clippers for all practical purposes ended with the depression of '57, which nearly destroyed shipbuilding all along the coast. The Civil War, following before the effects of the depression had worn off, and the destruction of much American shipping by British-built commerce raiders, were sufficient to depress the commercial shipbuilding industry in America for years afterward. It should be stated, however, that the clipper-ship

36

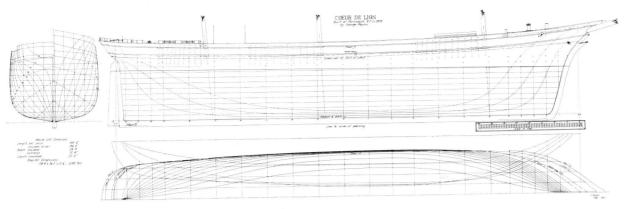

LINES OF THE MEDIUM CLIPPER *Coeur de Lion* built at Portsmouth, New Hampshire, in 1854. Taken off the half-model in the Portsmouth, New Hampshire, Athenaeum. A painting of this ship, in the Watercraft Collection, is shown, opposite.

building boom was almost fully deflated before 1857, for high freight rates were no longer obtainable in the California and China trades, owing to the huge number of ships competing for cargoes and the increasing ability of California and the Northwest coast to provide many of the necessities formerly brought from the East.

The whole development and decline of the American clipper ship occurred in the short period of 9 or 10 years. Although Americans did not build any extreme clippers after the Civil War, the British continued their development through the 1860's and into the 1870's. In the last years of British development many very extreme ships, some as extreme as the *Sunny South*, were built in England and Scotland, though of an entirely different model.

Attempts to make comparisons between British and American clipper ships are useless, for the two national types were designed to meet entirely different requirements of weather and sea and trade conditions. In the 1850's, when British and American ships were temporarily in the same trades, the Americans appear to have had the faster ships on the average but late in the 1850's the American advantage had almost disappeared in any of the trades where the ships competed. Such competition was so limited, however, that any conclusion based on relative speed of individual clippers is misleading. While the Americans can claim credit for introducing the extreme clipper and the clipper designs, they did not maintain a monopoly on the design of very fast merchant ships and many such were launched in Europe during the last years of the American clipper ship period and for about 10 years thereafter.

A reason for the American failure to resume building fast vessels after the Civil War lay in the fact that there were few American trades in which fast vessels were in demand. Of these few, the two most important were the fruit trade with the Bahamas, the West Indies, and Florida, and the coffee trade with Brazil. The latter in particular was carried on by vessels of some size, small barks and many brigantines and brigs being employed. Most of these were built at Baltimore, on the Chesapeake, and on the Delaware, but some notable coffee traders were constructed at New York and in New England. These vessels were usually fast sailers. The barks were sometimes almost medium clippers; the builders' model of the *Albemarle* in the Watercraft Collection (see p. 63) is a good example of the type of bark used; but few of the vessels, barks or brigantines or brigs, were very sharp-ended. Some brigantines were employed in the fruit trade, but most of the fruiters were schooners, and toward the last of the sailing fruit trade 3-masted schooners became popular. A particularly favored model was built at Bath, Maine, for this trade, and a few of these 3-masters were also built in Maryland. Fast fishing schooners and coasters were often employed in this trade, which was seasonal. The Bahamas and Florida fruit trade was mostly in pineapples; on the Florida east coast the Indian River country was being exploited in the years immediately following the Civil War, growing pineapples and, later, oranges.

Coasters

In colonial times the coasting trade was of very great importance. The small size of port villages and towns and the limited back country they served made

37

it difficult for them to gather cargoes for foreign trade that was needed to support the colonial economies. Gradually certain ports became developed enough to sustain some foreign trade, either through natural physical advantages or through the existence of certain products, such as tobacco for instance, in the back country. These ports at least as early as 1670 began, by means of a coastal trade, to draw upon other coastal areas to build up cargoes for their overseas trade and to supply local users. In the process, regular traders as well as coastal packets developed, so that by the time of the Revolution well designed coasters and packets were in operation.

The earliest coasters appear to have been ketches (or "catches"), sloops, and large shallops. As has been stated (p. 15), there is reason to suppose that the early ketches were in fact primitive schooners, and that the shallops were in this class also, though without headsails or bowsprit. The sloops seem to have appeared in colonial waters in a well developed state, and some of the early coasting sloops appear to have been rather large vessels for the time; records indicate that as early as 1690 some were about 50 feet on deck. The efforts of the colonial ports to support themselves, after trade with England was halted by the Civil War in Britain, led to the rapid development of a profitable West Indian trade even then operated as part of the coastal trade. This resulted naturally from the geographical distribution of the early American ports, for vessels proceeding to and from the West Indies could readily pick up and set down cargoes in a number of American ports along the way. This close relationship was characteristic of the American coastal trade on the eastern seaboard throughout the period of sail. There was in addition to the legal trade, a profitable smuggling trade in the West Indies from colonial times well into the 19th century, and beyond.

In the colonial period some river trade also developed, producing for the work, such craft as shoal-draft sloops, shallops, gundalows, and "flats," or scows. Some of these were of sufficient size to make short coasting voyages as well. The sloops and shallops built for use on the James River in Virginia, on the Delaware, on the Hudson, and on some New England rivers included some vessels of this description. A small-craft trade also developed along the coast, particularly on Long Island Sound and on the Chesapeake. The lack of plans, models, or even pictures, of colonial craft prevent us from knowing very much about them, though they are referred to in some colonial records.

Sloops and schooners predominated, though ships, brigs, and brigantines were also popular in the 18th-century coastal-West Indian trade. The growing importance of the lumber trade gradually produced coasting vessels suitable for carrying this merchandise. There appears to have been after 1740 a somewhat rapid increase in the average size of coasting vessels, and this led to an increase in the proportion of schooner-rigged vessel employed, as the large sloop required too many hands to work her. After 1825 sloops were limited to river and estuary trade, where the sloop-rigged carrier required fewer hands than in coastal waters. In the last quarter of the 18th century and throughout the 19th the most active coastal traders were the inhabitants of New England and of the Chesapeake region, though nearly all the Atlantic coastal ports carried on some coastal trade, particularly New York merchants.

After the Revolution the American coastal trade prospered, constituting a very great part of the total American merchant marine investment; and after the War of 1812 the rapid growth of many port towns and cities, the opening of canals and roads, and the development of the back country, caused a further expansion in coastal trade.

The New England trade to the West Indies after 1820 was carried on almost entirely by topsail schooners and brigantines. These vessels were usually large carriers and designed to carry lumber, as well as general cargo. In the period immediately after the end of the Napoleonic War and extending well into the 1830's the West Indies and the Gulf of Mexico was infested with pirates and freebooters, some masquerading as privateersmen out of the rebelling Spanish colonies. For that reason some New England West Indian trading vessels were modified carriers, designed to have a fair turn of speed, and many were also rather heavily armed. The Chesapeake traders used in this trade many small pilot-boat schooners as well as some quite large schooners and brigantines or brigs, all armed. As the British and American navies succeeded in suppressing piracy, armament went out of fashion, though some traders, particularly those smuggling, carried guns until as late as 1855.

The American West Indian trade extended to many of the old Spanish colonies on the mainland along the Gulf of Mexico.

Cargoes sent to the West Indies were at first salt fish, but they soon came to include flour, building and cooperage materials, farm produce, and manufac-

THE BLANCHARD SHIPYARD (LEFT) IN YARMOUTH, MAINE. Note the very fine example of 2-masted coasting schooner in the left foreground. (*Smithsonian photo 45095.*)

tured goods such as tools, stoves, hardware, and textiles. The vessels brought home dyewoods and mahogany as well as sugar and other merchandise.

Ownership of American sailing merchantmen in this period might be by individuals or by companies, or by a group who divided "stock" in a vessel. Some shipowners in the 19th century held a controlling but not complete interest in a ship or number of ships, and some merchants used this method to reserve to themselves reliable and controlled transportation for their goods. Individuals owning 100 percent of a fleet of large vessels were comparatively rare. In New England it was not uncommon for a shipbuilding community to build a large vessel and for the tradesmen to take shares or stock in her; the vessel was then operated by a vessel manager or by the captain, the latter being the more usual, who settled with the share owners at stated intervals. Shipbuilders often held shares in the vessels they built, and in a few cases, particularly in Maine, there were shipowners who built only on their own account. There were booms in vessel-owning, as in the clipper-ship period, and severe depressions, as in the late 1870's. Throughout the sailing ship period some vessels—ocean freighters, coasters, and even clipper ships—were built on speculation and sold after completion; but in general vessels were built under contract, the owner or owners financing the builder.

The brigantines and topsail schooners built in New England for the trade had a marked sheer, a somewhat raking and flaring stem rabbet fitted with a short head usually heavy in appearance, a slightly raking post, an upper-and-lower square transom stern with round tuck, a full convex entrance, and a long and sometimes fine run. The midsection usually showed small rise of floor and low and well-rounded bilges. Such vessels sailed moderately well. Generally speaking these vessels were cheaply and roughly built, though there were exceptions. The coasting vessels built in Maine were usually constructed at very low cost but, in spite of the rough finish, were very long-lived and made profitable vessels in the coastal trade. Those vessels built for the West Indian and lumber trades had short quarter-decks usually combined with high main-deck bulwarks; as a result the cabin sole of the trunk cabin was actually the maindeck, giving all space below the maindeck for cargo. Small schooners often housed the entire crew in the trunk cabin. Large schooners and brigantines usually had a small deckhouse at, or abaft, the foremast for a galley; sometimes this served to quarter the crew. In the large vessels there was sometimes a short forecastle below the main-deck. Some of the schooners and brigantines had quarterdeck bulwarks, others had merely the turned-stanchion-and-cap rail aft which eventually became very popular in all coasters. The West Indian traders were usually over 80 feet on deck.

39

The regular New England coasting trade, after 1825, was carried on to a very great extent by 2-masted fore-and-aft rigged schooners 50 to 75 feet long, having short, high quarterdecks with bulwarks or turned-stanchion rails. Some of the vessels had a strong resemblance to the old Marblehead schooner, but these were usually much less sharp.

The Chesapeake Bay coastal traders were Baltimore clippers, often of the modified model and commonly with flush decks and a low trunk cabin aft. These vessels as a rule had a small galley house just abaft the foremast; the crew was housed in the trunk cabin and in a short forecastle right forward, below the main-deck. Before 1850 coasters on the Baltimore clipper model were rarely over 80 feet and were commonly topsail schooners, in the West Indian coastal trade. Brigantines were rarely over 100 feet in length.

At an early period after the War of 1812, probably in 1815–25, the centerboard was introduced into the Chesapeake Bay schooner. Some of the early centerboard schooners were fitted with two boards, one forward and one abaft the mainmast, but by 1830 the single centerboard had come into use. In the Bay schooners this was often placed alongside the mainmast and off center so that the board passed through the garboard rather than through the keel. In such schooners the mainmast might also be off center, on the opposite side from the centerboard. By 1850 the standard Chesapeake Bay centerboard schooner hull had a straight keel, rather upright and flaring stem rabbet, upright post, round tuck, upper-and-lower-transom square stern, moderate sheer, flush deck, a short but usually sharp convex entrance, and a rather long, fine run. The midsection had a slightly rising straight floor, a low, full round bilge, and some tumble-home in the topsides. A short, heavy head complete with headrails and trails was used until about 1850, when the local fashion turned to the long and projecting cutwater that, exaggerated in time, came to mark all Chesapeake schooners and bugeyes.

A local type of Chesapeake Bay schooner, mentioned earlier (p. 25), that was employed in the Bay coasting trade and occasionally in the trade to the Bahamas, was the "pungy," the last survivor of the Baltimore clipper model in the cargo-carrying class of schooners. Known at first as an inexpensive example of the true Baltimore clipper, it was commonly flush-decked and usually with stanchion-and-cap rails aft but with a low log rail forward. The draft was rather deep, the ends quite sharp, and there was a good deal of rise in the floor amidships. But by 1850, at least, the most common pungy model was closely related to that of the Norfolk, or Virginia, pilot-boat schooner in that there was only moderate rise of floor amidships (the hull being relatively shallow), a low round bilge, and sharply flaring topside. The pungy was a very fast sailer, particularly in light and moderate winds, but was wet in blowing weather. Some of the pungies were employed in the sea fisheries for a short period in the 1840's and early 1850's, as well as in the fruit trade.

When the clipper ship became popular in the 1850's coasters soon showed the clipper-ship influence and many fine vessels were built of good model and well finished; for by this time the coasting trades were all very profitable and most owners could afford such refinements. The old round tuck stern, with its wide upper-and-lower transoms, went slowly out of fashion all along the coast; it was replaced, first by a flat and sharply raking transom with round tuck, then by a short counter with a raking transom curved athwartships and, in New England, elliptical in shape. Round fantail counters became popular in the 1850's in some areas, New York and Boston in particular.

In the last half of the 19th century the New England coasting schooner reached its maximum development and, from Maine to Connecticut, schooners were being built that had good capacity, construction, and sailing qualities combined with good looks. There were basically two models of the 2-master in New England in this period; one was the true schooner hull in which the depth of hull was not very great and the entrance and run were rather short, sharp, and well formed. In some trades another model was developed in large coasters; it resembled that of a square-rigged down-Easter, having great depth of hull and the run formed with marked reverse curves in the buttocks. In model such schooners were really in some instances medium clippers. The New England coaster of two masts then carried a fore-and-aft rig with two headsails (jumbo and jib) fisherman fashion, fore and main gaff-topsails in summer, and only a topsail in winter. Square sails were very rarely employed in these vessels after the Civil War. Two-masters of from 100 to 135 feet on deck were built during that period, but were found very expensive to operate, as they required large crews. By 1885 some had been fitted with a donkey engine and boiler used not only to raise the anchor but also to hoist sails. However, by then the gradual loss of the package trade to steamers required coasting schooners

THE 3-MASTED SCHOONER *J. S. Hoskins*, built by the New England Ship Building Company, Bath, Maine, for Emerson Rokes, of Baltimore, Maryland. Launched October 26, 1886, her register dimensions were 193.9' x 34.2' x 11.5', 411.56 gross tons. Her captain was Joshua A. Rich. (*Smithsonian photo 44588.*)

to be built almost entirely for bulk cargoes, so there was a need for schooners larger than was practical for the 2-masted rig.

The 3-masted schooner was found to be the solution, so far as economy in operation was concerned, to the shift to bulk cargoes in the sailing coasting trade of the 1850's. As has been noted (p. 21), the 3-masted schooner apparently came into being quite late in the 18th century. It had been popular at Baltimore and vicinity about 1800, but not elsewhere. Between that time and 1850, however, a few were built outside the Chesapeake; and during the 1850's and right after the end of the Civil War a number were built for coasting and ocean freighting. Most of the early ones were relatively sharp models with a rising straight floor amidships, a full, round bilge, and tumble-home in the topside. The entrance was moderately long and sometimes fairly sharp, with convex lines.

The run was of moderate length and often quite fine, and the sheer rather straight. These first 3-masters were, in fact, strongly influenced by the clipper-ship fashion and therefore many had very short and light heads, mere gammon knees fitted with some simple decoration.

It was soon found that the sharp-model 3-master did not pay in the coastal trade and for this reason the model had to be altered. By 1875 two types of 3-master were in use. One was the centerboard model, having a shoal-draft hull with rather flat floor amidships, a low and sometimes hard bilge, and tumble-home in the topside. Some of this type had a rather long and sharp convex entrance combined with a long and markedly flat run; the sheer was quite strong and the rig large. These were often very swift sailers. Some had two centerboards and others one; if a single one was used it was often placed

41

abreast the mainmast and either the case or the mast, or both, might be off center. Some of these schooners had a short quarterdeck and others a long one extending to the foremast or thereabouts. The second type was a keel model, usually with a hull like that of a down-Easter, in which there was very marked depth and in which the run showed reverse curves in the buttock lines.

In the lumber and coal trades the 3-masters proved very profitable, and many were built all along the American coasts, Atlantic and Pacific, from the end of the Civil War until the end of the first World War. A few, particularly on the Pacific coast, were fitted with square fore-topsails. By 1885 more schooners were being built in a single year than all other rigs together. The steadily increasing size of 3-masted schooners led to the introduction of the 4-mast rig in 1880; the first coasting schooner carrying this rig was the *William L. White* built at Bath, Maine. In 1888 the first 5-master, the *Governor Ames*, fitted with a centerboard, was built. In 1900 the first 6-master, the *George W. Wells* was built, and soon after that a steel 7-master, the *Thomas W. Lawson*. Because of their cost, only seven steel schooners were built on the Atlantic coast. By 1885 the large coasting schooners were employed almost entirely in the coal trade. Wooden 5-masted and 6-masted schooners proved generally unsatisfactory, as they were too long to have longitudinal strength, and were awkward to handle in confined waters. By 1920 the coal schooners had given way to steam colliers; by then the sailing coasting trade was a thing of the past.

The model developed for the 4-, 5-, and 6-masted schooners became almost standardized except for dimensions. The vessels had a strong sheer and a strongly raking stem rabbet on which was either a plain gammon knee with some carving or a light head fitted with trail boards and, in some cases, with single head rails. The post was nearly vertical and the stern was formed with a short and light counter having a wide elliptical transom. The entrance was sharp, convex, and of moderate length; the run was likewise rather short but often very well formed and as fine as in many of the clipper ships of the 1850's. These big schooners were sometimes fast sailers under favorable conditions, but were too lightly manned to allow them to be sailed hard; in addition their construction was rarely strong enough for such treatment.

The small 2-masted coasters lingered on in Maine, on the Chesapeake and on the Gulf coast, until well into the 20th century but the development of the type may be said to have ceased by about 1885, though 2-masted coasters were built as late as 1914. In the last years of the small sailing coasters, vessels built for specific coasting trades were employed in general trade, often far from their place of building and original employment. Thus, schooners built for the stone and brick trades at New York and in Massachusetts ended their days in the Florida or the Maine general coasting trade.

In the great period of the 2-masted sailing coaster, between 1825 and 1885, many special types were developed. One was the scow schooner. The early history of this vessel type in America is not known; scow sloops were employed from colonial times for river trade and were common on the Maine coast, on the Hudson River, the Gulf coast, at the head of Chesapeake Bay, and on the Great Lakes. As the scows grew in size the schooner rig became popular and a large number of scow schooners were in use by 1870. Most were fitted with centerboards but a few had leeboards, as had most of the scow sloops. After the Civil War the scow schooner became popular at San Francisco for Bay and river trading. At least one 3-mast scow schooner was built on Long Island Sound. Scow sloops and schooners were used in the Hudson River brick trade and scow sloops were once very common on the New England coast, carrying sand, stone, firewood, and ice.

The general coastwise schooner trade was in a huge variety of cargoes; lumber, flour, salt, sugar, grain, coal, wood staves and hoops, ice, firewood, salt fish, sand, stone, bricks, lime, hay, farm produce, manufactures, and "notions." Cotton, grain, and other bulk cargoes were often lightered to a loading port by coasting schooners. Livestock was often carried and on the Maine coast schooner loads of sheep were often carried between the mainland and the islands, which were once used as grazing grounds.

Coasting packets were once very profitable, and even after steamers had taken over the important runs between large ports, the schooner packet was able to serve the small coastal towns and villages. Some of these packets operated until after the Civil War, by which time the railroads and steamers had reached most of the coastal areas, and highway transport had also developed. The schooner packet, usually built for the purpose or a converted fisherman or coaster with a reputation as a smart sailer, generally was no more than a sharp-ended coaster in model. The rig was that of a coaster, of perhaps greater sail area than

THE 3-MASTED SCHOONER *Bertha Louise*, of Fall River, Massachusetts, built by Kelly and Spear of Bath, Maine, and launched March 1, 1890. A typical New England 3-masted coasting schooner of the date, her register dimensions were 115.2′ x 28.3′ x 8.7′, 231.42 gross tons. (*Smithsonian photo 44872.*)

usual. If the packet run was long enough to warrant sleeping quarters, the cabin was fitted for passengers, the after trunk being usually given up to passengers and the captain, and the crew being quartered forward as usual. The hold was fitted for light cargo, but some vessels had large hatches fitted with temporary ramps to allow carrying carriages and wagons in the hold as well as horses. Some of the packet operators, particularly in eastern New England, had arrangements with stage-coach lines that permitted the transfer of mail, packaged goods, and passengers.

Coastal passages by the sailing packets were far more comfortable and usually faster than by stage-coaches, particularly if the trip were long. A number of Chesapeake-Bay-built schooners were employed as coastal packets after 1840 even in New England, though New England builders were turning out very fast packet schooners themselves. A distinct period

existed, 1845–50, in which Maryland-built schooners were introduced into New England, particularly at Cape Cod and at Gloucester and one of the builder's models in the Collection (p. 78) shows a vessel built for the packet trade on this imported model.

The brigantines used in the coasting trades during the 19th century represent a most interesting class of vessel. During much of the century vessels of this rig were "jacks-of-all-trades," serving alternately as coasters, West Indian traders, and as ocean freighters. This rig had a very curious history. In the 17th century it appears in its accepted form—a 2-masted vessel square rigged on the foremast and fore-and-aft on the main. At some time late in that century, or early in the 18th century, the fashion arose for carrying a square topsail on the main, and later square topgallant sails were added to this mast so that, except for the main course, the fore and main masts carried the

THE 4-MASTED COASTING SCHOONER *King Philip* was built in 1886 at Camden, Maine. Her register dimensions were 211.0′ x 42.5′ x 20.4′, 1,163.65 net tons. From a painting by W. P. Stubbs, 1888, in the Watercraft Collection (USNM 76108). (*Smithsonian photo 44691–b.*)

square sails. The foremast, in this period, had no gaff sail. It was common practice, in naval reports, to refer to the brigantine in abbreviation, "brig.," and gradually "brig" (with period omitted) was used when actually a "brigantine" was meant. When in the 18th century a main course was added to the brigantine, the resulting rig came to be called "brig" by lexicographers. A variation of this rig was the "snow," a 2-masted vessel rigged exactly like the "brig" that had by then developed, except that on the after side of the mainmast, was placed a pole, or small mast, on which a main fore-and-aft gaff-sail, or spanker, was set, an arrangement that allowed the main yard to be lowered without interfering with the main fore-and-aft sail, as it did on the brigs and brigantines. Curiously enough, the snow rig became the naval rig known as the "brig," so that after 1810 nearly all naval brigs were, in fact, snows! In the 19th century a fore-and-aft gaff-sail of small size was added on the foremast and the result was called "schooner brig" or "brig schooner" by some and

finally, by most seamen, hermaphrodite. To add to the confusion, the British Navy as late as 1812 rated as "brigantines" vessels having the lexicographers' "brig" rig.

The American coasting brigantine was built in a variety of hull forms. The most common was that of the ordinary 2-masted topsail schooner, having a rather full entrance, long and often fine run, moderate sheer, slightly raking and flaring stem rabbet with a short and heavy cutwater, a somewhat raking stern-post, upper-and-lower raking transoms with round tuck, the rail quite full at the bow and the sides almost parallel for most of the hull length. The midsection was formed with a slight rise in the straight floor, a full round bilge, and some tumble-home in the topside. The high, raised quarterdeck, at main-rail height, was short and had solid bulwarks or the turned-stanchion-and-cap rail. Between 1820 and 1850 this was the most common New England coasting brigantine. To the southward the model used was that of the modified Baltimore clipper until about

44

1838, when the Chesapeake Bay region began to build brigantines very like the New England type, but with a much finer entrance and run and with a very flaring bow section. By 1840 they had produced a clipper brigantine having many of the hull-design features that were to mark the clipper class (see p. 73) of the 1850's, and as the clipper ships became fashionable, the New England brigantine builders followed the style set by the Bay builders.

By then however, the size of brigantines had increased and builders in New York, and later in New England and Maryland, were launching brigantines whose hull design was that of the clipper ship, in which the floor was carried well fore-and-aft and the buttocks had marked reverse curves as the counter was approached. These vessels sometimes had long quarter-decks reaching to the foremast, or beyond. Another variation, used in some New-England-built brigantines and 3-masted schooners, was to carry what had earlier been the raised quarter-deck from the level of the rail height aft to the level of the main-deck at stem,

in a long, flush deck that did not follow the outward sheer of the hull. The turned-stanchion-and-cap rail was carried to the foremast, or thereabouts, in these vessels and, eventually, this rail was brought to the knightheads.

A number of barkentines, 3-masted vessels with square sails on the foremast only and fore-and-aft rigged on the main and mizzen, were built for both coasting and for the ocean trades after 1850. This rig became popular on the West Coast, and some very fine wooden barkentines were launched on the Northwest Coast. On the Great Lakes, 2-masted schooners with square-topsails on the foremast gave place to 3-masters in the 1850's and 1860's. Gradually a distinctive type of 3-master developed in the Lake trades in which the hull was long, narrow and rather full ended and wall sided, the entrance short and moderately full, the run short but often rather fine, and the hull fitted with a centerboard. The rig sometimes had a short mizzen-mast, and a large square course was set on the foremast and above it either a square topsail or a

DECK OF THE 4-MASTED SCHOONER *Sam G. Mengel*, built in Maine, 1917. (*Smithsonian photo 38454-e.*)

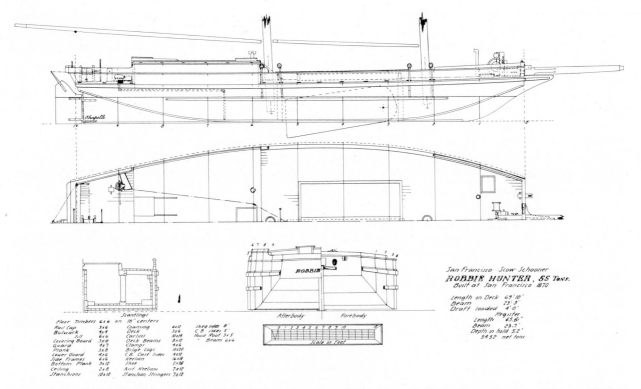

Scantlings

Floor Timbers	6x6	on 18" centers	
Rail Cap	3x6	Coaming	6x12
Bulwark	4x4	Deck	3x6
Sill	6x6	Carlins	10x14
Covering Board	3x10	Deck Beams	8x12
Guard	4x7	Clamps	4x6
Plank	3x8	Bilge Logs	16x20
Lower Guard	4x6	C.B. Case Sides	4x18
Side Frames	6x6	Keelson	14x18
Bottom Plank	3x12	Shoe	2x18
Ceiling	2x8	Asst Keelson	7x18
Stanchions	10x10	Stanchion Stringers	7x12

Skeg sides 8"
C.B. sides 5"
" Beams 6x6

Afterbody   Forebody

Scale in Feet

San Francisco Scow-Schooner
ROBBIE HUNTER, 55 Tons.
Built at San Francisco 1870

Length on Deck   69'10"
Beam   23'3"
Draft loaded   4'0"
Register
Length   65'6"
Beam   23'7"
Depth in hold   5'2"
54.52 net tons

LINES OF SAN FRANCISCO 2-MASTED SCOW SCHOONER *Robbie Hunter*, built in 1870. As taken off by the Historic American Merchant Marine Survey.

raffee, a triangular topsail with its apex at the topmast head.

In the late 19th century a number of variations in sail form took place in some localities; on the Pacific Coast many schooners had the mainsail of triangular form with a long, triangular topsail set above and abaft this, with its sheet made up to the end of the main boom. This rig was also used on the spanker in barkentines and brigantines built on the West Coast.

Auxiliary steam schooners were built on the Pacific Coast and on the Great Lakes. On the Lakes these were actually steam barges with a rather large sail plan and had a 3- or 4-masted schooner rig without a bowsprit. On the Pacific Coast the "steam schooner" was employed in the coastal lumber trade and eventually this name was so well established that it became the type-name of the lumber vessels there, even after they became steamers without a sailing rig.

The relation of Canadian builders to American builders requires mention, for there are a few Canadian half-models in the Watercraft Collection. From Colonial times, after Canada ceased to be a French colony, the relationship between shipbuilders of Canada and of the United States was very close, particu-

larly between those of Nova Scotia and New Brunswick builders and those of Maine, New Hampshire and Massachusetts. There were also very close relations between builders on both sides of the Great Lakes. The shipyards and boatshops of New England employed many Canadian-born carpenters, who worked on both sides of the border, as employment demanded. As a result the vessels built in New England and in the Canadian Maritime Provinces were quite similar in hull design, construction, and rig. In the 1840's and 1850's many fine vessels were built in eastern Canada, including the very fast *Marco Polo* and a number of medium clippers. The New Brunswick builders along the Gulf of St. Lawrence built fine ships, barks, brigantines, and some steamers in the period between 1850 and 1885. The fishing schooners built in Nova Scotia after about 1865 were on the same model as those built in Massachusetts. Small craft in eastern Canada were generally of a distinctive model and the boatbuilders of Nova Scotia, in particular, have had a reputation for skill.

It is worthy of mention that many shipbuilders who became famous in the United States were Canadian born or Canadian trained—Eckford, Donald McKay and Lawlor are examples. During the last quarter of the 19th century ship design was taught at a small trade school at Charlestown, Massachusetts, and the graduates of this school included many Nova Scotian and New Brunswick shipbuilders as well as many New Englanders, some of whom became prominent in their business.

During the last quarter of the 19th century the shipbuilders of eastern Canada built many fine coasting schooners and also some sharp-model 2-masters to carry salt fish to Europe. In the early 20th century, and particularly during the first World War, the Nova Scotia builders launched for this trade some sharp, fast sailing 3-masted, or "tern" schooners on yacht-like lines. While most of these schooners retained the traditional "clipper bow" quite a number were designed with the round bow profile of the contemporary sailing fishing schooner. The Nova Scotia 3-masted "fish carriers" were the last fast-sailing commercial vessel type to be launched in North America, and in this respect they may be said to be the "last of the clippers" as some of these vessels were extreme models for sharpness of form.

Ocean Freighters

Of far greater economic importance than North Atlantic packets and clipper ships in the development of the American sailing merchant marine were the ocean freighters, the regular traders and transients of the late 18th and 19th century. They included brigs, snows, and ships, and later barks, brigantines, and barkentines, and a few large, square-topsail schooners.

HUDSON RIVER BRICK SCHOONER of about 1890. (*Smithsonian photo 45785-b.*)

These ocean freighters carried on the bulk of the sea trade of the American colonies and, later, of the United States. The popular type of vessel varied with the times, and with the state of the times. When there was peace they were full-ended and slow sailers, for economical operation required large cargo capacity in relation to hull size, rather than speed and handiness. In times of unrest, the sea trader was often a Baltimore clipper, or at least a fairly fast sailer for her size, with cargo capacity limited by the necessity of sailing fast in order to have any cargo to deliver at all. This is not to say that such changes were universal, for there was always some use for the two extremes. The full-lined ship could be used in convoys in wartime, and so we find the pre-Revolutionary merchant ships of the colonials relatively full-ended vessels during the French wars because they had naval protection, whereas earlier, in the last years of the 17th century, and later, in the 18th century, fast ships had been built because of the lack of this protection. After the Revolution, insofar as a generalization may be made, the average merchant ship had lines fairly good for swift sailing. The unprotected state of most of the American merchant marine in the period 1786–1815, as has been explained, had made popular the Baltimore clipper model, and even the hull design of merchant ships, in which cargo capacity was thought most desirable, had felt the influence of this design.

As early as 1760, and before 1818, American merchant ships were commonly built in lengths of 75 to 100 feet on deck; and brigs were 60 to 90 feet. These vessels had a large midsection with some slight rise in the floor. As early as 1800 there was a difference of opinion among American shipbuilders as to the desirability of rising floors in square-rigged vessels, as has been mentioned. Before 1815 the stem and sternpost were usually well raked but there was no uniformity in proportion; in this there was also a difference in opinion as to what was most desirable in square-rigged vessels, and as early as 1760 many were built with nearly upright posts. The entrance was commonly very short and full and the run long and fine. Some sharp-built vessels were launched, as we have seen (p. 19), at least as early as the American Revolution and there can be little doubt that such ships were built much earlier. By the time of the Revolution, American ships no longer had high quarterdecks of more than one level, or deck. The fashion of having low raised decks at bow and stern lasted until about 1780; thereafter it gradually went out of style and, by 1790, flush decks were becoming in-

47

BRIGANTINE *San Blas* at East Boston in the 1890's. (*Smithsonian photo 45785.*)

creasingly common. Many vessels had open bulwarks on the main deck and some carried these to the stern. The average size of American ocean freighters grew gradually; ships of 110 to 115 feet on deck increased in number during the first decade of the 19th century.

The increased interest in improvement of design that competition among packet-ship builders had created in the period immediately after the War of 1812 (see p. 29) had a considerable effect on American shipbuilding, but all classes of ocean freighters, and particularly those in the European trade, did not benefit from this movement. The design of these ships and brigs was mainly influenced by efforts to evade the measurements of the existing tonnage law, so as to have more capacity in fact than the tonnage measurement indicated. There is not space to describe the law and its influence in detail; suffice to say that it produced a very deep and full-ended hull that gradually developed into the kettle bottom craft represented by some builders' models in the Watercraft Collection. Such vessels, though wretched sailers, could carry double their register yet be subject to far less taxes and port charges than a normal vessel. Even ships of less extreme model were often very full-ended to obtain great capacity for a given tonnage; and full-ended ships, barks, and brigs were built in very large numbers in New England between 1820 and 1850.

The common ocean trader of this period had a rather straight sheer, straight keel with little or no drag, a nearly upright stem above the load line with

a short curve at the forefoot, a moderately raking post, and an upper-and-lower transom square stern with round tuck below. The entrance was very short and quite full, and the rail line was almost square across at the bow and very sharply rounded at the shoulders. The stern was wide and the sides of the hull were almost parallel for most of the length. The run was very short and full. Ships of the period 1820-40 were commonly 100 to 135 feet long on deck, brigs 75 to 100 feet, and topsail schooners and brigantines slightly smaller in the European and South American trades. The cutwater was short and heavy, naval fashion, and the vessels had a heavy, blocklike appearance. Improved rigs were developed. Fore-and-aft gaff sails, were employed on all masts of ships and brigs; these were called spencers when on the fore and main masts of ships. Many schooners had fore booms. The bark rig was becoming popular. Vessels, in general, were fitted to be operated economically.

In the 1840's and 1850's the fashionable clippers caused a change in the appearance of ocean traders; ships 190 feet in length became common; and in model they took on the appearance of the clipper ship, with round sterns, light and simple heads and cutwaters, and well proportioned sail plans. The entrance and run were lengthened somewhat and made finer so that, on the average, their sailing qualities were improved. Many ocean traders were almost medium, or half, clippers. In some trades, particularly the South American and Pacific trades, a large proportion of rather sharp brigs, brigantines, and

48

THE 3-MASTED SALT-FISH CARRIER
E. P. Theriault, built in Nova
Scotia in 1919. (*Smithsonian photo
38794–b*).

topsail schooners were employed and some of these were fast-sailing craft.

The building of ocean freighting ships declined after the depression of 1857 and very few ships of any great size were built until after the Civil War, when there was a slow recovery and New England in particular began building ships over 190 feet and of a superior class. These down-Easters, as they came to be known, were fuller ended than earlier clippers and extreme clippers, approaching the medium clipper in form, and many were very large and well finished. The number of brigs, brigantines, and topsail schooners in foreign trade gradually lessened; brigantines and schooners in this period were built primarily for the coasting and the West Indian trades.

The down-Easter soon achieved high importance in the American merchant marine and in most respects represented the highest development of the sailing merchant ship. They were large carriers yet had lines that permitted quick passages on occasion. They had relatively smaller sail plans than the old clipper ships, but with their larger average size and greater power to carry sail, they were nearly as fast on long voyages as the more extreme ships of the 1850's. Builders' models in the Watercraft Collection illustrate this class of ship and show the perfection in hull form that the New England builders reached by 1885. Most of these ships had strong sheer compared to earlier vessels. The rather upright stem had a short flaring cutwater with very sparse adornment, in the form of a figurehead or billet and a little carving; often the trails and headrails were omitted.

The stern was often round or there was a light and well formed counter with an elliptical transom. The entrance was fairly sharp and convex, and of moderate length. The run was rather short but often very well formed.

The down-Easter remained supreme in the American merchant marine until well toward the end of the 19th century, when economic depressions and unwise taxes finally took their toll. By then the competition of steamers had also become very effective and the cost of operating ships under the American flag gradually rose so that they could no longer compete with foreign ships. The maritime interest of the American public had also declined very markedly after the Civil War. The opportunities for profit in the expansion in the West and the rise of American manufacturing in many areas produced a shift in economic interest; investors formerly supporting shipping now turned to railways, manufacturing, land speculation, timbering, and mining. By 1900 the American merchant marine was to a very great extent restricted to the coasting trade and to inland navigation.

Attempts to revive the seagoing merchant marine were made but it was not until the first World War that any real success was obtained, and this was accomplished by government subsidy. Standard models of freight steamers were built as part of the war effort and, for a period, America was again active in foreign trade. This declined for a time after the war but in the years prior to the outbreak of the second World War a strong merchant marine was

49

MERCHANT SHIP *Bazaar*, from a French print in the Watercraft Collection (USNM 76499). A good example of an American freighting ship of the period 1825–45, she was built at Medford, Massachusetts, in 1834 and employed in the European trade. Her register tonnage was 490, old measurement. (*Smithsonian photo 44638-g.*)

again developed. In the meantime the coastal trade had declined until, by 1940, it was almost non-existent. At the present time the American merchant marine represents an unusual condition—a seagoing trade development unsupported by any coastal trade of consequence. The modern merchant marine is referred to in more detail under steamships (p. 114).

Special Types

The 19th century saw the rise of a number of special types of sailing craft. Perhaps the most important or best known were the pilot boats. The first American pilots, active in the colonial period, were self-appointed and without legal responsibilities. At some ports the pilots cruised at sea in search of vessels needing their services, at others the pilots remained ashore until vessels came within sight of their lookout positions. Pilots were at work in some ports at least as early as 1650, employing any suitable type of small boat.

After the Revolution pilotage became a well estab-lished profession and each of the important ports had groups of pilots who used sloops or schooners of some size. The pilots at Norfolk appear to have established the initial standards of the profession; they developed a suitable model of small vessel, sloop or schooner rigged, for their service and as the geo-graphic conditions at the mouth of the Chespeake required them to cruise they also established the basic practice of operation.

These pilot boats carried a seaworthy dinghy or "canoe" that could be carried on deck (in early times, probably a dugout boat-canoe, hence the name, but later usually a ship's yawl boat). This boat was used to transfer pilots to and from the ships at sea and was rowed by apprentices, who also brought the pilot boat back to port after the pilots were all dis-charged. The small Norfolk pilot boats did not remain at sea long; and most were operated by a single pilot, hence accommodations aboard them were very limited and somewhat primitive.

Other ports, such as Charleston, Philadelphia, New York, and Boston developed somewhat larger and more comfortable boats, as their pilots ranged farther at sea; the common size of these pilot schooners up to 1825 was about 60 feet on deck. During the remain-ing century the schooners grew in size until boats

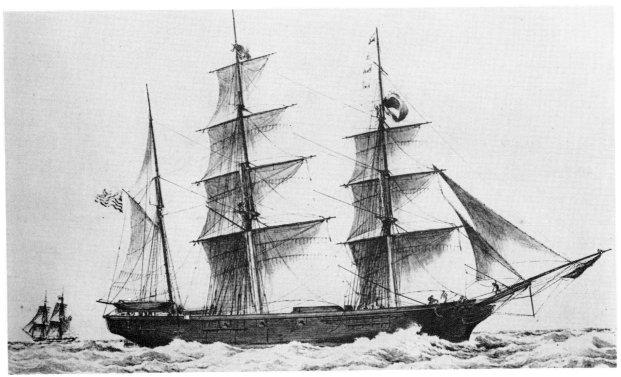

THE CLIPPER BARK *Race Horse*, from a French print in the Watercraft Collection (USNM 159926). She was built in 1850 by Samuel Hall, at East Boston, Massachusetts, for Boston owners. A medium clipper of small size and a good sailer, her register dimensions were 125' x 30' x 16', 530 tons. (*Smithsonian photo 44638-j.*)

over 100 feet on deck were not uncommon. At the end of the century the sailing pilot boat was gradually being replaced in some ports by specially designed steamers.

When the pilots operated singly, or in small groups aboard a pilot-boat schooner, there was much competition and the boats were raced in an effort to place a pilot aboard an incoming vessel. This produced classes of pilot boats having great speed as well as vessels of marked sea-keeping ability. The pilot-boat schooner soon developed into a remarkably fine class of small vessel approaching a yacht in most requirements.

By the middle of the 19th century pilot associations were being formed and competition ceased; each pilot going out in turn and the profits being shared by the association members. This led to a reduction in the number of pilots and pilot boats at each port.

In the early 19th century these schooners were from about 50 to 65 feet long with long, low, raised quarterdecks, and had a Baltimore-clipper hull form. At Boston a somewhat similar form was developed. In the South Atlantic ports and on the Gulf Coast the modified Chespeake model remained popular until

after the War of 1812. The pilot boats at Norfolk began to depart from their original model about 1806; the first change was to make the stem nearly upright, thus sharpening the entrance without lengthening the overall hull dimensions. This was copied elsewhere and, at New York the appearance of pilot-boat schooners changed rapidly after about 1835. Pilot-boat schooners with cutwaters, trails and headrails, and fitted with a billet head or a small figurehead, began to appear all along the coast. Yet the straight, upright stem, sometimes falling inboard a trifle at the head, became the hallmark of the pilot boats by 1860 at New York and, later, at Boston.

Between 1830 and 1860 the New York pilot boats, and those in some other ports, had the Chesapeake rig in which there was a very large sail area. The rig had two raking masts, supported by only one or two shrouds on a side, and a short bowsprit. On these, until about 1845, were set a gaff-mainsail with boom (this was a loose-footed sail secured to the boom only at tack and clew, but later the foot was laced to the boom), and a large gaff-foresail, having no boom, the clew of which came well abaft the mainmast. A single large jib was set. A main-topmast was carried

51

THE OCEAN FREIGHTING SHIP *William Lawrence*, 1874, from a French print in the Watercraft Collection (USNM 159930). This type was popular with American and Canadian shipowners during the period 1865–85. (*Smithsonian photo 44638–d.*)

but rarely a gaff-topsail; on the topmast was set a large staysail which became better known to modern yachtsmen as the fisherman staysail. The rig was designed so that in strong winds and fresh breezes the vessels would work on all points of sailing under foresail alone, the jib and mainsail being set only when the vessel was racing to put a pilot aboard a ship, or when the weather was light, at which time the topmast staysail would also be set.

These pilot schooners attracted international attention and were widely copied abroad. When yachting became an organized sport in America, a great many schooner yachts had pilot-boat hulls and rigs; indeed, two or three were former pilot boats or were used as pilot boats after a few years as yachts. By 1860 fore booms were being added and the size of the foresail reduced, so that the rig became the modern one now used in some yachts. By then the pilot boat was a rather stereotyped model having a short, straight keel with much drag, and a nearly upright post, above which was either a very short counter or a strongly raking V-shaped transom; the stem was nearly upright above the load line and unadorned with any head or carvings, the forefoot was usually much rounded and the curve of the forefoot was carried farther and farther aft along the keel in each new boat. The sheer was usually strong, the freeboard amidships quite low. The midsection was formed with a steeply rising floor, sometimes with hollow at the garboard, a high and often hard turn of the bilge, and a slight tumble-home in the topside. The entrance was usually long, very sharp and, sometimes, slightly hollow at the load line just abaft the stem. The run was less long but very fine, with almost straight buttocks where they crossed the load line aft. Some of the boats were flush decked; others had a long, low quarterdeck, with an oval cockpit for the helmsman. In the early part of the 19th century many pilot boats had a "sunk poop," the raised quarterdeck ending aft just forward of the steersman's position and dropping down to a level below that of the maindeck. Few pilot boats had a cabin trunk on the quarterdeck, a flush deck being preferred there.

The designers and builders of pilot schooners were often noted yacht builders as well. George Steers of New York and Dennison J. Lawlor of Boston were

52

DOWN-EASTER MERCHANT SHIP, name unknown, in drydock on the West Coast about 1885. (*Smithsonian photo 45785-c.*)

notable examples; both were also designers of other types of vessels.

George and Henry Steers were the sons of an English shipwright who came to the United States after the War of 1812 and became a shipbuilder at New York. The elder Steers, trained in an English naval dockyard, had adapted the Baltimore clipper model as his favorite. His sons followed his trade, Henry, the older, became a very famous shipbuilder who designed sailing ships, steamers, and at least two men-of-war; he also turned out some very fast yachts. George, the younger, specialized in pilot-boat schooners and yachts. In 1851 he designed the famous schooner yacht *America* whose success in England brought him great fame. He later designed and built the extreme clipper *Sunny South* and, with Henry, designed the notable American Navy steamer *Niagara*. He was killed in 1856, by being thrown from his carriage. The brothers were closely associated professionally from 1852 to 1856, and some vessel designs

have been credited to George that should have been assigned to Henry.

Dennison J. Lawlor was born in New Brunswick, Canada, and came to Massachusetts about 1848. He worked for various shipbuilders and began designing as early as 1849; in the 1850's he had become well known as a designer of fast schooners and began turning out notable pilot schooners. In the 1860's he designed and built some very fast fishing schooners, as well as commercial craft including coasting schooners and brigantines. During the Civil War he designed the *Meteor*, a very fine auxiliary steamer in her day, and after the war became one of the leading designers and builders of tugs and small steamers. He also achieved fame as a yacht designer, in New England. A number of his designs, including famous pilot boats and fishing schooners, a tug, the auxiliary steamer *Meteor*, steam yachts, and a launch, are represented by half-models in the Watercraft Collection.

BOSTON PILOT SCHOONER *Hesper*, built at Chelsea, Massachusetts, by Dennison J. Lawlor, in 1884. Her register dimensions were 92′ x 22′ x 12′, 98.94 gross tons. She is represented in the Watercraft Collection by the builder's half-model (USNM 76037; see p. 91). (*Smithsonian photo 37747–b.*)

Between 1830 and 1857 a small number of schooners was employed by the New York newspapers to obtain the latest news from incoming ships; these ranged from small schooner-rigged decked boats to small pilot schooners, some of which were built on the Chesapeake. These were all swift-sailing craft, as the competition between the newspapers was very great; the newspaper schooners raced for incoming ships in the same manner as the pilot boats of the period.

In the last half of the 19th century the use of the centerboard sharply increased; centerboards were to be found in coasters, pilot boats, fishermen, and yachts and even in vessels of large size or those intended for long voyages. The centerboard proved very useful in the 3-masted coasters, for it was found that those with a centerboard sailed much better when light than did those with a keel. The period between 1870 and 1895 was one in which the centerboard was most widely used in American commercial sailing craft, large and small.

Special types also appeared in some coastal and river trades during the 19th century. On the lower Mississippi sloop-rigged barges were used during the first half of the century; eventually these were built with leeboards or centerboards. A large variety of sailing barges also appeared; some had complete schooner rigs, but many carried the old shallop rig, without bowsprit or headsail. Some of these were actually canal-boat hulls fitted with masts that could be lowered to pass under bridges. Masts fitted in that way were employed at an early date, though not always in coasters. During the War of 1812 one pinky schooner thus fitted, as a privateer was thereby enabled to hide among the islands on the Maine coast, her spars lowered, and to pounce on passing English or Canadian vessels, either by using sweeps or by raising her rig and sailing.

Another curious type was the Piscataqua River gundalow (not to be confused with the 18th century gundalo), used in that river in New Hampshire. This was a shallow, log-built barge with spoon-shaped ends, fitted with a single triangular boomless sail laced to a spar that could be lowered to pass under bridges. This spar was hung on a stub mast by a short chain halyard and as a result the rig has a superficial resemblance to the lateen rig. These vessels had a single leeboard secured inside an iron rack to keep it from breaking away from the hull at the pivot on the off tack. These boats, which sometimes ventured a short distance coastwise, were good sailers. The name "gundalow" was also applied in New England to various sailing scows having this rig or a simple square sail on a pivoted mast that could be lowered.

There was a sharp increase in the use of vessels having the form of a flat-bottomed, sharp-bowed skiff rigged as a sloop or schooner, or with square sails. One of these, a gundalow used on the Kennebec River in Maine, had a mast that lowered, and was rigged with a square course and a topsail; the hull had one leeboard and a low trunk cabin aft.

Flat-bottomed skiff-shaped schooners, or sharpies, were developed on the Great Lakes and along the coasts of Georgia, the Carolinas, and Florida. Some of these had the above-water appearance of regular coasting schooners but the underbody of a skiff or sharpie. Sloops of the same form, used in the Carolinas and in Florida, were sometimes called "flatties," and a rather distinctive type was used for a period on the Chesapeake Bay as lighters to carry farm produce to ports that could be served by schooners and steamers. The log-bottom bugeye, an overgrown canoe, also developed on the Bay, had two masts, of almost equal height and standing with a sharp rake, fitted with leg-of-mutton sails and a large jib; they were employed in both fishing and freighting. Small sailing craft lasted in the coastal trade, until the introduction of gasoline engines early in the 20th century.

Catalog of the Collection—Merchant Sail

MERCHANT SHIP, 1818
BUILDER'S HALF-MODEL, USNM 76125

Atticus

The ship-rigged wooden merchant vessel *Atticus* was built on this half-model at Castine, Maine, in 1818 for the general ocean-freighting trade. She represented a class of such vessels that were developed in New England after the War of 1812 for the foreign trade. Though considered a large merchant vessel at the time of her launching, ships of the size of the *Atticus* were soon very common in the American trade with European and Mediterranean ports.

The half-model represents a burdensome vessel having a long body and full ends, moderate sheer, straight keel with very little or no drag, upright stem rabbet curved at forefoot, upright post, round tuck, and upper- and-lower-transom square stern. The entrance is short, bluff, and nearly round at the rail. The run is rather long but quite full. The midsection is well forward and is formed with slightly rising straight floor carried well out, well rounded bilge, rather straight and upright topside, and slight tumble-home. She had deep bulwarks and in proportion to her length was rather wide for ships of her type.

The half-model scales 132 feet moulded length at rail, 33 feet 4 inches moulded beam, and 16 feet 8 inches moulded depth; it represents a ship of about 298 tons, old measurement. Scale of model is ⅜ inch to the foot.

Given by James B. Crawford.

MERCHANT SHIP, 1827
BUILDER'S HALF-MODEL, USNM 76126

Lucas

The *Lucas*, a ship-rigged merchant vessel, was built on this model at Castine, Maine, in 1827, for general ocean freighting, and is typical of the largest class in her trade then popular with New England shipowners.

The half-model represents a wooden merchant ship having moderate sheer, a straight keel with little drag, nearly upright stem rabbet with well rounded forefoot, upright post, round tuck, upper-and-lower-transom square stern, and a long body with very full rail line forward and a wide stern. The midsection shows a slightly rising straight floor, low and well rounded bilge, and upright topside. The entrance is short and bluff; the bow sections flare heavily. The run is rather long and for so burdensome a hull is quite fine. The midsection is forward of the mid-length of the hull; in general this vessel was designed not for fast sailing but to have large capacity. Ships of this class and period had deep, heavy heads, usually fitted with a billet, though some had the more expensive figurehead.

The model is for a ship 132 feet 8 inches moulded length at rail, 30 feet 8 inches moulded beam, 17 feet 4 inches moulded depth, and about 290 tons, old measurement. Scale of model is ⅜ inch to the foot.

Given by James B. Crawford.

MERCHANT SHIP, 1830
BUILDER'S HALF-MODEL, USNM 76067

This half-model of a ship-rigged ocean-freighting vessel was made by Samuel Pattee about 1830. A ship, name unknown, was built on it by Thomas Harwood at Bath, Maine; the vessel is said to have been employed largely in the cotton trade between Liverpool, England, and New Orleans and other southern ports. Ships in this trade required large under-deck capacity; speed was not particularly necessary.

The half-model shows a very burdensome, wooden, ship-rigged merchantman having rather straight sheer, a straight keel with little drag, nearly upright stem rabbet with moderately rounded forefoot, upright post, round tuck, upper-and-lower-transom square stern, long parallel body with full rail line forward and a wide stern, a short and very bluff entrance, and a very short and full run. The midsection is well forward of the midlength of the hull and is formed with a slight rise in the straight floor, a rather quick, hard bilge, and a slight tumble-home in the topside.

Rather roughly made of white pine, the model is painted, and is mounted with a short, heavy head with trails, cutwater, keel, post, and rudder. Ships such as this were dull sailers and were disrespectfully described by sailors as having been "built by the mile and sawn off by the foot."

The model scales 131 feet moulded length at rail, 28 feet moulded beam, and 18 feet moulded depth to rail. Scale is ½ inch to the foot.

Given by William P. Pattee, shipbuilder, Bath, Maine.

MERCHANT SHIP, 1836
BUILDER'S HALF-MODEL, USNM 76066

Glasgow

The ship-rigged merchantman *Glasgow* of Bath, Maine, was built in that port in 1836 on this model. *Glasgow*, a typical cotton ship of her date, was employed for many years in the New Orleans-Liverpool trade. In outward appearance these ships often had some resemblance in profile to packet ships, but were usually smaller and had very full lines, so were not the fast sailers that most packets were by this date.

The half-model shows a burdensome, wooden vessel having graceful sheer, a straight keel with little drag, upright stem rabbet with rounded forefoot, upright post, round tuck, upper-and-lower-transom square stern and short quarterdeck. The midsection is well forward of midlength and is formed with a slightly rising straight floor, a round, full bilge, and is rather wall sided above, with some tumble-home. The entrance is short and bluff, the run short and full, and the body long and straight sided.

Mounted with a short, heavy head with billet, trail, cutwater, keel, post, and rudder; the stern carvings and name boards are shown. Painted in the fashion of the period: green (verdigris) bottom, black topsides with three narrow white bead lines, and one broad varnished strake; carvings all gilded as in original ship.

The model is for a vessel 138 feet moulded length as rail, 135 feet between perpendiculars, 31 feet 2 inches beam, 19 feet depth in hold, and 594⁵⁵⁄₉₄ tons register, old measurement. Scale of model is ½ inch to the foot.

Given by William P. Pattee, shipbuilder, and W. F. Weeks of Bath, Maine.

MERCHANT SHIP, 1850
BUILDER'S HALF-MODEL, USNM 76068

A ship-rigged merchant vessel, name unknown, was built on this model at Bath, Maine, about 1850. The model, in the long, narrow, and deep ship form that became popular in burdensome vessels in this period, represents the class of large ships built in Maine for the cotton trade, which demanded very large under-deck capacity without pretensions to fast sailing (it was not until well into the 1850's that many fast-sailing ships were built for this trade).

The half-model represents a large, ship-rigged, wooden vessel, burdensome and full ended, having a moderate sheer, straight keel with little or no drag, rather upright stem rabbet with small rounded fore-foot, upright post, round tuck, light and rather shallow square stern with upper and lower transoms, short and bluff entrance with much flare in the bow sections, long parallel-sided body, and short and full run. The midsection is formed with a slightly rising straight floor, round and rather hard bilge, and is wall sided above, with slight tumble-home.

Painted and mounted, with the short heavy head and cutwater typical of these Maine-built cotton ships until well into the 1850's.

The model scales 183 feet 4 inches moulded length at rail, 33 feet moulded beam, and 25 feet moulded depth. Scale of model ⅛ inch to the foot.

Given by William P. Pattee, shipbuilder, Bath, Maine.

PACKET SHIP, 1850
DECORATIVE HALF-MODEL, USNM 311307 (Griffiths' Collection)

Universe

This small decorative half-model of the clipper-packet ship *Universe* was made by the ship's designer, John W. Griffiths, of New York. It is not an actual builder's model. The lines and sail plan of this vessel are in Griffiths' *Treatise of Marine and Naval Architecture*, London, 1857 (new ed.).

The *Universe*, built in 1850 by Smith & Dimon at New York for Williams and Guion's Liverpool Line, was a 1,297-ton (old measurement) packet. She was the first of the American packet ships that might be classed as a "clipper" ship. Her registered length was 186 feet, her beam 38 feet 7 inches, and her depth 28 feet 6 inches. The model, which is only about 20½ inches in length at rail, is apparently on a scale of 1/10 inch to the foot.

The half-model shows a sailing ship hull having moderate sheer, straight keel with little drag, a raking and flaring stem rabbet with very small round at fore-foot, a nearly upright post, raking transom, round

tuck, the entrance sharp and slightly hollow at the forefoot and rather short, and the run short but fine. The midsection shows a slightly rising straight floor, a full and round bilge, and some tumble-home in the topside. The model is mounted with keel, rudder, and cutwater; channels are indicated.

Received from Marion H. Virnelson, granddaughter of the designer.

CLIPPER SHIP, 1851
BUILDER'S HALF-MODEL, USNM 76072

Comet

The noted American clipper ship *Comet* is represented by this decorative half-model presented by the builder and stated in the Museum records to be a duplicate of the builder's half-model. The *Comet* was built at New York City by William H. Webb in 1851 for the California and China trades. Noted for her speed and beauty, the *Comet* made many fast passages, such as:

New York to San Francisco	103 days (maiden voyage)
San Francisco to Hong Kong	37 days
San Francisco to New York	86 days
San Francisco to New York	76⅔ days
New York to Liverpool	19 days
Liverpool to Hong Kong	84 days

On one voyage she sailed 332 nautical miles in 24 hours and 1,512 nautical miles in 120 consecutive hours.

The lines and sail plan of this ship are in William H. Webb's *Plans of Wooden Ships*.

The half-model shows a moderate and graceful sheer, straight keel with very slight drag, raking and flaring stem rabbet, upright post, and a short, round, and light counter. The entrance is long, sharp and slightly hollow at forefoot; the bow sections have much flare; and the run is very long and fine. The mid-section has slightly rising straight floors carried well out, a well rounded and easy bilge, and a slight tumble-home above. This clipper, like many of her type, has a large midsection combined with very fine ends.

The model, mounted on a mirror to show the deck arrangement of the ship complete with bulwarks and deck furniture, is illustrated on p. 9. The figure-head, mouldings and cutwater, keel, post, and rudder are shown, and the stern carvings are also represented.

The model is for a ship 229 feet between perpendiculars, 42 feet extreme beam, 24 feet 10 inches depth,

BUILDER'S HALF-MODEL OF CLIPPER SHIP MOUNTED AGAINST MIRROR TO SHOW DECK ARRANGEMENT. *Young America*, USNM 160135. (*Smithsonian photo 20523.*)

and 1836 tons register. Scale of model is ⅛ inch to the foot.

Given by William H. Webb, shipbuilder, New York City.

CLIPPER SHIP, 1853
BUILDER'S HALF-MODEL, USNM 160135

Young America

This decorative half-model of the American clipper ship *Young America* is a duplicate of the original builder's half-model, complete with deck furniture and bulwarks. The figurehead, mouldings, cutwater, keel, post, rudder and stern carvings are shown. The model is mounted on a mirror.

The *Young America*, built in New York City by William H. Webb in 1853, was one of the most celebrated of American clipper ships. Employed in the California and Australian trades, carrying freight and passengers out of New York and Liverpool, the *Young America* made five passages from San Francisco to New York in from 83 to 92 days and five passages in from 97 to 101 days. The run from New York to Liverpool was made in 18 days and the return voyage in 23 days. Liverpool to Melbourne, Australia, was made in 81 days and runs from Liverpool to San Francisco in 102, 103, 105, and 106 days.

This ship was heavily sparred and canvassed; her lines and sail plan are in William H. Webb's *Plans of Wooden Ships*.

The model shows a clipper ship having a moderate and graceful sheer, straight keel with slight drag, the stem rabbet raking and flaring, vertical post, a short, light, round counter, the entrance long and sharp and somewhat hollow at forefoot, the run very long and fine. The bow sections show strong flare. The midsection is large, formed with slightly rising straight

floor carried well out, a full-round bilge, and slight tumble-home in the topsides.

The model is for a ship of 236 feet 6 inches between perpendiculars, 42 feet extreme beam, 28 feet 3 inches depth, and 1962 tons register. The deadrise amidships is 2 inches to the foot. Scale of model is ⅛ inch to the foot.

Given by William H. Webb, shipbuilder, New York City.

MERCHANT SHIP, 1853
BUILDER'S HALF-MODEL, USNM 76062

John N. Cushing

The full-rigged merchant ship *John N. Cushing* of Newburyport, Massachusetts, was built at that port in 1853 on this half-model and was intended for the general ocean-freighting trade. She was employed for some years in the New England, West Indies, and Europe trade. John N. Cushing, Sr., who owned the fleet of merchant vessels to which this ship belonged, was a firm believer in full-bodied carriers and continued to build such ships, even though they were out of date, and in spite of their slow sailing, well into the clipper-ship period. Five ships were built for the Cushing fleet on this half-model.

The half-model shows a very burdensome wooden merchantman, deep and narrow, rather straight in sheer, straight keel with little or no drag, upright stem rabbet with small rounded forefoot, nearly vertical post, round tuck, upper-and-lower-transom square stern with low cross seam, short and very bluff entrance, long body, short and heavy run, some flare in bow sections. The midsection is well forward and is formed with slightly rising floor, round firm bilge, and is wall sided above. The beam at rail is carried well into the ends.

The model scales 154 feet moulded length at rail, 28 feet moulded beam, and 24 feet moulded depth. Scale is ¼ inch to the foot.

Given by John N. Cushing, Newburyport, Massachusetts.

MERCHANT SHIP, 1855
BUILDER'S HALF-MODEL, USNM 160148

A ship-rigged merchant vessel was built from this half-model about 1855 at Bath, Maine, and although the model has the name "Mayflower" painted on it, this does not appear to have been the name of the ship. The model represents an improved form of vessel, built for the cotton trade in the middle 1850's, combining capacity and fair sailing qualities.

The half-model is of a wooden, ship-rigged merchantman of the half-clipper type, having graceful sheer, straight keel with very slight drag, upright and straight-stem rabbet with small forefoot, vertical post, short and light counter, square stern, moderately sharp entrance with strongly flaring sections, long parallel body, and a long but somewhat full run. The midsection is formed with slightly rising straight floor, full-round bilge, and considerable tumble-home in the topsides.

The model scales 131 feet 4 inches moulded length at rail, 28 feet 6 inches moulded beam, and 20 feet moulded depth. Scale is ¼ inch to the foot.

Mounted and painted in the style of the period and trade, with painted ports, naval fashion.

Given by the Board of Trade, Bath, Maine.

MERCHANT SHIP, 1857
BUILDER'S HALF-MODEL, USNM 76063

Elizabeth Cushing

The full-rigged merchant ship *Elizabeth Cushing* was built on this half-model in 1857 at Newburyport, Massachusetts, for John N. Cushing of that port. The vessel, intended for the East India trade, was a modified "kettle-bottom" model—deep, narrow and full ended, and of rather large dimensions. A very old-fashioned type of vessel at her date of building she illustrates the extreme conservatism of her owner.

The half-model represents a merchant ship of very burdensome form, having slight sheer, straight keel with little or no drag, rather upright stem rabbet flaring a little at the top and with small curved forefoot, slightly raking post, round tuck, upper-and-lower-transom square stern, short and full entrance, very short and full run, a long body, and flaring bow sections with very bluff rail line. The midsection is

formed with very slightly rising straight floor, rather hard bilge, and straight tumble-home in the topside.

Mounted with short and heavy head, cutwater, keel, post, and rudder.

The model scales 172 feet moulded length at rail, 36 feet moulded beam, and 28 feet moulded depth. Scale is ¼ inch to the foot.

Given by John N. Cushing, Newburyport, Massachusetts.

MERCHANT SHIP, 1874
BUILDER'S HALF-MODEL, USNM 76054

Exporter, Reporter

The merchant ships *Exporter* and *Reporter* were built on this half-model at Newburyport, Massachusetts, in 1874 by George W. Jackman, Jr., for the general ocean trade and were owned in that port. They belonged to that class of merchant sailing ships, known as down-Easters, that followed the extreme clipper ships in the American ocean trades. The down-Easters combined large cargo capacity with very good sailing qualities and thus were more profitable to operate than the extreme clippers of the California, Australian, and China trades of the 1850's, yet were capable of making almost as speedy passages. These ships were largely employed in the cotton trade. An earlier vessel named *Reporter*, a clipper ship, was built at Medford, Massachusetts. The *Exporter* was sold foreign in 1892.

The half-model shows a moderately burdensome ship having marked sheer, straight keel with very little drag, raking and flaring stem rabbet, upright post, short, light counter with elliptical transom, sharp entrance of moderate length, and fine run. The midsection is formed with a slightly rising straight floor carried well out, well rounded bilge, and moderate tumble-home above. Painted and mounted with long head, trail, cutwater, keel, post, and rudder.

The model is for a vessel 199 feet 6 inches between perpendiculars, 38 feet 2½ inches beam, 24 feet depth, and 1369.75 gross tons register. Scale of the model is ¼ inch to the foot.

Given by Sumner, Swasey, and Currier of Newburyport, Massachusetts.

MERCHANT SHIP, 1875
BUILDER'S HALF-MODEL, USNM 76065

Oregon, Hercules, C. C. Thompson, Highland Light

The full-rigged ship *Oregon* was built on this half-model by William Rogers at Bath, Maine, in 1875, and later the sister ships *Hercules, C.C. Thompson,* and *Highland Light* were built on her moulds. These merchant ships were down-Easters. Vessels of this type represented the highest development of the American square-rigged merchant ship, combining fine working qualities, speed, and capacity to an extent not generally achieved earlier. The *Oregon* was considered a superior vessel of the type.

The half-model represents a large wooden ship having strong sheer, straight keel with little or no drag, moderately raking and flaring stem rabbet, upright post, short counter with elliptical transom, sharp entrance of moderate length, and a rather long easy run. The midsection is formed with slightly rising straight floor, hard bilge, and a slight tumble-home above.

The model is mounted with stub bowsprit and masts, head and cutwater, keel, post, and rudder. Gilded and painted as on the original ship.

The *Oregon* measured 205.9 feet between perpendiculars, 30.9 feet extreme beam, and 24.01 feet depth in hold. She was 1431 tons register. Scale of the model is ⅓ inch to the foot.

Given by William Rogers, shipbuilder, Bath, Maine.

MERCHANT SHIP, about 1876
BUILDER'S HALF-MODEL, USNM 160150

A wooden ship-rigged merchant vessel, name unknown, was built on this model at Boston, Massachusetts, about 1876. She was a down-Easter, a class of vessels moderately sharp ended for carriers, yet of good capacity.

The half-model represents a vessel having marked and graceful sheer, a straight keel with little or no drag, a curved, raking, and flaring stem rabbet, upright post, short and light counter ending with an elliptical transom; sharp entrance of moderate length, and a rather long and easy run. The midsection shows a slightly rising straight floor of some length, a hard bilge, and a slight tumble-home in the topside.

The scale of this model is stated in the Museum records to be ⅜ inch to the foot; this gives a ship of only 172 feet moulded length at rail, which is very small for this type and date. It seems probable that the scale is ⅓ inch to the foot, giving a vessel about 202 feet 6 inches moulded length at main rail, about 35 feet 1½ inches moulded beam, and about 22 feet 5 inches moulded depth.

Given by R. G. F. Candage.

MERCHANT SHIP, 1884
BUILDER'S HALF-MODEL, USNM 76094

This half-model of a Canadian sailing merchant ship was exhibited at the World's Exposition at New Orleans in 1884–85 and represents a design of vessel intended for the New Orleans-European cotton trade. It closely resembles the general model of the American down-Easters of this date and is also rather typical of the ships built on the north shore of the Province of New Brunswick for the ocean carrying trade. Canadian-built ships of this type were often fast and rather sharp for their period, and many of these New Brunswick built vessels were constructed on speculation and sold in England, where they were very often employed in the Australian or South American trade.

The half-model shows a vessel having a rather straight sheer, straight keel with little or no drag, rather upright and flaring stem rabbet, slightly raking post, a light, round counter, a short, sharp and somewhat convex entrance, and a long, well formed run. The midsection has a slightly rising straight floor, rather easy round bilge, and is wall-sided above.

Mounted with head, cutwater, keel, post, and rudder. Painted and gilded.

The model scales 202 feet length on the load line, 40 feet moulded beam, and 24 feet 6 inches moulded depth. Rise of floor is 20 inches at half floor. Register tonnage would be about 1,650 and the deadweight tonnage about 2,200 tons. Scale of the model is ⅓ inch to the foot.

Given by W. Powers, shipbuilder, Kingston, Ontario.

MERCHANT BARK, 1836
BUILDER'S HALF-MODEL, USNM 76050

William Shroeder

The bark-rigged merchant ship *William Shroeder* was built on this model at Newburyport, Massachusetts, in 1836 for owners in that port and was intended for the West Indian trade. The *Shroeder* was considered a very good vessel for the trade, having the reputation of being an easy-working ship, of sailing very well, and of being profitable because of her rather large capacity. She ran chiefly between New England ports and Puerto Rico, carrying lumber south and sugar and molasses on the return voyage. About 10 or 12 years after her launching the *Shroeder* was sold to Salem owners and thereafter was employed in the Salem-Zanzibar trade.

The half-model has a rather straight sheer, straight keel with little or no drag, stem rabbet curved and with little rake, nearly upright post, round tuck, upper-and-lower-transom square stern, a rather short and full entrance, a fairly long and easy run, quite a long body with a broad stern, and a full, round rail line at the bow with much flare in the bow sections. The midsection is formed with a slightly rising straight floor, a rather easy round bilge, and a slight tumble-home in the topside.

Mounted, with a short, heavy head, cutwater, keel, post, and rudder, and the mouldings shown as in the original vessel. Painted, with painted ports, naval fashion.

The model scales 131 feet 8 inches moulded length at rail, 26 feet 8 inches moulded beam, and 15 feet moulded depth. Scale is ⅛ inch to the foot.

Given by Captain Charles M. Bayley.

MERCHANT BARK, 1845
BUILDER'S HALF-MODEL, USNM 76049

Edward Koppisch

The bark-rigged merchant vessel *Edward Koppisch* of Newburyport, Massachusetts, was built on this model at that port in 1845 for the West Indian trade. She was employed on the New England-Puerto Rico run, carrying lumber out and sugar and molasses home. About 12 years after her launching she was sold to Salem, Massachusetts, owners, and was employed in the African trade out of that port.

The half-model is of a bark-rigged vessel having a rather straight sheer, straight keel with little or no drag, curved and moderately raking stem rabbet, somewhat raking post, round tuck, upper-and-lower-transom square stern, entrance full and short, run moderate in length and slightly full, long body with wide stern, and an almost round rail at bow with much flare in the forward sections. The midsection has a slightly rising straight floor, easy round bilge, and a slight tumble-home in the topside.

Mounted with short, heavy head, cutwater, keel, post, rudder, and gilded mouldings. Hull painted, with black topsides and with painted ports, naval fashion. A monkey rail, or false hammock rail, is shown; this became fashionable in American merchant ships after the War of 1812 and continued in general use to the end of the clipper-ship period. American sailing ships in the West Indian trade in the period between 1825 and 1855, were usually copper-sheathed.

Model is for a vessel 125 feet moulded length at rail, 23 feet 4 inches moulded beam, 13 feet 4 inches moulded depth, and about 250 tons register, old measurement. Scale of the model is 3⁄10 inch to the foot.

Given by Captain Charles M. Bayley.

MERCHANT BARK, 1846
BUILDER'S HALF-MODEL, USNM 76071

Saone

The bark-rigged merchant vessel *Saone* was built on this model at Bath, Maine, in 1846 for owners in that port; she was intended for general ocean carrying out of New England, trading to Europe, the West Indies, and South America.

This half-model is of an extreme kettle-bottom vessel, a design developed to escape full payment of tonnage dues without any loss in carrying capacity, and following a basic principle of design, used in the much later turret steamers, of wide bottom and narrow upper deck. Depth, under the American tonnage law in force when the *Saone* was modeled, was an estimate of depth in hold as a proportion of the measured beam at deck, rather than a measurement of actual hold depth as in later years. Hence real depth was a tax free measurement to a great extent. As a result the hulls were formed with a deep midsection, having a wide, almost flat bottom, a firm round bilge, very marked tumble-home, and concave topside that under the tonnage law gave a very great cargo capacity but small register tonnage. The form resembling the profile of an old iron kettle, hence the name. There were disadvantages. For her maiden voyage the *Saone* was loaded with lumber but with insufficient ballast; when she filled away from the wharf, she fell over on her side with her lower yardarms in the water. She then had to be unloaded to right her, and ballast added.

These kettle-bottom ships were deep in proportion to beam and length; to the discomfort of their crews, even when properly ballasted they sailed with a sharp angle of heel, and were slow as well.

The body plan of the *Saone* is shown in Hall's *Report on Shipbuilding*.

The half-model shows a very burdensome vessel having very straight sheer, a straight keel with no drag, nearly upright stem rabbet and post, round tuck, upper-and-lower-transom square stern, excessively long body and wide stern, almost round rail at bow, and a very short and full entrance and run.

The *Saone* registered 292 tons, old measurement, 116 feet 10 inches moulded length at rail, 21 feet 9 inches moulded beam, 16 feet 9 inches moulded depth, 20-inch hollow in the tumble-home topsides, and carried 460 tons of cargo on a draft of 14 feet to the keel rabbet. Scale of the model is ⅜ inch to the foot.

Given by William P. Pattee, shipbuilder, Bath, Maine.

MERCHANT BARK, 1851
BUILDER's HALF-MODEL, USNM 76059

Hesper

The bark-rigged merchant vessel *Hesper* was built on this model at Newburyport, Massachusetts, in 1851 for John N. Cushing of that port. She was a kettle bottom and was employed in the European trade. Like the rest of her type she was a very large carrier but slow and unhandy, though reputedly profitable for her owner.

The half-model is of a very burdensome ship having very little sheer, a straight keel with no drag, upright stem rabbet with small, rounded forefoot, nearly upright post, round tuck, upper-and-lower-transom square stern, short full entrance and run, and a very long body. The midsection has a slightly rising straight floor, round firm bilge, a marked tumble-home, with the topside straight rather than concave. The *Hesper* was short, deep, and narrow.

The model scales 128 feet moulded length at rail, 25 feet moulded beam, and 21 feet moulded depth. Scale is ¼ inch to the foot.

Given by John N. Cushing of Newburyport, Massachusetts.

MERCHANT BARK, 1854
BUILDER's HALF-MODEL, USNM 76114

Crusader

The bark-rigged merchantman *Crusader* was built on this model at Millbridge, Maine, in 1854 for the European trade. She belonged to that class of sailing vessels sometimes called half clippers, having good capacity and some pretension to fast sailing. The *Crusader*, cost $85,000 to build and fit for sea; she was a well finished vessel and profitable in her trade, although too full in the run to be very swift. She was engaged in general ocean freighting and was finally burned at sea on a voyage between Rio de Janeiro and London.

The half-model shows a vessel having a rather straight sheer, straight keel with little or no drag, rounded stem rabbet becoming straight and vertical above the load line, upright post, round tuck, upper-

and-lower-transom square stern with little overhang, short and rather sharp entrance, short and full run, and a long body. The midsection shows a slightly rising straight floor and a rather hard bilge, and is wall sided above. The bow flares strongly.

The model scales 216 feet moulded length at rail, 28 feet moulded beam, and 19 feet moulded depth. Scale is ¼ inch to the foot.

Given by Captain Austin Dyer.

MERCHANT BARK, 1877
BUILDER's HALF-MODEL, USNM 76134

Julia

The bark-rigged merchant vessel *Julia* was built on this model in 1877 at Ellsworth, Maine, for local owners and was intended for general ocean freighting, an example of the smaller class of Maine-built down-Easters that followed the clipper-ship period, combining good capacity with beauty and speed. Vessels of this type for many years competed successfully, with the early, iron tramp steamers.

The half-model shows a merchant vessel having marked sheer, a straight keel with little drag, curved and raking stem rabbet, vertical post, short counter with elliptical transom, moderately sharp convex entrance, long, fine and well-shaped run, and a good length of body. The midsection shows a slightly rising straight floor and a well rounded bilge, and is rather wall sided above.

Mounted with long head, cutwater, keel, post, and rudder.

The model scales 164 feet moulded length at rail. The vessel was 155 feet 1 inch between perpendiculars, 34 feet extreme beam, 20 feet 1 inch depth of hold, and the net tonnage was 758.18. Scale of the model is ¹⁄₁₆ inch to the foot, unusually small for a builder's half-model.

Given by Isaac M. Grant.

MERCHANT BARK, 1878
BUILDER's HALF-MODEL, USNM 76095

Albemarle

The half-clipper bark *Albemarle* of Baltimore, Maryland, was built on this model by William Skinner and Sons of that city for Messrs. Wedbee and Dickerson. She was launched June 19, 1878. The *Albemarle* had wire-rope standing rigging and improved fittings; she was considered an advanced design when launched. Though economic conditions in the American shipping trades had, before 1860, brought an end to the

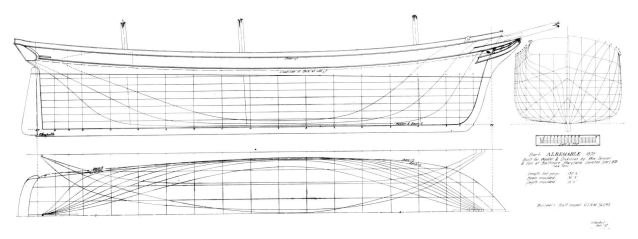

LINES OF THE COFFEE-CLIPPER BARK *Albemarle*, built at Baltimore, Maryland, in 1876. Taken off the builder's half-model USNM 76095.

construction of the very large California clipper ships, some trades still existed in which small clipper sailing vessels were profitable—one was the fruit trade to the West Indies, another, the Rio de Janeiro-American coffee trade. The latter trade employed the larger vessels, mostly barks, brigs, and brigantines. While few of these vessels were very extreme in design, some were quite sharp and many were very fast sailers. The *Albemarle* was long accepted as one of the fastest vessels in the Rio coffee trade and her design was much admired.

The half-model shows a medium-, or half-clipper bark having a moderate and graceful sheer, straight keel with slight drag, a raking, curved and flaring stem rabbet, nearly upright post, light and short counter with elliptical transom, long and sharp entrance, and a moderately long and fine run with no length of deadflat amidships; the bow sections show heavy flare. The midsection is formed with a slightly rising straight floor, firm round bilge, and curved tumble-home in the topside.

Mounted with long head, trails, cutwater, keel, rudder, and post.

The model scales 138 feet 10 inches moulded length at rail, 130 feet 6 inches between perpendiculars, 30 feet 9 inches moulded beam, and 15 feet 5 inches depth rabbet to underside of deck at side. The vessel would draw 16 feet 9 inches when loaded. The model is marked with what are, apparently, her register dimensions: "135 feet between perpendiculars, 30 feet extreme beam, 14 feet 11 inches depth of hold, 560 tons." Scale is ½ inch to the foot.

Given by William Skinner and Sons, shipbuilders, Baltimore, Maryland.

MERCHANT BRIG, 1817
BUILDER'S HALF-MODEL, USNM 76061

Dove

The merchant brig *Dove* was built on this model in 1817 at Newbury, Massachusetts, for John N. Cushing, Sr., of Newburyport. She was built for the West Indian trade in the period immediately following the Napoleonic Wars, when the West Indies were infested with pirates and freebooting privateers of the Spanish colonies then in the throes of revolution. Because of this condition it was necessary to construct West Indian traders with some speed. The *Dove*, an attempt to combine capacity with sailing ability, had sharper ends and a greater rise of floor than most New England traders of her time. However, this brig was by no means a clipper model, though she was the sharpest vessel ever owned by Cushing, whose fleet of brigs, as well as ships and barks, were all extremely full ended and burdensome.

The half-model represents a brig-rigged vessel having strong sheer, a straight keel with slight drag, curved and somewhat raking stem rabbet, slightly raking post, round tuck, upper-and-lower-transom square stern, short convex entrance becoming almost round at rail, and a short, but rather easy run. The midsection has a moderately rising and short straight floor, rather easy round bilge, and a slight tumble-home in the topside.

Mounted and fitted with a short, heavy head, cutwater, keel, post, and rudder, and with a quarterdeck rail. Painted as in the original vessel.

The model scales 76 feet moulded length at rail, 18

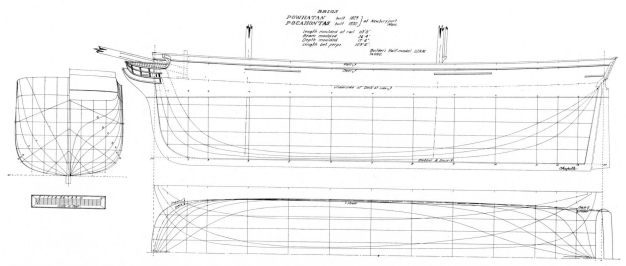

LINES OF THE NEW ENGLAND MERCHANT BRIGS *Powhatan* and *Pocahontas*, built at Newburyport, Massachusetts, 1829–30. An example of a model of burdensome freighting vessels favored in New England before the days of the clipper ships. Taken off the builder's half-model USNM 76060.

feet 6 inches moulded beam, and 10 feet moulded depth. Scale is ½ inch to the foot.

Given by John N. Cushing, Newburyport, Massachusetts.

MERCHANT BRIGANTINE, 1825
BUILDER'S HALF-MODEL, USNM 76070

Thomas Harwood built a merchant brigantine, name unknown, on this model at Bath, Maine, in 1825 for the West Indian sugar trade. Vessels built in Maine for this trade usually had short, high quarterdecks with a trunk cabin let into them so that the cabin sole, or floor, was at main deck level. The crew's quarters were in a small deckhouse abaft the foremast. Because the main deck was much lower than the quarterdeck, these vessels were referred to as "low-decked" in Maine shipyards. The bulwarks were high, permitting large deck-loads, so the low-decked vessels were popular in the Maine lumber trade. Since lumber was the usual southbound cargo in the Maine-owned West Indiamen, the vessels built for the sugar and molasses trade were commonly of this description.

The name "barrel bottom" was sometimes applied to such a vessel; some sailed well, particularly in light and moderate winds, but usually they would not carry sail well in a fresh breeze.

The half-model shows a burdensome vessel having marked sheer, a straight keel with little or no drag,

curved and slightly raking stem rabbet, slightly raking post, round tuck, upper-and-lower-transom square stern, and a short entrance and run. The midsection is formed with a slightly rising straight floor, well-rounded slack bilge, and an upright topside.

The model is for a brigantine 91 feet in moulded length at rail, 22 feet moulded beam, and 9 feet moulded depth. Scale of the model is ½ inch to the foot.

Given by William P. Pattee, shipbuilder, Bath, Maine.

MERCHANT BRIG, 1829
BUILDER'S HALF-MODEL, USNM 76060

Powhatan, Pocahontas

John N. Cushing, Sr., was a very successful merchant and shipowner of Newburyport, Massachusetts, who became prominent, after the War of 1812, as the operator of a large fleet of merchant vessels, the larger portion of which were full-rigged brigs. He engaged in the general ocean carrying trade and most of his vessels were employed in freighting out of Newburyport to Europe, the West Indies, and South America. Early in his career he decided that only burdensome vessels were profitable and began to have brigs built, and later barks and ships, that were extreme in design in this respect. The pioneer of the extremely burdensome brigs, in his fleet, were the sisters *Powhatan*, built at Newbury, Massachusetts, in 1829, and the *Pocahontas*, built there the following year, both on this half-model. The type of brig represented by this model was developed into an extreme kettle bottom in Cushing's later vessels.

The half-model represents a deep, narrow, brig-rigged vessel having a very slight sheer, straight keel with little or no drag, a rather upright and straight stem rabbet, small rounded forefoot, upright post, round tuck, upper-and-lower-transom square stern with small overhang, very short and bluff entrance, a long parallel body, and a short, very full run. The midsection shows a slightly rising floor, firm bilge, and a slight tumble-home in the straight topside.

The model is for a vessel 113 feet moulded length at rail, 26 feet 4 inches moulded beam, 17½ feet moulded depth, and about 268 tons register, old measurement. Scale of the model is ¼ inch to the foot.

Given by John N. Cushing, Newburyport, Massachusetts.

MERCHANT BRIG, 1832
BUILDER'S HALF-MODEL, USNM 76058

Palos

The brig-rigged merchant vessel *Palos* was built on this model at Newburyport, Massachusetts, in 1832 for John N. Cushing of that port. She was an extreme kettle bottom, narrow, deep and with very great tumble-home in the topsides. The brig was so profitable, largely because she carried cargo tonnage far in excess of her register tonnage (port dues were paid only on the latter), that fifteen brigs were afterwards built, most of them by Stephen Jackman, on the moulds, or model, of the *Palos*. Among the vessels built on this half-model, which may be said to have been the standard one for brigs in the Cushing fleet, were the *Carthage, Athens, Corinth, James Gray, Nicholas, James Caskie, Ark, Massachusetts, Salisbury, Smith*, and *Tuttle*. The brig *Keying* was the last; launched in 1845, she cost $22,264.98. These kettle-bottom brigs traded chiefly to Europe and the West Indies, bearing

KETTLE-BOTTOM BRIG *Salisbury*, built on the model of the *Palos* (builder's half-model USNM 76058) at Newbury, Massachusetts, in 1844. From a painting by Frédéric Roux, at Le Havre in the 1840's. (*Smithsonian photo 3394.*)

65

tobacco to Europe from Richmond, Virginia, and returning to New England with salt or coal or manufactures from Liverpool, or with marine stores and cordage from the Baltic, or with sugar and molasses from the West Indies. One of these brigs carried 700 tons of coal from Cardiff to Jamaica, though her register tonnage was a little under 300, and it was very common for this class of brig to carry twice her register tonnage in dead weight.

The half-model shows a very burdensome hull having a nearly straight sheer, straight keel with little or no drag, straight and nearly vertical stem rabbet, a small rounded forefoot, slightly raked post, round tuck, upper-and-lower-transom square stern with very little overhang, short and bluff entrance slightly hollow at the forefoot and almost square at the rail, a very long parallel-sided body, and a short and very full run. The midsection has a slightly rising straight floor, rather hard bilge, and a concave tumble-home in the topside.

The model is for a vessel 109 feet moulded length at rail, 24 feet moulded beam, 20 feet moulded depth, and about 277 tons register, old measurement. Some of the brigs built on this half-model measured 290 register tons. In these it is probable that length was added amidships by inserting two or more extra frames at the same spacing as the others. Scale of the model is ¼ inch to the foot.

The spar dimensions of the *Palos* were as follows:

Spars	Length	Diameter
Mainmast	62'	20'' at deck
Foremast	58'	20½'' at deck
Bowsprit	28'	20½'' at Gammon
Main topmast	33'6''	12½'' at cap
Fore topmast	33'	12'' at cap
Main topgallant mast	19'6''	7½'' at cap
Fore topgallant mast	19'6''	7'' at cap
Main royal mast	12'	5¼'' at cap
Fore royal mast	12'	5'' at cap
Jib boom	28'	12½'' at cap

Yards	Length	Diameter at slings	Length of arm outside lifts
Main	46'	13''	24''
Fore	46'	12½''	24''
Main topsail	36'6''	10¼''	26''
Fore topsail	36'6''	9¾''	26''
Main topgallant	24'6''	6¼''	15''
Fore topgallant	24'	5¾''	15''
Main royal	17'	4''	9''
Fore royal	16'	3½''	9''

950 sheets of copper were required to copper the bottom of the *Palos*. In addition to the sails indicated by the spars given above, the brigs often carried a spencer (boomless gaff-foresail) on the foremast and, of course, the usual boomed gaff-spanker and headsails. The brigs did not carry light sails, other than a few stunsails, for these would not help such dull-sailing vessels to any appreciable degree.

Given by John N. Cushing, Newburyport, Massachusetts.

MERCHANT BRIGANTINE, 1838
BUILDER'S HALF-MODEL, USNM 76127

Amethyst

The brigantine-rigged merchant vessel *Amethyst* was built on this half-model at Sullivan, Maine, in 1838 for the coastwise and West Indian trades. Intended to carry a large cargo on a moderate draft, in order to enter some of the rather shallow harbors to which she would trade, the *Amethyst* was a vessel of average size for her type and trade at the time she was built. When Maine-built these vessels usually were low decked and had short and heavy heads, usually fitted with a fiddlehead billet. Such vessels as the *Amethyst* were not designed to sail fast, though handiness in working in narrow waters was highly prized, and some full-bodied vessels were very capable in this respect.

The half-model is of a hull having moderate sheer, a straight keel of very little drag, curved and raking stem rabbet, slightly raking post, round tuck, upper-and-lower-transom square stern, short and bluff entrance, long body, and a short and very full run. The midsection shows a slightly rising straight floor and a heavily rounded bilge, and is rather wall sided above.

Length of Head	Rake
8'6''	1¼'' to 1'0''
8'6''	¾'' to 1'0''
5'	
5'	
5'	
3'	
3'	
6' pole	
5' pole	
2' pole	

The model scales 82 feet 7 inches between perpendiculars, 22 feet 9½ inches beam and 8 feet 6 inches depth. Scale is ½ inch to the foot.

Given by D. A. Simpson.

MERCHANT BRIG, 1841
BUILDER'S HALF-MODEL, USNM 76057

Chenamus

The brig-rigged merchant vessel *Chenamus* of Newburyport was built on this model at the neighboring village of Newbury, Massachusetts, in 1841 for John

N. Cushing and H. Johnson. She was intended for trade to the Pacific Coast, the Columbia River region, and the Northwest Coast. A somewhat smaller vessel than the standard Cushing brig, she was of the same extremely burdensome type that Cushing employed in his own fleet.

The half-model represents a brig hull having a very slight sheer, straight keel, upright stem rabbet with small rounded forefoot, slightly raking post, round tuck, upper-and-lower transoms, square stern, and a strong flare in the bow sections. The entrance is short and bluff, slightly hollow at the forefoot and becoming almost square across at the rail, the very short run is steep and full, and the body long and parallel. The midsection shows a slightly rising straight floor, firm bilge, and a strong tumble-home in the topside. In general, the half-model represents a slow sailing, burdensome kettle-bottom brig.

The model scales 97 feet moulded length at rail, 20 feet moulded beam, and 12 feet 9 inches moulded depth, and represents a vessel of about 202 register tons, old measurement. Scale is $\frac{5}{16}$ inch to the foot.

Given by John N. Cushing, Newburyport, Massachusetts.

BALTIMORE CLIPPER BRIG, 1845
Builder's Half-Model, usnm 76064

This builder's half-model is of an extreme Baltimore clipper brig of the period 1810–45. The model was submitted to John N. Cushing, Sr., in January 1845, as a proposal by a Baltimore builder for the construction of a full-rigged brig for use in the Pacific north-west coast trade, the estimated cost being $10,765. Cushing's preference for extremely full-ended vessels probably prevented his accepting the proposal; no vessel was built from this model for the Cushing fleet.

The half-model is of a flush-decked vessel designed to sail fast in moderate winds and its appearance and size are very similar to those of Baltimore clipper brigs built as privateers in the War of 1812. It represents the older type of Baltimore clipper in which the keel had much drag and the midsection showed a sharp rise in the straight floor. By 1825, at least, the Chesapeake Bay builders were producing for the merchant service brigs and brigantines in which there was little drag to the keel and only moderate rise in the straight floor at the midsection. This half-model, then, does not represent the most advanced ideas in the design of fast commercial brigs by Maryland builders in 1845 and, indeed, it may actually have been made much earlier than this date.

The half-model represents a brig having a rather straight sheer, straight keel with very marked drag, slightly curved and strongly raking stem rabbet with well rounded forefoot, sharply raking post, round tuck, and an upper-and-lower-transom square stern with very small overhang. The entrance is long, sharp and slightly convex, and the run is long and fine. The midsection is formed with the sharply rising floor briefly straight near the keel, a slack and well rounded bilge, and a slight tumble-home in the topside, but only above the maindeck level. The bow sections have moderate flare.

Model is mounted with a stub bowsprit, short and

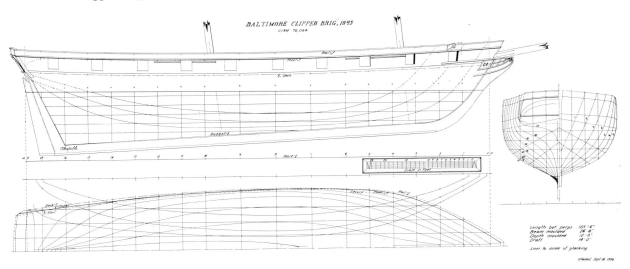

Lines Taken Off Builder's Half-Model USNM 76064, of a Baltimore clipper brig, 1845. Model is for a merchant brig or brigantine but shows a popular type that earlier (1812–15) was used for privateers.

deep head, trails and headrail, cutwater, keel, post, rudder, and false hammock rails. Ports are painted, naval fashion.

Brigs of this type had sharply raking masts and were very heavily sparred and canvassed; the antithesis of the Cushing fleet of brigs. The Baltimore clipper as early as 1790 had an international reputation, which it maintained well into the 1850's, for fast sailing and weatherliness.

The model is for a brig 112 feet moulded length at rail, 105 feet 6 inches between perpendiculars, 26 feet 6 inches moulded beam, 12 feet 8 inches moulded depth, 14 feet draft at post, and about 255 tons register, old measurement. Scale of the model is ⅜ inch to the foot.

Given by John N. Cushing of Newburyport, Massachusetts.

The original proposal for building this vessel was a simple statement of cost:

Hull and Spars	$6,400
Blacksmith's (bill)	500
Rigging	850
Blockmaker's (bill)	200
Joiner's (bill)	375
Riggers' (bills)	240
Plumber's (bill)	150
Copper etc.,	2,050
	————
	$10,765

This half-model is one of the few of Baltimore clippers that have survived from the period prior to 1850 and the only one known of a full-rigged brig other than a few half-models of naval brigs of this type. It is believed that many Chesapeake Bay builders were late in turning to the half-model as a method of design, and that they retained the old draught, or lines plan, far later than was usual elsewhere; hence there may have been relatively few builders' half-models before 1840.

MERCHANT BRIGANTINE, 1846
BUILDER'S HALF-MODEL, USNM 76140

Watson

The brigantine-rigged coaster *Watson* was built on this half-model at Sedgwick, Maine, in 1846. She was designed for the South Atlantic coastal and the West Indian trades, and was typical of a large number of small Maine-built traders of this period. Though she was only 146 tons register, old measurement, she was considered a large vessel of her class when built. These small Maine-built brigantines, usually low

decked, with a short, high quarterdeck, were very profitable for many years and were commonly long-lived and inexpensive craft. The *Watson* carried the usual cargoes in the West Indian trade: New England lumber (white pine building material, laths, and shingles) south and sugar and molasses north. The South Atlantic ports also received manufactures such as machinery, hardware, finished fabrics, furniture, and "notions" and shipped north yellow pine and tar or turpentine. By 1840 the New England shipyards were using the longleaf southern pine for planking and ceiling and, of course, the marine stores, tar and turpentine.

The half-model represents a brigantine-rigged vessel having moderate sheer, a straight keel of little or no drag, curved and raking stem rabbet, slightly raking post, round tuck, upper-and-lower-transom square stern, a short and rather full entrance, and a well formed run of moderate length. The midsection has a slightly rising straight floor, full round bilge, and a slight tumble-home in the topside.

Mounted with short, heavy head, cutwater, keel, post, and rudder.

The model scales 90 feet moulded length at rail, 22 feet moulded beam, and 8 feet 6 inches moulded depth. Scale is ½ inch to the foot.

Given by Joshua Watson, shipbuilder, Sedgwick, Maine.

MERCHANT BRIGANTINE, 1848
BUILDER'S HALF-MODEL, USNM 76124

Telula

The brigantine *Telula* was built on this hawk's-nest, or crow's nest, half-model in 1848 at Cherryfield, Maine, for the coastal trade. Vessels of this rig and date usually carried a gaff foresail, or spencer, and could work as well as a topsail schooner, yet with the wind aft could run as well as a full-rigged brig. The brigantine fitted with a spencer on her foremast was sometimes called a schooner, or hermaphrodite, brig. The trading brigantines of this date were fitted to give economical operation and were relatively inexpensive vessels to build and fit.

This half-model, a good example of the type, is made with a backboard upon which the profile is marked to show the height of the bulwarks, wales, and the half breadths of the level lines are marked on the sections, which are to deck level. The stations are marked and on each of these is a small board shaped to sectional form, or to the mould of the individual station. Battens are tacked to the sections, to hold them rigid and secure, and must be removed to take off the lines.

The half-model represents a vessel of very moderate sheer, having a straight keel with moderate or little drag, slightly raking stem rabbet curved below the load line, slightly raking post, round tuck, upper-and-lower-transom square stern, short and full entrance, long body, and a short and rather full run. The mid-section has a moderately rising straight floor, a low, well rounded and easy bilge, and a slight tumble-home in the topside. The head and cutwater are short and heavy.

The model is for a vessel 78 feet moulded length at rail, 22 feet moulded beam, and 10 feet 8 inches moulded depth to rail cap. Scale of the model is $\frac{1}{2}$ inch to the foot.

Given by G. R. Campbell and Company.

MERCHANT BRIGANTINE, 1852
BUILDER'S HALF-MODEL, USNM 76131

Iscarion

The brigantine *Iscarion* was built on this model by Hamen Cousins at Trenton (now Lamoine), Maine, in 1852 for the general coasting and West Indian trades. The low-decked vessel was particularly designed to carry lumber. The vessel is an excellent example of the small brigantines employed in the coastal trades in the 1850's out of Maine ports.

The half-model is of a brigantine hull having moderate sheer, a straight keel with slight drag, curved and raking stem rabbet, slightly raking post, round tuck, raking flat transom, square stern, moderately full entrance with flaring bow sections, no deadflat, and a rather short but easy run. The midsection has a slightly rising straight floor, a round, easy bilge, and a slight tumble-home in the topside.

Mounted with short and rather heavy head, cutwater, keel, post and rudder; a short quarter deck and rather deep bulwarks are indicated.

The model is for a brigantine 89 feet 8 inches moulded length at rail, 23 feet 8 inches moulded beam, and 9 feet moulded depth, about 198 tons register, old measurement. Scale of the model is $\frac{1}{2}$ inch to the foot.

Given by C. L. Young.

MERCHANT BRIGANTINE, 1852
BUILDER'S HALF-MODEL, USNM 76141

Abby Watson

The trading brigantine *Abby Watson* was built on this model at Sedgwick, Maine, in 1852 and was considered to be a very fine vessel and large for her type when launched. She was employed in the West Indian trade for some years and afterwards was in the lumber trade to South Atlantic ports. She was lost with all hands off Cape Hatteras about 1876.

The half-model shows a low-decked brigantine having moderate sheer, a straight keel with very slight drag, curved and raking stem rabbet, nearly vertical post, round tuck, raking-transom square stern, a rather sharp entrance with flaring bow sections, short deadflat, and a moderately long but somewhat full run. The midsection shows a slightly rising straight floor, a round, easy bilge, and a slight tumble-home in the topside.

Mounted with short heavy head, cutwater, keel, rabbet, and post. A short quarterdeck is indicated.

The model is for a vessel 109 feet 9½ inches between perpendiculars, 27 feet beam, 9 feet 3½ inches depth, and 213.87 gross tons register. Scale of the model is $\frac{1}{2}$ inch to the foot.

Given by Joshua Watson, shipbuilder, Sedgwick, Maine.

MERCHANT BRIGANTINE, 1852
BUILDER'S HALF-MODEL, USNM 160123

A merchant brigantine, name unknown, was built on this model at Bath, Maine, in 1852 for the West Indian and coastal trades. The half-model illustrates a popular hull form in this class of vessel in the period 1840–55, having good capacity and fair sailing qualities. This type of vessel had a short, high quarterdeck at rail-cap height.

The half-model shows a brigantine having moderate sheer, a straight keel with little drag, curved and raking stem rabbet flaring somewhat at the top, nearly vertical post, round tuck, upper-and-lower-transom square stern, short and full entrance with strong flare in the bow sections, and a moderate length of body and run, the latter somewhat full. The midsection is formed with some rise in the straight floor, a low, full round bilge, and a moderate tumble-home in the topside.

Mounted with a short, heavy head and cutwater, keel, post, and rudder.

The model is for a vessel 90 feet 6 inches moulded length at rail, 22 feet 6 inches moulded beam, and 8 feet moulded depth to deck. Scale of the model is $\frac{1}{2}$ inch to the foot.

Given by William P. Pattee, shipbuilder, Bath, Maine.

MERCHANT BRIGANTINE, 1854
BUILDER'S HALF-MODEL, USNM 76135

Fredonia

The trading brigantine *Fredonia* was built on this model in 1854 at Ellsworth, Maine, for the West Indian trade. She was an advanced design for her time and, in general, her model shows many of the characteristics that marked brigantines built in Maine and Nova Scotia 20 years later, combining cargo capacity with very good sailing qualities. Slightly narrower than contemporary Maine-built brigantines of her approximate length, the *Fredonia* was considered a very handsome vessel, and was profitable to operate.

The half-model represents a brigantine hull having moderate sheer, a straight keel, flaring and rather upright stem rabbet with rounded forefoot, nearly upright post, short counter and raking transom, moderately sharp entrance with much flare in the bow sections, giving a full rail line, practically no deadflat, and a long and easy run. The midsection shows a short and slightly rising straight floor, easy and round bilge, and some tumble-home in the topside. The model shows a short quarterdeck.

The model is for a vessel 103 feet moulded length at rail, 24 feet 6 inches moulded beam, and 10 feet moulded depth. Scale of the model is ½ inch to the foot.

Given by Abraham Lord.

MERCHANT BRIGANTINE, 1856
BUILDER'S HALF-MODEL, USNM 76115

Anita Owen

The brigantine-rigged merchant vessel *Anita Owen* of New York was built on this model at Millbridge, Maine, in 1856 by Ezekiel Dyer for the West Indian trade. She was a profitable and well built vessel, costing $20,000, of a type that carried a large cargo for her size yet sailed quite well. The *Anita Owen* was lost in 1870.

The half-model is of a burdensome brigantine-rigged trading vessel having moderate sheer, a straight keel, rather upright but flaring stem rabbet with a very small curved forefoot, nearly upright post, round tuck, a square stern with raking transom, a rather full entrance, and a moderately long, easy run. The midsection is formed with a slightly rising and very short floor developing into a rather easy and much rounded bilge, and a slight tumble-home in the topside. There is strong flare in the bow sections.

Mounted with a small, pointed longhead, trails, cutwater, keel, post, and rudder.

The model scales 117 feet moulded length at rail, 27 feet 5 inches moulded beam, 13 feet 6 inches moulded depth. Scale is 5/16 inch to the foot.

Given by Captain Austin Dyer.

MERCHANT BRIGANTINE, 1856
BUILDER'S HALF-MODEL, USNM 76100

Hurricane Bird

The trading brigantine *Hurricane Bird* was built at Baltimore, Maryland, by Pendergast and Brother in 1856 for the West Indian trade. The *Hurricane Bird* was a handsome and fast vessel on a clipper model that Maryland builders had developed, by gradual modification of the old Baltimore clipper hull form, brigs and brigantines in the late 1830's very similar in character to the later and better known clipper ships of the late 1840's.

The *Hurricane Bird* was launched November 3, 1856, and was lost at sea in 1859. She was heavily sparred and canvassed like most of the Maryland-built brigantines in the West Indian sugar trade. Speed in these traders was probably desired because many carried north fruit, as well as sugar and molasses.

The half-model is of a medium clipper brigantine having rather slight sheer, a straight keel with very slight drag, very flaring and raking stem rabbet, nearly upright post, a short counter with a raking square transom having some curve athwartships, rather long and sharp entrance, and a fine run of moderate length. The midsection is formed with a moderate rise in the straight floor, rather hard bilge, and a slight tumble-home in the topside. The bow sections flare considerably.

Mounted with a pointed longhead, cutwater, keel, post, and rudder; a short quarterdeck is indicated.

The model scales 111 feet moulded length at rail, 26 feet moulded beam, and 10 feet 10 inches moulded depth, deck to rabbet at side. Scale is ½ inch to the foot.

Given by William Skinner and Sons, shipbuilders, Baltimore, Maryland.

MERCHANT BRIGANTINE, 1858
BUILDER'S HALF-MODEL, USNM 76099

Alexander Kirkland, George Latimer

The trading brigantines *Alexander Kirkland* and *George Latimer* were built on this model in 1858 for the West Indian trade by William Skinner and Sons,

BRIGANTINES *GEORGE LATIMER* & *ALEXANDER KIRKLAND*
Built at Baltimore, Md. 1858
for the West Indian Trade

Length moulded at rail 110'9"
Length btl perpl 104'0"
Beam moulded 24'8"
Depth moulded 10'3"
Draft at post 11'8"

Kirkland lost at sea
with all hands

LINES OF THE BALTIMORE-BUILT BRIGANTINES *George Latimer* and *Alexander Kirkland*, built 1858 for the West Indian trade. The *Latimer* was destroyed by the Confederate cruiser *Florida*, and the *Kirkland* disappeared at sea. Taken off builder's half-model USNM 76099.

Baltimore, Maryland. The model represents a clipper brigantine of the period as developed by Maryland builders in which the rise of the straight floor and drag to the keel of their earlier Baltimore clipper model had been reduced to a minimum. The *Latimer*, a noted sailer in the West Indian-Baltimore sugar trade, was burned by the Confederate raider *Florida* in 1864. The *Kirkland* "went missing" and was probably overwhelmed in a hurricane. These Baltimore-built West-Indiamen were very similar in all respects to the brigantines in the coffee trade and carried a large spread of canvas.

The half-model is of a medium-clipper hull having a moderate and handsome sheer, straight keel with slight drag, slightly raking and moderately flaring stem rabbet, nearly upright post, short counter with raking elliptical transom curved athwartships, a long and sharp entrance with some hollow at the forefoot and much flare in the bow sections, and a long and fine run. The midsection is formed with a slightly rising straight floor, well rounded and rather easy bilge, and a marked tumble-home in the topside.

Mounted with a longhead, trails, cutwater, keel, post, rudder, and stub bowsprit.

The brigantines measured 110 feet 9 inches moulded length at rail, 104 feet between perpendiculars, 24 feet 8 inches moulded beam, and 10 feet 3 inches moulded depth, deck to rabbet at side. Scale of model is ½ inch to the foot.

Given by William Skinner and Sons, shipbuilders, Baltimore, Maryland.

MERCHANT BRIGANTINE, 1867
BUILDER'S HALF-MODEL, USNM 76118

Eva M. Johnson, Mary E. Pennel

The trading brigantine *Eva M. Johnson*, 235.84 register tons, was built on this model in 1867 and the *Mary E. Pennel*, 239.01 register tons, in 1868, at Harrington, Maine, for the West Indian and coastwise trades. The model is typical of the Maine-built brigantine traders, usually with a short quarterdeck, employed in the sugar and molasses trade in the decade following the Civil War.

The half-model represents a brigantine having moderate sheer, a straight keel with very slight drag, rather upright but flaring stem rabbet with slightly rounded forefoot, vertical post, short wide counter having raking elliptical transom rounded athwartships, short and rather full entrance, short and easy run, and a rather markedly long body. The midsection shows a slight rise in the straight floor, round and easy bilge, and some tumble-home in the topside. The bow sections have a good deal of flare.

Mounted with a small longhead, trails, cutwater, keel, post and rudder.

The model is for a vessel 114 feet 6 inches moulded length at rail, about 109 feet between perpendiculars, 27 feet moulded beam, and nearly 12 feet 4 inches moulded depth. Scale of the model is ⅜ inch to the foot.

Given by V. L. Coffin, of Harrington, Maine.

71

MERCHANT BRIGANTINE, 1866
BUILDER'S HALF-MODEL, USNM 76117

Antelope, Gazelle

The trading brigantines *Antelope* and *Gazelle* were built on this model at Harrington, Maine, in 1866 for the West Indian and coastwise trades. Vessels of this general model were good carriers and excellent seaboats; they sailed moderately well, and were considered by Maine shipowners to be very profitable in the West Indian trade. The *Antelope*, launched in July 1866 and wrecked on the Delaware Breakwater a few years later, and the *Gazelle*, launched in September 1866, measured 329.92 and 326.37 gross tons register, respectively.

The half-model is of a brigantine measuring about 117 feet moulded length at rail, 113 feet 9 inches between perpendiculars, 23 feet 3½ inches beam, and 14 feet moulded depth. Scale of the model is ⅜ inch to the foot.

The model has moderate sheer, a straight keel with very slight drag, slightly raking stem rabbet with moderate flare and a slightly rounded forefoot, nearly upright post, short counter with raking elliptical transom, rather full and short entrance, marked length of body, and a short and somewhat full run. The midsection shows a slightly rising straight floor, round and very easy bilge, and a slight tumble-home in the topside. The bow sections have marked flare.

Mounted with long head, cutwater, keel, post, rudder, and short quarterdeck monkey rail.

Given by V. L. Coffin, Harrington, Maine.

MERCHANT BRIGANTINE, 1871
BUILDER'S HALF-MODEL, USNM 76116

Minnie Smith

The brigantine *Minnie Smith* was built on this model by Ezekiel Dyer at Millbridge, Maine, in 1871 for the West Indian, coastwise and foreign trades. She cost $20,000 to build and was lost while entering the port of Salerno, Italy, from the West Indies, on her maiden voyage.

The half-model represents a brigantine having moderate sheer, a straight keel with little drag, somewhat upright and flaring stem rabbet with a slightly rounded forefoot, nearly vertical post, short and wide counter with thin elliptical transom, moderately sharp but short entrance, marked length of body, and a rather full run of moderate length. The midsection has a slightly rising straight floor, an easy,

round bilge, and tumble-home in the topside. The bow sections have considerable flare.

Mounted with longhead, cutwater, keel, post, rudder, and a short quarterdeck monkey rail.

The model is for a vessel measuring about 116 feet 8 inches moulded length at rail, 26 feet 8 inches moulded beam, and 12 feet moulded depth. Scale of the model is ⅜ inch to the foot.

Given by Captain Austin Dyer.

MERCHANT BRIGANTINE, 1874
BUILDER'S HALF-MODEL, USNM 76075

J. W. Parker

The trading brigantine *J. W. Parker* of Belfast, Maine, was built at that port by C. P. Carter and Company in 1874 on this model. This firm, noted for the fine design and construction of its vessels, had built many 3- and 4-masted schooners and barkentines, and at least one clipper ship, having started building in about 1851. The *J. W. Parker* was intended for general freighting in the coastwise, West Indian, and European trades, and was, therefore, a large vessel for her rig. Her model represents the final development of the American trading brigantine, combining swift sailing, weatherliness, and good handling qualities with excellent cargo capacity. The brigantines remained popular with some shipowners in the West Indian and European trades after the *Parker* was built; a number of fine vessels of this rig were built in Nova Scotia in the 1880's and 1890's. In the coastwise and, more slowly, in the West Indian trade, the brigantine was replaced by the 3-masted schooner, which benefited more by use of steam winches than the brigantine. The rising cost of manpower necessitated the use of a rig that could be handled by fewer men and, as size increased, by the additional help of the donkey engine and its winch. The mechanical aids combined to doom the brigantine in these trades, for the latter's square sails could not be handled by any practical arrangement of the steam winch.

The half-model represents a brigantine having strong sheer, a straight keel with slight drag, moderately flaring and raking stem rabbet with slightly rounded forefoot, nearly vertical post, short and light counter ending in a raked elliptical transom much curved athwartships, short and sharp entrance, moderate length of body, and a short but easy run. The midsection is formed with a moderately rising straight floor, firm round bilge, and tumble-home in

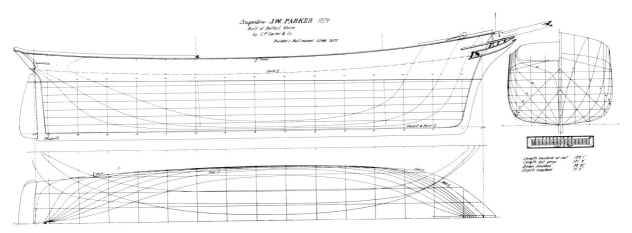

LINES OF THE BRIGANTINE, *J. W. Parker*, built at Belfast, Maine, in 1874. Taken off the builder's half-model, USNM 76075.

the topside. There is much flare in the bow sections. The model gives the impression of being rather deep and narrow for its length and it belongs to the down-Easter hull form.

Mounted with longhead, trails, cutwater, keel, post, rudder, and a short quarterdeck monkey rail, the latter indicating a turned-stanchion-and-cap rail above it.

The model scales 129 feet 1 inch moulded length at rail, 121 feet 3 inches between perpendiculars, 28 feet 10 inches moulded beam, and 15 feet moulded depth deck to rabbet. Scale is ⅜ inch to the foot. This model was given by the builders, C. P. Carter and Company, shipbuilders, Belfast, Maine.

SQUARE-TOPSAIL SCHOONER, 1845
BUILDER'S HALF-MODEL, USNM 76143

Ruth Thomas

The square-topsail trading schooner *Ruth Thomas* was built on this hawk's nest model at Frankfort, Maine, in 1845 for the coastwise and West Indian trades. She was low decked to suit the requirements of the lumber trade. Vessels of this rig had a square forecourse, square topsail and topgallant sails, as well as the usual schooner fore-and-aft foresail on the foremast; the main had a gaff mainsail and gaff topsail, in addition to the usual schooner headsails and main- and main-topmast staysails. The foresail on these coasters had a boom and some set a very deep square topsail on the foremast, omitting the topgallant sail. A fore royal was a great rarity in the New England-built topsail schooners of this period and employment. The square-topsail schooner went

out of fashion with New England owners about 1855, although as late as 1895, some vessels of this rig were built in eastern New England and in Nova Scotia for the coasting and West Indian trades.

The half-model, made up of plank sections mounted on a profile on a backboard, represents a schooner hull having moderate sheer, a straight keel with small drag, curved and somewhat raking stem rabbet with rounded forefoot, nearly vertical post, round tuck, upper-and-lower-transom square stern, short and full entrance, rather long and easy run, and a markedly long body. The midsection is formed with a slightly rising straight floor, easy bilge, and a moderate tumble-home in the topside.

Model is fitted with a short, heavy head, cutwater, keel, post, and rudder. A short quarterdeck is indicated.

The model scales about 88 feet moulded length at rail, 83 feet 7 inches between perpendiculars, 24 feet 2 inches moulded beam, and 7 feet 6 inches depth. Scale is ½ inch to the foot.

Given by F. L. Tyler.

SQUARE-TOPSAIL COASTING SCHOONER, 1847
BUILDER'S HALF-MODEL, USNM 76069

Arrowsic, Eagle

The square-topsail keel coasting schooner *Arrowsic* was built on this model at Arrowsic Island in the Kennebec River, Maine, in 1847 for the coastal lumber trade. The square-topsail packet schooner *Eagle* was also built on this model and employed in the run between New York City and Bath, Maine. Both vessels were built by master-builder Samuel Pattee,

73

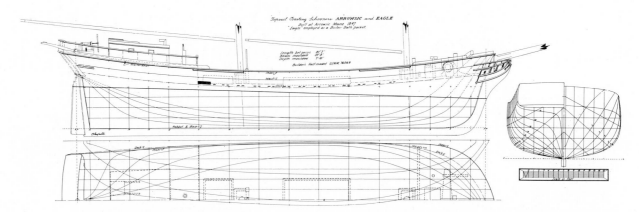

LINES OF THE SQUARE-TOPSAIL COASTING SCHOONERS *Arrowsic* and *Eagle*, built at Arrowsic Island, Kennebec River, Maine, in 1847. The *Eagle* was employed as a New York to Bath packet. Taken off the builder's half-model USNM 76069.

father of the donor of the half-model. The *Eagle* in particular had the reputation of being a fast sailer and on one occasion made the run from New York to Bath, outside Long Island and around Cape Cod, in 210 hours wharf to wharf. The *Arrowsic* was considered a good sailer; she capsized and sank off Block Island, sometime about 1860, through carrying too great a press of canvas during a gale.

The half-model represents a coasting schooner having marked sheer, a straight keel with moderate drag, slightly raking and flaring stem rabbet with a well rounded forefoot, slightly raking post, round tuck, and an upper-and-lower-transom square stern (the lower transom is unusually small). The entrance is short but moderately sharp at and below the load waterline, with a very full deck line and rail, and the run is long and rather fine for so burdensome a vessel. The midsection is formed with some rise in the straight floor, a well rounded and rather easy turn of bilge, and some tumble-home in the topside. The bow sections show great flare.

These schooners had deep bulwarks and a short, high quarterdeck. They had short heavy cutwaters fitted with trails, knees, head rails, and billets. The model is of the lift type, to represent waterlines or level lines, and the lifts are held together by wooden toggles through them, with wedges at bottom and top, instead of the iron screws usually employed to fasten the lifts together.

The model is for a vessel about 85 feet 9 inches moulded length at main rail, 22 feet 8 inches moulded beam, and 7 feet 10 inches moulded depth from rabbet to underside of deck at side, 81 feet 7 inches between perpendiculars, and 9 feet 8 inches draft at post when fully loaded. Scale of the model is ½ inch to the foot.

Given by William P. Pattee, shipbuilder, Bath, Maine.

TWO-MASTED COASTING SCHOONER, 1847
BUILDER'S HALF-MODEL, USNM 76109

Watchman

The 2-masted coasting schooner *Watchman* was built on this model at Tinker's Island, Maine, in 1847. A low-deck vessel intended for the general coasting trade, and particularly for carrying lumber from Maine to Boston and southern New England ports, she was a good example of the type of coaster employed in this trade in the 1840's and 1850's. Such vessels had high hatch coamings, as they were habitually loaded until the maindeck was nearly awash.

The model represents a burdensome schooner hull having moderate sheer, a straight keel with slight drag, a curved and raking stem rabbet, nearly upright post, round tuck, upper-and-lower-transom square stern, a short and full entrance with flaring bow sections, long body, and a short and full run. The midsection is formed with a very moderate rise in the straight floor, round and easy bilge, and a slight tumble-home in the topside. The stern in this model is deep for the depth of the hull, giving the vessel a very heavy appearance.

Mounted with a deep, heavy head, cutwater, keel, post, and rudder. A short quarterdeck is indicated.

The model scales 80 feet moulded length at rail, 22 feet 6 inches moulded beam, and 7 feet depth of hold. The scale is ½ inch to the foot.

Given by Joshua Watson, shipbuilder, Sedgwick, Maine.

74

TWO-MASTED TOPSAIL COASTING SCHOONER, 1847
Builder's Half-Model, usnm 76104

Marcia Tribou

The 2-masted, topsail-rigged coasting schooner *Marcia Tribou* was built on this model at Bucksport, Maine, in 1847. She was designed for the West Indian and coastal trades and is fairly representative of the large class of schooners employed in these trades and in general freighting along the Atlantic coast in the period 1825–50.

The half-model shows a burdensome schooner hull having a good deal of sheer, straight keel with very little drag, curved and raking stem rabbet, nearly upright post, round tuck, upper-and-lower-transom square stern, short and high quarterdeck, a short and full entrance with flaring bow sections, and a short but rather well formed run. The midsection shows a very slight rise in the straight floor, well rounded bilge, and a very small tumble-home in the topside. The model is mounted with a short and somewhat pointed head, cutwater, keel, post, rudder and a high quarterdeck bulwark.

The model scales 89 feet moulded length to taffrail, 85 feet between perpendiculars, 23 feet 8 inches moulded beam, 8 feet 9 inches moulded depth from deck at side to rabbet, and 10 feet 2 inches draft at post. Scale is ½ inch to the foot.

Given by John Swazey, Bucksport, Maine.

TWO-MASTED COASTING SCHOONER, 1852
Builder's Half-Model, usnm 76138

Lucy

The 2-masted coasting schooner *Lucy* was built on this model at Sargentville, Maine, in 1852. She was

built for the New England coasting trade, carrying lumber to southern New England and manufactures on the return voyage, and was of the low-decked type, with a short and high quarter-deck and a heavy stern. This vessel was eventually lost on a winter passage.

The half-model is of a very burdensome schooner hull having moderate sheer, a straight keel with very slight drag, curved and raking stem rabbet, nearly upright post, round tuck, raking square stern, short full entrance and run, and a long body. The midsection shows a very slightly rising straight floor, rather easy bilge, and a slight tumble-home above.

The model is for a vessel about 85 feet moulded length at main rail, 77 feet between perpendiculars, 23 feet 3½ inch beam and 7 feet 1¾ inches depth. Scale of the model is ½ inch to the foot.

Given by Robert Dority, shipbuilder, Sedgwick, Maine.

TWO-MASTED COASTING SCHOONER, 1855
Builder's Half-Model, usnm 76126

Wakeag

The 2-masted coasting schooner *Wakeag* was built on this model at Trenton (now Lamoine), Maine, in 1855 for the coastal and West Indian trades. The vessel was intended to have very large capacity for her length on a limited draft and to carry lumber profitably. The *Wakeag* was considered large for a coasting schooner at her date of launching.

The half-model shows a burdensome schooner hull having rather straight sheer, a straight keel with very slight drag, a flaring, curved, and raking stem rabbet, vertical post, round tuck, raking square stern, short and full entrance and run, with flaring bow sections,

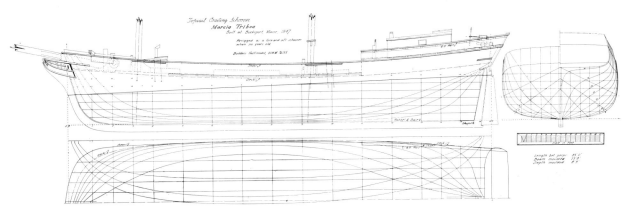

LINES OF THE SQUARE-TOPSAIL COASTING SCHOONER *Marcia Tribou* built at Bucksport, Maine, in 1847 for the lumber trade. Taken off the builder's half-model USNM 76104.

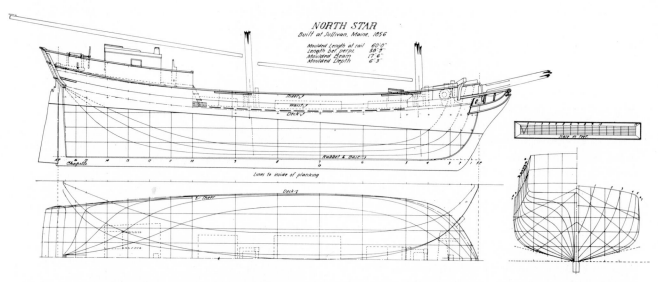

LINES OF THE 2-MASTED COASTING SCHOONER *North Star*, built at Sullivan, Maine, 1856. This vessel is somewhat similar to the early Marblehead type of fishing schooner. Taken off the builder's half-model USNM 76128.

and a long body. The midsection is formed with a slightly rising straight floor, a round and easy bilge, and some tumble-home in the topside. She has a notably long straight side and wide stern.

The model scales 102 feet moulded length at rail, 90 feet between perpendiculars, 25 feet 3½ inches extreme beam, and 8 feet 5½ inches depth in hold. Scale is ⅛ inch to the foot.

Given by Hamen Cousins, shipbuilder, Lamoine, Maine.

TWO-MASTED COASTING SCHOONER, 1855
BUILDER'S HALF-MODEL, USNM 76136

J. W. Hale

The 2-masted, keel coasting schooner *J. W. Hale* was built on this model in 1855 at Brooklin, Maine, for the general coasting trade. This vessel was designed primarily to carry lumber. She was employed for 2 years in the freighting of longleaf yellow pine from Jacksonville, Florida, and from Savannah and other southern ports to New England for shipbuilding and construction purposes. The vessels in this trade also freighted marine stores out of the Florida port and carried manufactured goods south. The *J. W. Hale* made two West Indian voyages, and was lost off Hatteras when she was 4 or 5 years old.

The half-model shows a wide, shallow schooner hull having very moderate sheer, a straight keel with very slight drag, a curved and raking stem rabbet, slightly raking post, round tuck, wide square stern with raking

transom, the entrance short and rather sharp, and the body long and the run short and quite full, with flaring bow sections. The midsection shows a slightly rising straight floor, full and rather easy bilge, and a slight tumble-home in the topside.

Mounted with a rather light head of moderate length, cutwater, keel, post, and rudder. A short quarterdeck is indicated.

The model scales 87 feet moulded length at rail, 23 feet moulded beam, and 7 feet 6 inches moulded depth. Scale is ½ inch to the foot.

Given by Moses B. Day, Brooklin, Maine.

TWO-MASTED COASTING SCHOONER, 1856
BUILDER'S HALF-MODEL, USNM 76128

North Star

The small 2-masted, fore-and-aft rigged coasting schooner *North Star* was built on this model in 1856 at Sullivan, Maine. She was intended for the coastal lumber trade. The model represents an obsolete type of coaster at the date she was built, but this hull form remained popular with some Eastern Maine owners until after the Civil War because of its sailing qualities. In general, the model was very nearly that of the old Marblehead fishing schooner of colonial times, with some additions. The coasters had the same marked sheer, heavy drag to keel, high and short quarterdeck, rising floor, full short entrance, and rather easy run. Like the old Marblehead schooner, these small Maine-built vessels were good sailers and very weatherly and handy. They were also fair carriers. The *North Star*, modeled by Richard Simpson, a notable builder of coasters and fishing schooners at Sullivan, was reported to have been a fast sailer and a fine sea boat.

The half-model represents a schooner having very great sheer, a straight keel with heavy drag, rather upright and curved stem rabbet, well rounded forefoot, slight rake to post, round tuck, upper-and-lower-transom square stern, short entrance with somewhat V–shaped waterlines, fair length of body, and a somewhat short but well formed run. The midsection is formed with rather marked rise in the straight floor, firm round bilge, and a slight tumble-home in the topside.

Vessels of this type had a short, heavy cutwater and much steeve in the bowsprit, a short, high and bulwarked quarterdeck; and, for their size high bulwarks on the maindeck. The old form of bow, having no flare, is very marked in the *North Star*. By 1856 this class of coaster had become better finished than the earlier fishing schooners; a head and billet with, sometimes, carved trails were often used, and the deck arrangement and deck fittings approached those of contemporary fishing and coasting schooners, of the then "modern" design, built in Maine and Massachusetts.

The model is for a schooner measuring 60 feet moulded length at rail, 58 feet 9 inches length between perpendiculars, 17 feet 6 inches moulded beam, 6 feet 3 inches moulded depth, and 8 feet 3 inches draft at post, loaded. Scale of the model is ½ inch to the foot.

Given by D. A. Simpson, Sullivan, Maine.

TWO-MASTED COASTING SCHOONER, 1858
BUILDER'S HALF-MODEL, USNM 76052

R. B. Sumner

The 2-masted keel coasting schooner *R. B. Sumner* was built on this model at Newburyport, Massachusetts, for owners in that port, in 1858. This vessel is said to have been intended for the general coastal freighting trade but she is unusually sharp for this employment; in any case she was found to be a fast sailer and was employed as a packet on the Boston-Newburyport run. It is probable that she was modeled and built as a packet rather than as a freighter.

The half-model represents a schooner hull having a slight and graceful sheer, straight keel with moderate drag, raking and flaring stem rabbet with slightly rounded forefoot, slightly raking post, round tuck, upper-and-lower-transom square stern, sharp convex entrance of moderate length, and a rather long and very fine run. The midsection is formed with a somewhat rising straight floor, full round bilge, and a moderate tumble-home in the topside. There is a moderate flare in the bow sections.

Mounted with a graceful longhead having trails and billet, cutwater, keel, rudder and post. A long quarterdeck monkey rail is shown. The schooner had a turned-stanchion-and-cap quarterdeck rail, packet-fashion.

The *R. B. Sumner* was about 84 feet 3 inches moulded length at rail, 79 feet 8 inches between perpendiculars, 21 feet 2 inches moulded beam, 8 feet 4 inches moulded depth, and had a draft, loaded, of 9 feet

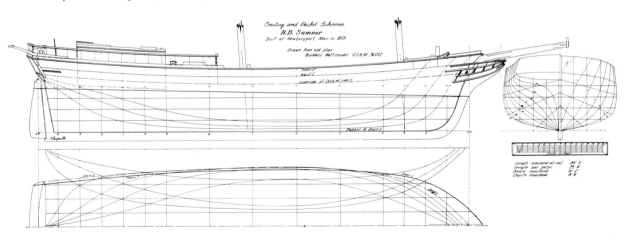

LINES OF THE COASTING AND PACKET SCHOONER *R. B. Sumner*, built at Newburyport, Massachusetts, in 1858. Taken off the builder's half-model USNM 76052.

4 inches at post. Scale of the model is ⅜ inch to the foot.

Given by Sumner, Swazey, and Currier of Newburyport, Massachusetts.

TWO-MASTED COASTING SCHOONER, 1858
BUILDER'S HALF-MODEL, USNM 76122

Aaron

The large 2-masted coasting schooner *Aaron* was built on this model at Lubec, Maine, by J. Kennedy in 1858. She was intended for the West Indian and coastwise trades and was employed for a time in freighting salt fish from eastern Maine to South Atlantic ports. She was eventually lost on a voyage to Africa. The *Aaron* was of the class of large 2-masted coasters, popular in the 1850's and 1860's, that were replaced by the 3-masters of the 1870's and 1880's.

The half-model is of a schooner hull having rather marked sheer, a straight keel with slight drag, raking stem rabbet, upright post, short counter and square transom sharply raked, short and full entrance, rather long body, long but rather full run, and flaring bow sections.

The midsection shows a slightly rising straight floor, much rounded and rather easy bilge, and a slight tumble-home in the topside.

Mounted with longhead, billet, cutwater, keel, post and rudder. Many schooners of this class had long quarterdecks.

The model scales 108 feet 9 inches moulded length at rail, 32 feet 10 inches moulded beam, and 14 feet 5 inches moulded depth. Scale is ⁵⁄₁₆ inch to the foot.

Given by J. Kennedy, shipbuilder, Lubec, Maine.

TWO-MASTED PACKET SCHOONER, about 1860
BUILDER'S HALF-MODEL, USNM 76053

Charmer

The 2-masted packet schooner *Charmer* was built at Newburyport, Massachusetts, about 1860 for the Boston-Newburyport packet service, carrying passengers and light freight. This trade required a fast and handy schooner, of moderate draft. These packet schooners remained profitable for many years after steamers had entered the coastwise trades, for the sailing packets were inexpensive to operate and had enough speed to compete with the majority of the early small steamers. The sailing packets often carried mail, package freight, and carriages and horses, as well as passengers.

The model of the *Charmer* was based on the lines of the packet schooner *Iowa;* her predecessor in the Newburyport packet trade. The *Iowa* was a Chesapeake Bay pungy schooner built in Dorchester County, Maryland, in 1854. She had been brought to Gloucester as a fishing schooner, but her speed and working qualities led to her immediate sale to owners in Newburyport. The *Iowa* became celebrated locally for her sailing qualities; she was considered very fast and weatherly. The model of the *Charmer* was made as an exact copy of the lines of the *Iowa*, but with a New England head and cutwater. The *Charmer* also became a celebrated schooner, with the reputation of being a very fast sailer and weatherly.

The half-model represents a Chesapeake pungy schooner having high bulwarks, a rather low freeboard, flush deck, slight sheer, straight keel with moderate drag, much rounded forefoot and sharply

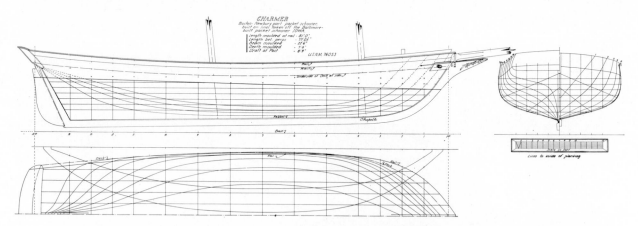

LINES OF THE PACKET SCHOONER *Charmer* of Newburyport, Massachusetts, built about 1860 on the lines of the pungy *Iowa*, which had been brought to Gloucester as a fishing schooner and converted to a packet late in the 1850's. Taken off the builder's half-model USNM 76053.

raking stem rabbet, strongly raking post, round tuck, and an upper-and-lower-transom square stern, the upper transom sharply raked and both well-rounded athwartships. The entrance is fairly sharp and convex, the run long and fine. The midsection has a rising straight floor, easy round bilge, and a moderate tumble-home in the topside.

Mounted with carved head and billet, cutwater, keel, post, and rudder.

The model is for a schooner 81 feet moulded length at rail, 77 feet ½ inch between perpendiculars, 61 feet on the keel, 22 feet 6 inches moulded beam, 7 feet 8 inches moulded depth; 6 feet 9 inches depth in hold, and 8 feet 9 inches draft. Scale of the model is ½ inch to the foot. This vessel was 116 tons register, old measurement.

Given by Sumner, Swazey, and Currier, Newburyport, Massachusetts.

TWO-MASTED COASTING SCHOONER, 1860
BUILDER'S HALF-MODEL, USNM 76051

A large 2-masted coasting schooner, name unknown, was built on this model at Newburyport, Massachusetts, in 1860. She was of the class of big 2-masted coasters, eventually replaced by 3-masters, many of which were employed in the coal trade.

The half-model is of a schooner hull having moderate sheer, a straight keel with slight drag, curved and raking stem rabbet, nearly upright post, short counter, raking elliptical transom, rather full entrance with flaring bow sections, moderate length of body, and a rather long and well shaped run. The midsection is formed with a slightly rising straight floor, well rounded and easy bilge, and tumble-home in the topside.

This class of schooner usually had a long quarterdeck at rail height, with a quarterdeck monkey rail and a turned-stanchion-and-cap rail above. The quarterdeck sometimes reached to a little forward of the foremast in such schooners, which usually had rather deep external keels in lieu of centerboards.

The model scales 106 feet moulded length at rail, 24 feet moulded beam, and 10 feet moulded depth. Scale is ⅜ inch to the foot.

Given by E. P. Goodwin.

TWO-MASTED COASTING SCHOONER, 1860
BUILDER'S HALF-MODEL, USNM 76137

E. Closson

The large 2-masted coasting schooner *E. Closson* of Bangor, Maine, was built on this model at Sedgwick,

Maine, in 1860 for the coastwise lumber trade. She had a sunken poop deck, as in some ships of this date, which is not indicated by the half-model.

The half-model represents a coasting schooner hull having moderate sheer, a straight keel with little drag, a flaring, curved and raking, stem rabbet, nearly upright post, short counter with elliptical ransom, a rather sharp entrance with flaring bow-sections, moderate length of body, and a short but rather easy run. The midsection is formed with a slightly rising straight floor, well rounded low bilge, and a slight tumble-home in the topside.

The model is for a vessel 95 feet 6 inches between perpendiculars, 26 feet 3½ inch beam extreme, 8 feet 11 inches depth in hold, and 135.37 tons register. Scale of the model is ½ inch to the foot.

Given by Robert Dority, shipbuilder, Sedgwick, Maine.

TWO-MASTED COASTING SCHOONER, 1867
BUILDER'S HALF-MODEL, USNM 76123

Ada S. Allen

The 2-masted coasting schooner *Ada S. Allen* was built on this model in 1867 at Dennysville, Maine, for the coastwise lumber trade. In Maine 2-masted coasters were not developed much further, as the large 2-masters were soon replaced by 3-masters, those in service being relegated, after about 1880, to the lime and granite trades, to short-haul freighting, and to the ice and firewood trades. The 2-masters built in Maine after 1885 were commonly under 85 feet on deck. Some centerboarders were built, mostly for the Stonington, Deer Isle, granite business, but most of the Maine coasters were keel vessels. To obtain weatherliness they had a fairly deep external keel rather than a strongly rising straight floor.

The half-model represents a schooner hull having moderate sheer, a straight keel with slight drag, raking stem rabbet with well rounded forefoot, nearly upright post, short counter with square transom, moderately sharp convex entrance, moderate length of body, and a rather long and shapely run. The midsection shows a slightly rising straight floor, moderately easy bilge, and a slight tumble-home in the topside. The bow sections have marked flare. This vessel had a short quarterdeck with turned-stanchion-and-cap rail.

The model is for a vessel 98 feet moulded length at rail, 94 feet between perpendiculars, 27 feet extreme beam, 9 feet 7 inches depth in hold, and 142.25 net tons register. Scale of the model is ½ inch to the foot.

Given by William Welch.

TWO-MASTED COASTING SCHOONER, 1868
BUILDER's HALF-MODEL, USNM 76130

Mountain Laurel

The *Mountain Laurel*, a large 2-masted coasting schooner, was built on this model at Trenton (now Lamoine), Maine, in 1868 for the coastwise trade. Her model and appearance somewhat resembled that of a contemporary fishing schooner of the full "Banker" type.

The half-model is of a rather burdensome schooner having moderate sheer, a straight keel with slight drag, curved and raking stem rabbet, upright post, short counter with wide and raking transom, fairly sharp and convex entrance, and a long but rather full run. The midsection is formed with a slight rise in the straight floor, a low and rather hard turn of bilge, and some tumble-home in the topside. The bow sections flare and the stern appears heavy.

Model mounted with billet, longhead, trails, cutwater, keel, post, and rudder.

The model is for a vessel 96 feet moulded length at rail, 88 feet 7 inches between perpendiculars, 25 feet 7 inches beam, 8 feet 4½ inches depth in hold, and 141.74 tons register. Scale of the model is ⅜ inch to the foot.

Given by Hamen Cousins, shipbuilder, Lamoine, Maine.

TWO-MASTED COASTING SCHOONER, 1869
BUILDER's HALF-MODEL, USNM 76121

Mable F. Staples, Alzema

The 2-masted coasting schooner *Mable F. Staples* of Machias, Maine, was built on this model in 1869 at Harrington, Maine, and in 1871 the sister schooner *Alzema* was built there on the moulds of the *Staples*. These were very large vessels for their rig and were intended for the lumber and coal trades. The *Alzema* was wrecked at Puerto Rico in April 1886, and the *Mable F. Staples* was lost at Nassau, Bahamas, in the hurricane of September 1887. Schooners with two masts and hulls of the size of these vessels were found to be expensive to operate, as they required large crews; in the coasting trade, the manning problem in these big two-masters led to the introduction of the steam-powered windlasses and winches that later made the large 3-masters so economical in manpower.

The half-model is of a deep ship-form hull showing rather marked sheer, a straight keel with small drag, curved and raking stem rabbet, nearly vertical post, short counter with a shallow and wide elliptical transom having much rake, fairly sharp and convex entrance, rather long body, and a short and hollow run. The midsection is formed with a slight rise in the straight floor, well rounded and rather easy bilge, and a slight tumble-home in the topside. The bow sections flare strongly.

Mounted with a rather pointed and light longhead, of moderate size for the length of the vessel, a billet, trails, cutwater, keel, post, and rudder. A long quarterdeck was usually found in this class of schooner.

The model is for a vessel about 124 feet moulded length at rail, 108 feet 5 inches between perpendiculars, 27 feet 3 inches beam, 11 feet 3½ inches depth in hold, and 268.16 net tons register. Scale of the model is ⁵⁄₁₆ inch to the foot.

Given by V. L. Coffin, Harrington, Maine.

TWO-MASTED COASTING SCHOONER, 1871
BUILDER's HALF-MODEL, USNM 76133

William H. Archer, Lenora

The 2-masted coasting schooner *William H. Archer* of Plymouth, Massachusetts, was built on this model at Ellsworth, Maine, in 1871 for the general coasting trade. In 1873 the schooner *Lenora* was built on the *Archer's* moulds at the same place. These schooners were representative, in model and dimensions, of the greater part of the Maine-built coasters of this period, having good capacity and sailing qualities, and being well fitted for the usual cargoes found in the general coastwise trade.

The half-model is of a hull having moderate sheer, a straight keel with very little drag, raking stem rabbet with rounded forefoot, nearly vertical post, short counter with rather wide elliptical and raking transom, a sharp convex entrance with flare in the bow sections and a long and rather easy run with fair length in the body. The midsection shows a slight rise in the straight floor, a well rounded and easy bilge, and some tumble-home in the topside.

Model is mounted with longhead, trails, cutwater, keel, post, and rudder.

The model is for a vessel of 89 feet moulded length at rail, 85 feet between perpendiculars, 25 feet beam, 7 feet depth in hold, and 90.69 net tons register. Scale of the model is ½ inch to the foot.

Given by Isaac M. Grant, shipbuilder, Ellsworth, Maine.

COASTING SCHOONER *Bloomer*, at Belfast, Maine, in 1936. Built at Eden, Maine, in 1855, her register dimensions were 64.3′ x 21.8′ x 6.2′, 51 gross tons. (*Smithsonian photo 45785–a.*)

TWO-MASTED COASTING SCHOONER, 1871
BUILDER'S HALF-MODEL, USNM 76132

D. S. Lawrence, City of Ellsworth

The 2-masted keel coasting schooner *D. S. Lawrence* was built on this model at Ellsworth, Maine, in 1871 for the general coasting trade and occasional packet runs. In 1875 the schooner *City of Ellsworth* was built on the same moulds at Ellsworth for coasting and packet service. The schooners, modeled and built by Isaac M. Grant, had the reputation of being prime sailers and proved to be profitable. Their model represents an important post-Civil War development in the design of small, 2-masted coasting schooners in New England.

The half-model is of a shoal-bodied keel schooner having rather straight sheer, a straight keel with moderate drag, slightly raking and strongly flaring stem rabbet with rounded forefoot, slightly raking post, long counter (for the period), raking transom curved athwartships, moderately sharp, convex entrance, and a rather short but very hollow and easy run. The midsection shows a rising straight floor (the dead rise rather great for a Maine-built coaster of this period), firm round bilge, and a slight tumblehome in the topside. Bow sections have a good deal

81

of flare. Model is mounted with longhead, trails and knees, cutwater, keel, post, and rudder. A rather long quarterdeck monkey rail is shown.

The model is for a vessel about 63 feet 8 inches between perpendiculars, 21 feet moulded beam, and 6 feet 10 inches moulded depth rabbet to deck. Scale of the model is ½ inch to the foot. In building these two schooners about 6 feet was added amidships.

Given by Isaac M. Grant, shipbuilder, Ellsworth, Maine.

TWO-MASTED COASTING SCHOONER, 1874
BUILDER'S HALF-MODEL, USNM 76120

Helen, Alta V. Cole, Pojara

The large 2-masted coasting schooner *Helen* of New York was built on this model and launched in June 1874, at Harrington, Maine. Her sister ship *Alta V. Cole* was launched at the same yard in November of that year and the *Pojara*, also built on these moulds, was launched there in October 1875. All were built for the West Indian and coastwise trades. The *Alta V. Cole* was wrecked in Salem Harbor, Massachusetts, in December 1886 and the *Pojara* was lost on her maiden voyage at Green Key, West Indies, December 18, 1875.

The half-model represents a hull having strong sheer, a straight keel with some drag, raking and nearly straight stem rabbet with slightly rounded forefoot, nearly upright post, short counter, wide elliptical transom with strong rake, rather sharp convex en-

trance, rather long body, and a short but rather easy run. Midsection shows a slightly rising straight floor, firm round bilge, and a slight tumble-home in the topside. Bow sections have much flare. Model mounted with billet, longhead, trails, cutwater, keel, post, rudder, and long quarterdeck monkey rail.

The half-model is for a vessel 119 feet 2 inches moulded length at rail, 109 feet between perpendiculars, 28 feet 11 inches beam, and 7 feet 1⅛ inches depth in hold. Scale of the model is ⁵⁄₁₆ inch to the foot.

Given by V. L. Coffin, Harrington, Maine.

TWO-MASTED COASTING SCHOONER, 1876
BUILDER'S HALF-MODEL, USNM 76152

Hunter

The 2-masted coasting schooner *Hunter* of Rockland, Maine, was built on this model at Orland, Maine, in 1876. Considered a good sailer and an excellent vessel of her class and type, she was intended for general coasting and, for a time, was employed in the lime trade out of Rockland and Rockport, Maine. The model is a fine example of the last development in the design of large Maine-built 2-masted coasting schooners.

The half-model shows a hull having a moderate and graceful sheer, straight keel with some drag, slight rake and a slightly flaring stem rabbet that is slightly rounded at the forefoot, nearly upright post, short counter, and a raking elliptical transom. The midsection shows a slight rise in the straight floor, a firm

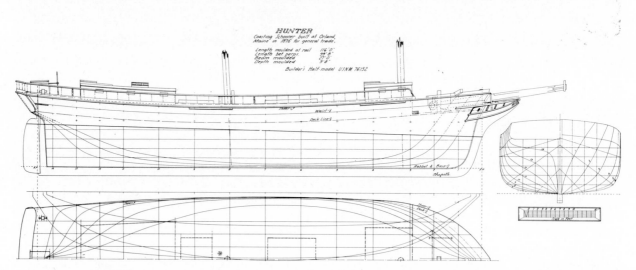

LINES OF THE LARGE, 2-MASTED COASTING SCHOONER *Hunter*, built at Orland, Maine, in 1876 for the general coasting trade. The plan shows a type popular in the early days of the coal trade. Taken off the builder's half-model USNM 76152.

82

low bilge, and a slight tumble-home in the topside. The entrance is rather sharp, convex, and moderately long, the body is long, and the run is short but fine. The bow sections are markedly flared. Model is mounted with a longhead, billet, trails, cutwater, keel, post, rudder, and a long quarterdeck monkey rail.

The model is for a vessel 116 feet moulded length at rail, 99 feet 8 inches between perpendiculars, 27 feet moulded beam, 9 feet 8 inches depth in hold, and 187.22 net tons register. Scale of the model is ⅜ inch to the foot.

The *Hunter's* customhouse dimensions were 105 feet between perpendiculars, 28 feet beam, 9 feet depth in hold, 197 tons gross.

Given by Harry H. Buck.

PUERTO RICAN TRADING SCHOONER, 1927
BUILDER'S HALF-MODEL, USNM 315713

Candelaria (1)

The 2-masted Puerto Rican trading schooner *Candelaria* (1) was built from this half-model near Mayagüez, Puerto Rico, in 1927 by a master ship-wright named Polito, a native of Caracoa, for Bartolo Cabanillas, of Mayagüez. The *Candelaria* was con-sidered a good schooner of her type, sailing well, a profitable carrier and a good looking vessel. She had high bulwarks and flush deck, to carry oil and gasoline drums on deck, and could sail with little ballast.

The half-model represents a shoal-bodied, keel schooner of good capacity, having moderate sheer, a straight keel rabbet, a rounded and raking stem rabbet, raking post, and a moderately long counter ending in a wide, shallow flat transom set at a slight rake. The entrance is long, full, and convex, and the run is long and easy. The midsection is formed with a straight floor of moderate rise, easy round bilge, and a slightly flaring topside.

The model is for a vessel of about 76 feet moulded length at rail, 23 feet 6 inches moulded beam, and 8 feet moulded depth. Scale of the model is ½ inch to the foot. The customhouse dimensions of this vessel are 74 feet length, 24 feet 9 inches beam, 8 feet 5 inches depth in hold, and 82 gross tons. Model is made to deck level and shows that frames were spaced 18 inches on centers.

The *Candelaria* was rigged with a large jib, foresail, mainsail, and main topsail; she had a spike bowsprit.

Given by Jose E. Echevarria, Aguadilla, Puerto Rico.

PUERTO RICAN TRADING SCHOONER, about 1942
BUILDER'S HALF-MODEL, USNM 315714

Candelaria (2)

The 2-masted Puerto Rican trading schooner *Candelaria* (2) was built about 1942 from this half-model at Mayagüez, Puerto Rico, for Bartolo Cabanillas, of that port.

The half-model is of a burdensome schooner having a straight keel rabbet, rounded and slightly raking stem rabbet, upright post, and a counter of moderate length ending in a wide, thin transom having very little rake. The sheer is slight. The entrance is short, rather full, and convex, and the run is short but well formed. The midsection is formed with a slightly rising straight floor, round and moderately firm bilge, and a slightly flaring topside. The schooner had high bulwarks and was flush decked.

The model is for a vessel of about 58 feet moulded length at rail, 19 feet moulded beam, 7 feet 6 inches moulded depth. The model is made to deck level and shows the frames to have been spaced 18 inches on center. Scale of the model is ½ inch to the foot.

Given by Jose E. Echevarria, Aguadilla, Puerto Rico.

THREE-MASTED COASTING SCHOONER, 1870
BUILDER'S HALF-MODEL, USNM 76078

Nellie S. Pickering, Fame Gorham

The 3-masted, centerboard, coasting schooner *Nellie S. Pickering* of Belfast, Maine, was built on this model in 1870 at that port, by C. P. Carter and Com-pany. This shipbuilding firm built clipper ships, down-Easters, brigs, brigantines, and coasting schooners, and was one of the few Maine shipbuilders to construct many centerboard vessels. The next year these builders launched a sister schooner *Fame Gorham*. The schooners were intended for the lum-ber trade out of Jacksonville, Florida. At the mouth of the St. Johns River there was then a shoal bar that limited the draft of vessels. As a result most of the 3-masted schooners built for this trade in the 1870's and 1880's had centerboards and, thus fitted, sailed very well on the wind when light, where most keel 3 masters did not. These centerboarders, many of which had fine ends and large sail areas, were handy, reliable vessels for the business, and it was claimed that they were the fastest of the 3-masted coasters.

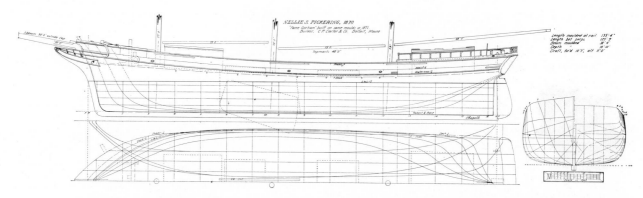

LINES OF THE 3-MASTED, CENTERBOARD, COASTING SCHOONER *Nellie S. Pickering*, built at Belfast, Maine, in 1870 for the Jacksonville lumber trade. The *Fame Gorham* was built on the same moulds. Taken off the builder's half-model USNM 76078.

The half-model shows a relatively burdensome hull of moderate depth, having a moderate and graceful sheer, straight keel with very slight drag, raking and flaring stem rabbet slightly rounded at the forefoot, nearly upright post, short counter, elliptical transom, a short and sharp and slightly convex entrance with flared bow sections, a rather long body, and a moderately long and fine run. The midsection is formed with a slightly rising straight floor, a low, firm bilge, and a marked tumble-home in the topside.

Mounted with a graceful longhead, billet, and trails, cutwater, keel, post, and a short quarterdeck monkey rail.

The model scales 135 feet 4 inches moulded length at rail, 125 feet 9 inches between perpendiculars, 31 feet 4 inches moulded beam, and 10 feet 10 inches moulded depth. Scale is ⅜ inch to the foot.

The length of her spars were: foremast 77 feet, mainmast 78 feet, mizzen 79 feet, topmasts each 48 feet, bowsprit outboard of rabbet 20 feet, jib boom outside of cap 30 feet, spanker boom 48 feet.

Given by C. P. Carter and Company, shipbuilders, Belfast, Maine.

THREE-MASTED COASTING SCHOONER, 1872
BUILDER'S HALF-MODEL, USNM 76119

James M. Riley, Susan P. Thurlow

The 3-masted, keel, coasting schooners *James M. Riley* and *Susan P. Thurlow* were built on this model at Harrington, Maine, in 1872 for the West Indian trade in the winter months and for the general coasting trade in summer. The *James M. Riley* was wrecked at Fortune Islands in 1886.

The half-model shows a hull having moderate sheer, a straight keel with little or no drag, a flaring

and raking stem rabbet slightly rounded at the forefoot, nearly vertical post, short counter with raking elliptical transom, moderately sharp and convex entrance with bow sections having marked flare, a long body, and a short but rather easy run. The midsection shows a slightly rising straight floor, low and rather hard bilge, and tumble-home in the topside.

The model is for a vessel 133 feet 10 inches moulded length at rail, 126 feet 5 inches between perpendiculars, 31 feet 1 inch beam, 16 feet 7 inches extreme depth, and 440.07 net tons register. Scale of the model is ⅜ inch to the foot.

Given by V. L. Coffin, Harrington, Maine.

THREE-MASTED COASTING SCHOONER, 1872
BUILDER'S HALF-MODEL, USNM 76076

John Bird

The 3-masted, shallow-bodied, keel, coasting schooner *John Bird* of Rockland, Maine, was built on this half-model by C. P. Carter and Company, of Belfast, Maine, in 1872 for the general coastwise trade, and was largely employed carrying lime out of Rockland and Rockport. This schooner is said to have been a very fast sailer.

The model represents a shoal and wide hull having a moderate and graceful sheer, straight keel with little drag, rather upright and flaring stem rabbet slightly rounded at the forefoot, slightly raking post and short counter with light elliptical transom, sharp convex entrance, moderate length of body, and a rather long and fine run. The midsection shows a slightly rising straight floor, rather quick and low bilge, and tumble-home in the topside. The bow sections flare strongly. This schooner had a long quarter-deck, though the model indicates a short one.

Mounted with graceful longhead, billet and trails, cutwater, keel, post, rudder, and a short quarter-deck monkey rail.

The model scales 131 feet 3 inches moulded length at rail, 123 feet between perpendiculars, 29 feet 6 inches moulded beam, and 9 feet 4 inches moulded depth to deck at side. Depth of bulwarks 4 feet. Scale is ⅜ inch to the foot.

Given by C. P. Carter and Company, shipbuilders, Belfast, Maine.

THREE-MASTED COASTING SCHOONER, 1873
BUILDER'S HALF-MODEL, USNM 311859

Emelie E. Birdsall

The 3-masted, centerboard, coasting schooner *Emelie E. Birdsall* of Wilmington, Delaware, was built at that port in 1873–74 by Jackson and Sharpe Company. She was modeled by Captain Edward Kershaw and was noted as a very fast sailer and handy vessel.

The half-model represents a hull having strong sheer, a straight keel with very little drag, raking and flaring stem rabbet slightly rounded at the forefoot, upright post, short counter having a raking elliptical transom, sharp convex entrance with hollow at forefoot, rather short body, and a long and easy run. The midsection shows a slightly rising straight floor, well rounded and somewhat easy bilge, and tumble-home in the topside.

Mounted with longhead, billet, trails, cutwater, keel, post, rudder, and a short quarterdeck monkey rail.

The *Birdsall* was 145 feet 9 inches between perpendiculars, 29 feet moulded beam, and 10 feet 6 inches moulded depth to rail. Scale of the half-model is ⅜ inch to the foot.

Given by the American Car and Foundry Company, Wilmington, Delaware, successors to Jackson and Sharpe Company.

THREE-MASTED COASTING SCHOONER, 1874
BUILDER'S HALF-MODEL, USNM 76074

William F. Frederick

The 3-masted, keel, coasting schooner *William F. Frederick* of Belfast, Maine, was built on this half-model by C. P. Carter and Company of that port in 1874 for the West Indian trade and for general coastwise service. This keel schooner was much deeper than the centerboard 3-masters built by this distinguished firm of shipbuilders and proved to be a fast and seaworthy trader, noted as a very easy vessel in heavy seas. She was built of hardwood, framed with beech, maple, and birch, and with hackmatack top-timbers to save weight; her planking and ceiling were southern yellow pine, and her deck white pine. She was abandoned at sea, October 4, 1895, during a very severe northeast gale, while on a voyage from the Saltilla River, Georgia, to Belfast, Maine, with a cargo of yellow pine lumber and marine stores. Her crew was rescued by the steamer *Franklin*. Because the steamer's boats could not approach the vessel, the schooner's crew, at great risk to themselves, had to jump into the sea and be picked up.

The half-model shows a very deep ship-form hull, having rather marked and graceful sheer, straight keel with little or no drag, slightly raking and moderately flaring stem rabbet very slightly rounded at the forefoot, a slightly raking post, short counter, wide and light elliptical transom, strongly raked, a rather sharp

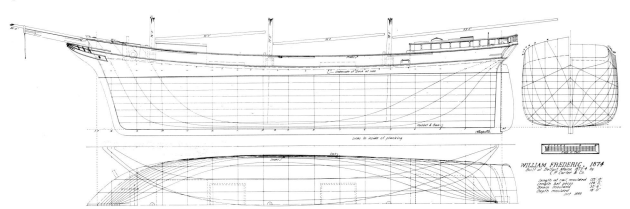

LINES OF THE 3-MASTED COASTING SCHOONER *William F. Frederick*, built, 1873–74, at Belfast, Maine, for the coastwise and West Indian trades. Taken off the builder's half-model USNM 76074.

and convex entrance with some hollow at forefoot, rather short body, and a moderately long and fine run. The midsection shows a slightly rising straight floor, rather quick, low bilge, and tumble-home in the top-side.

Mounted with longhead, billet, trails, cutwater, keel, post, and rudder.

The model is for a vessel measuring 135 feet 10 inches moulded length at rail, 120 feet on the keel, 30 feet 6 inches moulded beam, 18 feet moulded depth to deck at side, 15 feet depth in hold, and 430.38 net tons register. Scale is ⅜ inch to the foot.

Her spars measured: foremast 76 feet, mainmast 77 feet, mizzenmast 78 feet, bowsprit 34 feet (22 feet outboard of the rabbet) jib boom 30 feet outboard of the cap, topmasts each 50 feet, fore and main booms each 35 feet, spanker boom 53 feet.

Given by C. P. Carter and Company, shipbuilders, Belfast, Maine.

THREE-MASTED COASTING SCHOONER, 1876
BUILDER'S HALF-MODEL, USNM 311457

Daniel S. Williams Jr.

The 3-masted, keel, coasting schooner *Daniel S. Williams Jr.* was built on this model at Wilmington, Delaware, in 1876–77 by Jackson and Sharpe Company. She was a large coaster for her date and was designed for the general coastwise trade, particularly for the transportation of lumber and coal.

The half-model shows a coasting schooner hull having strong sheer, a straight keel with slight drag, raking and flaring stem rabbet with a slightly rounded forefoot, upright post, short counter, raking elliptical transom, sharp convex entrance with hollow at forefoot, a rather long body, and a short but easy run. The midsection is formed with a slightly rising straight floor, well rounded and rather easy bilge, and tumble-home in the topside. The bow sections have much flare.

Mounted with longhead, billet, trails, cutwater, keel, post, rudder, and a quarterdeck rail about one-fourth the length of the hull, with a monkey rail and turned-stanchion-and-cap rail above.

The *Williams* measured 165 feet 4 inches between perpendiculars, 34 feet extreme beam, 17 feet depth of hold, and 628.65 net tons register. Scale of the model is ⅜ inch to the foot.

Given by the American Car and Foundry Company, Wilmington, Delaware, successors to Jackson and Sharpe Company.

THREE-MASTED COASTING SCHOONER, 1883
BUILDER'S HALF-MODEL, USNM 76077

Meyer and Muller

The 3-masted, centerboard, coasting schooner *Meyer and Muller* was built on this model at Belfast, Maine, in 1883 by C. P. Carter and Company, and was intended for the lumber trade between the South Atlantic coast ports and New England. The schooner also traded to the Gulf ports, Mexico, and Central America. Like many of her type she was a notable sailer.

A somewhat similar schooner, the *William C. French*, was built at Newburyport, Massachusetts, in the same year by Atkinson and Filmore (her half-model was formerly in the Watercraft Collection, USNM 76048, but is now missing); she made three consecutive passages to Cape Breton from Boston, a distance of 675 nautical miles, in 72, 56, and 66 hours, respectively, at the overall average speed of 10½ knots. She also made the run from Philadelphia to Boston, dock to dock, in 56 hours, loaded with coal. This was a record in the trade. The *French* was 142 feet long.

The half-model shows a wide, shallow-bodied, centerboard coasting-schooner hull having marked sheer, a straight keel with little or no drag, a curved, flaring, and raking stem rabbet with slightly small rounded forefoot, nearly upright post, a short and rather heavy counter with raking elliptical transom, a rather sharp, convex entrance with some hollow at forefoot, moderate length of body, and an exceptionally long and easy run for a vessel of her type. The midsection shows a slight rise in the straight floor, a rather hard, low bilge, and moderate tumble-home in the topside.

The *Meyer and Muller* was 163 feet moulded length at the main rail, 140 feet on the keel, 34 feet moulded beam, and 10 feet moulded depth. Her spars measured: foremast 88 feet, mainmast 89 feet, mizzenmast 90 feet, topmasts each 52 feet, bowsprit outboard of rabbet 24 feet, jib boom outside the cap 26 feet, fore and main booms each 41 feet, and the spanker boom 52 feet, with its outer end about 12 feet outside the taffrail. Scale of the model is ⅜ inch to the foot.

Given by C. P. Carter and Company, shipbuilders, Belfast, Maine.

CHESAPEAKE BAY THREE-MASTED SCHOONER,
about 1890
BUILDER'S HALF-MODEL, USNM 315854

An unidentified 3-masted schooner was built for the lumber trade on this model in Wicomico County,

THE 3-MASTED SCHOONER *Cactus*, built at Bath, Maine, in 1890. Her register dimensions were 149.4′ x 34.7′ x 12.8′, 534.59 gross tons. (*Smithsonian photo 37382–a.*)

Maryland, about 1890. These schooners, called "rams," were intended to pass through the locks of the old Chesapeake and Delaware Canal; they usually had a centerboard and were limited in beam and length by the size of the canal locks then existing. This type of schooner normally had a short, high quarterdeck and some had lumber bow ports.

The half-model shows a rather long, narrow and shoal centerboard schooner hull having much sheer, a straight keel with little or no drag, a raking straight stem rabbet with small rounded forefoot, an upright post, short counter, and sharply raking and rather shallow, flat transom. The entrance and run are short and full; the hull is markedly parallel sided and boxlike for most of its length. The midsection is formed with a slightly rising straight floor, a low and sharply rounded (almost angular) bilge, and a straight and upright topside.

The model, on a scale of ⅜ inch to the foot, is for a vessel 140 feet moulded length at rail, 25 feet moulded beam and 9 feet 3 inches moulded depth, to deck.

Gift of James H. Allyn, Mystic, Connecticut.

THREE-MASTED TRADING SCHOONER, 1920–21
BUILDER'S HALF-MODEL, USNM 316107

Gaviota

The three-masted trading schooner *Gaviota* was built on the lines of this model at Catano, Puerto Rico, by Guillermo Valello, in 1920–21 for the inter-island trade. Considered a vessel suitable for her trade, and of good model, the *Gaviota* capsized in San Juan harbor, September 13, 1928, during the hurricane "San Felipe," and was a total loss.

The half-model shows a three-masted schooner hull having straight sheer (the model was made this way and so lofted; however, the hull was sheered after the frames were set up) a straight keel rabbet with moderate drag, angular forefoot, strongly raked stem rabbet, raking post, short counter, and a flat and strongly raking transom. The model is to the deck line. The entrance is sharp and rather short, the run short but rather easy. The midsection shows a moderately rising straight floor, a full round bilge, and a slight tumble-home in topside. The greatest beam is a little forward of midlength.

Scale of the model is ⅜ inch to the foot, for a vessel 124 feet 6 inches. Moulded length at deck, 30 feet 6 inches moulded beam, and 14 feet moulded depth. Dimensions of the *Gaviota* were: Register length 127.6 feet, beam 31.1 feet, depth in hold 11.7 feet, and 287 tons gross, 263 tons net. The vessel was apparently lengthened three frame spaces amidships.

Gift of Jose E. Echevarria, Aguadilla, Puerto Rico.

PILOT-SCHOONER YACHT, 1806–1950
BUILDER'S HALF-MODEL, USNM 315852

This half-model is of a proposed schooner yacht whose lines were drawn in 1950 as a modification of an 1806-design by Samuel Humphreys called "Yacht for Canton." The proposed yacht was to be named *Chasseur* but was not built.

The model represents a class of small pilot-boat schooners built in the United States in the early 19th century for any trade or purpose requiring fast sailing. The *Chasseur* was intended to test the hull form of these schooners in comparison with those of modern cruising yachts.

The model shows a small schooner having rather straight sheer, a straight keel with drag, curved and raking stem rabbet, raking post, upper-and-lower-transom stern with square tuck, rather short and moderately sharp entrance, and a long, easy run. The greatest beam is forward of midlength, the midsection is formed with sharply rising straight floor, a high, easy round bilge, and some flare in topside.

The half-model represents a schooner 54 feet between perpendiculars, 13 feet 1 inch moulded beam, and 6 feet 10 inches draft at post. Scale of the model is ¾ inch to the foot. It is illustrated on p. 9.

Given by William E. Geoghegan, Baltimore, Maryland.

PILOT SCHOONER, about 1812
BUILDER'S HALF-MODEL, USNM 316628

Snap Dragon

The "pilot-boat" privateer schooner *Snap Dragon* was built on this model, about 1812, at Wilmington,

North Carolina. Customhouse records of this schooner were destroyed during the Civil War. The *Snap Dragon* was one of the three privateer schooners, all pilot-boats, fitted out at Wilmington during the War of 1812, and the most successful. During her career she was commanded by Captains E. Pasteur, O. Burns, and N. Graham. In August and September 1813 she captured the British merchant brigs *Good Intent*, *Venus* and *Happy*, the barque *Reprisal*, and the schooner *Elizabeth*. She later took the brig *Ann* with a cargo of drygoods valeud at about five hundred thousand dollars. She also captured the brig *Jane*, the brig *Linnet*, and an unnamed schooner laden with mahogany. She was licensed as being of 147 tons, with 6 guns.

The half-model shows the hull of a typical pilot-boat schooner of the date having very little sheer, a straight keel with much drag, raking, curved stem rabbet, raking post, round tuck, and a square stern. The rake of the bow and stern are pronounced; the rudder was outboard of the transom, which is wide and shallow. The entrance is of moderate length and is convex and sharp, the run long and easy. The midsection is formed with a rising straight floor with a barely perceptible hollow at the garboard, a high, round, and slack bilge, and a flaring topside. The quarters are very thin and there is some flare in the bow sections. The schooner had a low log rail when built, and sat low in the water. The half-model, which is to deck level, is made of a solid block and one top lift. To loft the schooner, the lines were probably taken from the block by use of a lead bar.

Scale of the model is unknown. If ¾ inch to the foot, it would produce a vessel about 58 feet 9 inches on deck, 17 feet 2 inches moulded beam, and 7 feet 9 inches moulded depth. The model is one of the four known builders' models of American privateers of the War of 1812 and the only one of a Southern privateer. It is illustrated on page 11.

Schooners of this size and model, heavily sparred and canvassed and very fast, were quite popular with American vessel owners in the West Indian trade during the early 19th century. They usually had a curved stem, without knee or decorations, and with prominent knightheads and hawse timbers extending well above the rails. When fitted for a privateer, bulwarks were probably added, and a square course and topsail fitted on the foremast.

Lent by the U.S. Naval Historical Foundation.

NEW YORK PILOT SCHOONER, about 1835–45
BUILDER'S HALF-MODEL, USNM 315932

A large New York pilot schooner was built on this model, at some time between 1835 and 1845, for the Sandy Hook service. The name of the vessel is unknown. The model was preserved in the Brooklyn Athenaeum until taken possession of by the U. S. Navy Department and held at the U. S. Naval Academy, Annapolis, Maryland.

The half-model is of a rather typical New York pilot boat of the period, having slight sheer, a straight keel of moderate drag, much rounded and well raked stem rabbet, strongly raking stern post rabbet and an upper-and-lower-transom square stern, wide and shallow. The entrance is short but moderately sharp, the run is long and easy. The midsection is located well forward of midlength and is formed with sharply rising floors, slightly hollow at garboard, and a well rounded and rather slack bilge carried up round to deck level. The forward sections are nearly V-shaped.

The model, made to a scale of ½ inch to the foot, represents a schooner 80 feet moulded length at deck, 23 feet moulded beam, and 8 feet 9 inches moulded depth. Model is made to deck level, no bulwarks being shown.

Customarily the New York pilot schooners of this date and type had a very low rail, and were often long, low flush-decked boats, heavily sparred and canvassed. Their working rig was a large jib, gaff-foresail with no boom and overlapping the main, and a gaff-mainsail with boom. A short main-topmast supported a main-topmast staysail. The area of the foresail was large and the boats usually worked under this sail alone on the pilot grounds, setting full sail only when racing to meet an incoming vessel. The New York pilot schooners were long noted for their speed and sailing qualities.

Model lent by U. S. Navy Department.

PILOT SCHOONER, 1853
BUILDER'S HALF-MODEL, USNM 76032

Dancing Feather

The Boston pilot schooner *Dancing Feather* was built on this model by Dennison J. Lawlor at East Boston, Massachusetts, in 1853. The model represented an extreme clipper schooner design for the date and the vessel was celebrated for her speed, weatherliness, and seaworthiness. She was deeper bodied than was then common in her type. The *Dancing Feather*

carried the usual pilot-schooner rig of her date; in winter she had no foretopmast nor jib boom, so had neither fore gaff-topsail nor jib topsail. In summer she carried these spars and had mainsail, foresail without boom; with its clew overlapping the main; a large jib, main gaff-topsail, main-topmast staysail, fore gaff-topsail and a jib topsail.

The half-model is of a pilot-schooner hull having moderate sheer, straight keel with great drag, a raking and slightly flaring stem rabbet moderately rounded at the forefoot, slightly raking post, short and light-round fantail stern with flaring bulwarks, a long, sharp, and slightly convex entrance with hollow at forefoot, and a long and very fine run. The midsection is formed with a sharply rising floor with very slight hollow in the garboard, high and rather firm bilge, and tumble-home in the topside. Bow sections have rather marked flare. The model is mounted with a graceful longhead, billet, trails, cutwater, keel, post, and rudder.

The model scales 67 feet 6 inches moulded length at rail, 19 feet 6 inches moulded beam, and 8 feet 4 inches moulded depth. Scale of model ½ inch to the foot.

Given by Dennison J. Lawlor, shipbuilder, Chelsea, Massachusetts.

PILOT SCHOONER, 1865
BUILDER'S HALF-MODEL, USNM 76047

Edwin Forrest

The New York and Boston pilot-schooner *Edwin Forrest*, named after the noted American actor, was built at East Boston, Massachusetts, in 1865 by Dennison J. Lawlor to replace the *Edwin Forrest, No. 14*, of New York, lost off Long Island in 1862. She became a celebrated pilot boat, showing great speed on all points of sailing and was long considered a model of her type. After being employed for many years at New York and Boston, she was sold to the Pensacola, Florida, pilots.

The model shows a pilot-schooner hull having moderate and graceful sheer, straight keel with strong drag, a much rounded forefoot, nearly straight and slightly raking stem rabbet, vertical post, strongly raking V-shaped transom giving a short stern overhang. The entrance is sharp and rather hollow, and the run is very fine and long. The midsection shows a sharply rising and slightly hollow floor, high and hard bilge, and tumble-home in the topside. There is little flare forward and the bow is noticeably wedge shaped.

Mounted with straight and slightly raking stem, keel, post and rudder; the model has low bulwarks. Boats of this type had a low, long quarterdeck and a small cockpit aft; the freeboard was low.

The half-model scales 68 feet 9 inches moulded length at rail, 19 feet moulded beam, and 7 feet 9 inches moulded depth to deck at side. Scale is ½ inch to the foot.

Given by Dennison J. Lawlor, shipbuilder, Chelsea, Massachusetts.

PILOT SCHOONER, 1867
BUILDER'S HALF-MODEL, USNM 76033

Florence

The Boston pilot schooner *Florence* was built on this model in 1867 at East Boston, Massachusetts, by Dennison J. Lawlor. She was of the relatively shoal bodied model that many pilots preferred, believing that shoal draft allowed the vessel to drift, in a storm, so that the hull received less punishment from the seas when hove to. The *Florence*, very popular at Boston, was a fast and extremely able vessel.

The half-model represents a pilot-schooner hull having moderate and graceful sheer, low freeboard, a straight keel with heavy drag, slightly rounded forefoot, straight and slightly raking stem rabbet, nearly upright post, a small overhang at stern formed by a sharply raking V-shaped transom, a long entrance, sharp and slightly concave below the load line, and a long, fine and rather straight run. The midsection is formed with a sharply rising and slightly hollow floor, high and firm bilge, and tumble-home in the topside.

Mounted with a straight and raking stem, keel, post, rudder, and a low bulwark, the model being solid to the deck-at-side height.

The model is for a vessel 71 feet moulded length at rail, 19 feet moulded beam, and 8 feet 6 inches moulded depth to deck at side. Scale of the model is ½ inch to the foot.

Given by Dennison J. Lawlor, shipbuilder, Chelsea, Massachusetts.

PILOT SCHOONER, 1868–1869
BUILDER'S HALF-MODEL, USNM 76039

Phantom, Pet

The sister pilot schooners, *Phantom* and *Pet*, were built on this model by Dennison J. Lawlor, at East Boston, Massachusetts, in 1868–1869 for the New York pilots. These schooners were considered models

for their type and were handsome, able vessels with a great reputation for swiftness under sail. The *Phantom* was lost with all hands in March 1888; the *Pet* was wrecked in Narraganset Bay in 1889.

The half-model represents a pilot-schooner hull having a graceful and strong sheer, low freeboard, straight keel with marked drag, well rounded forefoot, rather upright and curved stem rabbet, nearly upright post, a short overhang at stern formed by sharply raking and V-shaped transom, a long, sharp, and slightly concave entrance, and a long and very fine run. The midsection shows a sharply rising and slightly hollow floor, high and firm bilge, and tumble-home in the topside.

Model mounted with curved and nearly upright stem, keel, post, rudder, and low bulwark.

The model is of a pilot-schooner hull 76 feet 6 inches moulded length at rail, 19 feet 10 inches moulded beam, and 9 feet 2 inches moulded depth to deck at side. Scale of the model is ½ inch to the foot.

Given by Dennison J. Lawlor, shipbuilder, Chelsea, Massachusetts.

PILOT SCHOONER, 1870
BUILDER'S HALF-MODEL, USNM

Thomas Howard

The Delaware Bay pilot schooner *Thomas Howard* was built on this model at Philadelphia in 1870. She was similar in form, size, and general appearance to the vessels used by the New York pilots at the time she was built. The *Thomas Howard* had a long career in the pilot service and was considered a fine example of her type.

The half-model represents a pilot schooner having considerable sheer, straight keel with much drag, well curved forefoot with a straight, slightly raking stem rabbet above the load waterline. The post is upright, the transom is sharply raking and V- or heart-shaped, with the rudder stock passing through it. The entrance is long, sharp, and hollow; the run is long and very fine. The midsection is located abaft the midlength and is formed with a sharply rising and slightly hollow floor, a high, firm bilge, and tumble-home in the topside. The flare forward is very moderate.

Mounted without appendages.

The model, on a scale of ½ inch to the foot, is for a pilot boat 82 feet moulded length at rail and about 79 feet between perpendiculars, 21 feet moulded beam, and 9 feet 3 inches depth. The frames were spaced 24 inches on centers. The register dimensions of the

90

Thomas Howard were 79.2 feet length, 20.6 feet beam, and 7.6 feet depth in hold, 50.59 gross tons.

Gift of James H. Allyn, Mystic, Connecticut.

PILOT SCHOONER, 1876
Builder's Half-Model, usnm 76038

Lillie

The Boston pilot schooner *Lillie* was built at East Boston, Massachusetts, on this model by Dennison J. Lawlor in 1876. She represented the trend toward deeper bodied pilot boats that appears to have started at Boston, beginning about this date and continuing into the 1880's. The *Lillie* was a very successful schooner in her business, and for many years was a well known Boston pilot boat. She was afterwards sold to the New York pilots and renamed *Richard K. Fox*.

The half-model shows a pilot-schooner hull having considerable sheer, a low freeboard, straight keel with marked drag, well rounded forefoot, curved and nearly upright stem rabbet, vertical post, a short overhang formed by the sharply raking V-shaped transom, a long and sharp entrance with much hollow at forefoot, and a long and very fine run. The midsection is formed with a sharply rising floor, quite hollow at garboard, a high and firm turn of bilge, and tumble-home in the topside. Very little flare forward and bow wedge shaped to a marked degree.

Mounted with a curved and upright stem, keel, post, and rudder, and with bulwark indicated by a lift.

The model is for a pilot boat 73 feet 11½ inches moulded length at rail, 66 feet 10 inches between perpendiculars, 19 feet 10 inches moulded beam, and

10 feet moulded depth. Scale of the model is ½ inch to the foot.

Given by Dennison J. Lawlor, shipbuilder, Chelsea, Massachusetts.

PILOT SCHOONER, 1884
Builder's Half-Model, usnm 76037

Hesper

The celebrated Boston pilot schooner *Hesper* was built on this model in 1884 by Dennison J. Lawlor at East Boston, Massachusetts. She was long considered the fastest pilot schooner in America and was the favorite opponent of every new schooner, yacht, or fisherman launched in Massachusetts. The *Hesper* had unusually sharp lines; she was longer, and was deeper and narrower in proportion, than previous pilot boats. She was designed to have all her ballast, lead and iron, inside, some years after her launching some was placed on her keel, outside. The *Hesper* had much influence on the Massachusetts-built fishing schooners and was one of the vessels that made depth, in proportion to length and beam, very popular in the New England fishing fleet, after 1885, as well as in later Boston pilot schooners. The *Hesper* (see p. 54) when old was sold by the pilots, became a yacht for a few years, and was broken up sometime after 1910.

The half-model is of a pilot-schooner hull having rather strong sheer, low freeboard, a rather short, straight keel with heavy drag, the fore end much curved and fairing into a well rounded forefoot, the stem rabbet becoming straight and upright at loadline. The post is vertical; the counter short, with a very raking V-shaped transom; the entrance long,

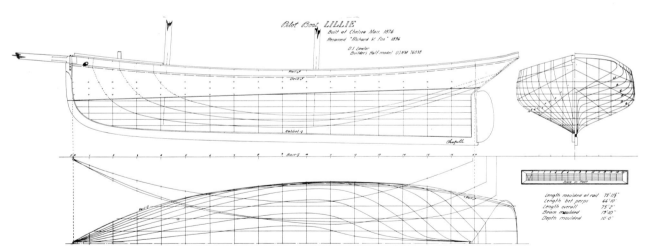

Lines of the Boston Pilot Schooner *Lillie*, built at Chelsea, Massachusetts, 1876. Taken off the builder's half-model USNM 76038.

91

sharp, and hollow at the forefoot; and the run is also long and very fine. In sailing trim the stem fell inboard slightly. The midsection shows a sharply rising and somewhat hollow floor, high and firm bilge, and tumble-home in the topside.

Mounted with straight stem, keel, post, and rudder.

The model is for a schooner 112 feet moulded length at rail, 22 feet 6 inches moulded beam, 13 feet 4 inches moulded depth, and drawing about 14 feet 3 inches in sailing trim. Scale of model ⅜ inch to the foot.

Given by Dennison J. Lawlor, shipbuilder, Chelsea, Massachusetts.

PILOT SCHOONER, 1884
BUILDER'S HALF-MODEL, USNM 160117

Glyn

The handsome pilot schooner *Glyn* of Brunswick, Georgia, was built on this model at Noank, Connecticut, in 1884 from the design of G. L. Daboll. A number of these pilot-schooners, of which this half-model is typical, were built for southern ports after the Civil War. Noank had a reputation for building fast vessels and, besides the sloop and schooner smacks for which the town was famous, built many yachts, schooner packets, and pilot schooners. The models used for yachts and pilot schooners had a strong resemblance, although when the *Glyn* was launched, Noank-built yachts were usually shoal centerboarders. In the 1880's the local trademark in schooner design was a V-shaped stern with unusually heavy quarters and heavily flared sections at the bow, features that mark the model of the *Glyn*. This schooner was notably fast and was a very successful vessel in her business.

The half-model represents a clipper schooner having moderate and graceful sheer, a straight keel with some drag, well rounded forefoot, a flaring and markedly raked stem rabbet, upright post, and a short counter ending in a strongly raked and flat V-shaped transom. The entrance is sharp and rather hollow, and the run is long, flat, and fine. The midsection shows a sharply rising floor, with hollow at the garboard, a rather firm bilge, and little tumble-home in the topside. The bow sections flare strongly; the dead rise in the floors in the sections in the run is parallel, or of "constant deadrise," a feature found in the models not only of Daboll but also of Lawlor and other noted American designers.

Mounted with a long head, billet, trails, cutwater, keel, post, bulwarks, and rudder.

The model scales 79 feet 8 inches moulded length at rail, 69 feet 6 inches moulded waterline length, 19 feet 8 inches moulded beam, 8 feet 8 inches moulded depth to deck at side, and is for a vessel drawing about 8 feet 3 inches in sailing trim. Scale of the model is ½ inch to the foot.

Given by G. L. Daboll, shipbuilder, Noank, Connecticut.

PILOT-BOAT SLOOP, 1898
BUILDER'S HALF-MODEL, USNM 311520

A pilot-boat sloop was built from this half-model by "Bat" Fogarty in 1898 at Bradenton, Florida, for the pilots at Bay Rest, Florida. The model was intended for a swift-sailing sloop, and the form resembles that of sloop yachts of the period 1860–85.

The half-model represents a yacht like centerboard sloop of moderate sheer, wide and shoal, having a keel-rabbet straight forward but sweeping up aft in a fair curve to the round fantail stern. A skeg is shown with an upright post well inboard the extreme stern. The bow rabbet rakes, and there was probably a long head; the entrance is long and sharp; and the run long and fine. The midsection shows a rising floor, an easy turn of bilge, and a rather upright topside. The greatest beam is about at midlength.

The sloop measured 35 feet 7 inches moulded length at deck, 11 feet 10 inches moulded beam, and about 4 feet moulded depth. Scale of model is 1 inch to the foot.

Given by "Bat" Fogarty, boatbuilder, Bradenton, Florida.

YACHT and PILOT SCHOONER, 1846
BUILDER'S HALF-MODEL, USNM 76040

Coquette

The noted Boston schooner yacht and pilot schooner *Coquette* was built on the lines of this model at Boston, Massachusetts, in 1846. She was designed by Lewis Winde, a Swedish naval architect who settled at Boston and was a member of the shipbuilding firm of Winde and Clinkard, which built many fast schooners, yachts, pilot boats, and coasters. This model was made from plans by Dennison J. Lawlor, who is said to have been employed in the Winde and Clinkard yard as a young man, and is probably accurate as to form, though in error as to head and other details.

The *Coquette* was a very fast sailer and won wide attention by beating the big New York centerboard sloop yacht *Maria* in a match race to windward. The *Coquette* was later sold to the Boston pilots and was long a favorite boat with them; the pilots have

<92></92>

92

a fine painting of this schooner in their office at Boston. Plans of the vessel also exist and these and the painting show the errors in the model's longhead and details.

The half-model shows a clipper schooner hull having rather straight sheer, a straight keel with strong drag, rounded forefoot, raking stem rabbet, a nearly straight and nearly upright post, and a short counter with raking elliptical transom. The entrance is sharp and convex, the run long and fine. The midsection shows a rising straight floor with much dead rise, a high and rather hard bilge, and tumble-home in the topside.

Mounted with head, keel, post, and rudder. The vessel had a long, low quarterdeck and cockpit aft.

The model measures about 67 feet moulded length at rail, 19 feet moulded beam, 8 feet moulded depth, and is for a vessel drawing 10 feet at post and about 5 feet 6 inches forward. Scale of the model is ½ inch to the foot.

Given by Dennison J. Lawlor, shipbuilder, Chelsea, Massachusetts.

YACHT and PILOT SCHOONER, 1853
BUILDER'S HALF-MODEL, USNM 76035

Olata

The clipper schooner *Olata* was built on this model at East Boston, Massachusetts, in 1853 by Dennison J. Lawlor. It is believed that she was built on speculation and was intended for a yacht. However, very soon after her launching, she was employed as a packet, running between Boston and Provincetown, and in that service she attracted much attention because of the manner in which she outsailed fast yachts, pilot boats, fishermen, and coasters. She was chartered in 1856 to carry the American consul out

from Boston to St. Thomas in the West Indies. Just before departure her foresail was so damaged that it could not be used, and she therefore sailed under her large jib and mainsail, making the passage in 7 days. In 1858 she was sold to the New Orleans pilots; her later career has not been traced.

The half model represents a very extreme clipper schooner hull, of the yacht or pilot-boat form, having graceful sheer, a straight keel with moderate drag, well rounded forefoot, a rather upright and flaring stem rabbet, upright post, a short and rounded counter having flaring bulwarks, very sharp entrance with marked hollow particularly just abaft the forefoot, and a very fine run. The midsection is formed with a very marked hollow at garboards and a sharply rising floor, the bilge is high and quite hard, and the topsides have a marked tumble-home. The bow sections show marked flare. The *Olata*, which appears to have been flush decked, sat low in the water and had a graceful longhead, trails, billet, and head rails.

Mounted with longhead, trails, cutwater, keel, post, and rudder.

The model is for a vessel 73 feet 2 inches moulded length at rail, 69 feet 10 inches between perpendiculars, 20 feet 8 inches moulded beam, 9 feet 4 inches moulded depth, rabbet to underside of deck at side, and drawing about 10 feet at post. Scale of the model is ½ inch to the foot.

The *Olata* is described as having raking masts rigged "pilot-boat fashion," with a large single jib, loose-footed foresail (no fore-topmast), boomed mainsail, and with a main gaff-topsail and a main-topmast staysail.

Given by Dennison J. Lawlor, shipbuilder, Chelsea, Massachusetts.

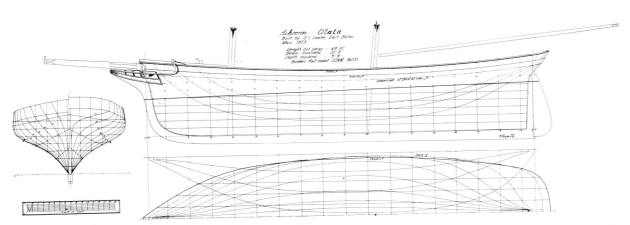

LINES OF THE PILOT SCHOONER AND YACHT *Olata*, built at East Boston, Massachusetts, in 1853. Taken off the builder's half-model USNM 76035.

SCHOONER YACHT, 1884
BUILDER'S HALF-MODEL, USNM 76093

This builder's half-model is a design for a very large, seagoing sailing yacht of topsail schooner or brigantine rig, exhibited at the World's Exposition, New Orleans, Louisiana, in 1884–85. No vessel was built from the design; the model represents an extreme clipper form—deep, narrow, and sharp—intended for fast sailing. It is an interesting example of a yacht design by a Canadian builder, W. Powers, whose work was usually in commercial vessels.

The half-model is of a large clipper yacht hull, having rather straight sheer, a straight keel with some drag, well rounded forefoot and raking stem rabbet, upright post, short counter with elliptical transom, long and very sharp entrance, and a very fine run. The midsection is formed with a strongly rising straight floor, high and rather hard bilge, and tumble-home in the topside.

Mounted with a long and pointed head, billet, trails, cutwater, keel, post, rudder, stub masts, and bowsprit. The position of the masts suggests that a brigantine rig may have been intended.

According to a card accompanying the model, it is for a vessel 125 feet on the load line, 25 feet moulded beam, and 12 feet moulded depth. The straight floor shows a dead rise of 20 degrees. Scale is ⅛ inch to the foot.

Given by W. Powers, shipbuilder, Kingston, Ontario.

SCHOONER YACHT, 1880
BUILDER'S HALF-MODEL, USNM 54462

This builder's half-model is of a keel, clipper, fore-and-aft rigged schooner yacht of large size designed by C. B. Harrington, shipbuilder, of Bath, Maine, in 1880; no vessel was built on this design. The designer was locally prominent as a builder of fast sailing yachts.

The half-model represents the hull of a sharp-lined schooner yacht having strong sheer, a straight keel with some drag, a raking straight stem rabbet with moderate round at forefoot, upright stern post, a long and round fantail counter with flaring bulwarks, a sharp and long hollow entrance, and a long and extremely fine run. The midsection has a sharply rising straight floor, high and hard round bilge, and tumble-home in the topside. There is much flare in the forward sections, and the forefoot is very thin and fine.

Mounted with longhead, cutwater, keel, post, and rudder.

The model scales 100 feet moulded length at rail, 26 feet moulded beam, and 9 feet 6 inches moulded depth. Scale is ½ inch to the foot.

Given by C. B. Harrington, shipbuilder, Bath, Maine.

CENTERBOARD SLOOP, about 1905
BUILDER'S HALF-MODEL, USNM 311522

Eclipse

The small centerboard sloop *Eclipse* was built on this model at Bradenton, Florida, sometime between 1898 and 1910 by "Bat" Fogarty. This model was also used to build a number of sloops, names unknown, for the coastal fisheries and for general service.

The half-model is of a centerboard sloop having moderate sheer, a rockered keel rabbet (the keel is straight with a large skeg aft), raking post, round fantail counter (the fantail is added to the model, which probably had originally a raking V-transom), a rather upright flaring stem rabbet, a short and rather hollow entrance, and a short but rather well formed run. The midsection is formed by a rising straight floor, a slack round bilge, and a flaring topside.

The scale of the model is believed to be 1 inch to the foot, at which scale it represents a sloop approximately 29 feet 3 inches moulded length at deck, 11 feet beam, and about 3 feet 6 inches moulded depth.

Given by "Bat" Fogarty, boatbuilder, Bradenton, Florida.

CENTERBOARD SLOOP, about 1910
BUILDER'S HALF-MODEL, USNM 311521

Mermaid

The small centerboard sloop *Mermaid* was designed and built on this model by "Bat" Fogarty at Bradenton, Florida, sometime between 1900 and 1915. Boats of this type were used in the Florida fisheries and for carrying produce alongshore. The sloop had a trunk cabin and large cockpit, and its form is that of American centerboard fishing sloops of similar size in the 1880's.

The half-model represents a shoal centerboard sloop having moderate sheer, a rockered keel rabbet with a straight keel forming a skeg aft, raking straight stem rabbet, vertical post, overhanging stern formed by a raking flat V-shaped transom, with the rudder stock passing through the apex of the V, a long and sharp entrance, and a rather short but well formed run. The midsection is formed with a markedly rising straight floor, high and firm bilge, and a nearly upright topside.

The scale of the model is believed to be 1 inch to the foot, at which scale it represents a sloop about 28 feet 6 inches moulded length at deck, 9 feet beam, and 2 feet 9 inches moulded depth.

Given by "Bat" Fogarty, boatbuilder, Bradenton, Florida.

CENTERBOARD SLOOP, 1903
BUILDER'S HALF-MODEL, USNM 311240

Pathfinder

The centerboard sloop yacht *Pathfinder* was built on this model at Oxford, Maryland, in 1903 by Charles W. Langdon and was intended for cruising on Chesapeake Bay. The *Pathfinder* was typical of a large number of American centerboard sloop yachts of the period 1895–1906, a class which had trunk cabins and large centerboards.

The half-model has moderate and graceful sheer, a rockered keel rabbet fairing into the overhanging and curved stem rabbet and into a rather long counter, which ends in a flat and strongly raking transom, and a large skeg with the rudder hung on its after end. The entrance is sharp and convex, and the run long, flat, and easy. The midsection shows a short straight floor with some rise, a round and easy bilge, and a nearly upright topside. The dead rise is carried into the run with slight change.

The model is for a sloop 31 feet 9 inches moulded length at deck, 9 feet 6 inches moulded beam, and 2 feet 9 inches moulded depth at side. Scale of the model is 1 inch to the foot.

The usual rig in these sloop yachts was jib and gaff mainsail. Sometimes a topmast was fitted, or the head of the mast made with a long pole and a gaff topsail and jib topsail could then be carried.

Given by Charles W. Langdon, boatbuilder, Oxford, Maryland.

CENTERBOARD SAILBOAT, 1920
BUILDER'S HALF-MODEL, USNM 311256

A shoal draft, centerboard sailboat was built on this model at Apalachicola, Florida, by Samuel Johnson, about 1920. The boat was probably sloop or cat rigged and intended for pleasure sailing.

The half-model represents a centerboard sailing hull having a moderate sheer, a rockered keel rabbet,

rounded forefoot, nearly straight and upright stem rabbet, raking flat transom, short and sharp entrance, and an easy run of moderate length and having a large skeg with rudder hung on it and the transom. The midsection shows a rising straight floor, a slack round bilge, and a nearly upright topside.

The model is believed to be on a scale of 1 inch to the foot, at which scale it represents a boat measuring about 21 feet 7 inches moulded length at deck, 8 feet 1½ inches moulded beam, and 2 feet 6 inches moulded depth.

Given by Samuel Johnson, boatbuilder, Apalachicola, Florida.

CENTERBOARD SLOOP, 1919
BUILDER'S HALF-MODEL, USNM 307423

This half-model shows the hull form of a class of centerboard half-decked racing sloops built at Essex, Connecticut, in 1919 by Dauntless Shipyard, Inc. Known as the "Essex class," this popular form of small racing sloop in various designs, is to be found in most American yachting centers.

The boats of this class were 15 feet 9 inches long over the gunwales, 5 feet 7 inches beam, and about 18 inches depth. They had a jib and gaff-headed mainsail rig. The mast stood about 15 feet above deck.

The half model shows a centerboard sloop hull of marked sheer, the keel is rockered fore and aft and fairing into a rather upright curved stem rabbet, and the transom is flat and raking. The entrance is easy and the run flat and rather short. The midsection is formed with a rising straight floor, easy round bilge, and a slightly flaring topside. The bow sections show flare, but there is a slight tumble-home in the topsides as the transom is approached. The dead rise is at a constant angle in the run. Scale of the model is 1 inch to the foot.

Given by Dauntless Shipyard, Inc., Essex, Connecticut.

CENTERBOARD SLOOP, 1922
BUILDER'S HALF-MODEL, USNM 315703

This model is a design for a small centerboard sloop for pleasure sailing made by Otis A. Palmer of East Moriches, Long Island, New York, about 1922. It is not known whether boats were built on this model.

The half-model represents a jib-and-mainsail rigged centerboard boat having rather straight sheer, a rockered keel rabbet, a curved, raking, and overhanging stem rabbet, and a small and flat raking V-shaped transom. The entrance is of moderate length and convex. The run is long, easy, and slightly rockered in the buttocks. The midsection is forward of midlength and shows a short, straight and gently rising floor, slack round bilge, and slightly flaring topside.

Scale of model 1 inch to the foot, for a vessel of 21 feet moulded length at deck, 6 feet 5 inches moulded beam, and 1 foot 10 inches moulded depth. It was probably intended to carry a knockabout rig, with oval cockpit. Small sloops of this type were very popular in the period 1918–32 as a one-design racing class and for general pleasure sailing.

Gift of Mrs. Otis A. Palmer, East Moriches, Long Island, New York.

CENTERBOARD SLOOP, 1897
RIGGED MODEL, USNM 310829

Ariel

The *Ariel* was designed by Arthur Binney of Boston, Massachusetts, and built by George Lawley and Son, Neponset, Massachusetts, in 1896–97. She was a gaff-rigged, centerboard, knockabout sloop of a type popular in the United States at the end of the 19th century and in the early years of the present century.

The model represents a wooden, caravel-planked centerboard sloop of moderate sheer, having a short, straight keel with much drag (formed by a skeg), and the keel rabbet cambered fore-and-aft to fair into the overhanging bow and counter. The stem is curved and the counter long and thin, ending with a wide, shallow, elliptical transom raking sharply. The entrance is rather sharp and convex, and the run is long and easy. The bow sections are U-shaped. The midsection has a rising straight floor, hard round bilge, and an upright topside.

The model is mounted on glass representing water, and shows the boat in process of picking up or dropping her mooring. The topsides are white, bottom green, and deck varnished. The outboard sides of the trunk and the cockpit (elliptical in plan) are white, and the cabin trunk roof yellow. There is a slide hatch companionway for the cabin trunk. A small flat-bottomed skiff-tender is shown in the case with the model.

The model is fully rigged and details are well shown. The mast is forward of the trunk. There is no bowsprit. The sails include a large jib with club laced to the foot, a gaff-mainsail with boom laced, and a small club gaff-topsail.

The *Ariel* was 38 feet overall, 10 feet beam, 23 feet length in the waterline, and drew 2 feet 4 inches with the centerboard raised and about 6 feet 6 inches with it lowered. Scale of the model is ¾ inch to the foot.

Bequest of Major John W. Loveland, Washington, D. C.

J–CLASS RACING SLOOP, 1934
RIGGED MODEL, USNM 313627

Rainbow

This is a model of the *America's* Cup defender *Rainbow*, which sailed against the English challenger *Endeavour* in 1934, winning a series of six races, of which the *Endeavour* won the first two. This big sloop was designed by Starling Burgess, naval architect, and was built by the Herreshoff Manufacturing Company, Bristol, Rhode Island. Large sloops of this size and general type were built to race for the *America's* Cup which had been won in a squadron race at Cowes, England, in 1851 by the New York schooner-yacht *America*.

The model shows a large racing sloop of the J-class of the Universal Rule having slight sheer, a very short and heavy ballast keel, a long, pointed bow with some reverse curve in the profile below the load line, a raking straight post, a long and thin counter ending in a small elliptical raking transom with an athwartship curve in its face, and no bulwarks but a low grab rail along the planksheer. The midsection is somewhat Y-shaped, with a thick ballast keel, or fin, and strongly rising floor, a slack and easy round bilge, and a nearly upright topside. The entrance is fine and convex, the run long and very fine.

A dinghy is carried on deck at the stern, forward of which is a small hatch, steering wheel, and binnacle, companion hatch with skylights on each side of it, main skylight, mast, and a small hatch. The forestays come to deck well inboard of the stemhead.

The *Rainbow* measured 126 feet 7 inches overall, 82 feet on the waterline, 20 feet 11 inches beam, 14 feet 11 inches draft, and had a mast 152 feet 6 inches, deck to center of halyard sheave in mast. The measured sail area was 7,549 square feet. Scale of the model is ¼ inch to the foot.

Given by Chandler Hovey, Boston, Massachusetts.

INLAND LAKE RACING SCOW, 1900
RIGGED MODEL, USNM 316086

Minnezitka

This model is of an early racing scow developed for the Inland Lake Yachting Association (founded in 1898), an association of yacht clubs located on lakes

INLAND LAKE YACHTING ASSOCIATION RULE racing scow *Minnezitka*, built in 1900. Rigged model USNM 316086. (*Smithsonian photo 45606–f.*)

in Wisconsin and Minnesota, with four more clubs situated in nearby States.

The racing scow first appeared as a fast, shoal, centerboard sloop in the early 1890's and the type had a period of popularity on the Atlantic coast, particularly on Long Island Sound and in Massachusetts Bay. There has been international racing in this type, between American and Canadian clubs, since 1896. In the late 1890's it was introduced in a primitive form on the so-called Inland Lakes of Wisconsin and Minnesota, and also in lower Canada.

The development of organized racing of scows was very rapid under the guidance of the Inland Lake Yachting Association and various classes of boats were established. In 1959 there were six classes: "A" 37⅞ to 38 feet in length, "E" 27¾ to 28 feet, "D" 19¾ to 20 feet, "C" 19¾ to 20 feet, "X" 15.83 to 16 feet, and "V" 18.83 to 19 feet. These classes produce the fastest sailing boats in the world, over a triangular racing course.

The class "A" scow *Minnezitka*, was built in 1900 at White Bear Lake, Minnesota, by John O. Johnson. She was a candidate for an international race for the Seawanahka Cup, but was not chosen, though the fastest of the American candidates. A very successful boat in interclub racing for some years, she was jib-and-mainsail rigged, with a gaff-mainsail.

The hull of the model has a sled-profile bow, vertical flat transom, and straight sheer. The bottom is cambered, giving a flat run and entrance. On deck the hull is approximately rectangular, the bow being square across but narrower than the stern transom. The sides are on a long, fair sweep in plan, and the hull is deliberately designed to sail at a given angle of heel. The midsection shows a nearly flat floor, with the bilge on a long sweeping curve, and a curved and flaring topside.

Scale of the model is ¾ inch to the foot. The boat was 38 feet overall, 7 feet 9 inches beam and 1 foot 5 inches deep at side.

Gift of John O. Johnson, boatbuilder, White Bear Lake, Minnesota.

INLAND LAKE RACING SCOW, 1959
RIGGED MODEL, USNM 316087

This model is the 1959 version of the class "A" Inland Lake racing scow. Boats built on this plan have been successful in club racing and are considered very fine craft of their type for competition sailing. It is claimed that a modern scow has been timed at 28 miles per hour with wind on the quarter.

INLAND LAKE YACHTING ASSOCIATION RULE class A racing scow, 1959. Rigged model USNM 316087. (*Smithsonian photo 45606–g.*)

97

These boats plane under suitable conditions and usually are very weatherly under all sailing conditions. The scow is entirely an American development in racing types of sailing yachts, and the designer-builder appears to have introduced bilge boards and to have introduced features that mark the modern Inland Lake scows.

The model shows the usual scow form, but with a sharp bow (both pointed and square bows are employed). The sheer is straight, the deck heavily crowned. The bottom is rockered, fairing into a curved, raking stem. The flat transom is vertical. The greatest beam is just a little abaft midlength. The midsection is formed with a short, flat floor, a sweeping bilge hardening in curve outboard, and a curved and flaring topside.

The model has bilge boards—two centerboards abreast, each in the bilge and so arranged as to be nearly vertical when the hull is heeled to the designed sailing angle. It is rigged with a jib-headed mainsail; the end of the main boom and the foot of the forestay are well inboard of the hull ends.

Scale of the model is ¾ inch to the foot, for a boat 37 feet 10½ inches overall length, 8 feet 2 inches beam, and 1 foot 9 inches depth at side.

Gift of John O. Johnson, boatbuilder, White Bear Lake, Minnesota.

WHITEHALL BOAT 1880
RIGGED MODEL, USNM 25001

The Whitehall boat, a type of rowboat once very popular in the United States, originated in New York City and was developed for the professional boatmen of that port. From the place of its origin on Whitehall Street, hence the name, the Whitehall boat spread to Boston and other eastern ports and to the Pacific Coast. It is believed that the type came into existence soon after the War of 1812 and that the model was developed from naval gigs built at the old New York Navy Yard. By 1825 the Whitehall was fully developed and was used by watermen of all classes, boarding-house runners, mercantile brokers, salesmen, ship-news reporters and others who required a boat in their business in the large ports. The boats varied to some extent in form and appearance and in size according to their intended use. The length was commonly between 14 and 18 feet but occasionally was as long as 22 feet. They were rowed by one to six oarsmen, depending on their size. Some were caravel planked, but most were clench planked. Some were fitted with sails and centerboards. Late in the 19th

century the Whitehall boat was much used for pleasure rowing and as tenders for large yachts. The type is now extinct.

The model represents a caravel-planked 4-oar rowing boat of moderate sheer, having a straight keel, upright stem with rounded forefoot, and a slightly raking heart-shaped transom stern. The entrance is long, fine, and slightly hollow, and the run is also rather long and very fine. The midsection is formed with a slight rise in the straight floor, a round, slack bilge, and a slightly flaring topside. The rudder is hung outboard on the transom and is operated by a yoke and steering lines. The model has four thwarts, with sternsheets and backboard, and a bow grating forward of the foremost thwart.

The model is of a boat of rather common size, 18 feet long at gunwale, 4 feet 9¾ inches beam and 19 inches deep from ceiling alongside keel to top of gunwale, with oars 11 feet 6 inches long. Scale of model is 2 inches to the foot.

Gift of Nash and Sons, boatbuilders.

ADIRONDACK SKIFF, 1885
RIGGED MODEL, USNM 25053

This model represents an open, double-ended skiff, from the Adirondack Mountain area of New York, which was developed for fishing on the lakes and streams and was also employed by hunters. The model varied somewhat according to the ideas of the builders. Some used caravel planking but most boats of the type were clench built of thin white cedar. The Adirondack skiff became a popular hunting boat during the last quarter of the 19th century and was produced as a stock boat by many small-boat builders in Northern New York State. It was usually light enough to be carried by two men, the common length being 14 to 16 feet at gunwale. Some of these skiffs were fitted with centerboards and rigged for sailing, usually with a small boomed spritsail with mast well forward.

The model shows a light, open, double-ended skiff of moderate sheer, having a straight keel, rather upright stem, slightly raking post, and a fine entrance and run. The midsection has a slight rise in the straight floor, a slack round bilge, and a slightly flaring topside. The model is not fitted for sailing and appears to represent a pleasure boat, not one used by guides for hunting or fishing. Fitted to row with two pairs of oars it has thwarts and seats; at each end is a very short deck.

It represents a skiff 22 feet long, 3 feet 10 inches beam, and 12 inches depth amidships, an unusually long boat of the type. Scale of model 1½ inch to the foot.

Given by Cornwall and Weston, boatbuilders, Alexandria Bay, New York.

NEW JERSEY SNEAKBOX, 1890
Rigged Model, usnm 26623

This type of hunting skiff was developed by commercial duck hunters, during the 19th century, on Barnegat Bay, New Jersey, and was intended to be rowed or sailed. The boat carried a single gunner and his gear, including a large-bore gun, ammunition, decoys and supplies for at least a day. The boats, built of white cedar, were about 12 or 13 feet long and were light enough to be dragged over the mud flats.

The sneakbox was a fast sailer, having many of the characteristics of a racing "scow," and has continued in use, not only as a gunning skiff but also (in modified form) as a racing sailboat and afternoon sailer on Barnegat Bay. Some are rigged as jib-and-mainsail sloops. Like the melon seed, the sneakbox steered with a yoke and steering lines. Folding oarlocks were employed. The rig was a single boomed spritsail, the mast stepped well forward in the boat.

The model shows a square-sterned caravel-planked skiff, fitted with a dagger-type centerboard and decked except for a small cockpit about amidships. The sheer is nearly straight and the deck much crowned, the keel is rockered, and there is a small skeg, the rudder being hung outboard. The stem is formed by the keel being brought up in a sweep to meet the sheer. The transom is upright and flat. In appearance the entrance is somewhat like the end of a teaspoon; the run is easy and flat. The midsection, which shows a moderate rise in the floor, a very slack round bilge, and much flare in the topside, may be described as "dish-shaped." Washboards are shown fitted along the gunwale aft to hold decoys from falling overboard. The spray cloth for the cockpit and its hatches are shown.

The model represents a skiff about 11 feet 9 inches long, about 4 feet 3 inches beam, and nearly 13 inches depth to crown of deck. Scale of model is probably 1¼ inch to the foot.

Given by J. D. Gifford, Tuckerton, New Jersey.

AU SABLE RIVER SKIFF, 1877
Rigged Model, usnm 25899

This model represents a fishing skiff of a type once used in the Au Sable River region in Michigan for trout and grayling fishing in rapid streams. The boat was related in form to the lumbermen's drive boat, or lumbermen's bateau. It is described in *Forest and Stream* (vol. 3, August 1877, p. 33) by Thaddeus Norris, author of *The American Anglers' Book.*

The model is of an open, double-ended, flat-bottomed skiff or plank canoe which was made of white pine; the bottom in profile is somewhat rockered; the sheer is moderate and the stem and stern are strongly raked; the sides have marked flare. The bottom is flat athwartships. A small live-well, usually about 2 feet long, was built about one-third the length from the bow; the model shows widely spaced floor timbers, one at a semibulkhead abaft the well and two at the well bulkheads. Breasthooks are fitted bow and stern at the gunwale, and inboard of these at the gunwale hand grips are cut through the sides, port and starboard, bow and stern. The bottom is planked fore-and-aft. The sides are each of a single plank and the bottom of two or three planks. No side frames are shown nor are there gunwale stringers or chine timbers.

The boats usually had two or three thwarts. When used on lakes these boats were sometimes fitted with oarlocks or tholes and some were fitted to sail with a small spritsail and a shifting leeboard. The construction was that of the "drive boat," or dory, and was quite light; these boats could usually carry a fisherman and guide and about 200 pounds of baggage or gear. Normally the boats were paddled or poled.

The scale of the model is 2 inches to the foot, so that the skiff represented was 18 feet 6 inches long at gunwale, 3 feet 6 inches extreme beam, and 1 foot 1½ inches deep amidships.

Given by D. A. Fitzhugh, Jr.

EGG HARBOR MELON SEED, 1885
Rigged Model, usnm 25658

The Egg Harbor melon seed, a name apparently suggested by the shape of the hull, was a type of wildfowl hunting boat developed at Egg Harbor, New Jersey, for use on lower Barnegat Bay. This form of sailing-rowing skiff, particularly designed for use in rough-water shooting, was developed by professional duck hunters who sold game to commercial markets during the last half of the 19th century. Designed to be manned by a single gunner, the melon seed gunning skiffs were excellent sailing boats and rowed well; they were lightly built of cedar, and the rudder

Egg Harbor Melon-Seed Gun-ning Skiff from lower Barnegat Bay, New Jersey. Rigged model USNM 25658 showing a typical boat of this type. (*Smithsonian photo 44697-a.*)

was controlled by a yoke and steering lines, as in the sneakbox.

The model shows a square-sterned caravel-planked centerboard boat having a moderate sheer, rockered keel with skeg, curved stem, raking transom with rudder hung outboard, sharp entrance, and an easy, well formed run. The midsection shows a slightly rising straight floor, slack rounded bilge, and flaring topside. The centerboard is of the curved dagger type, not pivoted. The boat is decked except for small cockpit nearly amidships which has covers and a spray cloth.

The rig is a single boomed spritsail, the mast well forward as in a catboat.

The model is of a skiff 13 feet 4½ inches extreme length at gunwale, 4 feet 3 inches beam, and about 13½ inches depth from rabbet to centerline of deck amidships at fore end of cockpit. Scale of model is 2 inches to the foot.

Given by P. Brasher.

WOODEN CANOE, 1880
FULL-SIZED BOAT, USNM 160315

Sairey Gamp

This very small canoe was built by J. H. Rushton of Canton, New York, about 1880 for George W. Sears, who, under the pen-name "Nessmuk," wrote for American sporting magazines about woodland travel, hunting, and fishing. The canoe was designed to be as light and small as was practical for a single woodsman to carry and use in long expeditions in the forest. Its notable builder specialized in canoes and light rowing craft. The *Sairey Gamp* (named for the midwife and nurse in Charles Dickens' *Martin Chuzzlewit*) was the third and last of a series of such canoes built for the owner.

The canoe, clench-planked of thin white cedar, is a small double-ender of moderate sheer, having a straight keel and moderately raking stem and stern posts. The stem has a slight curve in profile and is

100

slightly rounded at the forefoot. The ends are sharp and the entrance is slightly longer than the run. It has a shallow outside keel, a very slight rise in the straight floor amidships, a rather easy round bilge, and a slightly flaring topside. The canoe has two thwarts, placed to leave the middle third of the hull clear of obstruction, and no seats. The frames are slight and steam-bent.

The canoe is 9 feet in overall length, 26 inches beam, 6¾ inches deep inside, and weighs 11 pounds, dry, without equipment. The paddles exhibited are one very small single-bladed hunting-and-fishing sneak paddle, 17 inches long with a blade 3 inches wide, and a double-bladed traveling paddle with jointed shank, 6 feet 1 inch in length.

This canoe is described in some detail in the well-known book, *Woodcraft*, by "Nessmuk."

Donor not recorded.

WOODEN CRUISING CANOE, 1880
RIGGED MODEL, USNM 76083

Capital

This model represents a wooden, sailing and paddling canoe, decked and with small cockpit, of a type that was popular in the 1880's for racing and cruising. These canoes, developed in the 1870's out of adaptions of the Eskimo kayak, had become more a sailing boat than a paddling canoe. The user could sleep in the hull, whether afloat or ashore, by crawling partly under the deck, the cockpit being then covered with a tent or canopy. These canoes were fitted with two masts and lateen sails and steered, when sailing or being paddled, by a rudder fitted with a yoke and steering lines; the latter were fitted to a foot yoke inboard so the user could steer with his feet while paddling and with his hands or feet while sailing.

The model shows a clench-planked double-ended canoe hull, decked except an oval cockpit located about amidships. The boat has a long, sharp entrance and an easy sharp run, a straight keel, a stem nearly vertical and with very rounded forefoot, a raking straight post, and graceful sheer. The midsection is formed with a slightly rising straight floor, an easy round bilge, and an upright topside.

The model, representing the canoe *Capital*, which was built at Washington, D. C., by J. Passeno, an amateur builder, shows a craft 18 feet 10 inches overall length, 3 feet 6 inches beam, and 1 foot 5 inches extreme depth, and having the foremast 6 feet

1½ inches above deck, fore yard 14 feet 7½ inches and the fore boom 12 feet long, the mainmast 3 feet 4½ inches above deck, main yard 7 feet 8 inches and main boom 6 feet 9 inches long. The double-bladed paddle scales 9 feet 3 inches long. Scale of the model is 2 inches to the foot.

Given by J. Passeno, Washington, D. C.

CANVAS-COVERED WOODEN CANOE, 1907
RIGGED MODEL, USNM 248063

This model represents a type of canvas-covered wooden canoe, manufactured by the Old Town Canoe Company, Old Town, Maine, about 1907. This class of canoe was intended for propulsion by paddle only and was used for pleasure as well as for hunting, fishing, and for woodland travel. In general form they resembled the birch-bark canoes of the American Indians, and the first of them produced at Old Town for general sale were built by Penobscot and Malecite Indians, but the model shown more nearly resembles the last birch-bark canoes built by the Chippewa and St. Francis tribesmen. The construction, as developed, employed wide and thin, closely spaced bent-frames overlaid with a complete planking system and made watertight by a cover of canvas stretched over and tacked to the hull.

The model represents a canoe having a sharp entrance and run, straight keel with ends semicircular in profile, and a sheer strong at the bow and stern and moderate in the midbody. The midsection is rather U-shaped, having an almost flat floor, an easy round bilge, and a slight tumble-home in the topside. The middle third of the length is unobstructed; on each end of this open space are narrow thwarts and caned seats, with two more thwarts and seats near each end of the hull. Gunwales are formed of two strips each, one inside the frames and one applied over the canvas cover. In the model is a cap rail over all, producing a "closed gunwale," but the cap rail was normally omitted; woodsmen preferred the "open gunwales," which allowed the canoe to be easily cleaned of sand or mud that collected inboard.

Scale of the model is 3 inches to the foot (¼ full size), so that the model represents a canoe about 16 feet 4 inches overall length, 3 feet extreme beam, and 1 foot 2 inches depth. Model is painted green outboard with varnished outer gunwale, cap, and exposed inboard surfaces.

Given by the Old Town Canoe Company, Old Town, Maine.

SINGLE-SCULL RACING SHELL, 1897
FULL-SIZED BOAT, USNM 311024
OARS, USNM 311395

This single-scull, or one-man racing shell, was used by Edward Hanlon Ten Eyck to win the "Diamond Sculls" at Henley, England, in 1897. E. H. Ten Eyck was the son of the professional oarsman James Ten Eyck and was the fastest amateur sculler of his day. After winning a large number of races in America he entered the Diamond Sculls at Henley, England in 1897, rowing as a member of the Wachusett Boat Club of Worcester, Massachusetts, his home. He was then 18 years old and won the race in record time. He trained in a professional manner and this, and other conduct, led the English to refuse his entry in 1898, apparently on the grounds of semiprofessionalism. Ten Eyck continued rowing and was unbeaten until he retired from active competition in 1901.

The boat was built by J. H. Clasper at Putney, England, for the owner and to his specifications.

Craft of this class and model were developed to allow the highest possible speed under oars in smooth water, and the boat exhibited is of the type rowed by a single oarsman using two sculls, or oars, and steering with his feet.

The boat is a long and very narrow double-ended hull having a U-shaped midsection, cambered keel, straight sheer, curved and very raking stem, shallow upright post, and a very sharp entrance and run. The hull is built of veneer (some were built of paper) and has steam-bent ribs of very small scantling, closely spaced. The deck is of varnished muslin or cotton, the cockpit has flaring side coamings, with a V-shaped breakwater at the fore end. Also provided are a sliding seat for the rower and oarlocks outrigged on each side by means of a tubular frame. The hull is 31 feet 6 inches long, 10½ inches beam, and weighs 30 pounds, dry. Oars are 9 feet 5½ inches long; the blades are 2 feet long and spoon-shaped in a hollow curve to give a better grip on the water.

Given by James A. Ten Eyck.

OUTRIGGED ROWING BOAT, 1890
FULL-SIZED BOAT, USNM 309501

Saunterer

This boat is of a type once much employed in pleasure rowing by skilled oarsmen who had been trained in outrigger shells with sliding seats. Known as working boats, or "wherries," they had a wide seat aft for a cockswain or passenger and were capable of great speed in smooth water. Such boats were used for training crews for pair-oars racing shells, or for pleasure rowing.

The *Saunterer*, very lightly built of thin cedar plank and slight, bent frames, has a straight keel, curved and upright stem, raking and very narrow V-shaped transom about 6 inches wide at gunwale, very slight sheer, and a long and very sharp entrance and run. The midsection has a slight rise in the straight floor, a slack round bilge, and a flaring topside. There is a stern seat with cane back, two sliding seats, each outrigged on both sides, for rowers and a seat facing aft at bow. The boat steered with a rudder having a yoke (missing) and steering lines. Outriggers are of tubing and rod.

The boat is 24 feet long, 3 feet 1½ inches beam at gunwale, 5 feet 5 inches over the outriggers, and depth of the hull amidships about 11 inches.

Gift of Charles G. Warden, Washington, D. C.

PISCATAQUA RIVER PACKET BOAT, 1865
RIGGED MODEL, USNM 311147

This model, made by the donor from memory, is one of the last of a type of small sailing packets once used on the Piscataqua River, in New Hampshire, to carry passengers, mail, and light freight to the river villages above Portsmouth, N. H. These small packets, which remained in use until about 1870, were in fact the marine counterpart of the stagecoach in this area. The boats, some of which were fast under sail, usually operated between Portsmouth and an individual village, each boat serving a given section in the Great Bay region. The regular river packet service had been in larger sloops and schooners until steam packets came into use in the 1850's on the run between Portsmouth and Dover.

The model represents a hull having the form of a ships' yawl-boat of more than usual depth. It has slight sheer, a straight keel with some drag, an upright stem with a slightly rounded forefoot, raking post, and a heart-shaped flat transom with rudder stock inboard. The entrance is full and convex and the run rather easy but short. The midsection is formed with a rising straight floor, a firm round bilge, and a nearly upright topside. The model, roughly made, represents a boat with lines somewhat fuller than was usual in this type. The deck arrangement however, is typical; the mast is well forward in the "eyes" of the boat, with its heel over the fore end of the straight part of the keel. On this short mast a triangular lateen-type sail is shown slung from a strong halyard, the heel secured by a tack tackle setting up on the face of the stem and with fall leading inboard. Abaft the mast is a small square hatch and well abaft amidships is a companion hatch; here the deck is lowered to form a shallow cockpit. The boat steered with a tiller, now missing in the model. The loose-footed sail is brailed to reef. Sweep locks, fitted amidships to permit rowing in a calm, are omitted in the model. The raised portion of the deck had a low log rail, or chock rail, carried to the transom, where there was an iron mainsheet horse.

The scale of the model is uncertain, probably ½ inch to the foot, and the boat was therefore about 26 feet long, 10 feet 9 inches beam, and about 4 feet.

Given by Captain Edward H. Adams, Adams' Point, New Hampshire.

PISCATAQUA RIVER GUNDALOW, 1886
RIGGED MODEL, USNM 311148

Fanny M.

This model represents the Piscataqua River gundalow *Fanny M.* built at Adams Point, New Hampshire, in 1886 by Edward H. Adams for his own account.

The builder-owner desired an improved vessel and made this model to carry out sailing tests. When tests showed the model would sail fast, the model's lines were taken off and used to build the full-sized gundalow.

The history of the development of the gundalow is not fully known. It is believed that this type developed from ordinary river scows in colonial times and that the rig was a gradual evolution from a leg-of-mutton to allow the mast and sail to be quickly and easily lowered to pass under low bridges. This form of gundalow (the name was applied to many forms of flat-bottomed craft in America in the 18th and early 19th centuries) was a river freighter having a characteristic sail plan and a single leeboard. The early gundalows were open boats and some were no more than ordinary square-ended scows having the single leeboard and peculiar rig shown in this model. Later many gundalows had large single hatches and were partly decked. The last built, and the largest gundalows like the *Fanny M.*, were decked and had only a small entry hatch to the hold, being deck-loading. These sailing gundalows carried coal and freight from Portsmouth upriver to Dover and into Great Bay,

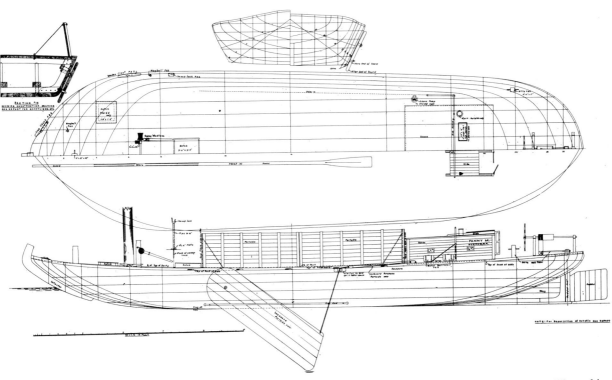

LINES AND ARRANGEMENT OF PISCATAQUA RIVER GUNDALOW *Fanny M.* built at Adams Point, New Hampshire, in 1886. Drawn from builder's model, and under supervision of the builder, by the Historic American Merchant Marine Survey. (HAMMS 2-171-A.)

103

SAIL PLAN OF PISCATAQUA RIVER gundalow *Fanny M.*, showing rigging details. Drawn, under supervision of the builder of the gundalow, by the Historic American Merchant Marine Survey. (HAMMS 2–171–B.)

returning to the coast with manufactured goods, farm produce, and timber. Sometimes gundalows ventured along the coast to York, Maine, but usually confined themselves to the river trade.

The model is correct as to hull form and to hull and sail proportions but does not show details accurately. Drawings of the *Fanny M.* made from this model and measurements of the full-sized gundalow are in the *Historic American Merchant Marine Survey* material (see bibliography) and show this gundalow in great detail.

The model represents a shoal, flat-bottomed, scow-like hull having ends much like the tip of a teaspoon, a slight sheer, slightly rounded bilges, and a flaring topside. A single leeboard on the port side only is held to the side by an iron staple or rod. There is a false cutwater at the bow. The hull is decked, with mast well forward, and a small hatch just abaft. The high, removable side boards on the cargo deck amidships are not shown on the model, which shows aft on this space a small hatch the full-sized gundalow did not have. Near the stern is a small trunk cabin with a large iron mainsheet horse astraddle it. At the extreme stern is a steering wheel and tiller, the rudder post coming up through the stern overhang inboard

the rail. The greatest beam of the hull is abreast the mast; the sides from this point to the trunk are nearly straight in plan, but with decreasing beam. On a skeg at the stern a nearly rectangular rudder is hung.

The rig is characteristic of the Piscataqua gundalow. The mast is very short; its height being determined by the lowest bridge clearance which, for many years, was that of the long wooden bridge at the mouth of Great Bay now replaced by the modern "General Sullivan Bridge." From the stub mast was slung by a chain halyard a long yard with a triangular sail, loose footed and fitted with both brail lines and reef points. To the yard head extended a single vang; the mainsheet was of peculiar lead. A heel tackle topped the yard so that it stood almost vertically. In some gundalows the heel of the yard was counterweighted to aid in raising the spar and sail after passing under a bridge. It is common to consider the gundalow sail as a lateen but it had so little sail forward of the stub mast that it cannot be properly so classed. The plan of the *Fanny M.* shows this more correctly than the model.

The cargo deck of large gundalows like the *Fanny M.* were covered with an asphalt surface to protect the wooden deck. The gundalows of the largest class usually worked with a captain and one or two hands; the *Fanny M.* worked very often with only the owner and his wife aboard. The crews were often French Canadians who were not sailors but only roustabouts.

The model is on a scale of ½ inch to the foot and represents a gundalow about 67 feet 6 inches long on deck, 18 feet beam, and about 4 feet 6 inches depth. The vessel's hull was built of hewn logs edgebolted and secured to heavy single-futtock frames, the construction being marked by massive strength. The gundalows were very fast sailers and were very handy in narrow waters. They were fitted with two long sweeps with tholes forward of the mast, to permit them to be rowed in calm weather.

Given by the builder, Edward H. Adams, Adams' Point, New Hampshire.

SIDE-WHEEL STEAMER *Orizaba* BUILT AT NEW YORK BY JACOB & WESTERVELT IN 1854, 1,355 TONS. (*Photo courtesy Union Title Insurance Company, San Diego, California.*)

MERCHANT STEAM

AMONG THE EARLY experiments in the construction of steamboats the American efforts were probably the most important and effective. The earliest known American experimenter was the gunsmith William Henry, of Lancaster, Pennsylvania, who in 1763 proposed a steamboat, though little is known of the engine or of the method of propulsion he planned, other than that he proposed using paddle wheels. Apparently he accomplished little; at least his efforts drew little attention.

James Rumsey has usually been credited with being the first successful experimenter in America, but this is doubtful. A house-builder and miller at Berkeley Springs, Virginia, he made a working model of a "mechanical boat" or "stream boat," about 1784, which he showed to visitors; this was not a steamboat but, rather, a mechanically driven craft employing setting poles. In 1787 he was able to construct a steamboat; the boiler and engine were built by the Catoctin Iron Furnace in Frederick County, Virginia.

Rumsey employed a pump, operated by a steam engine, to propel the boat by means of a primitive hydraulic jet which drew in water at the bow and expelled it at the stern. He had some success and, after dismantling his boat, he went to England to obtain financial backing. Here he designed an improved boat and started construction, but died before the craft was completed. The boat, when finished, was exhibited on the Thames and apparently was considered successful, but nothing further developed from this experiment.

Thus it appears that not until 1787 did Rumsey produce a steamboat. But in 1785 John Fitch had developed an idea for a steamboat and had built models, as well as a manually operated boat employing paddle wheels. Papers, including the specifications, and a model of a steamboat were presented to the American Philosophical Society in August of 1785.

Fitch organized in 1786 a steamboat company and in July of that year completed a skiff with a steam engine operating a bank of oars on each side of the boat. This boat he placed in operation to demonstrate the invention, and in the following month began a second boat, 45 feet long, which was demonstrated in August 1787, when a run was made in the presence of members of Congress at Philadelphia. In 1788 a third boat, 60 feet long and 12 feet beam, was built and fitted with stern oars, as illustrated. She made 14 trips to Burlington and back, from Philadelphia, covering between 2000 and 3000 miles, by the spring of 1790. A fourth boat, about the same size as the third, was started in the fall of 1790 but this boat was wrecked in a storm. and never repaired.

It is not clear that Fitch used the mechanical rowing system of propulsion in all his boats, for he experimented with endless-chain paddles and paddle wheels, as well as with the mechanical oars usually associated with his boats. In 1793 Fitch went to France and left plans there which Robert Fulton later saw. Fitch returned to the United States and died in 1798.

It will be seen that Fitch had a steamboat constructed a year before Rumsey, thus making him the first American to produce an operating steamboat. Others were interested in steamboats; Samuel Morey about 1790 built a steamboat, with a paddle wheel at the bow, that was tried out on the Connecticut River; a few years later he built another steamboat with a stern paddle wheel which made about 5 miles per hour. This he showed to Chancellor Robert Livingston, who was later associated with Fulton. Morey patented a steam engine in 1795 which was intended to operate paddle wheels. In 1797 he built a boat with two paddle wheels on each side. Nicholas J. Roosevelt also experimented with paddle wheels; he built a small boat, or large model, propelled by paddle wheels operated by a spindle on the axle, which was revolved by a cord attached to a wood-and-whalebone spring. His experiment took place sometime prior to 1798 and Roosevelt showed this boat to Chancellor Livingston.

It should be noted that a number of other Americans were active in steam engine construction and in steam propulsion problems after 1800. Oliver Evans built many experimental engines and finally produced the "grasshopper" engine in some number after 1820. It was employed in a couple of American steamboats but did not become very popular in America, though a number of early French steamboats were fitted with this type of engine. Evans was the first American to produce a standardized steam engine. The walking-beam engine was tried in America, but the first successful design was imported from England, and after about 1832 this type of engine became very popular in American steamers.

The lack of proper tools and of facilities for working large masses of metal appears to have caused the early

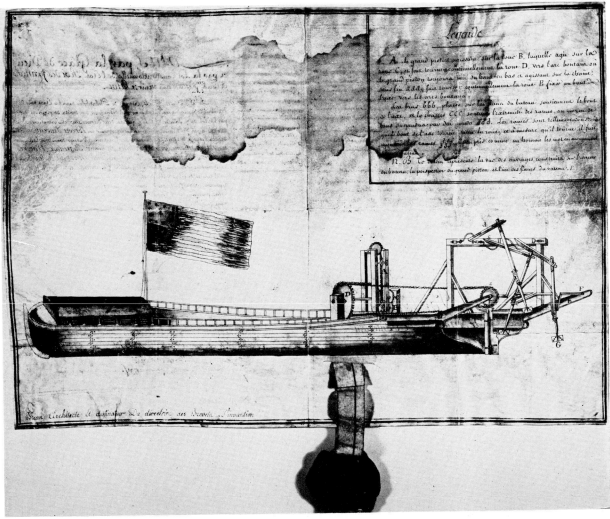

PATENT GRANTED TO JOHN FITCH BY LOUIS XVI OF FRANCE, November 29, 1791 (the original is in the Watercraft Collection USNM 130032). Propulsion is by "duck leg" paddles from the stern. The paddles are operated by cranks and pitman rods, driven by a chain, sprockets, and cranks from the steam engine. (*Smithsonian photo 44795–a.*)

American experimenters great difficulty in producing suitable engines for steamers. Hence early engines employed in steamboats were crude, of low power, and slow turning. Americans gave much attention to boilers; Fitch apparently had designed a water-tube boiler in 1785 and others worked on this idea.

John Stevens of Hoboken, New Jersey, probably began experimenting about 1791; his first attempt was with the hydraulic jet but he soon turned to a screw propeller. Stevens was a very brilliant man and invented, among other things, a tubular boiler (patented in 1791) and improvements (in 1805). In 1803–04 he built a twin-screw steamboat or rather, launch, with which he made tests on the Hudson in

the spring of 1804 and his boat reached a speed of about 4 miles per hour. He apparently had trouble with the engine and as a result, turned to side paddle wheels in place of screws and in 1807–09 built the steamboat *Phoenix*. While Stevens was still constructing his engine, Fulton and his backers obtained a monopoly on the use of steamboats in New York waters, and Stevens had no recourse but to send the *Phoenix* to the Delaware River. This vessel in making the passage by the coastal route, became the first American steamer to venture on the open sea. In spite of his own pioneering work Stevens gave full credit to Fulton for having produced the first practical paddlewheel steamboat.

109

Stevens retained his interest in the screw propeller but his inability, with the tools and skills available, to obtain a fast-turning engine, caused him to give up the experiment. In 1844, after some repairs and replacements of parts had been made, his original engine and boiler, with screws, was placed in a new hull, and a speed of 8 miles per hour was obtained, showing that the principles of Stevens' designs were sound. Stevens plans called for use of a multitube boiler, high-speed engine, and 4-bladed propellers, in a twin-screw installation, gear-driven in opposite directions. His experimental machinery has been preserved in the U. S. National Museum.

A Practical Steamboat

Robert Fulton's success in producing the first practical steamboat in America has given him popular credit for "inventing" the steamboat but in fact, as has been shown, many experimental steamboats able to run satisfactorily for a short period had been built previous to his. Fulton's boat, however, was able to operate for a prolonged period, though the hull was rebuilt during the first winter (1807–08) after her launching.

Fulton had studied the problem of constructing a steamboat for some years and had gone to England and France in an effort to obtain financial backing for experiments. While in France he had built a small boat, but this was not successful because the engine was too heavy for the hull. However, he succeeded in purchasing a Boulton and Watt steam engine, the third the British government allowed to be exported, and with this he was able to construct his steamboat at New York, aided by his backer there, Chancellor Robert Livingston. He and his associate were also able to obtain a state monopoly

PATENT DRAWING SUBMITTED IN 1790 BY JOHN FITCH AND HENRY VOIGT to the New Jersey State patent office. It represents the *Experiment*, Fitch's third boat, 60 feet long, 12 feet beam, built in 1788. By 1790 this vessel had traveled over 2,000 miles in river packet service between Philadelphia and Burlington, New Jersey. The patent drawing shows clearly the mechanical arrangement of paddles in Fitch's French patent. The flag shown flying on the vessel was presented to Fitch on September 4, 1790, by the President of Pennsylvania, the secretary of the State, and several members of the Pennsylvania Council. It is one of the earliest known contemporary representations of the flag of the 13 States. (*Smithsonian photo 45539.*)

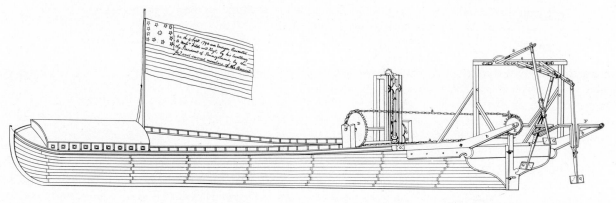

CONTEMPORARY VIEW OF FULTON'S STEAMBOAT. The *North River* (popularly known as the *Clermont*) passing West Point, showing the vessel as rebuilt in 1807–08 with figurehead, wheelboxes, and leeboards. From a lithograph by F. Berthaux, Dijon, of a work attributed to Saint-Memin. (*Photo courtesy of New York Public Library.*)

on steamboat navigation that gave them time to perfect their boat and its operation without financial trouble. Apparently Fulton had intended his boat for operation on the Mississippi, and although he later began operations there, the more profitable opportunity for the boat in New York waters diverted him at the time from any western navigation.

The exact dimensions of the boat as first built are unknown; one report gives her dimensions as 133 feet long, 16½ feet beam, and 7 feet deep. She was apparently a "Durham boat"; this type was used, with some variations in detail, in Pennsylvania, Ohio, and New York for inland water navigation under oars and sail—having a long, narrow, shoal, flat-bottomed hull with little sheer, the bottom straight or nearly so fore-and-aft and flat athwartships, the

sides somewhat flaring and sometimes curved vertically, the bilges angular, with chines, or very slightly rounded, and the stem and post raking, the stem sometimes having the same curve as the side frames. This form of hull was called a "praam" in some parts of Europe and was widely used there for craft operating in shallow water. When rebuilt in 1807–08 Fulton's vessel measured 149 feet between perpendiculars, 17 feet 11 inches beam, and 7 feet depth of hold. She does not appear ever to have been named *Clermont;* originally known as "The North River Steamboat of Clermont" she was registered after her rebuilding as the *North River*.

The model of this vessel in the Watercraft Collection was reconstructed for the Hudson-Fulton Celebration of 1907.

The second Fulton steamer, the *Raritan*, was built in 1808 by Charles Brown of New York after Fulton's design; a plan of this vessel has survived and shows that the Durham boat hull form was retained in her. The plan of the *Raritan* in Griffiths' *Marine and Naval Architecture* shows a flat-bottomed hull having a stem curved in profile, raking post, no rocker in the bottom, slight sheer, short and rather full entrance, and a short run. The stern is square and has the same type of platform used in the *North River*. The side frames amidships are straight vertically and the sides flare markedly. The crude plan shows that the side paddle wheels were housed and placed well forward and that the hull was trussed in way of the engine and boiler. The vessel was about 124 feet overall and 21 feet beam at the gunwale, and about 5 feet 6 inches headroom was allowed in the cabins. The wheels were about 15 feet in diameter and the paddles were about 3 feet 9 inches wide. (Custom-house dimensions: 124' x 21' x 6'8", 163⁹⁵⁄₉₅ tons, eagle figurehead, round tuck, square stern, no galleries.)

She was followed by the *Car of Neptune*, of 295 tons, 157 feet long on the bottom, 171 feet 6 inches on deck, 22 feet beam on the bottom, and 26 feet on deck. This vessel was built in 1808 by Brown, who also built the Fulton-designed *Paragon*, of 331 tons, in 1811. Another steamer, the *Firefly*, was built in 1812, as was a ferryboat of 118 tons, with ramps at each end.

Fulton also designed and supervised construction of the first steam man-of-war for the United States Navy, a catamaran with the paddle wheel between the hulls, 156 feet long, 56 feet beam and 20 feet deep. The paddle wheel was 16 feet diameter and the blades were 12 feet wide. The ship made 5½ miles per hour. Wood was used for fuel in these boats; the first known use of coal was in the *Car of Neptune* in 1816.

After Fulton's vessels had demonstrated the steamboat to be practical, a large number of steamers were built in the United States. Fulton's monopoly in New York did not last long, and his patents were worthless, so there were soon competitors. Speed in steamboats was important very early; the first race between steamers on the Hudson occurred in 1809. The first boats were all relatively narrow for their length but soon the beam was increased and the ends sharpened, to give a more easily driven form.

All the early American steamers were built for use in rivers or in relatively protected waters such as Long Island Sound, Delaware Bay, and the Chesapeake, the greatest number being built for river service. By 1832 Hudson River steamers were being built in lengths between 250 and 272 feet, with beam between 22 and 26 feet. Robert L. Stevens took much interest in the Hudson River steamers and through his experiments the models were much improved. In 1836 vessels for Long Island Sound were as large as 212 feet 6 inches long and 27 feet 10

RIGGED MODEL (USNM 309409) of a reconstruction of Robert Fulton's *North River*, commonly called the *Clermont*. The reconstruction was built for the Hudson-Fulton Celebration of 1909. For a view forward, see p. 126. (*Smithsonian photo 44957–a.*)

112

STEAMER BUILT FOR LIVINGSTON AND FULTON in 1811, the *Paragon*. She was the third steamboat built for the Hudson River service, and the fourth designed by Fulton. A flat-bottom vessel like the *Clermont* and *Raritan*, her register dimensions were 167′ x 26′10″ x 7′9″. She was built by Charles Brown. From D. T. Valentine's *Manual*, 1852. (*Smithsonian photo 44791–a.*)

inches beam. The construction of steamboats spread very rapidly; two had been built on the St. Lawrence by 1813. The first steamer for Mississippi River service was built in 1811. After about 1835 larger diameter side wheels with narrow blades came into use and experiments were made with blade shapes and feathering buckets or blades.

L. M'Kay in his *Practical Shipbuilder* shows the lines of a steamer of 1838, a sharp river vessel 173 feet long which he describes as "being only" that length, suggesting that she was small for the time and service. She was 161 feet between perpendiculars, 20 feet moulded beam and 12 feet 3 inches moulded depth. The plan shows a long, narrow, low, shoal-draft vessel diagonally strapped (apparently with iron) along her sides inboard above the bilge, straight sheer and keel, upright stem with rounded forefoot, vertical post, upper-and-lower transom, and round tuck. The midsection is formed with slightly rising straight floor, a low and hard bilge, and a vertical, straight topside. There is no flare at bow, the sections there being slightly V-shaped, with moderate curve from rabbet to rail. The entrance is very long and sharp, and convex, and the run is also long and very fine, but shorter than the entrance. The designed midship section is abaft midlength, about 64 feet from the after perpendicular, and the deadflat extends from here forward for about 12 feet.

The paddle-wheel shaft is about 61 feet from the after perpendicular and the wheel diameter is nearly 24 feet. The deckhouse extends from within some 6 feet of the extreme stern to about 109 feet forward, leaving a long forward maindeck uncovered by any structure; the small pilothouse is at the fore end of the deckhouse, on its roof. A large boat on davits was carried on each side, well aft. The side wheels were operated with a walking beam and the stacks and boilers were probably forward of this on the

guards, as in the *Empire of Troy*, to trim the boat. This plan is interesting in that it shows how early a good form had been developed in the Hudson River type of river steamer, a form that changed remarkably little for seventy years. By 1838 some river steamers were capable of a speed of 20 miles per hour.

Ocean Steamers

Americans were much slower than the English to develop ocean-going steamers. The need for swift river transportation over long distances and for coastal services in relatively protected waters was, of course, the reason why American steamers were built almost entirely for such work; sailing vessels that were large, well built, and cheap to operate, were already in use in the ocean trade and as ocean packets. In England there were no long navigable rivers and little protected water; the nearby Continent was the attractive destination which required open sea operation. Hence the early English steamers were designed for ocean service.

However, in 1818 an attempt was made to produce an American ocean-going steamer. In that year a company, formed under the name of the Savannah Steamship Company, of Savannah, Georgia, purchased a coastal packet ship under construction at New York by Francis Fickett; one of the leading builders of this class of vessel. The ship was fitted with an inclined, direct-acting, low-pressure 90-horse-power engine made by Stephen Vail at the Speedwell Iron Works at Morristown, New Jersey. The boilers were made by Dod, at Elizabeth, New Jersey.

Side paddle wheels without wheelboxes were fitted; and as it was expected that the ship would have trouble with the wheels in heavy weather, these were designed to be readily dismounted at sea. Each wheel had eight arms pivoted to the hub flanges; on these

113

flanges were two fixed arms with blades. To keep the pivoted arms open, a chain was secured to the arms near the blades, from arm to arm. Thus the paddle wheel could be folded fanwise in two sections, one on each side of the hub and parallel to the load line. In addition, the folded wheels could be uncoupled and lifted on deck. The stack had a movable hood or elbow which was intended to be rotated to prevent sparks reaching the rigging.

This ship was named the *Savannah;* when complete she was taken to Savannah, Georgia, and she sailed from there May 22, 1819, for Liverpool, England, where she arrived on June 20. She did not steam the whole distance, sailing most of the way. Under steam, in smooth water, she could make but 5 or 6 knots and had insufficient fuel capacity. The vessel visited Sweden and Russia and then returned to Savannah. The venture was unsuccessful financially, and therefore the engine and boilers were removed and the ship employed as a sailing packet between Savannah and New York until her loss by stranding on Fire Island, off Bellport, Long Island, in 1821. She was apparently a typical packet ship and quite fast under sail; her low-powered engine was rather ineffective so far as speed was concerned.

The only drawings of the ship that have been found are of the engine and wheels, and of the ship's profile above the waterline; these are contained in the *Mémoire sur les Bateaux a Vapeur des États-Unis d'Amérique,* by the French naval constructor Marestier, who in 1824 made a report on American steamers. The Marestier drawings show that an existing rigged model of this ship in the Watercraft Collection, of the U. S. National Museum, and also a picture accompanying it, do not represent correctly the ship or her details.

The next attempt to build a commercial steamer for ocean trade in the United States was in 1843, when the *Massachusetts,* of 751 tons, was fitted as an auxiliary packet ship for service between Boston and Europe. This ship was fitted with an Ericsson screw (abaft the rudder) which pivoted on a strut that allowed the wheel to be swung sidewise and upward to above the load line for sailing, the propeller shaft being off center and alongside the sternpost. The ship was a regular packet model of good form, 157 feet 5 inches between perpendiculars, 32 feet moulded beam, and 20 feet depth of hold, built by Hall, at Boston, Massachusetts. Her stack was between the main and mizzen mast on a long quarterdeck that reached almost to the mainmast. The ship was not

a financial success, for auxiliary steamers were usually unable to compete with sailing vessels in ocean trade, not only because of their higher initial cost but also because the auxiliary cost more to operate. The *Massachusetts* was sold to the U. S. Government and became a storeship, with her engine removed, under the name *Farralones.* Later she became a merchant ship under the name *Alaska,* in the wheat trade.

In 1847 two ocean-going steamers, the *Washington* and *Hermann,* of 230 and 241 feet length on deck respectively; side-wheel auxiliary steamers; were built at New York for the New York and Europe packet run. These were subsidized by mail contracts. Two more steamers, the *Franklin* and *Humbolt,* side-wheel auxiliaries 263 and 292 feet long on deck, respectively, were built in New York in 1850 for the New York to Bremen run. They were employed in the Le Havre run, however. In 1847 the Webb-built steamer *United States* entered the trans-Atlantic service also. With the establishment of these projects, a steam packet line to Liverpool was set up by Edward K. Collins.

With mail contracts available and with the intent of producing steamers that could serve as men-of-war when necessary, Collins built four side-wheel steamers; the *Arctic, Atlantic, Baltic,* and *Pacific.* These ships, of over 2700 tons and larger than competing English steamers then in the North-Atlantic service, were all about 280 feet or more on the main deck and made the run to Europe, or the return voyage, on an average of 11 days 3 hours. The ships were built at New York, the *Arctic* and *Atlantic* by William H. Brown under the supervision of Henry and George Steers, who probably designed them, and the *Baltic* and *Pacific* by Brown and Bell.

The *Arctic* was lost, with heavy loss of life, through a collision at sea in 1854 and the *Pacific* disappeared in 1856 on the way home from Liverpool. Collins in 1855 replaced the *Arctic* with the *Adriatic,* a huge wooden sidewheeler, designed by the Steers brothers, of over 4000 tons, 345 feet long, and 50 feet beam. She once ran from St. Johns, Newfoundland, to Galway, Ireland, in 5 days, 19¾ hours and would have been capable of making the New York to Liverpool run in a few hours over 8 days. The withdrawal of the mail contracts by the U. S. Government in 1857, a year of great economic depression, put the American steamship lines out of business, for the British continued to subsidize their steamer lines.

Commodore W. K. Vanderbilt for a short time beginning in 1856 operated a single steamer, the *Vanderbilt,* in the European run and afterwards added two more ships to the run, but this line was not profitable and the ships were withdrawn. After the Civil War, in 1866, a Boston to Liverpool line was established with the *Erie* and *Ontario*, two large screw steamers built at Newburyport, Massachusetts; however, the English operators soon lowered their freight rates and after a few voyages this line also withdrew. In 1873 the Pennsylvania Railroad Company began operation from Philadelphia to Liverpool with four iron steamers built by Cramp, at Philadelphia, and in 1874–75 a number of iron steamers were built at Chester, Pennsylvania, for the trans-Pacific trade and two were built for a short-lived South American trade run. Other individual ships were built for ocean trade. Steel slowly replaced iron in United States shipbuilding beginning about 1878.

York. The next steamer was built on the Canadian side, and the third steamer on the American side, the *Walk-in-the-Water* at Black Rock, New York, in 1818. These were followed by other steamers and in the next 10 years about 20 steamers were afloat on the Lakes. When the Welland Canal was opened, soon after 1829, the width and length of its locks fixed limits to the dimensions of steamers and sailing vessels alike for many years, particularly after 1831. The construction of large steamers began about 1845, when fast side-wheelers were built for the passenger trade. After 1857 propellers rather than side paddle wheels were used, the first being on the *Vandalia*, built in 1841 at Oswego, New York.

The growing trade in iron ore, grain, lumber, and coal produced a special type of lake steamer whose

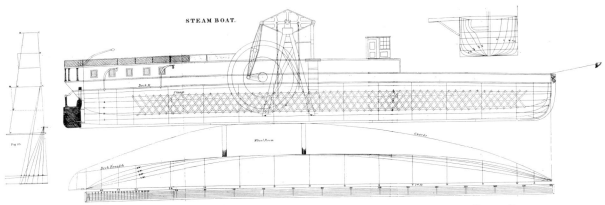

PLAN OF A SMALL HUDSON RIVER STEAMER OF ABOUT 1838, SHOWING DIAGONAL STRAPPING AND SHARP-ENDED FORM. After plate 7, in L. M'Kay, *Practical shipbuilder*, New York, 1838.

The American steamers of the 1840's and 1850's were of a distinctive national character, but those built of iron and steel, after the Civil War, of necessity resembled English steamers, for Britain had taken the lead in producing such ships. American production of seagoing steamers was very limited until the first World War when a large number of freighters were built and a few passenger vessels as well. From then to the second World War the number of American-built ocean steamers steadily increased in all classes.

Inland and Coastal Steamers

Coastal and inland steamers developed rapidly in the United States after Fulton had shown that serviceable steamboats were possible. On the Great Lakes steamboat construction began in 1816 with the *Ontario*, of 232 tons, built at Sackett's Harbor, New

dimensions were controlled by the changes made in the Welland Canal and by other restrictions. This vessel had its machinery well aft; it was a flat-floored, wall-sided, rather straight-sheered vessel with short, full ends; the hull was long and narrow and was heavily trussed to give longitudinal strength. The design was largely established by the steam barge, which had a long and narrow, full-ended hull of moderate sheer with short counter, usually round or elliptical, a vertical straight stem, and was schooner rigged with two to four masts, but without a bowsprit. The engine and boiler was right aft, where there was a 2-deck superstructure. Many of the barges carried topmasts and some of the 4-masters had no sail on the after mast, it being employed as a derrick mast only.

About 1880 wooden shipbuilding became very expensive on the Lakes and there was a gradual shift to iron and then to steel construction. Late in that decade the use of sail on lake steamers went out of

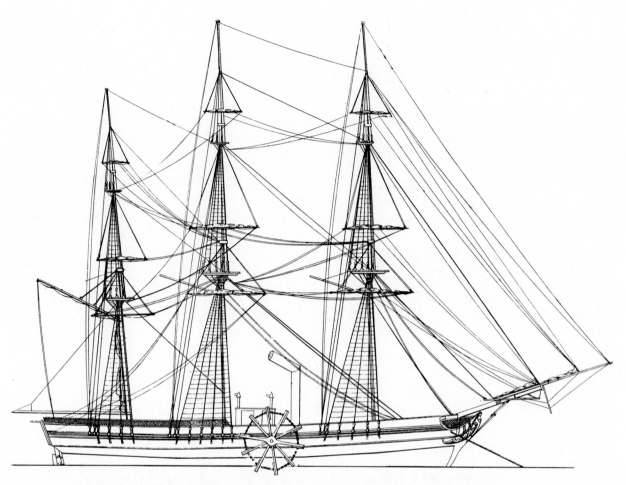

FIRST STEAMSHIP TO CROSS THE ATLANTIC, the *Savannah*, as drawn by the French naval constructor Marestier in 1820 and published in 1824 in his report on American steamers. (*Smithsonian photo 45434–a.*)

fashion and within a few years the forerunner of the modern ore and bulk cargo carrier of the Lakes appeared, with pilothouse right forward and the engine, boiler, fuel, and a deckhouse for crew's quarters at the extreme stern.

The steamboats of the Ohio and Mississippi and their tributaries have had a remarkable development. Fulton and Livingston had built the *Orleans* at Pittsburgh in 1811 in hopes of obtaining a monopoly in steam navigation on the Ohio as they had on New York waters. The *Orleans* was fitted with side paddle wheels and was of about 200 tons, measured for register. She was fitted with masts and sails. The hull was probably like that of the *Raritan* in form; the cabins were in the hold and there were port holes in the sides. According to a contemporary description, the vessel had one stack and no superstructure.

A stern-wheeler, the *Comet* was built at Pittsburgh in 1813. Fulton built the *Vesuvius* there in that year,

and steamboat construction soon spread along the Monongahela and the Ohio, the boats gradually increasing in power as they began to take the now well known form of the Mississippi River steamboat. Racing of these steamers began in about 1830, the size of vessels rapidly increased as it had on the Hudson, and after about 1839 cabins on top of the deckhouse came into fashion and high-pressure boilers were usually installed. On the lower Ohio and on the Mississippi the side-wheeler was popular; on the upper Ohio and on the tributaries the stern-wheeler was preferred.

By 1852 steamers on the lower rivers had become very large. The *Eclipse*, built that year, was 363 feet long, 36 feet beam and 9 feet deep; she was capable of making 16 miles per hour against the current, so that her speed in still water must have been about 19–20 miles per hour. In model such side-wheelers were shallow hulls having a straight keel, a curved and slightly raking stem, short vertical post with

116

round counter, the entrance sharp and long, and the run long and easy. The midsection was formed with little or no rise to the floor, a firm round bilge, and some flare in the straight topside. The side wheels were abaft midlength and were 40 to 42 feet in diameter, covered by wheelhouses, or wheelboxes, the latter name being the shipbuilders' term. Vessels such as the *Eclipse* had a cabin atop the main deck-house with a pilothouse on the cabin roof abaft the stacks, which were two abreast. These river packets were well finished and fitted; they attracted much attention at home and abroad. Stern-wheelers of somewhat lesser size and magnificence were built on the Ohio and Missouri and innumerable small side-wheel and stern-wheel freighters were built.

During the Civil War some river steamers were converted to ironclad gunboats by both the Federal and Confederate navies. The construction of iron vessels began on the upper Mississippi and Ohio during the war, though iron vessels had been built at Pittsburgh as early as 1840. After the war, large river steamers, including the famed *Robert E. Lee* and the *Natchez*, were built, and the river trade boomed.

Stern-wheel towboats had been built on the Ohio in the 1840's, and after the Civil War these grew in size and power, as the river barge traffic increased. By 1880 highly developed stern-wheel towboats or "push-boats" were being built of wood or iron and steel; the bow was long and sharp and the run short and straight, or formed with a tunnel with skegs at the sides. Early in the 20th century the tunnel-stern screw-propelled boats were developed, and these have taken the place of stern-wheelers, particularly after the introduction of the diesel engine.

In the last 45 years great efforts have been made to develop better river craft and to improve the rivers for inland navigation, with the result that towboats are now of even greater power than the old steamers and can draw more water, which allows the use of screw propellers, many modern boats having as many as four. Few major changes, other than the tunnel stern, have been introduced to alter the basic hull design of river craft, already well developed at the time of the Civil War.

The number of steamers in the coasting trade in the East gradually increased after the Civil War. Vessels were built for coastwise passenger service, and those intended for such voyages as from New York to Charleston, Savannah, or Jacksonville, resembled the oceangoing steamers of their time and were usually screw propelled. The side-wheelers remained popular in some coastal trades for a few years after the Civil War, but the screw gradually replaced them. Many notable steamers were built for the Long Island

SIDE-PADDLE-WHEEL STEAMER *Fulton*, from a French print in the Watercraft Collection (USNM 160010). Built by Smith and Dimon in 1856 for the New York-Le Havre service, her register dimensions were 290′ x 42′4″ x 31′6″, 2,300 tons. She was broken up in 1861. (*Smithsonian photo 44638-e.*)

SHIPYARD OF THE NEW ENGLAND SHIPBUILDING COMPANY, Bath, Maine, in 1890. Under construction is the steamer *Portland*, lost with all hands November 26–27, 1898 in a storm that became known as the "Portland Gale." A 3-masted coaster is building in background. (*Smithsonian photo 44792–e.*)

Sound service, New York to Fall River for example. After 1880 few wooden steamers were built, and the then still popular iron vessels soon gave way to steel. Vessels employed as freighters were the last coasting steamers to be built of wood.

The Pacific Coast shipbuilding industry was late in developing and it was not until after the Civil War that many yards were established. The shipbuilders and carpenters were mainly from the East, and in the 1880's the yards were producing from native timber vessels having local characteristics. The sailing craft of the Pacific Coast were often very handsome and some were notable sailers. Likewise, the Pacific Coast shipbuilders produced for both coastal and ocean trade, a number of very fine wooden steamers whose form was much admired at home and in Europe. Steel shipbuilding did not become well established on the Pacific Coast until the 1890's.

On the Gulf of Mexico shipbuilding was largely centered at New Orleans and the nearby region. In the years after the War of 1812, New Orleans shipyards had produced small, fast sailing vessels of the Baltimore-clipper type and a few freighting vessels of fuller model. After 1825 a few small steamers were also produced, but after the Civil War shipbuilding almost ceased and only small craft were built—luggers, sloops, schooners, scows, barges, and tugs.

In the 1890's some of the coastal trades began to feel the competition of the railroads, as did some of the river steamship lines, and between 1888 and 1910 the railroads obtained control of many lines, as well as many ferries, liquidating those that competed with their rail traffic. Some roads laid their rails up both banks of a river to cut off the steamers from their shore connections, and thus force them to cease operations. A common practice was to purchase a controlling interest in a coastal or river steamship line and then, by raising the water freight rates, put the line out of business. Another practice was for the railways to reduce their freight rates to a ruinous level, so that the steamship lines had to cease operations, for they were commonly small companies dependent upon a limited area of coast for their income whereas the railways, drawing support from operations elsewhere, could take a loss in a limited area for a long period.

118

After 1918 the improvement of highways and the use of automobile trucks and, later, of prime-movers and trailers, not only gave serious competition to the railroads but also to the remaining small-vessel coasting trades. By 1935 the trucking operators had eliminated the small-vessel coasters in nearly all areas, and the American coasting trades were practically extinct. All that now remains of these once prosperous operations are some small coastal tanker runs and a moderate amount of barge transportation on the intercoastal waterways. Highway competition with door-to-door delivery on the one hand and controlled freight rates on the other have prevented any rebirth of the coasting trades, even at times when governmental stimulus is being given the ocean freight trades.

Special Types

Several of the many special types of steamers developed in various parts of the United States require particular mention. Tugboats in great numbers were built in the United States after steamboat construction started. The earliest steamers built for towing were small side-wheelers built in the 1830's and employed to do harbor towing and to supply ships with fresh water; two of these were in service at New York in 1839. In the 1840's a large number of side-wheel steamers were built as towboats and the hull form and fittings of such boats became somewhat standardized. The early side-wheel tug usually had a low-sided hull with sharp ends; the wheels were abaft midlength and the boat was fitted with a deckhouse extending from about a quarter the length of the hull abaft the stem to a little more than that short of the stern. The pilothouse might be either part of this superstructure but somewhat raised or a small house atop the deckhouse. The boats usually had one stack and the hulls had heavy guards. Some old river steamers were cut down in their old age and converted to towboats, with reduced superstructures. Screw tugs were built in the late 1840's but powerful paddle-wheel tugs remained quite numerous until after the Civil War.

The first vessel to have Ericsson screw propellers in America was the small iron steamer *Robert F. Stockton*, built at Lairds, Birkenhead, Liverpool, England, in 1838 for the private account of Captain Robert F. Stockton, U.S.N. This vessel had twin screws. After running her trials she was fitted as a topsail schooner and was brought to the United States

where, in 1840, she was sold to the Delaware and Raritan Canal Company and, shorn of her sailing rig, was employed as a tug on the canal and on the Delaware and Schuylkill Rivers. She was capable of 11 to 12 miles per hour running free and could tow four scow coal-barges at 5½ miles per hour. The success of this boat as a tug undoubtedly influenced many to build screw tugs, and soon after the end of the Civil War the standard American harbor tug had been developed. This had a rather narrow deep-draft hull, having drag to the keel, a more or less upright stem with rounded forefoot, a nearly vertical post, round or elliptical counter, strong sheer, sharp ends, a rising straight floor at the midsection, with a firm round bilge and a slight tumble-home in the topside. A long deckhouse was placed on the main deck; the pilothouse might be part of this or be mounted on the deckhouse roof. Usually the boats had a single stack and two pole masts, but a few large tugs used in coastal towing had two stacks and some had a schooner rig without a bowsprit. American builders of tugs had developed great skill in the design of these craft and by 1875 there were many fine wooden tugs at Boston, New York, and elsewhere on the coast.

Various attempts to build high-speed passenger steamers in the United States were made in the 1850's. George Steers and John W. Griffiths each prepared designs for "7-day steamers" intended to cross the Atlantic either way in less than a full week. A vessel was started from Griffith's design but was not completed as planned and so was not suitable for such a run. In appearance the two designs were somewhat similar to the cross-channel express steamers the British had begun building, but the American ships were to have been larger, more powerful and faster than any channel steamer then afloat. However, the high speed reached in river steamers led to the construction of some fast coastal passenger ships as early as the 1830's. In the 1880's and 1890's some very large and fast Long Island Sound steamers were built as well as some express boats for the Chesapeake.

On the Lakes, in the 1890's the curious "whaleback" freighters were built; their hulls were rather cigarshaped with a pilothouse and deckhouse forward and another deckhouse aft, over the engine and boilers. These boats were intended to cheat the tonnage laws and had a short vogue; they all were built of steel, and all but one of these ships were bulk carriers.

After the first World War liquor smuggling became very active on the coasts of the United States and many fast motorboats were built for this illegal business. These boats were often 50 to 125 feet long; long, low straight-sheered boats capable of high speed and fitted with high-speed gasoline engines of great power. Some large boats were double-enders and of moderate speed; these brought cargoes to offshore rendezvous where they were met by fast "runners" which attempted to land the cargoes clandestinely. Liquor smuggling became highly organized during the 1920's and in this respect resembled the organized smuggling in Britain at the end of the 18th century.

Engineering and Design

In the period directly after the Civil War the maritime interests of the United States had reached a low ebb, yet a great deal of ingenuity was being shown in marine engineering and shipbuilding. In the 1870's Americans were experimenting with cycloidal propulsion and geared propeller shafting; quick-steaming and "flash" boilers and high-speed reciprocating engines were produced. Many patents were granted to American inventors for improvements in marine engineering and for deck equipment.

The introduction of gasoline engines into marine propulsion occurred in the last quarter of the 19th century. There is evidence that the earliest application of the gasoline engine in the marine field was at San Francisco, California, where Daniel Regan and Mora Barrett began to build and sell marine gasoline

engines sometime in the 1880's. These were small engines. In the 1890's a large number of experimenters were at work developing gasoline and kerosene engines and by 1906 a large number of practical engines were on the market.

During the first two decades of the 20th century gasoline and kerosene engines gradually replaced steam in small commercial craft. These motors were particularly suited for auxiliary power in schooners, fishing and coasting. As increased power became available, these engines were employed in other small craft.

The use of oil engines in American commercial craft developed most rapidly after the introduction of the diesel engine. At the present time practically all small commercial craft, ferries, tugs, small coastal tankers, excursion boats, and small freighters, as well as most fishing craft above launch size, are now diesel powered. However, large diesel-powered ships are less popular in the American merchant marine than abroad and relatively few such vessels have been built in this country.

The development of the geared-turbine propeller drive and the introduction of oil-burning boilers early in the 20th century were perhaps the most important improvements before the first World War. The American merchant marine was not in a state to play much part in the development of these until during the first World War, when the American merchant marine was quickly expanded. Since that time the use of reciprocating engines has almost ceased in large American vessels, though in the

RIGGED MODEL (USNM 203712) made in the National Museum about 1900, to represent the popular concept of the appearance of the first steamboat Fitch tried out on the Delaware River, in July 1786. (*Smithsonian photo 26756–k.*)

second World War the need of quick expansion of the merchant fleet caused these to be employed in the "Liberty Ships." The modern American merchant marine employs the turbine-electric drive as well as geared turbines, and marine engineering has reached a high level of effectiveness in the United States.

Though the speed of ships has increased, much of this increase has been due to improved powering and engineering rather than to better hull design. The difficulties in designing an efficient hull were recognized very early in the development of modern naval architecture. In Europe, in the 17th and 18th centuries, the idea was put forward of using models of ships to predetermine the performance of full-sized vessels and a number of experiments were made; in 1721 the first known proposal for the use of towed models was made by Swedenborg but without effect. About the middle of the 18th century Chapman, an eminent Swedish naval architect, carried out some model experiments. Others were Bird in 1756, Benjamin Franklin in 1764, and d'Alembert, Condorcet, and Bossut, who built a test tank in 1775 at the Paris École Militaire; this was operated at least until 1779 and perhaps longer. In 1790 a "Society for the Improvement of Naval Architecture" was formed in England and between 1793 and 1798 Beaufoy carried out experiments for the Society in the Greenland Dock at London which were reported privately in 1799. Charles Gore continued these experiments and reported upon the effect of length in proportion to beam; he designed a large, 3-mast lugger to illustrate the application of the results of his tests.

About 1830 Alexander Hall and Company, at Aberdeen, Scotland, established a private model-testing tank and as a result of experiments this firm built some very fast sailing vessels. At about the same time Robert L. Stevens was carrying out extensive model testing at New York with both sailing and towed models; using the latter method he also experimented with steamboat hull forms. Other experimenters used model testing in various ways; among them William Froude, who began testing models privately in 1862–63. In 1870, obtaining aid from the British Admiralty, he established a model testing tank at Torquay. Froude's work and general methods may be said to have established the basis for modern model-testing techniques. In 1886 a larger tank was built in England; by that time one was in use in Holland and another in Scotland.

The first model tank in the United States was established at the Washington Navy Yard in 1900 and was operated under the supervision of Rear Admiral David W. Taylor. Since that time many model-testing tanks have been established in this country, at the University of Michigan, Northwestern University, Webb Institute of Naval Architecture, Massachusetts Institute of Technology, Stevens Institute of Technology, Newport News Shipbuilding Company, and the very large testing facility operated by the United States Navy at Carderock, Maryland—the David Taylor Model Basin.

The use of these test facilities has raised the standards of boat and ship design in the United States. Although there is still much to be done, not only in tests but in improvement of testing technique, American designers now have facilities for scientific study equal or superior to any country in the world.

Catalog of the Collection—Merchant Steam

JOHN FITCH'S STEAMBOAT, 1786
RIGGED MODEL, USNM 203712

This model was made in the Museum to represent the first steamboat Fitch tried out in July 1786 on the Delaware River. The boat is supposed to have been about 34 feet long and was propelled by two banks of oars, one on each side, operated by a ratchet-chain-and-drum drive. In August 1786 a second boat, 45 feet long and 8 feet beam, was begun and in 1788 a third boat, 60 feet long and 12 feet beam, was

launched. A fourth boat was started in 1790 but was wrecked before its trials and never repaired. The third boat ran as a packet between Philadelphia and Trenton. She is described as having stern oars, as indicated in the drawing for the French patent granted Fitch (see p. 109). This is apparently the steamboat referred to by a Philadelphia newspaper. She was named *Experiment*.

In its issue of Monday, July 26, 1790, the Federal Gazette and Philadelphia Daily Advertiser had the following notice: "*The Steamboat* sets out tomorrow at

10 o'clock from Arch Street Ferry, in order to take passengers from Burlington, Bristol, Bordentown and Trenton, and return the next day." It is probable that the maintenance of Fitch's boats caused much trouble and expense, for the steamboat packet service appears to have lasted only three or four months and then was not resumed.

The model represents a double-ended open boat having a straight keel, raking curved stem, raking straight post with rudder hung on it, moderate sheer, sharp entrance and run, midsection with some rise in the floor, firm round bilge, and an upright topside. There is no authority to be found for the hull form of this model; the engine in it does not agree with contemporary descriptions.

The model scales 34 feet overall length, 8 feet beam,

and 3 feet 6 inches depth; the oars six to a side, are each 12 feet long. Scale of model 2 inches to the foot.

The boat was driven by the oars, which were stroked by a crank and rod arrangement, the crank being driven by a gear and endless chain operated by the engine. The many moving parts in this mode of propulsion, as well as the crude workmanship common to machinery of the period, must have made maintenance difficult, so that in a short time the boats became unreliable.

The model was made in the Museum.

JAMES RUMSEY'S STEAMBOAT, 1787
RIGGED MODEL, USNM 203711

This model is a reconstruction of the steamboat that James Rumsey of Berkeley Springs, Virginia,

RIGGED MODEL (USNM 203711) of reconstruction of James Rumsey's steamboat. His vessel was built in 1787 and tested in 1788 on the upper Potomac River near Berkeley Springs. (*Smithsonian photo 44440.*)

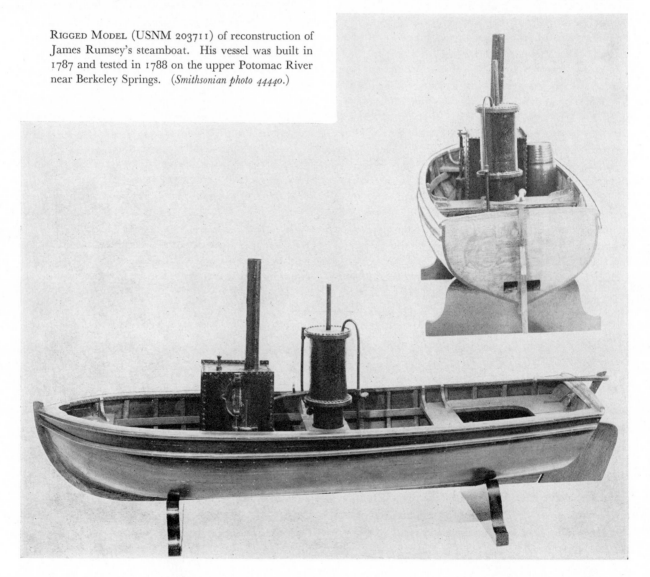

122

invented in 1787 and experimented with the following year on the Potomac River. The boat was driven by a steam pump on the hydraulic-jet principle and its trials appear to have been considered successful. Rumsey is usually credited with inventing this boat in 1784 but recent research indicates that his first boat was probably mechanically propelled and intended to demonstrate only a mode of propulsion employing setting poles. After Rumsey completed the tests of his steamboat he went to England and obtained backing that permitted him to start construction of another boat there. However, he died before it was completed. The boat was tried out on the Thames by his backers but the demonstration did not impress onlookers enough to create any great interest, and nothing developed from this final experiment.

Supposed to represent the second boat, built for the Potomac River trials, the model is no more than a rowboat somewhat like a contemporary ship's longboat, having a full entrance, a short and heavy run, and a square stern with the rudder hung outboard. The engine and other details are not in agreement with contemporary descriptions. The authority for the form of the model is unknown. Scale of model is 2 inches to the foot.

The model was made in the Museum.

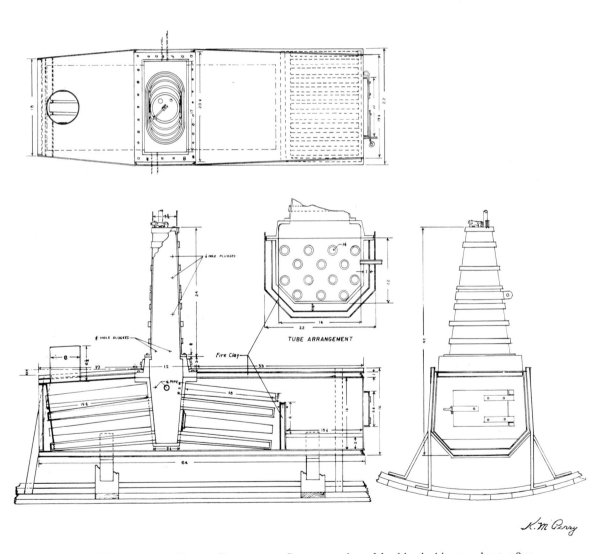

SCALE DRAWING OF MULTITUBULAR BOILER DESIGNED BY STEVENS and used by him in his steamboat, 1804. Original boiler (USNM 181179) is in the Watercraft Collection. (*Smithsonian photo 45368.*)

STEVENS' MULTITUBULAR BOILER, and STEAM ENGINE, 1804
FULL-SIZED MACHINERY, USNM 181179

The machinery consists of the original boiler and engine employed in a twin-screw steamboat designed by Colonel John Stevens and built at Hoboken, New Jersey, in 1803–04. The boat was tested in in New York Harbor in May 1804, when a speed of 4 miles per hour was obtained.

The boiler is of the multitubular design patented by Stevens in 1791 and 1803, having 28 copper tubes each $1\frac{1}{2}$ inches in diameter and 18 inches long. The boiler has a small rectangular chest, 14 tubes project from each of two sides of it. The grate is at one end of the projecting tubes; the heat passes around these, under the chest, and then around the tubes at the opposite end and to the smokestack. The Stevens boiler was designed for higher pressure than the Watts boilers used in England, and his boilers were the forerunners of the American high-pressure boilers used later on American locomotives and steamboats.

The engine is a single-cylinder, high-pressure type, having a cylinder $4\frac{1}{2}$ inches in diameter and a stroke of 9 inches, noncondensing and fast turning. The engine and propeller shafts are in one unit.

The difficulties that discouraged Stevens from following up the tests of 1804 with a larger boat can be understood by inspection of the engine and boiler. Both are crudely built. There were at that time neither tools nor skilled workmen in the United States that would enable him to produce machinery and boilers well enough made to withstand high-pressure steam and to produce the speed of engine revolution desirable in Stevens' plan of using twin-screw propulsion.

In 1844 the boiler and engine were repaired, only defects in workmanship being corrected and these were identified by being painted yellow. Many of these defects were in soldered pipe joints. Some worn parts were duplicated and replaced. A test was then made, on the Hudson in October 1844, of the machinery installed in a new hull, and a speed of 8 miles per hour was obtained.

The exhibit was preserved in the Stevens Institute from 1844 until it was exhibited in the World's Columbian Exposition in 1892, after which it was transferred to the Smithsonian Institution and placed in the Watercraft Collection.

STEVENS' SCREW PROPELLER, 1804–05
FULL-SIZED COPY, USNM 180597

This full-sized copy of an experimental screw propeller designed by John Stevens complies with a description written by Stevens to Dr. Robert Hare of Philadelphia, Pennsylvania, dated November 16, 1805. The wheel has blades separately attached to the hub by a bar or shank fitting into a hole in the hub. The pitch could be adjusted by turning the blade on its shank and the wheel could be tried with two or four blades.

Stevens had made numerous trials of the screw propeller, using manually operated cranks to turn the propellers, before attempting his steam engine trials of 1804. Stevens' letter to Dr. Hare shows he knew the value of pitch in propeller design as well as the desirability of curved faces on the blades as opposed to flat surfaces. Stevens tests apparently included a long screw but before his twin-screw tests of 1804, he had concluded that this modern-style short screw was the better.

Purchased.

STEVENS' TWIN-SCREW STEAMBOAT, 1804
RIGGED MODEL, USNM 160306

This is a model representing a twin-screw steamboat designed by Colonel John Stevens and built at Hoboken, New Jersey, in 1803–04. The steamboat was tried in the spring of 1804 in New York Harbor and made a speed of 4 miles per hour. The great difficulties Stevens met in the construction of the high-pressure, fast-turning engine, required for his screw propulsion, discouraged his work in this direction, and he turned to paddle-wheel propulsion in his first large steamboat, the *Phoenix*.

The model may not represent the form and appearance of the orginal boat accurately but the model's boiler and engine, etc., are based on the original machinery now preserved in the Watercraft Collection (USNM 181179).

The model is of an open boat having a straight keel and skeg, curved stem, rather upright flat transom, nearly straight sheer, rather full entrance and run, twin screws set abaft the post, and with the iron rudder set off from the transom on outriggers to clear the wheels. Engine and boiler are located a little abaft amidships. The boat is rather flat floored, with a firm round bilge and upright side. No drawings or pictures of the original boat exist and all that is known about the hull is that it was of a then common rowing Whitehall type, which this model does not represent, being probably of a longer boat.

Under the direction of Colonel Stevens' sons, the boiler and engine were overhauled in 1844 by Isaac Dripps, who was Superintendent of Machinery on the Camden and Amboy Railroad and afterwards held the same position on the Pennsylvania Railroad. He was under strict orders not to change or improve upon the original but merely to correct damaged parts. A new hull was built, and in October 1844 boat and machinery were tested on the Hudson River; a speed of 8 miles per hour was obtained.

The model represents a boat 24 feet 8 inches overall, 6 feet 1 inch beam, 4 feet 11 inches width of transom, 2 feet 4⅛ inches depth. Scale of model is 2 inches to the foot.

Model made in the Museum.

Engine and Boiler (USNM 181179) Designed by John Stevens and used in his first steamboat, tested in New York Harbor, 1804. The propeller (USNM 180597) is a full-sized replica of the one used in tests in 1804–05. (*Smithsonian photo 6151.*)

RIGGED MODEL USNM 309409. Reconstruction of the *North River*, commonly called the *Clermont*, built for the Hudson-Fulton Celebration of 1909. For a view aft, see p. 112. (*Smithsonian photo 44957.*)

ROBERT FULTON'S STEAMBOAT, 1807–08
RIGGED MODEL, USNM 309401

North River, ex *Clermont*

This model, an attempt at reconstruction of Robert Fulton's steamboat *Clermont* after her rebuilding during the winter of 1807–08, represents the full-sized reconstruction made for the Hudson-Fulton Celebration in 1907. The rebuilding corrected faults in both machinery and in hull revealed by the experimental runs started in August 1807 and alterations were made.

The model shows a "praam" type vessel, flat bottomed athwartships and fore-and-aft, having chines instead of a round bilge. The sides are slightly flaring and in section these are apparently all on the same moderate curve. There is a shallow external keel. The stem is nearly upright and slightly curved, the post straight and raking. At the stern is a false counter, made by a "bustle," a structure somewhat like the "patent stern" of the later Chesapeake Bay bugeyes, that makes the sharp stern into a square stern at deck, the stern structure ending in a wide, shallow, rectangular transom with the whole of the false counter being well above the load line. The sheer is almost straight and the entrance convex and sharp, the run the same but finer. An open rail along the sheer is formed by a turned-stanchion-and-cap-rail. The vessel is decked; forward is a low cabin trunk and the foremast, the latter with topmast, yard,

gaff, and boom. About amidships is the engine space, with engine, boilers, and drive machinery. The gear-driven fixed-blade paddle wheels are just forward of midlength and the high stack just abaft midlength. The paddle wheels have no guards or wheelboxes; after her rebuilding guards and wheelboxes were fitted. Aft is a long, low cabin trunk and the mainmast, which has only a boom and gaff. A tiller is right aft. The vessel appears long, low, and narrow.

This model is in error in not having guards and wheelboxes, in having outboard flywheels, and in the omission of leeboards. The eagle figurehead has also been omitted.

The register dimensions of the *North River*, as the *Clermont* was renamed after the rebuilding of 1807–08, were 149 feet between perpendiculars, 17 feet 11 inches extreme beam, and 7 feet depth in hold. Scale of model is ¼ inch to the foot.

From the Hudson River Day Line.

STEAMBOAT, 1807–09
RIGGED MODEL, USNM 160303

Phoenix

This model is a reconstruction of the steamboat *Phoenix* that was built under the personal supervision of Col. John Stevens in 1807–09. Originally the vessel had a crosshead engine with twin condensing cylinders, 16 inches in diameter and 36 inches stroke. The boiler was set in brickwork and was a cylindrical shell with one return flue. After making the run from

CONTEMPORARY VIEW OF FULTON'S STEAMBOAT (see also p. 111). The *North River* after her reconstruction in 1807–08, with leeboards and figurehead omitted. From a watercolor said to have been made by Simeon De Witt under the supervision of the *North River's* engineer. (*Smithsonian photo 37977.*)

Sandy Hook to Philadelphia in the summer of 1808 the double cylinders were replaced by a single cylinder 24 inches in diameter and a flywheel was added to the engine. The *Phoenix* was under construction soon after Fulton returned from Europe with the engine made for him by Watt in 1806; the third steam engine that Britain allowed to be exported; which Fulton used in the *Clermont*. As a result of having the English engine Fulton was able to complete and test his boat a short time before Stevens could fit out the *Phoenix* and therefore obtained a monopoly of steam navigation in New York waters. Stevens sent the *Phoenix* to Philadelphia by sea, making her the first steamboat to navigate in American coastal waters, and very generously gave credit to Fulton as the first to apply paddle wheels to a steamboat and the first to produce a useful vessel, in spite of his own lengthy pioneering work with steam propulsion. Stevens had primary interest in the screw propeller, but his inability to build a good engine with the tools and workmen available in the United States had caused him to turn to paddle wheels in the *Phoenix*.

The *Phoenix*, which had been employed as a packet between Philadelphia and Trenton since her arrival on the Delaware River in 1808, was wrecked in 1814 near Trenton, New Jersey.

The model shows a steamboat having side paddle wheels in wheel boxes protected fore and aft by short overhanging guards, the wheels slightly forward of midlength, a straight keel, stem curved and raking, with small gammon knee head, an upright post, and a round tuck, and an upper-and-lower transom square stern. The entrance is moderately sharp and the run rather short but straight. The midsection is formed with a slight rise in the straight floor, a hard turn of bilge, and a rather upright topside. The sheer is moderate and the hull is flush-decked, with a small pilot house forward, a single stack of very small diameter, and the companionway to cabins well aft. Square ports are shown in the sides of the hull.

Rigged with two masts, with a square course on the foremast and a boomed gaff-sail on the mainmast.

The *Phoenix* was about 101 feet long on deck, 16 feet beam, and 6 feet 9 inches depth. Scale of model is ½ inch to the foot.

Made in the Museum from a supposedly contemporary picture of the vessel; the data on which the model was built was inadequate. The hull is very poorly formed, and in this respect, at least, the model is undoubtedly incorrect.

SIDE-WHEEL STEAMER, 1816
RIGGED MODEL USNM 316742

Chancellor Livingston

The *Chancellor Livingston* was built by Henry Eckford at New York for Robert Fulton and asso-

127

ciates, the North River Steamboat Company, and was launched in 1816. She was the last vessel for which Fulton planned; he died early in 1815. The hull was designed by Eckford in consultation with Isaac Webb and was built by the latter under a subcontract. The engine was of the Fulton type, designed by Fulton's foreman Charles Stoudinger and built by James P. Allaire, with whom Stoudinger had entered a partnership. Her joinery was done by David Cook, of New York. Costing $120,000, she was considered the fastest and finest steamer that had yet been built at the time of her launch.

She was intended for service on the Hudson River and, as originally fitted, had a single stack. Her engine was rated at 75 horsepower, having a cylinder 40 inches in diameter and a stroke of 60 inches. The boiler was copper, 28 feet long and 12 feet front, and weighed about 44,000 pounds. There were two 14-foot diameter flywheels, and the paddlewheels were 18 feet in diameter and 5 feet 10 inches wide. Her speed was about 8½ miles per hour and under normal conditions she carried 25 to 30 pounds of steam in her boiler. Her fuel consumption was about 1½ cords of hardwood per hour.

In the fall of 1827 she was rebuilt and provided with new engine and boilers. Her new engine, rated at 120 horsepower and also built by Allaire had a cylinder 56 inches in diameter and a stroke of 72 inches. She was also fitted with three small boilers and three stacks placed athwartships, and in addition was provided with a jib boom, three masts with topmasts, and a 3-mast schooner rig with a square course on the foremast. In 1828 she was placed on the New York-Providence run, where she made three round trips weekly during the next five years. Sold in 1832, she underwent extensive alterations, after which she was placed on the Providence-Boston run. In 1834 she was again sold, and in the fall of that year ran onto a rock in Boston Harbor and was abandoned to the insurance underwriters. Her engine, salvaged in 1835, was fitted to a new vessel, the *Portland*, owned by the Cumberland Steam Navigation Company and operated on the Boston-Portland run.

The *Chancellor Livingston* was about 165 feet long on deck, 157 feet long on the waterline, 154 feet on the keel, 33 feet 6 inches moulded beam, 10 feet 3 inches depth, 7 feet 3 inches service draft, and 494 tons register. She was built of oak, cedar, and locust, copper fastened and copper sheathed. Her

principal cabin was 54 feet long, the ladies cabin was 36 feet long, and the forward cabin 30 feet long, with 38 berths in the principal cabin, 24 in the ladies cabin, and 56 in the forward cabin. Scale of the model is ¼ inch to the foot.

The model shows the vessel as originally built and using wood for fuel. (She burned coal as early as September 8, 1816.) The hull is formed with rather straight sheer, straight keel with slight drag, short and moderately full entrance, short but fine run, and raking stem rabbet with head and man's bust figurehead, trails, and headrail. The stern is square, with round tuck and quarter galleries. The midsection has a slightly rising straight floor, firm round bilge, and vertical topsides. The sponsons, formed by carrying the deck beams outboard, extended nearly the full length of the hull.

Built for the museum by F. Van Loon Ryder from plans in Marestier's *Mémoire sur les Bateaux á Vapeur des États-Unis d'Amérique*, Paris, 1824.

IRON, SCREW CANAL TUG, 1838
RIGGED MODEL, USNM 160404

Robert F. Stockton

This model is a reconstruction of the iron, screw, steam canal tug *Robert F. Stockton* built at the Birkenhead Ironworks in England in 1838 and fitted with Ericsson's screw propeller, to the order of Lt. Robert F. Stockton, U.S.N., to serve as a canal tug on the Raritan Canal, in the construction of which Lt. Stockton was interested. When the vessel was completed she was schooner rigged, the propeller unshipped, and the voyage from Liverpool to New York was made under canvas. The vessel was owned by the Delaware and Raritan Canal Company and she was built under the supervision of F. B. Ogden, American consul at Liverpool. The *Stockton* was 40 days in making the Atlantic crossing, leaving Liverpool on April 11 and arriving at New York May 21, 1839. Her crew consisted of Captain Crane, four men, and a boy. On arrival her propeller was shipped and she was employed in towing canal boats and vessels. She was renamed *New Jersey* when an Act of Congress, May 8, 1840, admitted her to American registry.

The model does not agree with contemporary pictures of the *Stockton* in many respects and the information employed to construct this model has not been found. It shows an iron, single-screw steamer having straight keel, nearly straight raking stem with angular forefoot, slightly raking post, round fantail counter with vertical bulwarks, sharp entrance and full run, slightly rising straight floor, full round bilge, and vertical topside amidships. A high stack of small diameter is shown.

The *Stockton* was 63 feet 5 inches overall, 10 feet beam, 7 feet depth, 33 tons register, and 30 horsepower. The model is $\frac{1}{10}$ full size.

Model built in the Museum.

SCREW STEAM PACKET, 1844
BUILDER'S HALF-MODEL, USNM 76055

Decatur

The steam screw packet *Decatur* was built on this model by Stephen Jackman at Newbury, Massachusetts, about 1844 for the Boston-Newburyport service, to carry passengers and freight. The half-model is of importance in that it shows the hull-form of a very early screw coasting vessel. No information is given on the power and speed of this steamer.

The half-model shows a steam, screw, coasting vessel hull having very straight sheer, straight keel, upright straight stem rabbet very slightly rounded at forefoot, upright post, short round stern counter, sharp but short and convex entrance, long body, and a short and somewhat full run. Midsection has very slightly rising straight floor, a well rounded and easy bilge, and an upright topside.

The model scales 132 feet moulded length at rail, 24 feet 4 inches moulded beam, and 8 feet 8 inches moulded depth. Scale is $\frac{3}{8}$ inch to the foot.

Presented by Sumner, Swazey, and Currier, Newburyport, Massachusetts.

SIDE-WHEEL STEAM PACKET, 1846
BUILDER'S HALF-MODEL, USNM 76056

Ohio

The side-wheel steam packet *Ohio* was built on this model in 1846 by Stephen Jackman at Newbury, Massachusetts, for the Boston-Newburyport run, to carry passengers, mail, and freight. She was a shoal, full-ended vessel with wide, full-length guards and represents a class of steamer popular in some coastal trades in the 1840's.

The half-model has straight sheer, straight keel, upright straight stem rabbet very slightly rounded at forefoot, upright post and very short overhanging round stern, a short and full convex entrance, long body, short and full run. Midsection has a flat floor, a short, quick, almost angular turn to the bilge, and an upright topside. Model shows the wide guards running the length of the hull.

The model is for a vessel 133 feet 4 inches moulded length at gunwale, 29 feet 8 inches beam over the guards, 19 feet 4 inches moulded beam at gunwale, and 6 feet 8 inches moulded depth. The *Ohio* was 225 tons register, old measurement. Scale of model is $\frac{3}{8}$ inch to the foot.

Given by Sumner, Swazey, and Currier, Newburyport, Massachusetts.

HUDSON RIVER STEAMER, 1852
RIGGED MODEL USNM 316204

Francis Skiddy

The Hudson River steamer *Francis Skiddy* was built by George B. Collyer, at New York in 1848–49 for the day run between New York and Albany. She was intended to have a rotary type engine but failures in its manufacture not only delayed the vessel's completion but also led to the substitution of a vertical beam engine. In 1852 she was completed as the *General Taylor* but before her first run she was renamed the *Francis Skiddy*. Considered the handsomest Hudson River steamer that had yet been built, she was capable of averaging 23 to 24 miles per hour, and was for many years considered the fastest and finest steamer of her type. In 1855 the *Skiddy* was rebuilt into a night boat, another cabin-deck being added. This slowed her somewhat, so she was again changed by building another hull around the old one, but after the changes she was never as fast as when built. On November 25, 1864, the *Skiddy* hit a rock 4 miles below Albany and was then beached and stripped.

The model shows a 4-stack, side-wheel Hudson River passenger steamer having a shoal hull with rather straight sheer, straight keel with no drag, rounded stem, vertical sternpost with small overhang to the stern and transom, a very sharp, long entrance, and a long and fine run. The midsection has a slightly rising straight floor, firm bilge, and nearly upright topside. The hull is fitted with a low superstructure with boilers on the guards. The model shows the boat as first built, as a day boat.

Scale of the model is $\frac{1}{8}$ inch to the foot. The vessel was 325 feet long, 322 feet on deck, 312 feet 7 inches on the keel, 38 feet 10 inches beam, 10 feet 4 inches depth in hold, and 5 feet 6 inches draft, and was fitted with a Belknap and Cunningham vertical beam engine having a 70-inch cylinder with a 14-foot stroke. Four iron boilers, two on each side, operated at 40 pounds pressure; each was supplied with a small

FAMOUS HUDSON RIVER STEAMER *Francis Skiddy*. Launched in 1849, she was capable of steaming 23–24 miles per hour. Wrecked in 1854. Rigged model USNM 316204. (*Smithsonian photo 45666–h.*)

steam blower. Paddle wheels were 40 feet in diameter and had 26 buckets 11 feet wide and 33 inches deep. The vessel was 1,235 tons, old measurement.

Built for the Museum from the builder's lines by F. Van Loon Ryder.

SCREW STEAM FRIGATE, 1858
BUILDER'S HALF-MODEL, USNM 160139

General Admiral

The single-screw, wooden steam frigate *General Admiral* was built on the lines of this half-model at New York by William H. Webb in 1858 for the Imperial Russian Navy. She carried 64 guns and at the time of her launching was one of the largest and most powerful ships of her class in the world, being then considered the finest man-of-war to have been built in the United States. She was full ship-rigged with a large spread of canvas and was intended to steam fast and sail swiftly. Her lines and other drawings are shown in Webb's *Plans of Wooden Ships*.

The half-model shows an auxiliary steam frigate hull having little sheer, a straight keel with little or no drag, straight and slightly raking stem rabbet, slightly founded at forefoot, upright post, short counter with round stern, long and sharp entrance, short body, long and easy run. Midsection shows a slightly rising straight floor, a low hard bilge, and a slight tumble-home in the topside. Model mounted with long-head, billet, trail, cutwater, keel, post, and rudder.

The model is for a frigate 316 feet 6 inches moulded length at rail, 302 feet 10 inches load waterline length, 54 feet 6 inches extreme beam, 34 feet depth,

22 feet draft loaded, 4600 tons measurement. Scale ⅛ inch to the foot.

Given by William H. Webb, shipbuilder, New York, N. Y.

WOODEN, SCREW STEAMSHIP, 1864
BUILDER'S HALF-MODEL, USNM 76045

Meteor

The ship-rigged, wooden, single-screw clipper steamship *Meteor* was built on this model at Portsmouth, New Hampshire, and was launched May 21, 1864, apparently under the name of *U. S. Grant*. She was designed by Dennison J. Lawlor and her building was financed with funds raised by subscriptions from vessel-owners and merchants of Boston, New York, and other ports. She was built for the purpose of destroying the Confederate States' raiders like the *Alabama*, then preying on American shipping, and it was intended to present her to the United States Navy as an armed seagoing cruiser of great speed and heavy armament. The vessel was the result of a designing competition in which were entered three of the best known American ship designers and builders, Henry Steers and William H. Webb of New York City and Dennison J. Lawlor of East Boston and Chelsea, Massachusetts. Lawlor's design was considered most suitable but he did not build the vessel himself; she was built by Tobey and Little-field, at Portsmouth, N. H.

The ship was designed to have a large cruising radius and to be capable of great speed under either steam or sail or both. She was to carry one heavy

130

Steam Screw Clipper, From a Painting in the Watercraft Collection (USNM 76113). The *Meteor*, represented in the collection by builder's half-model USNM 76045, was built at Portsmouth, New Hampshire, in 1864 by Tobey and Littlefield from a design by Dennison J. Lawlor. Intended for a cruiser to capture Confederate commerce-destroyers, she was not completed in time to be of service, and was sold to South America, where she took part in the war between Chile and Peru. There she was scuttled to prevent capture. (*Smithsonian photo 44649.*)

11-inch muzzle-loading pivot gun amidships on her lower deck, placed just forward of the mainmast and firing through long ports on either side, or, as an alternative, to have two 10-inch guns there, firing on the broadside. Forward of this she was to have two gunports on each side for 8- or 9-inch muzzle-loading Dalgren guns, and abreast the engine hatch abaft the mainmast two more ports on each side for 24- or 32-pounder muzzle-loading columbiads or howitzers. On her spar deck forward she was to have two 30-pounder rifled Parrott guns, muzzle-loaders, as chase guns. She had four tubular boilers and an engine having two 62½-inch by 30-inch cylinders; her propeller was 13 feet 6 inches in diameter and 23 feet pitch. All her machinery and her boilers were built in Scotland. She was about 400 tons register larger than the Confederate steamer *Alabama*, and with a speed of about 13 knots was considered to be the fastest ocean-going screw steamer in America at the time she ran her trials off New York. She

was also said to have been very fast under sail alone; she had a Forbes rig and was heavily sparred.

The vessel was completed too late to be of service in the Civil War. She made several short voyages as a merchant ship but was thought too fast and expensive to operate for that purpose, and was then laid up. There were no buyers when she was offered for sale in 1865, but on January 23, 1866, she was seized by the U. S. Marshal at the request of the Spanish Ambassador, it being alleged that negotiations were then underway for her purchase by revolutionists of the rebelling Spanish colonies in South and Central America. The court actions growing out of this incident lasted almost three years. The steamer was sold, however, ostensibly for use in China, but she did not reach there; eventually she took part in the war between Chile and Peru under another name and was destroyed to prevent capture.

The *Meteor* was much admired, when building, for her hull form, which was considered a great advance on that of all previous steamers designed for swiftness, such as the U. S. S. *Niagara*, designed by George Steers and built before the Civil War.

The half-model shows a wooden, single-screw, auxiliary steamer hull having very moderate and graceful sheer, a straight keel with slight drag, upright stem rabbet with a much rounded forefoot, upright post, short round counter with flaring bulwarks, a very long and sharp entrance with marked hollow adjacent the forefoot, a short body, and a very long and remarkedly fine run. The midsection is large, having a very slightly rising floor, a quick, low turn of bilge, and moderate tumble-home in the topside.

The *Meteor* was rigged as a ship, having the Forbes rig and a large spread of sail, comparable to that of some of the earlier clipper ships, it being intended that she sail equal to any sailing vessel in the world, as well as that she steam faster than any ocean-going steamer of equal gun power then afloat. There were then some side-wheel steamers faster under steam, but the *Meteor* would have been their superior in fighting qualities. She resembled some of the fast wooden cruisers built for the U. S. Navy at the end of the Civil War.

The model is for a ship 198 feet moulded length at rail, 48 feet moulded beam, 18 feet 6 inches moulded depth, and 1440 tons register. Scale of model is ½ inch to the foot.

Given by the designer, Dennison J. Lawlor, shipbuilder, Chelsea, Massachusetts.

IRON, PASSENGER and FREIGHT STEAMER, 1878
RIGGED MODEL, USNM 160201

Cuba

The iron single-screw steamer *Cuba* was built in 1878 by Neafie and Levy at Philadelphia, Pennsylvania, for freight and passenger service in the Philadelphia-Havana run. The museum records state that the model also represents the *Oriental*, built by the same firm over ten years earlier, but this is not supported by the register dimensions.

The model is of a single-screw, iron steamer, brigantine rigged, having a moderate and flush sheer, a straight keel with slight drag, upright straight stem with rounded forefoot, vertical post, round fantail counter, long sharp entrance, and a long and easy run. The midsection shows a slightly rising straight

RIGGED MODEL, USNM 160201, of the iron screw steamer *Cuba*, built in 1878 at Philadelphia to carry passengers and freight in Havana trade. (*Smithsonian photos—top, 44956–f; bottom, 44956–g.*)

132

floor, a hard, round bilge, and a slight tumble-home in the topside. There are short whaleback decks at bow and stern.

A long main deckhouse with the pilothouse and a small deckhouse on its roof, a single stack, ventilators, skylights, a life raft, fire buckets in a rack, and six lifeboats in davits are shown. The maindeck rail is an open one without bulwarks.

The *Cuba* was 246 feet 9 inches overall, 28 feet 4 inches beam, 17 feet 3 inches depth. The spar dimensions were: foremast above deck 51 feet, fore-topmast heel to truck 36 feet, fore yard 49 feet 4 inches, fore topsail yard 42 feet 9 inches, fore top-gallant yard 38 feet 3 inches, mainmast above deck 53 feet 3 inches, main topmast heel to truck 36 feet 9 inches, and main gaff 34 feet 4 inches. The boats were 19 feet 4 inches long and 5 feet 9 inches beam. Scale of model ¼ inch to one foot.

Given by the *Cuba's* builders, Neafie and Levy, shipbuilders, Philadelphia, Pennsylvania.

AUXILIARY, SCREW STEAMER
BUILDER'S HALF-MODEL, USNM 311456

Amiral de Joie

This half-model of a fast auxiliary steam screw vessel named *Amiral de Joie*, having dimensions in French and with an indistinct flag and seal or coat of arms on the backboard, was found in the shipyard of the Jackson and Sharpe Company. No record of the vessel having been built there has yet been found; the model is a decorative one representing a fast, wooden steamer, probably rigged as a 3-masted topsail schooner having a single screw. The model may represent a dispatch boat or government mail packet of 1853–65 belonging to the French government. The general appearance is that of a British Navy dispatch vessel of about 1858.

The half-model shows a hull having a strong, graceful sheer, a straight keel with drag, and a raking and flaring stem rabbet with rounded forefoot. The stem is fitted with a longhead and trails, the post is vertical and the stern formed with a round fantail with flaring bulwarks, the entrance is rather long and quite sharp, and the run is fairly long and very fine. The mid-section is formed with a rising straight floor, a rather slack round bilge, and tumble-home in the topside.

The model is mounted with stub masts, and a stack on a round boiler housing located between the fore and main masts; the general deck arrangement is indicated. The lettering on the backboard states

that the vessel was "175 pieds" length between perpendiculars, "30 pieds" beam, and "18 pieds" depth. The scale is apparently ¼ inch to the foot, giving in English feet a moulded length at rail of about 192 feet, 32 feet moulded beam and 18 feet moulded depth, rabbet to rail, by measurement.

Given by the American Car and Foundry Company, Wilmington, Delaware; successors to Jackson and Sharpe Company, shipbuilders.

WOODEN, OCEAN STEAMER, 1870–85
BUILDER'S HALF-MODEL, USNM ———

This half-model of an unidentified wooden, ocean-going steamer is in the Watercraft Collection, without markings or information as to source or donor. The model resembles the steamer *Mexico* built by Dickie Brothers, San Francisco, in 1881, whose lines are shown in Hall's *Report on Shipbuilding*. It is of a smaller ship, however, judging by the apparent scale, which is believed to be ⅜ inch to the foot.

The half-model shows a wooden, single-screw steamer hull having marked sheer, a straight keel with little or no drag, a straight upright stem rabbet with slightly rounded forefoot, upright post, round fantail counter with flaring bulwarks, sharp convex entrance of moderate length, a rather long body and a short and well formed run. The midsection shows a slightly rising straight floor, a low and hard round bilge, and a slight tumble-home in the topside.

Assuming the scale to be ⅜ inch to the foot and the lift lines spaced at 24 inches, the vessel would have been about 202 feet 8 inches moulded length at rail, 30 feet 8 inches moulded beam, and 24 feet depth, rabbet to rail cap.

SCREW CARGO STEAMER, about 1880–90
EXHIBITION HALF-MODEL, USNM 313330

Calderon

This is a decorative half-model showing deck structures and layout of an iron or steel steamer, probably English built, of about 1880–90. No information on this vessel has been found in the Museum.

The model is of a single screw steamer having moderate sheer, a straight keel, cutaway forefoot, upright straight stem, upright post, round fantail counter, and an easy entrance and run. The body is long and the midsection is formed with a slightly rising straight floor, a hard round bilge, and a slight tumble-home in the topside.

The model shows a short raised forecastle and poop, with a short island amidships. There is one deckhouse, a pilothouse and bridge, two masts, and one stack.

Model may be on a scale of ⅜ inch to the foot making the measurements about 261 feet 10 inches overall, 33 feet 4 inches beam and 23 feet 4 inches depth.

Given by U. S. Post Office Department.

SIDE-WHEEL MISSISSIPPI RIVER STEAMER, 1871
Rigged Model, usnm 308426

James Howard

The flat-bottomed, side-wheel Mississippi River steamer *James Howard*, was built at Jeffersonville, Indiana, by the Howard Shipyards and Dock Company in 1871 for the St. Louis-New Orleans run. She was intended to carry both freight and passengers as a river packet and was the largest vessel of her type when built.

The model represents a wooden Mississippi River steam packet having side paddle wheels and a straight keel, slight sheer, curved upright stem, upright post with round fantail counter, wide guards extending out to outer face of wheelboxes, a sharp and long entrance, and a short easy run.

The wheels are about one-third the hull length from the stern, and there is a two-deck house with a pilot's wheelhouse on its roof abaft the twin stacks set abreast one another. There is a short forward deck, and the guards are carried fair from the bow to the fantail rim.

The vessel was 330 feet long, 56 feet beam over the guards, 10 feet depth, and had two engines with pis-

Rigged Model (USNM 308426) of the Mississippi River packet steamer *James Howard*, built at Jeffersonville, Indiana, 1871, for the St. Louis to New Orleans run. (*Smithsonian photo 30949–b.*)

tons 34 inches in diameter by 10 feet stroke, 7 locomotive-type boilers 42 inches in diameter and 32 feet long; the sidewheels were each 32 feet in diameter and 15 feet wide at the blades. Scale of the model is ⅛ inch to the foot.

Given by Howard Shipyards and Dock Company, Jeffersonville, Indiana.

SIDE-WHEEL OHIO RIVER STEAMER, 1892
Rigged Model, usnm 160323

Grey Eagle

The side-wheel wooden packet steamer *Grey Eagle*, represented by this model, was built at Jeffersonville, Indiana, in 1892 as a river packet and she ran for some years on the Ohio River, between Louisville and

Ohio River Mail and Passenger Packet *Grey Eagle*, built at Jeffersonville, Indiana, in 1892, and employed in the mail run between Louisville and Henderson. Rigged model USNM 160323. (*Smithsonian photo 23168.*)

134

Henderson, Kentucky, carrying mail, freight, and passengers. The *Grey Eagle*, typical for her date of building, was similar in every way to the famous Mississippi River side-wheel packet steamers. This type had become well developed by 1850 and played an active part in river operations by both the Confederate and Federal armed services during the Civil War. These packets were often fast, and on both sides some were converted into steam rams. The great period of these river packet steamers was in the 1850's but for at least 25 years after the Civil War the packet trade was prosperous on the Ohio, Mississippi, and Missouri Rivers, as well as on the Tennessee and Red Rivers. With the development of the railroads, the packets slowly disappeared; the last survivor ceased operations some time about 1955.

The model shows a shoal-draft, side-wheel, wooden, river steamer having a straight keel, curved stem, vertical post, a round fantail counter, slight sheer, a moderately sharp convex entrance, and an easy run: The midsection is formed with a flat floor, an easy round bilge, and a flaring topside. The hull, at the main deck, is fitted with wide overhanging guards fairing almost round into the stem and counter. The side paddle-wheels are about one-fourth the length of hull from the stern.

The model has a large deck structure consisting of a 2-deck house reaching from the stern to a point about one-fifth the hull length from the bow, the lower portion of the house being quite high. This was the main-deck freight space, on which were also the boilers, engine, and fuel space; the upper deck contained a promenade, cabins, and saloon; and the long deckhouse on its roof also contained cabins. On the deckhouse roof are two high stacks side-by-side and another small house, containing cabins or public spaces, on which is the pilot or wheelhouse, well abaft the stacks. The two decks fitted with promenade areas have turned-stanchion-and-cap rails, with ornamental posts, or columns, supporting the upper deck.

The *Grey Eagle* measured 250 feet long, 40 feet beam at gunwale, 60 feet 6 inches beam over the guards, 5 feet 6 inches depth of hold, and about 54 feet extreme height from rabbet to roof of pilothouse. Scale of model is $\frac{1}{4}$ inch to the foot.

Model made in the Museum from plans not now in the Museum files. It was built to float and was intended to be self-propelled, but was never completed.

SIDE-WHEEL HUDSON RIVER EXCURSION STEAMER, 1906
RIGGED MODEL, USNM 309408

Hendrick Hudson

The *Hendrick Hudson* was a steel, side-wheel Hudson River excursion steamer built in 1906 by the Marvel Shipbuilding Company at Newburgh, New York, under subcontract with W. and A. Fletcher, of New York, who built her engines. The steamer was designed by Frank E. Kirby and was built for the Hud-

TOPSIDE DETAIL OF RIGGED MODEL (USNM 160323) of river packet *Grey Eagle*. (*Smithsonian photo 32867–a.*)

135

THE STEEL SIDE-WHEEL HUDSON RIVER STEAMER *Hendrick Hudson* was built by the Marvel Shipbuilding Company, Newburgh, New York, in 1906. Licensed to carry 5,500 persons, she ran for many years between New York City and Albany. Rigged model USNM 309408. (*Smithsonian photo 45162.*)

son River Day Line of New York. She ran for many years on the New York City to Albany run and was a well known vessel in her day. She was licensed to carry 5500 persons.

The model represents an excursion steamer having three flush decks running from bow to stern. On the upper deck is a deckhouse, extending about three-fifths the hull length, on which is a 2-deck bridge-and-wheelhouse structure, a small 1-deck house, and two stacks in line fore and aft. Wide guards, with exposed iron braces to the hull sides below, house feathering paddle wheels forward of midlength. The guards are faired into both bow and fantail rim. The keel is straight with no drag; the forefoot is much cut away

and rounded, and the stem is straight and upright above the load line; the keel aft is cut up in a straight line for a considerable length; and there is a short vertical post with a balance rudder hung on it and a short, round, fantail counter above. The sheer is slight, the entrance is long and very sharp, and the run is long and very fine. The midsection had a nearly flat floor, an easy round bilge, and an upright topside.

The *Hendrick Hudson* was 400 feet long, overall, 379.1 feet between perpendiculars, 45.1 feet beam at gunwales and 82 feet over the guards, 14 feet 5 inches moulded depth, her depth in hold was 13.4 feet, and her draft 7 feet 6 inches. The vessel had a 3-cylinder

STERN-WHEEL RIVER STEAMER BUILT OF WOOD AT APALACHICOLA, FLORIDA, in 1901. The *Thomas A. Edison* is represented in the Watercraft Collection by builder's half-model USNM 311260. (*Smithsonian photo 34432.*)

136

compound direct-acting engine of 6200 indicated horsepower and made 23 statute miles per hour on trials. She had a register tonnage of 2847 gross tons, 1598 net tons. Scale of model ¼ inch to the foot.

From the Hudson River Day Line.

STERN-WHEEL RIVER STEAMER, 1908
Builder's Half-Model, usnm 311260

Thomas A. Edison

A stern-wheel steamboat for river navigation in Florida was built on this model about 1908 by Samuel Johnson at Apalachicola, Florida, and named the *Thomas A. Edison.* The model represents an attempt to improve upon the usual hull-form of this type of vessel, and is supposed to have been made from plans furnished the builder by the engine manufacturer.

The model shows a shallow, flat-bottomed hull having nearly straight sheer, a straight keel tucked up aft to form a short but easy run, an upright straight stem rabbet, a slightly rounded forefoot, vertical flat transom, long and sharp entrance, flat floor, a hard bilge on a short radius, and an upright topside. The flare becomes very marked near the bow and stern, as the bilges are made easy there. It was thought that a slack bilge aft would make the vessel turn quickly, a desired characteristic in these river steamers.

The model is for a vessel 80 feet moulded length at gunwale, 20 feet moulded beam at gunwale, and 3 feet 6 inches moulded depth. Scale of model is ½ inch to the foot.

Given by Samuel Johnson, boatbuilder, Apalachicola, Florida.

WOODEN, STERN-WHEEL RIVER STEAMER, 1908
Builder's Half-Model, usnm 311526

Uneeda

The wooden stern-wheel river steamer *Uneeda* was built by H. Hansen on this model on Orange River, near Fort Meyers, Florida, in 1908, for local river service. The model shows a very shoal stern-wheel steamer hull having straight sheer, a straight keel with the run formed by an angular rake, or "tuck-up," aft, the stem rabbet slightly curved and rather upright, the transom wide, flat, and upright. The entrance is short but rather sharp; the run formed by the tuck-up is straight, but short. The deck outline, in plan, shows almost parallel sides from the stern almost to the bow. The midsection is rectangular, the bilges being rounded on a very small radius to save labor in building.

The model is believed to be on a scale of ⅜ inch to the foot and the vessel would then measure about 84 feet 6 inches moulded length, 20 feet 6 inches beam, and 3 feet 6 inches moulded depth.

Given by Captain H. Hansen.

STEEL, SCREW LIGHTHOUSE TENDER, 1893
Builder's Half-Model, usnm 311829

Maple

This is the plating model used in building the single-screw, steel, steam lighthouse tender *Maple* for the U.S. Lighthouse Service by Samuel L. Moore & Son Co. at Elizabethport, New Jersey, in 1893. The steamer replaced a sailing-schooner tender of the same name.

The half-model represents a steel, single-screw steamer hull having moderate sheer, a straight keel with little drag, an upright straight stem slightly rounded at the forefoot, a vertical post, a round fantail counter with flaring bulwarks, easy entrance, and a short and full run. The midsection is formed with a moderately rising straight floor, a firm round bilge, and a nearly straight and vertical topside.

The model is to the main rail and indicates the short open space in them forward used to bring buoys aboard with minimum lift.

The *Maple* was 155 feet between perpendiculars, 30 feet beam, and 12 feet depth; she was 392 gross tons register, and had a 650-horsepower reciprocating engine. She was employed on the northern Atlantic coast during most of her career. Scale of model is ¼ inch to the foot.

Given by U. S. Coast Guard.

STEEL, SCREW LIGHTHOUSE TENDER, 1903
Builder's Half-Model, usnm 311828

Larkspur

This half-model was used for laying off the plating of the steel single-screw, steam lighthouse tender *Larkspur* built at Port Richmond, N. Y. in 1903. Vessels of this type were employed to supply lighthouses along the coast, for attending lifesaving stations, and for maintaining buoys and other navigation marks.

The half-model represents a hull having strong sheer, a straight keel with little drag, upright curved stem, vertical post, round fantail counter, sharp entrance of moderate length, and easy run. The midsection shows a rising straight floor of moderate deadrise, an easy round bilge, and a rather upright topside.

A long deckhouse, reaching from a little forward of midlength to within a short distance of the stern, is shown, and on the deckhouse roof is a pilothouse, with a small house abaft.

The *Larkspur* measured 162 feet length between perpendiculars, 30 feet beam, and 14 feet depth; she was 685 gross tons; and had a 750-horsepower reciprocating engine. Scale of model is ¼ inch to the foot.
Given by U. S. Coast Guard.

STEEL, SCREW LIGHTHOUSE TENDER, 1903
BUILDER'S HALF-MODEL, USNM 311830

Heather

This is the plating model employed by Moran Bros. & Co. in building the steel, steam, single-screw lighthouse tender and buoy boat *Heather* for the U. S. Lighthouse Service at Seattle, Washington, in 1903.

The half-model to main-deck height only, is of a hull having moderate sheer, a straight keel, an upright and nearly straight stem, vertical post, round fantail counter, a sharp entrance of moderate length, and an easy short run. The midsection is formed with a moderately rising straight floor, a firm round bilge and an upright topside.

The *Heather* measured 165 feet between perpendiculars, 28 feet beam, and 15 feet depth; she was 631 gross tons register and had a 685-horsepower reciprocating steam engine. Scale of model is ¼ inch to the foot.
Given by U. S. Coast Guard.

STEEL, SCREW LIGHTHOUSE TENDER, 1906
BUILDER'S HALF-MODEL, USNM 311831

Aspen

This is the plating model for the steel, steam lighthouse tender *Aspen*, built at Toledo, Ohio, in 1906 for service on the Great Lakes.

The half-model shows a steel, single-screw steamer having strong sheer, with a short, high raised deck at the bow, a straight keel with some drag, an upright post, a short round fantail counter like that of a tug but with upright bulwarks, an upright and curved stem, a rather short but sharp entrance, and an easy run. The midsection is formed with a slightly rising straight floor, a low hard bilge, and a slight tumble-home in the topside.

The *Aspen* was 118 feet between perpendiculars, 25 feet beam, 12 feet depth, and had a 440-horsepower reciprocating engine; she was 227 gross tons register. Scale of model is ¼ inch to the foot.
Given by U. S. Coast Guard.

STEEL, STERN-WHEEL LIGHTHOUSE TENDER, 1924
BUILDER'S HALF-MODEL, USNM 311886

Greenbrier

This is the plating model of the river lighthouse tender and buoy boat *Greenbrier* built at Charlestown, West Virginia, in 1924 for service on the Ohio and upper Mississippi Rivers. She was used to supply lighthouses and to attend to the buoys and navigation aids along these rivers.

The half-model represents a steel, stern-wheel, river steamer of traditional type, having moderate sheer, straight keel, upright and nearly straight stem, shallow square stern, sharp entrance of moderate length, and a short straight run formed by a tuck-up of the bottom close to the stern. The midsection is formed with a flat floor, a quick hard bilge formed on a short radius, and a vertical topside. There is very great flare in the forward sections to form the almost rectangular deck outline forward.

A large deckhouse and stern wheel are shown.

The *Greenbrier* measured 140 feet between perpendiculars, 32 feet beam, and 5 feet depth; she was 305 gross tons register and had 350-horsepower engines. Scale of model is ¼ inch to the foot. Her plans are in the Watercraft Collection.
Given by U. S. Coast Guard.

U. S. LIGHTSHIP 82, 1908
BUILDER'S HALF-MODEL, USNM 311832

This is the builder's plating model of the *U.S. Lightship 82*, a single-screw, steel steamer. She was built at Muskegon, Michigan, in 1908 and sank on the Buffalo station.

The model shows a lightship hull having much sheer, a straight keel with drag, a strongly curved and raking stem, upright post, round fantail counter with flaring bulwarks, a turtleback deck at the bow, and an entrance and run both short and full. The midsection is formed with a slightly rising straight floor, a round and easy bilge, and a slight tumble-home in the topside. The model shows the low hawse at the bow common in American lightships.

The length of the vessel was 80 feet, beam 21 feet,

depth in hold 8 feet 11 inches, and she was powered by a 90-horsepower steam engine. Scale of model is ¼ inch to the foot.

Given by U. S. Coast Guard.

U. S. LIGHTSHIP 89, 1908
BUILDER'S HALF-MODEL, USNM 311835

This is a builder's plating model employed in the construction of the *U.S. Lightship 89*, a steel, steam single-screw vessel, built in 1908 and employed on the Great Lakes at Martin Reef and North Manitou.

The half-model shows a lightship hull having strong sheer, a straight keel with some drag, rather upright and curved stem, vertical post, round fantail counter with flaring rail, moderately sharp entrance, and a short and full run. The midsection is formed with a rising straight floor, a low firm bilge, and tumble-home in the topside.

The length of the vessel was 80 feet, beam 21 feet, depth in hold 10 feet, and she was powered by a 90-horsepower steam engine. Scale of model is ¼ inch to the foot.

Given by U. S. Coast Guard.

U. S. LIGHTSHIP 98, 1914
BUILDER'S HALF-MODEL, USNM 311834

This is the builder's plating model for *U. S. Lightship 98*, a steel, steam single-screw lightship of moderate size. She was built in 1914 and employed at Buffalo, Lansing Shoals, and Handkerchief Shoal.

The half-model shows a lightship hull having strong sheer, straight keel with drag, a curved and flaring bow, upright post, a round stern with flaring bulwarks (the overhang of the fantail counter is short), and a full entrance and run. The midsection is formed with a slightly rising straight floor, a low, round, and rather easy bilge, and tumble-home in the topside. A large mooring hawse is shown low in the bows.

The length of the vessel was 101 feet 6 inches, depth in hold 11 feet 5 inches, and she was powered with a 100-horsepower steam engine. Scale of model is ¼ inch to the foot.

Given by U. S. Coast Guard.

U. S. LIGHTSHIP 99, 1920
BUILDER'S HALF-MODEL, USNM 311833

This is the builder's plating model of the *U. S. Lightship 99*, a steel, single-screw vessel, employed on Poe Reef.

The half-model shows a lightship hull having much sheer, a straight keel with marked drag, a curved and raking stem rabbet, upright post, round fantail counter with upright bulwarks, and a short and full entrance and run. The midsection is formed with a slightly rising straight floor, a low full bilge, and a slight tumble-home in the topside. The large mooring hawse low in the bow that marked many of the steel lightships is shown.

The length of the vessel was 91 feet 8 inches, beam 22 feet, depth in hold 10 feet, and she was powered with a 125 horsepower oil engine.

Scale of model is ¼ inch to the foot.

Given by U. S. Coast Guard.

TRANS-ATLANTIC LINER, 1889
RIGGED MODEL, USNM 271111

Philadelphia, ex *City of Paris,* ex *Yale*

The trans-Atlantic liner *City of Paris* was built by James and George Thompson at Clydebank, Glasgow, Scotland, in 1889 for the Inman Line. One of the distinctive liners built for this British firm during the 1880's, having lines like a steam yacht and a clipper bow, she was purchased by the International Mercantile Marine Company and transferred to the American flag under the name *Philadelphia*. In 1898, when under charter at $2,000 a day to the U. S. Navy during the Spanish-American War, she was renamed *Yale* and employed as an auxiliary armed cruiser. After the war she was returned to her owners and renamed *Philadelphia*. In 1900, after running ashore, she was rebuilt at Belfast, Ireland, and much altered, the number of stacks being then reduced from three to two. She ran between New York and Liverpool for about 18 years before being broken up.

The model shows a twin-screw, steel passenger steamer having a straight keel with little or no drag, graceful clipper bow with trails, false rails and scrolls, vertical sternpost, fantail counter with much overhang, propeller shafts housed, and the housings faired into the hull. The vessel has a long, sharp and hollow entrance, a very short body, or dead flat, and a long and very fine run. The sheer is moderate and unbroken. The midsection is formed with a slightly rising straight floor, a hard bilge, on a short radius and a slight tumble-home in the topside, above the main deck.

The forecastle and quarterdecks are connected by a continuous boat deck, though the rail line is broken at the ends of the forecastle and quarterdecks.

MORGAN LINE PACKET, THE COASTWISE STEAMSHIP *Louisiana*, built by John Roach & Son, Chester, Pennsylvania, in 1880 for the New York to New Orleans run. Length 320', beam 39', depth 28'6". (*Smithsonian photo 3511.*)

A long deckhouse on the boat deck, domed forward over the main saloon, reaches from the foremast to abaft the mainmast. On this are upper and lower bridges, a wheelhouse, two stacks, and trunk gratings. On each side the vessel carries four boats on davits with gratings out to them from the top of the deckhouse. Between the main and mizzen masts are two small deckhouses and four boats in davits, two on each side.

The vessel measured 576 feet between perpendiculars, 63 feet beam, and 10,786 tons register. She had two triple expansion engines. Scale of model is ¼ inch to the foot.

The vessel is rigged as a 3-masted schooner with pole bowsprit and standing gaffs; the sails are furled to the masts. This model shows the ship after her rebuilding in 1900, with two, instead of three stacks.

Transferred from the U. S. Post Office Department.

TRANS-ATLANTIC LINER, 1907
RIGGED MODEL, USNM 311006

Mauretania

The *Mauretania* was built by Swan, Hunter, and Wigham Richardson in 1907 at Wallsend-on-Tyne, Scotland, for the Cunard Line. Turbine driven, she

was coal-burning when built, and was converted to oil fuel in 1919. The *Mauretania* held many speed records in her day and was, for many years, a popular liner on the trans-Atlantic run out of New York. The ship was broken up in 1935. She was one of the famous "four-stackers" of the Cunard Line, and was a sister-ship of the *Lusitania*.

The model shows a large, four-stack, quadruple-screw liner, having a straight keel with no drag, upright straight stem slightly rounded at forefoot, which is cut away slightly, at an angle to the keel, a vertical post, a round fantail counter with a "bustle" above the rudder, steam-yacht fashion, a balanced rudder, shafts without struts, housed and faired into the hull. The entrance is long and sharp, the run long and fine. Midsection formed with a slightly rising straight floor, a hard bilge on a short radius, and a nearly vertical topside with a slight tumble-home near the main deck. The sheer is broken, the long forecastle and its deck extending almost to the stern.

The model is shown with two masts, four raking stacks, and a long double-deck deckhouse, with bridges and wheelhouse forward.

The vessel measured 790 feet overall, 87 feet 6 inches moulded beam, and 60 feet 6 inches depth to

140

RIGGED MODEL USNM 311006, OF THE TRANS-ATLANTIC LINER *Mauretania*, built at Wallsend-on-Tyne in 1907 for the Cunard Line. When a passenger liner suffers a disaster, it is customary to change the name of the model to that of her sister ship. The claim is made that this model was originally of the *Lusitania*. (*Smithsonian photo 32069.*)

upper deck. Her gross tonnage was 31,940. Scale of model is ¼ inch to the foot.

Her indicated horsepower was 70,000 and her service speed 25 knots. Her maiden voyage to New York in November 1907 was accomplished in 5 days, 5 hours and 10 minutes, then a record. In March 1909 she ran from Queenstown to New York in 4 days, 12 hours and 6 minutes, and for years held the speed records for both eastward and westward passages until the North German Lloyd liner *Bremen* made her maiden voyage in July 1929. She was later employed for cruising service out of New York, and made her last voyage in the fall of 1934. Exclusive of wartime service, she made 269 double crossings of the Atlantic. Affectionately known as the Grand Old Lady of the Atlantic, she was broken up at Rosyth.

Given by Franklin D. Roosevelt.

SINGLE-SCREW STEEL FREIGHTER, 1919
RIGGED MODEL, USNM 306999

American Merchant, ex *Cambrai,* ex *Shohokin*

This model of a steel single-screw freight steamer represents a class of 12 prefabricated army transports, built by the American International Shipbuilding Corporation at Hog Island in Philadelphia, Pennsylvania, for the U. S. Shipping Board, Emergency Fleet Corporation, of which 11 were delivered to the U. S. Army and one to the U. S. Navy. The model is of the *Shohokin*; her keel was laid November 9, 1918, and she was commissioned October 30, 1920. The design was intended to produce a swift freighter and transport for wartime use. Later named *Cambrai*,

the vessel was renamed *American Merchant* when transferred to private operators.

The model shows a steel single-screw cargo steamer having a straight keel with no drag, straight sheer with well decks forming a 3-island deck arrangement, an upright straight stem with slightly rounded forefoot, vertical sternpost, upright cruiser stern slightly rounded at deck, keel cut off at an angle at sternpost, dagger-type rudder. The entrance is short and sharp, with some hollow at forefoot; the run is rather long and hollow; and the dead flat is about one-third the total hull length. The midsection is formed with a slightly rising straight floor, a hard bilge on a small radius, and a slight tumble-home in the topside.

On the long deckhouse amidships is the bridge, pilothouse, a single stack, boats, and ventilators. The four pairs of derrick masts, cross-trussed in pairs, carry 14 cargo booms in all.

Scale of model is ⅛ inch to the foot.

The vessels measured 450 feet overall, 58 feet moulded beam, and 40 feet depth to upper deck; the loaded draft was 28 feet. Weight of steel hull was 3400 tons, machinery with water 760 tons, joinery and outfit 300 tons, giving a total ship's weight of 4460 tons; the displacement loaded was 12,460 tons and the estimated measured gross tonnage 6200 tons. These ships had six boilers, each of 1740 horsepower. and a single turbine of 6000 shaft horsepower. The boilers burned oil, the tankage capacity was 1600 tons, the consumption of fuel on trial 70½ tons in 24 hours, and the cruising radius 8132 nautical miles. Maximum speed was 15 knots.

Model transferred from U. S. Senate Committee on Commerce.

141

TWIN-SCREW TRANS-ATLANTIC LINER, 1924
RIGGED MODEL, USNM 311900

Statendam

The *Statendam* was a twin-screw liner laid down in the Harlan and Wolff, Ltd., shipyard at Belfast, North Ireland, in 1921. A depression in the shipping business delayed construction and the hull was not launched until 1924, after which work ceased on the ship until 1927, when the hull was towed to Holland and the vessel completed in Wilton's Yard, at Rotterdam, in 1929. The steamer owned by the Holland-America Line and employed on the North Atlantic run, was destroyed by the Germans at Rotterdam on May 10, 1940.

The model is of a vessel with straight keel, a straight upright stem slightly rounded at forefoot, upright post and cruiser stern, with the propeller shafts housed, a sharp entrance, long body and moderately long run, and broken sheer. The long deckhouse bears three stacks, two masts, and two sets of derrick posts. The midsection is formed with a very slight rise in the straight floor, a hard bilge on a small radius, and a slight tumble-home high in the topside.

The liner measured 698 feet extreme length, 91 feet moulded beam, 34 feet depth, and 28,291 gross tons register. She was gear-turbine driven, and her speed was 20 knots. Scale of model is ⅛ inch to the foot.

Given by Holland-America Line through Franklin D. Roosevelt.

MAIL and PASSENGER LINER, 1924
RIGGED MODEL, USNM 308324

Empress of Asia, Empress of Russia

These quadruple-screw turbine-driven passenger and mail steamers *Empress of Asia* and *Empress of Russia* were launched in 1924 at the yard of the Fairfield Shipbuilding and Engineering Company, Ltd., Glascow, Scotland. Built for the Canadian-Pacific Railway Company's trans-Pacific service they were two of a series of *Empress* liners popular in the passenger service.

The model shows a large, quadruple-screw liner having a straight keel, upright straight stem, vertical post, cruiser stern, balanced rudder, propeller shafts with housings faired into the hull, and a rather straight sheer breaking off just short of the stern. The entrance is long and sharp, the dead flat is about three-fifths the hull length, and the run is both long and fine. The midsection is formed with a slightly rising

straight floor, a sharp turn of bilge on a small radius, and a slight tumble-home in the topside.

The long deckhouse has a dome at its after end; on this deckhouse are a bridge structure and wheelhouse, three raking stacks, and two raking pole masts.

The vessels measured 592 feet overall, 68 feet 4 inches moulded beam, 46 feet moulded depth to upper deck, and 16,700 gross tons register; the trial speed was 21 knots. Scale of model ¼ inch to the foot.

Model loaned by the Canadian Pacific Railway Company.

FREIGHT and PASSENGER STEAMER, 1925
RIGGED MODEL, USNM 308363

President Polk

The *President Polk*, one of a standard design of freight and passenger steamer established by the U. S. Shipping Board, Emergency Fleet Corporation, and known as the 502 Class, was built in 1925 by the New York Shipbuilding Corporation, Camden, New Jersey, for the United States Lines. These ships were intended to serve as army transports in time of war.

The model represents a twin-screw, combination freight and passenger steamer having straight sheer, a straight keel, upright straight stem, upright post, and upright cruiser stern. The entrance is sharp, the dead flat is about one-third the hull length, the run is fine, and the propeller shafts are fitted with a strut. There is a balanced rudder. The midsection shows a slightly rising straight floor, a hard bilge on a small radius, and a slight tumble-home in the topside.

The vessel is well-decked, with three islands: a short forecastle; a low middle island, at the fore end of which is a 3-decked bridge-and-wheelhouse structure, and abaft this a 2-decked house with a stack on it and with a wireless house abaft the stack; and a short raised poop. There are five pairs of derrick masts and six cargo hatches.

The ship measured 522 feet 8 inches overall, 62 feet beam, 42 feet moulded depth to upper deck, and 10,633 gross tons register; her speed was 14 knots. Scale of model is ⅛ inch to the foot.

Model transferred to Museum from U. S. Shipping Board, Emergency Fleet Corporation.

GREAT LAKES ORE and BULK CARRIER, 1925
RIGGED MODEL, USNM 312827

William G. Mather

The steel single-screw Great Lakes ore and bulk carrier *William G. Mather* was built by the Great Lakes

SINGLE-SCREW GREAT LAKES ORE AND BULK CARRIER *William G. Mather*, built at River Rouge, Michigan, in 1925. Rigged model USNM 312827. (*Smithsonian photo 36710–b.*)

Engineering Works, River Rouge, Michigan, in 1925 for the Cleveland-Cliffs Iron Company, Cleveland, Ohio. Vessels of this class made about 30 trips a season.

The model shows a long, almost straight-sheered, narrow, bargelike steamer having a straight keel, straight upright stem, vertical post, round fantail counter, a short and full entrance, an abnormally long and parallel-sided body, and a very short and full run. Midsection is almost rectangular, with a very slight rise in the straight floor, the bilge on a very short radius, and a wall-sided topside.

Forward is a short raised deck on which is a 2-decked bridge-and-wheelhouse structure bearing a light signal mast. At the stem is a bowsprit-like "guiding pole," required by the position of the wheelhouse so far forward. On the long main deck are 18 ore hatches; well aft are a short deckhouse, a single large stack, signal mast, and boats.

The *William G. Mather* measured 618 feet ½ inch overall, 62 feet moulded beam, and 32 feet moulded depth. Her tonnage was 8662 gross, 6110 net register, and 13,300 tons capacity; and her nominal horsepower 2600. She drew 21 feet 5½ inches loaded and had a quadruple-expansion engine. Scale of model is ⅛ inch to the foot.

Given by the Cleveland-Cliffs Iron Company, Cleveland, Ohio.

PASSENGER LINER, 1929
RIGGED MODEL, USNM 314251

Uruguay, ex *California*

A turbo-electric drive steamer for passenger service was built as the *California* by the Newport News Shipbuilding Company, Newport News, Virginia, in 1929 for the United States Lines. Converted to a transport at the outbreak of the last war, she was renamed *Uruguay.*

The model shows a 2-stack liner having a straight keel, raking straight stem, vertical post, twin screws with shafts housed, balanced rudder, cruiser stern, sharp entrance, medium length of body, and a fine run. Midsection has a slightly rising straight floor, a hard bilge on short radius, and a vertical topside with a slight tumble-home high up.

There is a short, raised forecastle deck. A long, midship island is carried almost to the stern; on it is a 2-deck superstructure, atop which are a single-deck house, a 2-deck bridge structure, and two stacks. Derrick-winch houses and derrick masts are on the main deck forward and on the island deck well aft. There is a docking bridge aft.

The *Uruguay* measured 610 feet length, 80 feet beam, and 20,329 gross tons, and her speed 18 knots. Scale of model is ⅛ inch to the foot.

Given by United States Lines, New York.

DIESEL-POWERED TRANS-ATLANTIC LINER, 1935–36
RIGGED MODEL, USNM 311978

Pilsudski, Batory

This model represents two diesel-powered transAtlantic liners designed and built in Italy for the Polish Gdynia-American Line; the *Pilsudski* was launched in 1935 and the *Batory* in 1936 by the Monfalcone Shipyards at Trieste, Italy. Both ships were employed on the North Atlantic; the *Pilsudski* was sunk by a magnetic mine November 26, 1939, but the *Batory* remains in service (1959) and has often been in the news.

The model represents a twin-screw passenger vessel having a straight keel, forefoot cut away at an angle, raking straight stem of the rounded "soft-nose" design, a skeg and an upright post, cruiser stern, twin shafts housed, a long and sharp entrance, body one-third the hull length, and a moderately long, fine run. Midsection formed with a slight rise of straight floor, a hard and low bilge, and an upright topside with a slight tumble-home high up.

The vessel has flush sheer, a long 2-deck deckhouse with bridge structure forward, two low stacks, two pole masts, and two sets of derrick posts.

These ships measured 514 feet in length, 76 feet moulded beam, 25 feet moulded depth, and 14,200 gross tons register. Their speed is 18 knots. Scale of model is 1/80.

Given by Gdynia-American Line.

STANDARD AMERICAN MERCHANT SHIP, C-1 CLASS
Rigged Model, usnm 313021

This model represents the first design of a standard turbine-driven, single-screw merchant steamer developed by the U. S. Maritime Commission before the last war. A number of ships were built to this design with some variation in arrangment for American ship-owning companies who obtained financial aid from the government to expand their fleets or to replace out-dated ships. It was intended that the C-1 Class would serve as freighters and transports in event of war.

The model which shows the basic arrangement employed in this class of merchant vessel, is of a cargo steamer having a straight keel, straight raking stem with small "soft-nose," vertical post, round fantail counter, flush sheer with moderate camber, sharp entrance, body less than a third the hull-length, and a long and fine run. Midsection formed with a slight rise in the straight floor, a low and hard bilge on a small radius, and tumble-home in the upper topside only.

A large rectangular deckhouse, two decks high, is placed a little abaft midlength. On it is a bridge structure and deckhouse containing officers' quarters, a single stack, and lifeboats. The three holds forward and two aft have each a single large hatch.

These ships measured 417 feet 9 inches long, 60 feet beam, 37 feet 6 inches moulded depth, 26 feet 6 inches draft loaded, 12,889 tons displacement to load-line, 9125 tons deadweight, and 6710 gross tons register, 4000 shaft horsepower, and 14 to 15 knots speed. Scale of model is $\frac{1}{8}$ inch to the foot.

Given by U. S. Maritime Commission.

STANDARD AMERICAN MERCHANT SHIP, C-2 CLASS, Type C-2-S-B1
Rigged Model, usnm 313024

This model represents an improved design for a standard class of geared-turbine-driven, single-screw merchant ship developed by the U. S. Maritime Commission before the last war. Like the C-1 Class, a number of vessels of this design, but with variations in arrangement for American ship-owners, were built before and early in the war, and the class proved very useful for freighting and as emergency transports.

American Merchant Ship, Class C1–B, Modified for Use of a Private Operator. Rigged model USNM 313021 shows the basic design of the class. (*U.S. Maritime Administration photo 2106.*)

AMERICAN MERCHANT SHIP, CLASS C–2, MODIFIED FOR USE OF A PRIVATE OPERATOR. Many of this design were employed in war service. Rigged model USNM 313024 shows the basic design of the class. (*U.S. Maritime Administration photo 1416.*)

The model shows a merchant steamer, having a straight keel, rather upright flaring bow with small "soft-nose" and very angular forefoot, vertical post, well rounded cruiser stern, sharp and short entrance, body about a third hull length, and a long and easy run. Midsection formed with a slight rise in the straight floor, a low firm bilge on a small radius, and tumble-home in the upper topside only.

The model has a low, raised deck forward, three cargo hatches, and a midship island on which is a 2-deck deckhouse having on it a single stack and a bridge structure. Aft are two cargo hatches and a low raised poop. The sheer is unbroken. Two pairs of derrick masts forward and one pair aft act as vents.

Vessels of the C–2 Class measure 459 feet 2½ inches length overall, 63 feet beam, 40 feet 6 inches moulded depth, 25 feet 9 inches draft loaded, 13,898 tons displacement to load line, 9250 deadweight tons, 9222 gross tons register, 6000 shaft horsepower, 15½ knots speed, and 18,850 nautical miles cruising radius. Scale of model is ⅛ inch to the foot.

Given by U. S. Maritime Commission.

STANDARD AMERICAN MERCHANT SHIP, C–3 CLASS, TYPE C–3P
RIGGED MODEL, USNM 303025

This model represents an improved C–Class design, prepared before the last War by the U. S. Maritime Commission, for a turbine-driven, single-screw steamer for use in freight and limited passenger service and as a wartime cargo and transport ship. As merchant vessels they were intended particularly for the West Indian and Central American services. The standard plan provided accommodations for 122 in the crew and 111 passengers.

The model shows a single-screw steamer having a straight keel, straight raking stem with "soft-nose," upright post, and broad cruiser stern. The entrance is sharp, the body short, and the run long and easy. The midsection shows a slight rise in the straight floor, a hard bilge on a small radius, and a very slight tumble-home in the upper topside.

The deck line shows moderate sheer. On the long island amidships is a short deckhouse, atop which is a smaller 2-deck house, containing the bridge and wheelhouse structure and a large and tapered single stack. Two cargo hatches, one derrick mast, and two derrick posts are forward as well as abaft the island.

Vessels of the C–3 Class measured 489 feet overall, 69 feet 6 inches moulded beam, 45 feet 6 inches moulded depth, 16,730 tons displacement to load line, 9975 deadweight tons, and had 8500-shaft-horsepower geared turbines, giving them a speed of 16½ knots and a cruising radius of 17,692 nautical miles. Scale of the model is ⅛ inch to the foot.

Given by U. S. Maritime Commission.

STANDARD AMERICAN MERCHANT SHIP, C–3 CLASS, TYPE C–3–S–A2
RIGGED MODEL, USNM 313035

This model represents a standard class of turbine-driven single-screw cargo steamer designed by the U. S. Maritime Commission before the last war for general trade.

The model shows a steamer having moderate sheer, a straight keel, slightly raking straight stem with small

145

"soft nose," vertical post, and a cruiser stern. The entrance is sharp and slightly hollow, the body is long and begins well forward of midlength, and the run is rather long and easy.

There is a raised deck forward. Abaft this the sheer is broken, with no bulwarks; amidships is an island house, two decks high, on which is a 2-deck superstructure containing the bridge structure. There are three cargo hatches forward and two aft, four pairs of derrick posts forward and three aft. The ship has a single stack.

These ships measured 492 feet overall, 69 feet 6 inches beam, 42 feet 6 inches moulded depth, 28 feet 6 inches draft to load line, 17,615 tons displacement loaded, 12,343 tons deadweight, 7949 gross tons register, and had 8500 shaft horsepower geared turbines which gave them a speed of 10½ knots and a cruising radius of 12,000 nautical miles. Scale of model is ⅛ inch to the foot.

Given by the U. S. Maritime Commission.

STANDARD AMERICAN TANKER, TYPE 2–SE–A1
RIGGED MODEL, USNM 313036

This model represents a standard design turbine-driven, single-screw tanker prepared by the U. S. Maritime Commission before the last war. These vessels were faster than most earlier American tankers and were intended to serve the Navy in time of war.

The model shows a tanker having moderate and broken sheer, straight keel, straight raking stem with a small "soft nose" and very angular forefoot, an upright post, and cruiser stern.

There is a short raised deck forward, with a break in the sheer, a catwalk to the midship island, which is two decks high and has upon it a superstructure two decks high, containing the wheelhouse and bridge, and a signal mast. A catwalk leads from the island to the raised poop, one deck high, on which is a large deckhouse, a smaller one, and a stack. Forward is a derrick mast, and the ship also has a mast and two pairs of derrick posts.

This class of ships measured 523 feet 6 inches length overall, 68 feet beam, 39 feet 3 inches moulded depth, 21,670 tons displacement loaded, 16,765 tons deadweight, 10,172 gross tons register, and had 6000 shaft horsepower geared turbines which gave the vessel a speed 14½ knots and a cruising radius of 12,600 nautical miles. Scale of model ⅛ inch to the foot.

Given by the U.S. Maritime Commission.

STANDARD AMERICAN CARGO STEAMER, LIBERTY SHIP, TYPE EC2–S–C1
RIGGED MODEL, USNM 311022

This model is of a standard design of wartime single-screw vessel. Known as "Liberty ships," they were built in American shipyards by mass production methods. The design, a modification of a successful British class of ships, was prepared under the direction of the U. S. Maritime Commission to fit American production requirements. The ships were commonly of all-welded construction and had reciprocating steam engines, as turbines were required for other vessels. Liberty Ships served throughout the war as cargo carriers and even as emergency transports; many were lost through enemy action.

The model represents a cargo steamer having moderate and flush sheer, straight keel, straight raking stem, upright post, cruiser stern, a long body and deadflat, a short and full entrance, and a short but easy run. Midsection formed with a slight rise in the straight floor, a low and hard bilge on a short radius, and an upright topside.

There are three cargo hatches forward and two aft to serve the five cargo holds; a single deckhouse stands a little abaft midlength, and on it is a 2-deck superstructure containing wheelhouse and bridge, a single stack, and a signal pole to port of the foreside of the stack. There are three derrick masts, and a small deckhouse lies right aft on the main deck. Some variation existed in the deck arrangement of vessels of this design.

Liberty Ships measured 441 feet 6 inches length overall, 56 feet 10¾ inches moulded beam, and 37 feet 4 inches moulded depth, drawing 27 feet 8⅞ inches when loaded. The ships were of 14,257 tons displacement and 10,865 tons deadweight. The reciprocating engines developed 2500 shaft horsepower, giving a speed of 10½ to 11 knots and a cruising radius of about 10,000 nautical miles. Scale of model is ⅛ inch to the foot.

Given by the U. S. Maritime Commission.

STANDARD AMERICAN CARGO STEAMER, VICTORY SHIP, TYPE VC2–S–AP
RIGGED MODEL, USNM 313023

This model is of a standard design of turbine-driven single-screw merchant ship prepared by the U. S. Maritime Commission early in the last war. This design was the result of experience with low-speed cargo ships, which suffered heavy losses from enemy sub-

LIBERTY SHIP CLASS EC2–S–C1, FITTED FOR WAR SERVICE.   Rigged model USNM 313022 shows the original design of the class.   (*U.S. Maritime Administration photo 4423.*)

marine attacks. The Victory Ship was intended as a mass-produced ship of sufficient speed to avoid such attacks, and with the same shaft horsepower as the Type C–3–S–A2, but with finer lines. Ships of this class were capable of making 16½ knots as compared to the 10½ knots of the C–3–S–A2.

The model shows a cargo steamer having a straight keel, straight raking stem with a small "soft-nose," a

VICTORY SHIP, CLASS VC2–S–AP–2, FITTED FOR WAR SERVICE.   Rigged model USNM 313023 shows the basic design of the class.   (*U.S. Maritime Administration photo 3969.*)

147

vertical post, cruiser stern, sharp entrance, long body, and fine run. Midsection has a slight rise in the straight floor, a low firm bilge on a small radius, and a slight tumble-home in the upper topside.

The vessel has a raised forecastle deck with break in the moderate sheer and flush sheer abaft the break. There are a deckhouse amidships with a single stack and bridge structure, a small house aft, three derrick masts, and two pairs of derrick posts. A large number of ships were built on the Victory Ship lines during the war, but differed a good deal in appearance and arrangements. Since the war some ships of this type have been converted to passenger service.

The Victory Ships measured 455 feet 3 inches length overall, 62 feet moulded beam, 38 feet moulded depth, 28 feet 6¾ inches draft loaded, 15,194 tons displacement to load line, 10,850 deadweight tons, and 7612 gross tons register. The geared turbines produced 8500 shaft horsepower, and the ships were capable of maintaining a speed of 16½ knots; some of the class were said to have made 18 knots in emergencies. The ships had a cruising radius of about 20,500 nautical miles. Scale of model is ⅛ inch to the foot.

Given by the U. S. Maritime Commission.

PASSENGER LINER, 1951
RIGGED MODEL, USNM 316198

Independence, Constitution

The passenger liners *Independence* and *Constitution*, represented by this model, were built at Quincy, Massachusetts, in 1950–51 by the Bethlehem Steel Company, Shipbuilding Division, for the American Export Lines. These vessels were designed for the Mediterranean service by the U.S. Maritime Administration, classified as Type P3–S2–DL2. At the time of their launch the ships were considered the most advanced of their type.

The model is on a scale of ⅛ inch to the foot, representing a liner 683 feet overall, 89 feet beam, 30 feet draft loaded, 12,310 tons deadweight, 23,720 tons register, licensed for 1,007 passengers. The ships are driven by steam turbines and have a service speed of 22½ knots; the trial speed was over 26 knots. Passenger interiors were designed by Henry Drefuss.

The model is of a modern liner having rather straight, broken sheer, straight keel with little or no drag, a raking straight stem of the "soft nose" type, a round fantail stern of the "bustle" profile, a long, fine entrance and a long, easy run, and twin screws

with shafts faired into the hull by shrouding. Midsection is formed with a straight, slightly rising floor, a hard turn of bilge, and a slight tumble-home in the topside.

The model shows two stacks, a pair of derrick ports fore and aft, and one mast. The vessels had their superstructure altered in 1958–59. These ships were designed so that they might be converted into troop ships in time of war, each to carry 5,000 men.

Lent by the American Export Lines.

GREAT LAKES ORE and BULK CARRIER, SELF-UNLOADING EQUIPMENT, 1950
RIGGED MODEL, USNM 314497

This model represents, in simplified detail, a typical Great Lakes ore and bulk carrier and is intended to show the fittings and the method of operation of the patented self-unloading machinery developed for such vessels by the donor of the model, the late Leatham D. Smith.

The ship represented has a short, full entrance, an abnormally long parallel-sided body and a short and full run.

Forward there is a short raised deck, on which are a deckhouse with wheelhouse and bridge and a small pole mast; the body of the ship has cargo hatches; well aft is a large deckhouse on which is a large, single stack, a mast, and boats. The model shows a self-unloading boom and lifting frame, with endless-belt delivery; the forehold is exposed by a plastic panel to show the pick-up gear employing drag-line scoop buckets and housings.

Scale of model is probably ¼ inch to the foot, representing a ship about 400 feet long.

Given by the Leatham D. Smith Shipbuilding Company, Sturgeon Bay, Wisconsin.

WOODEN, SCREW CANAL TUG-BARGE, 1872
RIGGED MODEL, USNM 308435

William Baxter

The wooden, twin-screw steam canal tug and barge was a type developed on the Erie Canal, in New York as the result of a prize competition. It was produced to reduce cost of transportation by moving a number of barges at once, and the design was intended to allow use of a low-power engine and screw propellers without damage to canal banks. The first successful steam barges were built in 1871. The *William Baxter*, built at Fishkill, New York, in 1872, was the basic design of William Baxter for the first seven boats

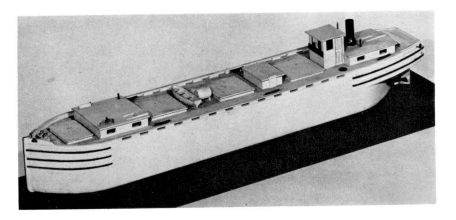

built. She was used, for part of her career, as a yacht and demonstrator on the canal and the Hudson River. Twin screws were eventually abandoned; single screws were employed in the last seven of the fourteen boats built on Baxter's designs. The standard Baxter boats were 96 feet long, 17 feet beam, and 9 feet depth in hold and were able to carry 215 tons of freight on a draft of 6 feet. These boats could tow barges from New York to Buffalo and return in 16 days, as compared with 25 to 30 days by horse-drawn boats on the canal and river tugs on the Hudson.

The model shows a vessel of the old canal-boat form, having parallel sides, a very full and very much rounded, convex, V-shaped entrance, and a similar run; the hull is basically double-ended. A false counter, in the same general manner as Fulton's steamer *North River*, is placed high on the stern, which shows enough overhang to protect the propeller and rudder in the locks. The wide and rectangular transom is flat and nearly vertical, the bottom is straight fore and aft and flat athwartships, and the stem straight and vertical, as is the post. The sheer is straight except at the ends, where it sweeps a little upward to the posts. The midsection is rectangular, with the chines slightly rounded.

At the bow is a small trunk cabin for the crew; abaft are three large cargo hatches, a pilothouse, and a small trunk cabin with a low single stack on it, with engine and boiler below. A skiff is carried on deck between the midship hatches, where there is also a hold-ventilating hatch. Heavy guards protect the sides and ends of the hull.

The *William Baxter* was 97 feet long overall, 95.7 feet between perpendiculars, 17.2 feet beam, and 9.5 depth; she was 116.93 tons gross, 73.76 tons net, and had two 42-horsepower reciprocating engines. Scale of model is ¼ inch to the foot.

Given by W. L. Christian, Binghamton, New York.

WOODEN, SCREW TUG, 1873
Builder's Half-Model, usnm 76043

Atlantic

The wooden, single-screw steam tug *Atlantic* was built on this model at East Boston in 1873 for the U.S. Army Quartermaster's Department at New York City. Her designer and builder was Dennison J. Lawlor, who had a reputation for designing fine tugs as well as other types of wooden vessels, and the *Atlantic* is an excellent example of his tug designs. Vessels of this type were then commonly employed in towing in coasting schooners. The tugs were required to go some distance to sea, so that besides towing well, they were also required to steam fast, running free, and to have some claim to seaworthiness.

The half-model represents a tug hull having strong sheer, straight keel with marked drag, an upright and straight stem rabbet with a well-rounded forefoot, upright post, a round, fantail counter with bulwarks tumbled-in, a long, sharp entrance, hollow at the forefoot, a short body, and a long and very fine run. The midsection shows a moderate rise in the straight floor, a low and rather hard turn of bilge, and tumble-home in the topside. The very easy lines of the hull show that the principles of good tug design were known by the time the *Atlantic* was modeled.

The model is of a tug measuring 78 feet 3 inches extreme moulded length, 18 feet moulded beam, and 9 feet moulded depth. Scale of model is ½ inch to the foot. The *Atlantic* drew about 8 feet 9 inches to 9 feet at post, in cruising trim.

Given by Dennison J. Lawlor, shipbuilder, Chelsea, Massachusetts.

IRON, SCREW TUG, 1879
RIGGED MODEL, USNM 160167

Rattler

This model represents the iron, single-screw steam tug *Rattler* built at Philadelphia, Pennsylvania, by Neafie and Levy in 1879. The *Rattler* was a large tug for her day and was intended for coastwise towing. The invasion of the coastal trade by the barge tow began in the 1870's and by 1880 the tug and barge were becoming common in short-haul runs in the coal trade. Though the large sailing schooner continued in this trade until into the 20th century, the tug and barge slowly displaced the large schooners of three, four, five, and six masts in all but the longest runs and even in these, finally, the steam collier doomed the sailing schooner. Tugs of the *Rattler's* type, but of smaller size, had been developed, ironically enough, as a necessary aid to the coasting schooner; these seagoing tugs went out to tow in coasters when the wind failed them or the schooners had been damaged. Tugs engaged in this work were well developed in the decade following the Civil War and by 1875 were fast, powerful and seaworthy vessels easily capable of coastwise towing in open water.

The model shows an iron steam-tug hull having a single screw, straight keel with marked drag, stem straight and nearly vertical with forefoot much rounded, vertical post, a round fantail counter with tumble-home in bulwarks, a long and sharp entrance slightly hollow near the stem at load line, and a long, very fine run. The sheer is marked and graceful. The midsection is formed with much rise in the straight floor, a firm bilge, and tumble-home in topside.

The model has a long deckhouse, on the roof of which is a pilothouse, a single large stack, and a pair of small boats in davits. On the flush main deck, forward and abaft the house, are heavy iron towing bollards. The arrangement of this tug on deck is standard for her type and date. Model is painted in the fashion of her day.

The *Rattler* was 102 feet 6 inches between perpendiculars, 22 feet moulded beam, and 11 feet depth; her gross tonnage was 139.68; and her nominal horsepower 350 according to Hall's *Report on Shipbuilding*. Scale of model is ½ inch to the foot, by which she is approximately 115 feet long, 25 feet extreme beam.

Gift of Neafie and Levy, shipbuilders, Philadelphia, Pennsylvania.

SEAGOING TUG, 1904
RIGGED MODEL, USNM 309521

Conestoga

This model is of the seagoing tug, *Conestoga*, built at Sparrows Point, Maryland, in 1904, for coastwise towing of coal barges. Steel and iron tugs of this class used the same hull model as earlier wooden tugs employed in towing the large coasting schooners of the coal trade. The *Conestoga* was typical of her class, which was employed largely in towing large wooden seagoing barges whose hulls were often built on the same model as the large 4- or 5-masted schooners; this type of coal carrying lasted until about 1918, when steam colliers and rail transportation put an end to the barges.

Barges were towed in line, the leading barge from towing bitts located just abaft the deckhouse on the main deck of the tug; American tugs did not use a towing winch until recent years. Barge tugs in the

IRON STEAM TUG *Rattler*, built in 1879 at Philadelphia, Pennsylvania, by Neafie and Levy. This tug, was intended for coastwise towing. Rigged model USNM 160167. (*Smithsonian photo 44693–d.*)

150

The half-model shows a wooden, single-screw tug-boat hull having moderate sheer, straight keel with drag, well rounded forefoot, nearly straight and upright stem rabbet above, upright post, a round fantail counter, a short and rather full entrance, and a short and heavy run. The midsection is formed with very short, rising, straight floor, a very easy round bilge, and an upright topside.

The model is made to deck height; the bulwarks are not shown.

A tug about 64 feet 6 inches moulded length at deck, 16 feet 8 inches moulded beam, and 7 feet 6 inches moulded depth to deck at side is represented. Scale of model is ½ inch to the foot.

Given by Levingston Shipbuilding Company, Port Orange, Texas.

HARBOR TUG, 1938
RIGGED MODEL, USNM 312088

Thomas E. Moran

This model represents the steel, single-screw, diesel harbor tug *Thomas E. Moran* built at Bay City, Michigan, in 1938 for the Moran Towing and Transportation Company, Inc., of New York City. The tug was designed by Tams, Inc., of New York.

The *Thomas E. Moran* has a straight keel with some drag, rather upright curved stem with rounded forefoot, vertical post, single screw, a round fantail tugboat stern with tumble-home in the bulwarks, strong sheer, sharp entrance, no apparent deadflat, and a clean run. Midsection formed with a marked rise in straight floor, a round easy bilge, and a nearly upright topside.

The tug had a large deckhouse amidships with a pilothouse at its fore end, slightly raised above the rest of the house. On the deck house was a dummy stack, one boat on davits and two pole masts. The model is complete in detail to show fitting of a tug of this type and date.

The tug was 89.4 feet between perpendiculars, 25.2 feet extreme beam and 10 feet depth in hold; 158 tons gross, 62 tons net. Scale of model is ¼ inch to the foot.

Given by the Moran Towing and Transportation Company, Inc. of New York City.

RIGGED MODEL (USNM 312088) OF THE MODERN STEEL, DIESEL HARBOR TUGBOAT *Thomas E. Moran*, 1938. Tugs of this type have displaced the older wooden and steel tugs in the large American ports. (*Smithsonian photo 44697–j.*)

153

SEAGOING TUG AND SALVAGE VESSEL, CLASS V–4, FITTED FOR WAR SERVICE. Rigged model USNM 313020 shows basic design of class. (*U.S. Maritime Administration photo 5059.*)

SEAGOING TUG, V–4 TYPE, 1942
RIGGED MODEL, USNM 313020

The model represents a modern seagoing, raised-deck tug designed during the late war by the United States Maritime Commission, as a standard design. It had a diesel engine of 2250 horsepower, and a single screw with Kort nozzle. A number of these were laid down in 1942–46 to be used for ocean towing and salvage work. The vessels were diesel-powered and resembled the large European seagoing tugs and salvage vessels.

The model shows a seagoing steel tug hull having marked sheer, a straight keel with some drag, a straight, upright, and "soft nose" stem, a round fantail counter with tumble home in the bulwarks, and a cutaway skeg with shaft exposed for some distance. The entrance is moderately sharp and the run fine. The midsection is formed with a rising straight floor, a low hard bilge, and a slight tumble-home in the topside.

The sheer line is broken by a raised forecastle deck, running to a little abaft amidships, on which is a rather large deckhouse with a wheelhouse and bridge structure at its fore end. A low, oval dummy stack is fitted, with a pole mast forward and a derrick pole and boom aft. A towing winch is located abaft the break of the raised deck and under an overhang.

These tugs were 194 feet 9 inches long, 37 feet 6 inches beam, drew 16 feet 4½ inches at the post, and had a tonnage depth of 21.5 feet. Their displacement tonnage was 1613, and their registered tonnage 1117 gross. Scale of model is ⅛ inch to the foot.

Given by the U. S. Maritime Commission.

NAVAL STEAM LAUNCH, 1862–63
BUILDER'S HALF-MODEL, USNM 76044

This half-model was made by Dennison J. Lawlor, shipbuilder, late in 1862 for the purpose of building, by contract, several steam launches for the U. S. Navy. The launches were built at East Boston, Massachusetts, during the winter of 1862–63 and one of these boats was used by Lt. W. B. Cushing, U. S. N., in the torpedoing and sinking of the Confederate States steam, ironclad ram *Albemarle*, a notable naval incident in the Civil War. The launch, fitted with a spar torpedo mounted on a swivel at the bow, was run up on to the log-raft boom around the ram; the spar-torpedo was then placed under the casemate-overhang of the ironclad and there exploded. When the ram was later raised it was found that the explosion had blown a hole in the side of the ram as well as doing other damage. The launch used by Cushing had a vertical boiler and is said to have had a maximum speed of between 7 and 8 knots. It was destroyed by gunfire in the attack.

The half-model shows a launch hull of the cutter form, having moderate sheer, a straight keel with some drag, well rounded forefoot with straight, upright stem rabbet above, slightly raking post, and a very short counter ending in a shallow, flat,

154

and slightly raking transom. The rudder post is shown in the counter, just inboard of the transom, but this may be an error. The entrance is quite long and sharp, the run is rather full but quite long. The midsection shows a slightly rising floor, a low and hard bilge, and an upright topside.

Model is mounted with straight stem, keel, post, propeller and rudder.

The model is for a steam, single-screw launch measuring 33 feet 6 inches moulded length at gunwale, 7 feet 8 inches moulded beam, and 3 feet 7½ inches moulded depth. Scale of model is 1 inch to the foot.

Given by Dennison J. Lawler, shipbuilder, Chelsea, Massachusetts.

EUROPEAN STEAM LAUNCH, 1875
RIGGED MODEL, USNM 311396

Trio

The steam launch *Trio* is of the type once built in Northern Europe for timber inspection. The model was built by a German engineer and is of a launch of 1875.

The model represents a launch having a fine entrance and run, a straight keel with some drag, curved and rather upright stem, vertical post, single screw, round fantail counter with knuckle at deck level, and moderate sheer. The midsection is formed with much rise in the straight floor, a rather slack round bilge, and an upright topside. The propeller is of large diameter by modern standards, and has its shaft low on the sternpost, so that the propeller extends well below the keel and is therefore protected by the skeg bar that extends below the deepest part of the keel itself.

The vertical boiler is fitted with a high stack having a copper top. The steering-wheel is abaft the boiler, which is just forward of midlength. Forward of the boiler is a cockpit with side seats having paneled backs. Abaft the steersman's position is another seating space, in which are seats with plain staved backs. The engine and boiler were close together and were operated by the helmsman and a fireman. There were short decks at bow and stern and narrow washboards along the sides.

The model (its scale is unknown) measures 40 inches overall and appears to represent a launch between 42 and 50 feet length.

Loaned by Walter A. Thompson, Baltimore, Maryland.

STEAM LAUNCH, 1883
BUILDER'S HALF-MODEL, USNM 160131

This half-model of an unidentified steam launch is in the Watercraft Collection without detailed information. The half-model represents a swift steam-launch hull having slight sheer, straight keel with some drag, upright straight stem rabbet with slightly rounded forefoot, upright post, round fantail counter, a long and sharp convex entrance, and a long and very fine run. The midsection shows a straight rising floor, a rather high and hard bilge, and a slightly flaring topside.

The lift spacing suggests that the model is on a scale of 1 inch to the foot, at which this model would be for a launch of 29 feet 6 inches moulded length at gunwale, 5 feet moulded beam, 2 feet 9 inches moulded depth, and about 2 feet 6 inches draft.

Gift of U. S. Fish Commission, 1883.

STEAM LAUNCH, about 1880–85
BUILDER'S HALF-MODEL, USNM 160130

The half-model is of a swift, low-powered steam-launch hull of about 1880–85, having graceful and moderate sheer, a slightly rockered keel and keel rabbet, a much rounded forefoot with nearly straight and upright stem rabbet above, a rounded and raking sternpost rabbet with the post itself raking, and a round fantail stern of moderate overhang. The entrance is long, sharp, and quite hollow in the vicinity of the forefoot, and the run is easy and rather long. The midsection is formed with much rise in the straight floor, a high and easy bilge, and a nearly upright topside. This is a single-screw boat; the boiler and engine were slightly abaft midlength and the launch was probably half-decked, with a large oval cockpit.

Model is mounted with straight stem, keel, semi-skeg post, and rudder.

The scale of the half-model appears to be ½ inch to the foot, at which the launch would have been 36 feet moulded length at gunwale, 9 feet 6 inches moulded beam, and 5 feet 1¼ inch moulded depth.

Supposed to be part of a builder's proposal to some department of the government, but no evidence exists to show that a launch was built on the model.

The donor is unknown, probably it was the U.S. Fish Commission.

STEAM YACHT, 1881
BUILDER'S HALF-MODEL, USNM 76031

Adelita

The wooden, single-screw steam yacht *Adelita* was built on this model at East Boston, Massachusetts, in 1881 by Dennison J. Lawlor, for Boston owners. She was designed for high speed and carried a light schooner rig of small sail area for steadying purposes only.

The half-model is of a steam-yacht hull having moderate and graceful sheer, a straight keel with marked drag, a well rounded forefoot with the stem rabbet nearly straight and upright above, an upright post, and a long and thin round fantail counter with flaring rail. The entrance is long, sharp and hollow at forefoot, and the run is long and very fine. The midsection shows a sharply rising straight floor, a high and rather hard bilge, and a slight tumble-home in the topside.

Model is mounted with longhead, cutwater, keel, post, and rudder.

The model is for a yacht 88 feet moulded length at rail, 82 feet between perpendiculars, 16 feet beam, 7 feet 9½ inches depth, and 27.55 net tons, 55.09 gross tons register. Scale of model is ½ inch to the foot.

Gift of Dennison J. Lawlor, shipbuilder, Chelsea, Massachusetts.

STEAM YACHT, 1884
BUILDER'S HALF-MODEL, USNM 76042

This half-model was a proposal for constructing a large 3-masted steam yacht, having light pole masts with small steadying sails and intended to steam fast. It was made by Dennison J. Lawlor at East Boston, Massachusetts, in 1884. No vessel was built on the model, which represented very advanced ideas for this class of yacht at the time.

The half-model is for a large, single-screw, wooden steam-yacht hull having moderate and graceful sheer, a straight keel with marked drag, a well-rounded forefoot with the stem rabbet curved and raking above. The stern rabbet is curved and raking at the skeg, which has a vertical trailing edge. The long, light, and narrow fantail counter ends in a round and flaring bulwark to form the rail. The entrance is long, sharp, and hollow at the forefoot, and the run is long and very fine. The midsection shows a rising floor with hollow at garboard, a high and firm bilge, and a slight tumble-home above.

The model is mounted with graceful longhead, billet, trails, cutwater, keel, skeg, and balanced rudder.

The scale of the model is ⅜ inch to the foot, representing a vessel 160 feet moulded length at rail, 28 feet moulded beam, and 15 feet moulded depth to rail.

Given by Dennison J. Lawlor, shipbuilder, Chelsea, Massachusetts.

STEAM LAUNCH, 1890
BUILDER'S HALF-MODEL, USNM 76300

Kara

The steam pleasure launch *Kara* was built on the lines of this model at South Boston (Neponset), Massachusetts, in 1890 by George Lawley and Son. The launch was intended for sport fishing as well as for general yachting purposes.

The half-model shows a single-screw, wooden steam launch, half-decked, and having moderate sheer, a straight keel with some drag, a well-curved forefoot and a raking and slightly curved stem rabbet, an upright post, round fantail stern, the post rabbet well curved, and a marked skeg. The entrance is long and fine, as is the run, and the midsection shows a rising straight floor, a high and firm bilge, and a slight tumble-home in the topside.

Model is mounted with curved stem, keel, and skeg.

The launch was 40 feet on deck, 6 feet beam, draft aft 3 feet 6 inches, draft forward 1 foot 3 inches. Speed 10 statute miles per hour. Scale of model is ¾ inch to the foot.

Given by U.S. Bureau of Fisheries.

STEAM YACHT, 1890
BUILDER'S HALF-MODEL, USNM 76301

Princess

The steam yacht *Princess* was built on the lines of this half-model at Boston, Massachusetts, in 1890. She was a wooden, schooner-rigged, single-screw steam yacht having moderate and graceful sheer, a straight keel with some drag, a well curved forefoot and a straight and nearly vertical stem rabbet, upright post, moderately long counter with elliptical transom, a long and sharp entrance, a short body, and a long and very easy run. The midsection is formed with a rising straight floor, a high and rather hard bilge, and slight tumble-home in the topside.

Mounted with straight stem, keel, post, and rudder.

This yacht did not have a bowsprit and her small rig was for steadying purposes only.

156

The model scales 76 feet 3 inches between perpendiculars, 15 feet 2½ inch beam, and 6 feet 5 inches depth. Scale of model is ¾ inch to the foot.

Donor not recorded.

GLASS-CABIN LAUNCH, 1902
BUILDER'S HALF-MODEL, USNM 311241

A gasoline-powered cabin launch, name unknown, was built on this model in 1902 at Oxford, Maryland, by Charles W. Langdon for cruising on Chesapeake Bay. Launches of this type strongly resembled the older steam launches in hull form. Popularly known as glass-cabin launches, they had long and rather high trunk cabins with large rectangular ports and windows and were well suited for hot-weather cruising in protected waters, or where shelter could be quickly reached.

The half-model shows a hull of the same form as the older steam launches, having moderate sheer, a straight keel with some drag, a rounded forefoot with nearly straight and upright stem rabbet, upright sternpost, a round fantail counter of moderate overhang, and a short and full entrance and run. The midsection is formed with a short straight rising floor, an easy round bilge and an upright topside. This launch is somewhat fuller-ended than usual in her type, and also above the average in proportion of beam to length.

The model is for a launch 45 feet 4 inches moulded length at deck, 10 feet moulded beam, and 4 feet moulded depth at side. Scale of model is ½ inch to the foot.

Given by Charles W. Langdon, boatbuilder, Oxford, Maryland.

GLASS-CABIN LAUNCH, 1905
BUILDER'S HALF-MODEL, USNM 311242

Comfort

The double-ended glass-cabin launch *Comfort*, powered with a gasoline engine, was built on this model in 1905 by Charles W. Langdon at Oxford, Maryland, for use on the Chesapeake. She was an unusually burdensome and roomy boat of her type, sharp at both ends and with the usual long and rather high trunk cabin, having full standing headroom.

The half-model shows a launch hull sharp at both ends and having moderate sheer, a straight keel with some drag, rounded forefoot with nearly straight and vertical stem rabbet above, an upright post, and a "canoe stern" formed with the overhanging

and curved post becoming nearly vertical before the deck is reached—a form of stern first introduced in sailing boats and at the turn of the century popular also in launches. The entrance is short and full, the run is unusually heavy. The midsection shows a short straight floor with moderate rise, a low and well rounded bilge, and an upright topside.

The launch represented was 40 feet moulded length at deck, 8 feet 10 inches moulded beam, 4 feet moulded depth. Scale of model is ¾ inch to the foot.

Given by Charles W. Langdon, boatbuilder, Oxford, Maryland.

FERRY LAUNCH
BUILDER'S HALF-MODEL, USNM 311523

Nymph

The single-screw wooden ferry launch *Nymph* was built on this model at Bradenton, Florida, sometime between 1918 and 1930 by "Bat" Fogarty. This boat was powered with a gasoline engine and was intended to carry passengers only.

The half-model is of a small launch, shaped much like a sailing boat, having moderate sheer, a straight keel fairing into the stem in a long and easy curve, the stem rabbet becoming upright at deck, an upright post, round fantail counter, long and sharp entrance, and a short but easy run. The midsection shows a rising straight floor, a slack round bilge, and an upright topside.

The model is believed to be for a launch 35 feet 3 inches moulded length at gunwale, 8 feet moulded beam, and 3 feet 6 inches moulded depth. The scale of the model 1 inch to the foot.

Given by "Bat" Fogarty, boatbuilder, Bradenton, Florida.

BILOXI FREIGHT BOAT, 1925
BUILDER'S HALF-MODEL, USNM 311222

A gasoline-powered freight boat of the launch type was built on this model about 1925 at Biloxi, Mississippi, by Anson Holley for local owners. The name of the boat is unknown.

The half-model represents a large launch hull having a single screw, moderate sheer, straight keel with slight drag, slightly rounded forefoot, straight and upright stem rabbet above, upright post, slightly raking flat transom, sharp entrance, and a long easy run. The midsection shows a straight and rising floor and an easy round bilge, wall-sided above.

The model, which resembles the local fishing launches, is for a larger boat measuring 43 feet moulded length at gunwale, 13 feet moulded beam, 4 feet 6 inches moulded depth. The scale of the model is ½ inch to the foot.

Given by Anson Holley, boatbuilder, Biloxi, Mississippi.

CRUISING LAUNCH, 1925
BUILDER'S HALF-MODEL, USNM 315700

Pawnee

The cruising launch *Pawnee* was built on this model at East Moriches, Long Island, New York, in 1925 by Otis A. Palmer. The boat was intended for overnight cruising and for inshore sport fishing, and was built to be seaworthy and to have moderate power and speed. It had a cuddy (small trunk cabin) forward and a large cockpit, with the engine under a box in the cockpit.

The half-model shows a short, wide, motorboat cruiser hull having moderate sheer, a rockered keel rabbet (a skeg was employed), and a curved and raking stem rabbet with a well rockered forefoot. The transom is flat and raking. The entrance is sharp, convex and rather short. The run is long and slightly cambered in the buttocks. Midsection is formed with a short, slightly rising straight floor, a slack round bilge, and a flaring topside.

Scale of the model is 1 inch to the foot, producing a moulded length of 22 feet, moulded beam of 8 feet, and moulded depth of 2 feet 11 inches.

The model is marked by a freeboard that is high for the hull length.

Gift of Mrs. Otis A. Palmer, East Moriches, Long Island, New York.

CRUISING LAUNCH, 1925
BUILDER'S HALF-MODEL, USNM 311258

A raised-deck, single-screw cruising launch, name unknown, was built on this model about 1925 at Apalachicola, Florida, by Samuel Johnson. She was powered with a gasoline engine. The model represents a general type of motor boat popular for pleasure cruising in the period 1912–30.

The half-model represents a motor launch hull having a long raised deck forward, a rather straight main sheer, a rockered keel-rabbet with skeg aft, a raking curved stem rabbet, a shallow vertical transom, curved athwartships, a short and sharp entrance, and a long but rather full run. The raised deck is high above the main sheer and extends about a third the length of the hull from the bow. The midsection

is formed with a rising straight floor, a slack round bilge and a nearly upright topside.

The model is supposed to be to the scale of ½ inch to the foot and to represent a boat 44 feet long at gunwale, 10 feet moulded beam, and about 5 feet depth.

Given by Samuel Johnson, boatbuilder, Apalachicola, Florida.

CRUISING LAUNCH, 1927
BUILDER'S HALF-MODEL, USNM 311259

A raised-deck, single-screw, cruising launch, name unknown, was built on this model about 1927 by Samuel Johnson at Apalachicola, Florida. According to the builder, this boat was powered by a converted automobile engine.

The half-model is of a launch hull having a rather long raised deck forward, nearly straight sheer, rockered keel rabbet with skeg aft, upright and nearly straight stem rabbet, wide, raking flat transom, short and full entrance, and a long and flat run. The midsection has a rising straight floor, a hard round bilge, and an upright topside. The raised deck is about one-third the whole length of the hull.

The model is believed to be on a scale of 1 inch to the foot and to represent a boat 30 feet 3 inches moulded length, 7 feet moulded beam, and 2 feet 1½ inch moulded depth.

Given by Samuel Johnson, boatbuilder, Apalachicola, Florida.

MOTOR CRUISER, 1927
BUILDER'S HALF-MODEL, USNM 315697

This half-model represents a small, raised-deck, motor cruiser, name unknown, designed and built by Otis A. Palmer of East Moriches, Long Island, New York, in 1927. This type of small cruiser was very popular from about 1910 to 1932, having a cabin under a raised deck forward and a standing canopy over the cockpit. The boats were usually low-powered, inexpensive craft and of varying degrees of seaworthiness. The model is fairly typical of many of this class, particularly of the relatively inexpensive boats. The boats of this general model would make about 8 to 9 knots with a gasoline engine of 15 to 25 horsepower.

The half-model shows a cruiser having a rather high raised foredeck with a break abaft midlength. The keel rabbet is rockered and the boat had a skeg, with the rudder hung outboard. The stem rabbet is rounded and flaring, the transom flat and raking, the entrance moderately sharp, and the run rather flat and long. The midsection is abaft midlength and shows a very short, straight rising floor, a round easy bilge, and a slightly flaring topside. The freeboard is high for the hull length.

Scale of the model is 1 inch to the foot, giving a moulded length overall of 28 feet, a moulded beam of 8 feet 10 inches, and a moulded depth abaft the break of deck of 4 feet 1½ inches.

The boat had berths for four, and a toilet and galley.

Gift of Mrs. Otis A. Palmer, East Moriches, Long Island, New York.

MOTOR CRUISER, 1928–29
Builder's Half-Model, usnm 315698

Two cruising launches, names unknown, were built from this model in 1928–29 by Otis A. Palmer, East Moriches, Long Island, New York. They had different arrangements, and were of two sizes. The model was designed to produce a boat 32 feet 3 inches moulded length on a scale of 1 inch to the foot, or 20 feet 6 inches long on a scale 1½ inch to the foot. This use of two scales has been quite common among American small-boat builders.

The half-model represents a launch hull designed for moderate speed and power, having rather straight sheer, a slightly rockered keel rabbet (with skeg aft), a well rounded forefoot with a raking, curved stem rabbet, a wide flat, raking transom, sharp convex entrance, and a long and rather flat run. The freeboard is high for the length of hull. Midsection is formed with a very short and slightly rising straight floor, a slack round bilge, and flaring topside. The model is a solid block, with only a top lift added. On a scale of 1 inch to the foot it is for a boat 32 feet 3 inches moulded length at rail, 8 feet 4 inches moulded beam, and 4 feet moulded depth; on a scale of 1½ inch to the foot the boat would measure 20 feet 6 inches moulded length at rail, 5 feet 8 inches moulded beam, and 2 feet 8 inches moulded depth. A seaworthy launch for the dimensions is indicated.

Gift of Mrs. Otis A. Palmer, East Moriches, Long Island, New York.

PASSENGER and FREIGHT LAUNCH, 1930
Builder's Half-Model, usnm 311236

A passenger and freight carrying launch, name unknown, was built on this model at Port Arthur, Texas, by John H. Cram about 1930. This launch was single screw, with gasoline engine.

The half-model is of a V-bottom launch hull having moderate sheer, straight keel with skeg aft, upright straight stem rabbet slightly rounded at forefoot, nearly upright flat transom, the chine carried high forward, the entrance short and sharp, and the run long and straight. The midsection shows a straight deadrise, angular chine and slightly flaring straight topside. The form of hull indicated by this model has been popular on the coast of the Gulf of Mexico for many years, V-bottom construction having been in use before 1880 in Louisiana, Mississippi, and Texas.

The model is for a launch measuring about 45 feet 4 inches moulded length at gunwale, 12 feet 6 inches beam, and 5 feet depth. Scale of model is ½ inch to the foot.

Given by John H. Cram, boatbuilder, Port Arthur, Texas.

SPORT FISHING BOAT, 1938
Builder's Half-Model, usnm 311252

A V-bottom, gasoline-powered, sport fishing tender was built on this model about 1938 by Patrick Moore at Galveston, Texas. The launch was intended to accompany a larger boat and to engage in sport fishing in the Gulf of Mexico.

The half-model is for a single-screw launch having straight sheer, a rockered keel rabbet fairing into a rather upright curved stem rabbet, a nearly upright transom, curved athwartships, a sharp entrance, and a long and flat run. The chine, in profile, is high at the stem and is formed in a shallow sweep, rising slightly in the run. The midsection is formed with a straight and rising floor, an angular bilge, and a flaring straight topside.

The model is for a launch 20 feet 4 inches moulded length at gunwale, 7 feet moulded beam, and 3 feet 1 inch moulded depth. Scale of model 1 inch to the foot.

Given by Patrick Moore, boatbuilder, Galveston, Texas.

NEW JERSEY GARVEY, GASOLINE-POWERED,
about 1950
Rigged Model, usnm 315246

This model is of a motor garvey built about 1950 near Tuckerton, New Jersey, for fishing and pleasure boating. This design originated in southern New Jersey and has spread to Delaware, Maryland, and Virginia along the Atlantic beaches and inlets, replacing the earlier sailing garvies, with or without a trunk cabin. In Maryland and Virginia it is used in the oyster fisheries, particularly in the vicinity of Chincoteague Island, and variations are built in New Jersey from Barnegat southward. Now being rather extensively used for pleasure, it is built in lengths from 12 to about 40 feet, and for these dimensions is inexpensive and, when suitably powered, produces a very shallow-draft and fast motor boat.

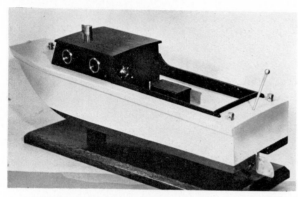

MOTOR GARVEY, a low-cost craft for fishing and pleasure boating, built about 1950, near Tuckerton, New Jersey. Rigged model USNM 315246. (*Smithsonian photo 45605-a.*)

The model shows a scow-hulled motorboat having slightly flaring sides, a flat bottom with a very slight V in the forward rake, a style of bow called "chicken-breasted" in southern New Jersey. The profile of the hull is like that of a sled; the bow rake is curved, and the bottom profile is straight from the bottom of the rake to the nearly vertical transom. The sheer is straight in the model, but some boats of the type have moderate sheer. The bow is always narrower than the stern; the model has a stern as wide as the mid-section. A semitunnel stern, of rather primitive design, is employed in this model, following the stern design used in some of the garvies.

The model is of a rather small boat of the type, measuring 23 feet total length, 6 feet 6 inches beam and 4 feet deep forward, 2 feet aft, and 6 inches draft to chine. Scale is 1 inch to the foot.

Gift of W. R. Main, Waretown, New Jersey.

COLLECTION OF SCREW PROPELLERS and PADDLE-WHEEL MODELS

The Watercraft Collection contains a series of screw propeller models showing, in general, the development of the screw propeller, though all stages of the development are not covered, the Ericsson designs, as well as some others, being omitted. The following designs are included: Robert Hooke 1681, Joseph Bramah 1785, William Lyttleton 1794, John Stevens (two) 1804, Perkins 1825, Beard 1829, Smith 1831, Woodcroft 1832, Burk (two) 1834–35, Smith (two) 1835–36, Burcher 1839, Rennie 1843, Steamboat 1845, Beard 1853, Swartz 1857, Colborn 1865, Cary and Cary 1875, Tyson 1877, Tanner 1878, Steamboat 1880, Stevens 1889, Steamboat 1890, and Hancock (no date).

Models of paddle wheels include two showing side wheels and one of a stern paddle wheel. The stern of a screw vessel fitted with two banded propellers, of the Ericsson type, abaft the rudder, and on a single shaft is also part of this exhibit. The paddle-wheel models show details of the housing and drive of the various paddle wheels. A number of patent models of propellers or propulsion methods are also in this collection.

SCHOONER *Mary D. Dyer*, BUILT AT EAST BOSTON BY DONALD D. McKAY IN 1860. *Photo courtesy The Mariners' Museum, Newport News, Virginia.*

FISHING CRAFT

THE DEPRESSION IN trade and the almost complete cessation of emigration to the American colonies that followed the Civil War in England, during the 1640's, led to the rapid growth of the New England fisheries and colonial maritime trade. To support themselves in this period, the colonials began trading in the West Indies, and as fish was an article-in-trade much in demand there and as the New England colonies could produce the article, the fisheries soon assumed great importance. As a result, the New England fishing fleet began to invade Nova Scotian waters; in 1670 there were 30 New England shallops reported on the Nova Scotian coast, by 1708 the number reported was 300.

Colonial Craft

Very little is known about colonial fishing craft of the 17th and early 18th centuries. Customhouse records and colonial reports show that the fishing fleet was largely made up of brigantines and ships ("gallies"), sloops, shallops, and "catches." The "gallies" were fast-sailing ships and brigantines designed to permit rowing and these, from about 1695 to 1720, were employed by merchants, first to catch fish on the Banks and secondly, to carry the catch to a foreign market, often one of the Mediterranean countries. The sloops were single-masted vessels, perhaps having a gaff- or sprit-mainsail and one or two headsails according to size. They made up the bulk of the colonial whaling fleet until after the Revolution. The shallops were a 2-masted decked boat of some sort, perhaps sprit- or gaff-rigged, without a headsail. They were 30 to 40 tons burden at the end of the 17th century; later, about the middle of the 18th century, the name shallop was sometimes applied to small schooner-rigged craft as well as to 2-masted decked boats having no headsail. The "catches" were apparently 2-masted boats and many writers have assumed these were the same as the later ketches of the 18th century. However, there is some reason to doubt that the fishing catches and the 18th century bomb and merchant ketches were alike; the fishing catch was commonly a small vessel below 30 tons register and thus too small to be rigged bomb-ketch fashion.

The records also show that the fishing catches often carried small crews (four men in one case) when making relatively long voyages. The catch must have been more burdensome than the shallop, as a rule, for catches are reported to have often carried fish to the West Indies. The possible rig of the fishing catch is suggested by the colonial lists of ships, on which it appears that a large number of catches were carried until about 1710–20 when, suddenly they are replaced by "scooners." Hence it may be that the fishing catch was a fore-and-aft rigged vessel which about 1715 became known as the "scooner," or schooner, as has been mentioned earlier (p. 14).

Early in the 18th century the New England and Canadian inshore fisheries were being carried on by small sloops and shallops, the offshore fisheries by schooners and a few large sloops. The schooners soon became vessels of some size and by 1770 the New England fishing schooner was often 60 feet in length. As far as can be discovered, the shallop or "two mast boat," was something like the Chebacco boat and dogbody, to be referred to later (p. 164). It is apparent, from contemporary accounts, that there were a number of shallops and small schooners with the pink stern, a sharp stern with overhanging bulwarks aft that later marked the New England pinky schooner. The large fishing schooners appear to have all been square-sterned.

As early as 1721 Marblehead, Massachusetts, had 120 schooners in the fisheries averaging 50 tons register and by 1741 Marblehead had 160. In the colony of Massachusetts, in 1741, 400 schooners were owned, besides about an equal number of decked and undecked small craft all employed in the fisheries. Sometime before 1760 the large fishing schooner had developed marked characteristics and had become known as the "Marble Head scooner."

The history of the development of the early fishing schooners has been clouded by tradition. The alleged "invention" of the schooner at Gloucester, Massachusetts, in 1715 was accepted as an historical fact for many years, until it was finally challenged by the production of old paintings and drawings showing that the schooner-rig had existed long before 1715. It has been traditional that the fishing schooner improved in size, speed, and all good qualities as time passed and knowledge increased, whereas the facts were that the schooner developed or receded in size, speed, and good qualities, as the economics of the fisheries required, or as international conditions made necessary

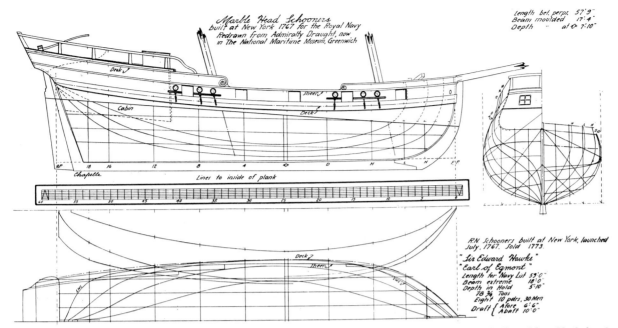

LINES OF THE MARBLEHEAD-TYPE SCHOONERS *Sir Edward Hawke* and *Earl of Egmont*, built at New York for the British Navy in 1767. This type had a reputation for speed. Redrawn from the original British Admiralty building draught, courtesy of the Trustees of the National Maritime Museum, Greenwich, England.

Marblehead Schooner

During the early years of the New England fishing schooner, from perhaps 1745 to 1770, the American offshore fisheries were harassed by foreign cruisers and raiders; earlier, wandering pirates and freebooters had been troublesome. Just as the lack of naval protection had caused New England merchants to resort to the fast-sailing galley-ship at the end of the 17th century, so the same lack in the 18th century produced the fast-sailing Marblehead "Scooner," or schooner. Early newspaper references and notices to mariners refer to these schooners as privateers, indicating fast-sailing qualities. During the American Revolution and in the years just preceding it the Marblehead schooner was employed where swiftness was necessary; the British Navy built two in 1767 at New York, the *Sir Edward Hawke* and the *Earl of Egmont*, and to this circumstance we owe the existence of the one plan of a pre-Revolutionary Marblehead schooner (see above). Early in the Revolution General Washington commissioned Marblehead schooners to capture British supply ships trying to reach the besieged port of Boston. Even the French had employed these fast schooners, as is shown by a mariners' notice in the *Boston Gazette*, Monday, Aug 24, 1761, regarding French cruisers on the northern coasts:

A Schooner of 12 guns, formerly a Marblehead Fisherman, one side of her upper Works black, and the other yellow and white streaks; a Seahorse on her Hase-holes, and looks very much like a Fisherman on the painted Side.

During the Revolution the Canadians fitted out some privateers against the Americans; in the October 20, 1777, issue of the *Boston Gazette* this warning appeared:

We have intelligence that a schooner mounting 12 carriage guns with 40 men lately sail'd from Halifax to cruise this coast. She is about 70 tons burthen, Marblehead-built, white bottom, with lug foresail and two standing topsails. Ten of her crew belonged to Commodore Manly and about as many more are young lads.

In the years of unrest that followed the Revolution the Marblehead schooner evidently maintained her reputation for speed, for President John Adams, writing from Quincy, Massachusetts, on the 5th of August, 1799, suggested to the Secretary of the Navy that, "we must have Bermuda Sloops, Virginia Pilot Boats or Marblehead schooners" for light cruisers against the French. The inclusion of the Marblehead schooner with such swift-sailing types as the Bermuda sloop and Virginia pilot boat speaks for itself. Yet, in spite of this evidence, tradition is firm that the Marblehead "heel-tappers," or schooners, were barrel-shaped, full-ended, and slow-sailing craft.

Chebacco Boat, Pinky, and Schooner Smack

In the years after the Revolution, many of the fishermen in Massachusetts were unable to replace the large fishing schooners lost during the war. At the same time, the coastal fisheries became very active. The resulting demand for small craft, led to an improvement in the old shallop, or 2-masted boat. This improvement appears to have originated at Essex, Massachusetts, then called the Chebacco Parish of Ipswich. It is probable that the improvement was largely a mere increase in size and some refinement in model and rig, but the resulting craft were found to be very efficient fishing boats and the type soon became the "Chebacco boat," in the fishermen's vernacular. Tradition supposes the Chebacco boat was "invented" at Essex and goes so far as to claim that the first one was built in an attic of one of the houses in the village, quite a feat considering the size of a Chebacco boat and of the Essex houses.

The Chebacco was built in two basic models—one was referred to as a Chebacco, or "Jebacco," boat, and was pink-sterned, the other was called the "Chebacco dogbody," or just "dogbody," and was square-sterned. The rig was 2-masted, schooner fashion but with the foremast in the eyes of the hull; there was no bowsprit, no headsail and no topsails. The boats were decked, the smaller craft under 40 feet length had "standing rooms," or cockpits, in which fishermen stood when fishing and the helmsman also had a "steering room"; the boats above 40 feet were usually decked and were without these "rooms." Commonly the square-sterned dogbody was smaller than the contemporary pink-stern Chebacco; the square stern gave equal deck room in less length.

At the end of the 18th century the Chebacco boats rarely exceeded 23 tons register and most were between 36 and 38 feet length, 11 and 12 feet beam, 5 and 5½ feet depth. By 1810 the average boat was still under 30 tons register; 39 to 42 feet on deck, 11½ to 12½ feet beam, and 5½ to 6 feet depth in hold. During the War of 1812 some large Chebaccos were built, up to 45 feet length and 13 feet beam, of about 35 tons. The small boats had low rails; the large boats had bulwarks. The Chebacco was often a fast-sailing boat and very seaworthy. As a result, boats of this type are known to have made voyages to the West Indies and fishing trips to the Gulf of St. Lawrence. The type was at its height of popularity in the decade 1800–10.

The Chebacco boats were marked by a curved stem profile, raking post, drag to the keel, and usually a marked sheer. Often the low bulwarks or chock rails were cut short of the stem; the latter stood high and could be employed as a mooring bitt. The masts were usually raked and the sails were rather square-headed. The boats usually had a raised cuddy-deck forward, but the rail line might be flush at sheer in spite of this; in the small boats the rail stopped at the break of the cuddy-deck and the fore rail was a low log rail, or bow chock-rail, carried almost to the stem.

SMALL CHEBACCO BOAT, 1790–95, a type much used in the Massachusetts inshore fisheries from 1785 to 1815. This old and somewhat crude rigged model (USNM 39198), of indeterminate scale, shows the basic features of a small boat of the type. (*Smithsonian photo 44697-c.*)

In their home ports the Chebacco boats employed a mooring made of a large block of granite, of 3 or 4 tons weight, having a hole in its center about 8 inches in diameter; in this a white oak timber was set and secured at the butt, below the granite block, with a fid. Over the head of this oak timber, which was about 14 to 18 feet long, to stand 3 or 4 feet above high tide, was placed a short timber, 18 to 24 inches long, in which was a hole large enough to fit loosely over the top of the long timber; it was held in place by a fid through the head of the long piece. This short block, or "crab," could revolve on the upright oak piece. A piece of well-tarred cable, about two inches in diameter, was made fast to one end of the

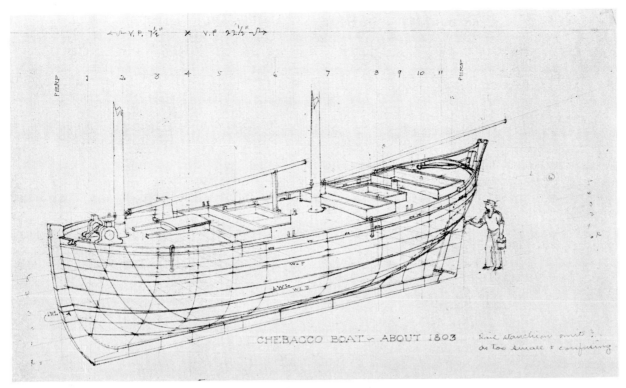

MEASURED PERSPECTIVE DRAWING OF A CHEBACCO BOAT, 1795–1805, showing form and arrangement of hull. Drawn by the late George C. Wales.

crab by passing it through a small hole, made in the crab for the purpose, and splicing it in place; the free end was made up in a large eye-splice. This cable was usually about 4 to 5 fathoms long and the eye-splice was buoyed. In mooring, when the Chebacco boat picked up the buoy, the large eye-splice was dropped over the high stem-head of the boat, thus securing her. In some boats a removable fid was passed through the stemhead athwartships to prevent the eye-splice from coming adrift, but in most boats the stemhead was so high this was not necessary.

Though the center of Chebacco boat construction was at Cape Ann, copies of the type were built elsewhere, on the "South Shore" of Massachusetts at Hingham, Scituate, and Kingston as well as to the eastward in Maine, New Brunswick, and Nova Scotia. The old sailing fishing boats of the northern end of the Gaspé Peninsula, Quebec, were certainly descendants and a form of Chebacco is said to have existed there late into the last quarter of the 19th century. The Chebacco lost its popularity in Massachusetts at the end of the War of 1812 as the increase in size of hull began to make the rig heavy to work; as a result, in the inshore fisheries the schooner-rigged

pinky surplanted the pink-sterned Chebacco and the square-stern schooner the dogbody.

It is not known when this type of schooner, later known as the "pinky," originated. But the pink-sterned hull with schooner rig appears to have been used in the New England fishing fleet before the Revolution. It is probable, however, that it existed throughout the whole period of development of the square-stern schooner. At the end of the War of 1812 the pinky had a period of popularity and a great many were built. The pinkies were at their height of popularity in New England between 1815 and 1840. The invention of the mackerel jig in 1816 by Abraham Lurvey of Pigeon Cove, Cape Ann, made this fishery popular and profitable. As the mackerel work to windward, vessels in this fishery had to be weatherly. The pinkies were notable for this quality and so a great many were employed in this fishery, a fact that led to their being called "jiggers." Pinkies were employed in all New England offshore fisheries except the Grand Banks, in the period 1815–35.

The Chebacco boats and pinkies had open fireplaces in the cuddy forward and life aboard them was often hard. The fare may be imagined by a list

165

of provisions, supplies for a week, placed aboard a Chebacco boat in 1811: 2 quarts of molasses, 5 pounds of fat salt pork, 4 pounds of flour, 7 pounds of hard crackers, ½ barrel of water, and an unstated supply of rum. Beans were sometimes supplied and cooked aboard the boats.

Throughout the colonial period and after, until well into the 1840's, the consumption of rum aboard New England fishing vessels was enormous. It was said that this often had serious effects upon fishing, causing loss of time and gear. Occasionally an incident appeared in the newspapers, as in the *Boston Gazette*, Monday, August 12th, 1771:

The beginning of last Week a Fishing Schooner arrived at Marblehead, having on board 4 Men and 2 Lads, who gave an Account, that about a Week or Fortnight before they got in, one Saturday Evening, after the Crew had made a Supper of Pork and boiled Dumplins, their Skipper, Mr.........., and one Russell, died very suddenly, the former immediately after Supper and the latter the next Morning. Although the Men and Lads agreed in the Circumstances relative to these Deaths, yet the Magistracy tho't proper to make a legal, particular Enquiry into the Affair, which was done last Saturday, when it appeared that Russell, after the Men had finished their Supper, challenged the Skipper, or any other, to drink Bumpers of Rum with him; which being accepted, a Pint Mug was filled and Russell drank it off, and the Skipper then drank the same Quantity. Russell repeated the fatal draught which completed a Quart; before the Skipper had Time to drink his second Draught he fell and immediately expired. His Champion dropt very soon after, continued in a lethargic State till the Next Morning and then died. The 4 Men and 2 Lads agreed to Conceal the unhappy cause of these Deaths; which they did until examined by Authority.

In the years between 1815 and 1840 the peaceful state of the seas and the steadily increasing demand for fish made cargo capacity more important than speed. Under these conditions, what was generally needed was a burdensome vessel that would lie at anchor safely on the banks and sail at a moderate rate. In 1821 the first attempt was made by a Massachusetts fisherman to anchor on Georges Bank, as had long been done on the Grand Banks; previously the strong tides on the Georges had led to a belief that a vessel anchoring there would be pulled under by the tide. The importance of the salt fishery caused the construction of many large, burdensome schooners having a short, full entrance and run, a rather round, full bottom, a moderate sheer, and a short quarterdeck. On the whole these schooners were very slow under sail and it was these, perhaps,

NEW ENGLAND PINKY of 1820–45, rigged model USNM 57586, showing a typical deck arrangement. The mainsheet horse forward of the tiller, however, is unusual and probably an error of the model builder. (*Smithsonian photo 44694.*)

that caused the veteran fishermen later (in 1885) to describe Marblehead-built schooners as slow and barrel-shaped and thus to establish the tradition that all the old Marblehead schooners, without regard to date, were tubby craft.

Sharpshooter and Clipper Fishermen

Several factors arose to change this picture and to create a demand for faster vessels. The invasion of Canadian waters by New England fishermen and the various international disputes over treaty rights of Americans to fish in Canadian waters finally led to attempts to exclude the New Englanders from some of the desirable fishing areas on the coasts of Nova Scotia, New Brunswick, and Labrador. This was done by use of fishery patrol vessels and British naval craft. The New Englanders resisted this, first employing some fast pinkies to poach on the forbidden fishing banks and then demanding that builders produce smart sailing craft that could escape the patrol and naval vessels. Another factor placing emphasis on the value of fast-sailing in fishing schooners was the demand for fresh fish occasioned by the rising population of the coastal cities. This demand was further stimulated, about 1836, by the construction of a railroad into Boston and, some 10 years later, to Gloucester. With the possibility for rapid delivery of fish inland, the market-fisheries

OLD FASHIONED Grand Banks cod-fishing schooner with crew hand-line fishing. Vessel is of about 1825. Drawn by H. Elliott under the direction of Capt. J. W. Collins. From G. Brown Goode, *The fisheries and fishery industries of the United States*, Washington, Government Printing Office, 1884–87.

thus assumed very great importance. The first effort to produce suitable vessels resulted in a large number of smacks, or schooners having live-wells. As most of these vessels were built on the old, slow model, they did not prove very satisfactory. In the midddle 1840's an effort was made to increase the supply of ice at the Boston and Gloucester fish piers, and to introduce better ways of handling iced fish, with the result that by 1847 the market-fishing schooners were almost entirely fitted for icing their catch. The use of ice, which made short, quick trips necessary, added to the demand for speed.

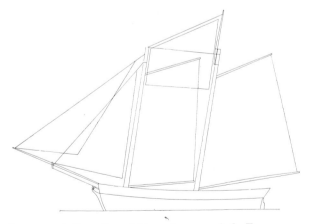

SAILMAKER'S PLAN for a fishing schooner, 1836. From a drawing, made for the U.S. Fish Commission, in the Watercraft Collection.

A third factor creating a demand for swift schooners resulted from the trend in the 1840's toward combining the summer mackerel fishery at Cape Cod with the winter transport of oysters in the shell from the Chesapeake to Cape Cod. This combination of operation had led to the purchase of a number of Chesapeake Bay schooners, some keel and some centerboard, designed and built to conform to the Chesapeake tradition that speed was a necessity in a schooner. Of these, the most popular model in the Cape Cod ports was the shoal-draft keel schooner known in the Chesapeake Bay country as the "pungy." Chesapeake Bay keel schooners, or "Baltimore clippers," were also purchased by Gloucester owners engaging in the summer mackerel fishery, so that by 1845 the fast-sailing clipper-schooner was very well known in Cape Ann waters as well as at Cape Cod. However, the Bay schooners, which were rather shoal bodied and low sided, had proved to be very wet and uncomfortable in winter weather, and to meet this objection and satisfy the demands for fast fishing schooners, the Essex, Massachusetts, builders produced a deep, keel schooner having great dead rise amidships, hard and powerful bilges, a sharp entrance and long easy run, heavy flaring sections forward above the waterline, and drawing much more water aft than forward. The model may have been influenced by the contemporary Chesapeake schooners but probably was more affected by the large and deep

167

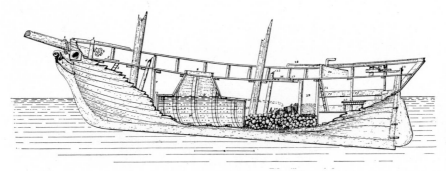

NEW ENGLAND WELL-SMACK for the fresh halibut fishery on Georges Bank, 1836–47. Longitudinal section, drawn by H. Elliott under the direction of Capt. J. W. Collins. From G. Brown Goode, *The fisheries and fishery industries of the United States*, Washington, Government Printing Office, 1884–87.

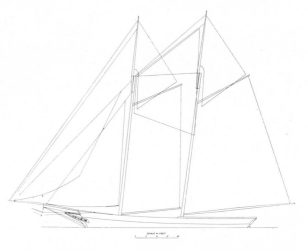

SAILMAKER'S PLAN for a fishing schooner of the clipper model, built in late 1850's. From a drawing, made for the U.S. Fish Commission, in the Watercraft Collection.

SAILMAKER'S PLAN for the sharpshooter fishing schooner *Romp* built at Essex, Massachusetts, 1847. From a drawing, made for the U.S. Fish Commission, in the Watercraft Collection.

pilot-boat schooners then employed in nearly all New England ports. The new class of fishing schooner was named by the fishermen "sharpshooter" or "file bottom," to indicate the V–form of the schooner that resembled a triangular file.

The first sharpshooter appears to have been the *Romp*, built at Essex, in 1847 by Andrew Story for Gloucester owners. Traditionally her crew is sup-

posed to have refused to sail in her because she was so sharp but no actual record has yet been found of this. The *Romp* was a most successful vessel and remained at Gloucester for many years. She must have made a great impression while building, for she was immediately followed by a great number of similar schooners, and soon all classes of new schooners, Grand Bankers, Georgesmen, and market boats were being designed as sharpshooters, or file-bottoms. The sharpshooter attracted much attention in Canadian waters and authorities complained that the new and superior class of New England schooner could outsail the fishery patrol vessels and that the lawless American crews were driving Canadian fishermen from their fishing grounds. It was reported that the sharpshooters had heavily ironed bowsprits and that their captains threatened to run down Canadian fishermen; the worst of the American vessels were commanded by "Whitewashed Yankees" who, said the Canadian report, were Nova Scotians who had become American citizens.

Late in the 1850's, the demand for relatively shoaldraft and large keel schooners, to replace the old Chesapeake Bay clippers at Cape Cod, led to the

HALIBUT-FISHING SCHOONER BEING TRIPPED BY A HEAVY SEA. Usually this caused loss of vessel and crew. Drawn by H. Elliott under the direction of Capt. J. W. Collins. From G. Brown Goode, *The fisheries and fishery industries of the United States*, Washington, Government Printing Office, 1884–87.

construction of a new class of clipper fishermen. These were much sharper and longer in the entrance than the older sharpshooter, though with the same long and easy run; and were very straight in the buttocks. The new schooners, however, had less depth and dead rise in the midsection, and had low and hard bilges. The model resembled that of a centerboard schooner having some dead rise but with a deep keel outside the rabbet in lieu of a centerboard. It was quickly found that the new model could carry a large sail area and was stiff, and that the new schooners were very fast. By 1859 the building of the sharpshooter had almost ceased and all but the "salt bankers" were being built as clippers. The clipper model was to predominate for about 25 years.

In the 1860's a few rather deep schooners were built for the market fishery, but the trend in design was generally toward the extreme clipper having a very shoal-draft body for a keel sailing vessel. The greatest beam was now well abaft the midlength, the stern was wide and the quarters heavy, the freeboard was low, the entrance became very long and sharp with much hollow at the forefoot, the run was also long and hollow near the post, and the buttocks were often extremely flat and straight.

The Fast, Safe Fisherman

However, it soon began to be apparent that something was wrong. The rise in prosperity in the New England fisheries was general from the late 1840's on and the banks had become so crowded with schooners that when a severe gale swept the fishing grounds heavy losses through collisions, caused by vessels going adrift, could be expected. But it became apparent that this condition was not the sole cause of the growing loss in lives and vessel property. Vessels were knocked down and either capsized or swamped, usually with the loss of all or most of the crew, because the shoal-bodied schooners could not recover from a sharp angle of heel. In a heavy gale, furthermore, the popular shoal model could not carry her heavy spars and large sails and the knowledge that the vessels could capsize caused captains to heave to and try to ride out the gale. Under such conditions, the shoal draft caused the vessels to drift unmanageably to leeward, a frequent cause of collision on the banks. In the 1870's a number of disastrous gales swept the New England coasts and the losses were very heavy.

About 1880 a former Gloucester fisherman, Captain Joseph W. Collins, joined the U.S. Fish Commission.

169

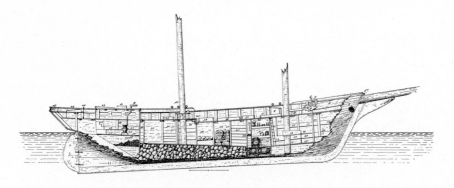

A Clipper of the 1880's, the Mackerel-Seiner *Daniel Marcy*, 1882, out of Gloucester. (*Smithsonian photo 43816–d.*) →

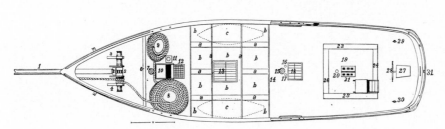

← Inboard Profile and Deck Layout of a halibut-fishing schooner 1880, for fishing on Georges Bank. From G. Brown Goode, *The fisheries and fishery industries of the United States*, Washington, Government Printing Office, 1884–87.

His experience as commander of some of the extreme clipper fishing schooners, and his knowledge of the causes of the extensive losses in lives and vessels that had occurred had led him to begin a campaign to bring about safer and better schooners. Writing in newspapers and later in the publications of the Fish Commission, he effectively centered attention upon the shortcomings of the fashionable model of schooner. He obtained the aid of a number of competent designers such as Lawlor, John Bishop, and Thomas Irving, and he also modeled schooners himself to illustrate what could be produced in a schooner having more depth, lower ballast, and a greater range of stability than was possible with the existing model. The speed of the shoal clipper was too well appreciated for his campaign to be successful, if based upon safety alone, so it was also necessary to prove that the new, deep, safe schooner would be as fast or faster than the fashionable type.

The Fish Commission planned to build a smack-schooner and, from 1883 to 1886, Collins exhibited a number of his designs for such a vessel to serve as a model for the ideal fishing schooner. Lawlor was very much interested in the subject and aided Collins with his designing; in 1884 Lawlor built on speculation the deep and improved fishing schooner *Roulette*, which attracted much attention. She was fast, weatherly, and able to carry sail. In 1885 Lawlor designed a number of fast schooners having the straight, upright stem of the pilot schooner; these were the schooners *Arthur D. Story*, *John H. McManus*, and the *A. S. & R. Hammond*. These schooners were fast and though less deep than the *Roulette*, they were nevertheless much deeper than average in proportion to length.

In 1886 the Fish Commission finally built its research smack, the *Grampus*. She was obviously influenced by Lawlor's work and had a straight upright stem, much dead rise, a deep draft and low ballast, and a narrow stern. In 1887 the Boston yacht designer, Edward Burgess, designed a notable fishing schooner, the *Carrie E. Phillips*, which introduced a number of improvements. She was a plumb-stem vessel in the Lawlor fashion and had iron standing rigging, a spike bowsprit, and improved ironwork. The success of this schooner led to the Burgess design of the *Nellie Dixon* and *Fredonia*, sister schooners built in 1889; they were so highly approved that the "Fredonia Model" as it was called, remained popular well into the early 1900's. These efforts during the period 1884–89 to improve schooner design had produced fast, safe, and handsome schooners that were universally admired throughout the world.

The years between 1875 and 1895 had also been a period of experimentation in fishing methods. A number of 3-masted salt bankers had been launched, a ketch-rigged beam trawler had been built and tried out; improvements had been made in the small schooners and smacks employed in the alongshore

fisheries, and great efforts had been expended upon improving mackerel seines, dories, and trawl gear.

Thomas F. McManus, son of a noted Boston sail-maker, began designing fishing schooners as a hobby in 1892. A fish dealer at the time, his first designs were for schooners that were fast-sailing but not very good fishing vessels, a problem he soon overcame; by 1896 he was designing excellent schooners. He introduced the rounded stem profile of the contemporary small yacht into the fishing fleet with notably successful schooners known as "Indian Headers"; the first of these was launched in 1898. The name of this type was the result of the early schooners having the names of noted American Indians.

Another designer of note was Captain George "Mel" McLain of Rockport, Massachusetts. He had turned to modeling schooners in the early 1880's and, after the *Fredonia* was built, employed the basic principles

of her form to produce extremely handsome schooners of great speed, superior in every way to the *Fredonia*. McLain turned out the designs of some of the noted flyers of the Gloucester fleet during the heyday of the sailing schooner, 1890 to 1910.

In 1900 another yacht designer, B. B. Crowninshield of Boston, began designing fishing schooners. He introduced the long overhang of the contemporary sailing yacht, as well as a short, straight keel having very great drag, a very raking sternpost, and a much cut away forefoot formed with an angular break at the fore end of the keel and continuing to the rail at the stem in a fair, unbroken line; this profile was found so practical and satisfactory that it soon became standard and was long known as the "fisherman profile."

McManus, who until the Crowninshield schooners appeared had made his keels a fair curve from heel of post downward and then upward, fairing them into a

rounded stem having a very moderate overhang, adopted the new underwater profile. In 1901 he designed the first "knockabout" fishing schooner, the *Helen B. Thomas*, launched in 1902 at Essex. This design had no bowsprit; the stem was projected forward enough in a very long bow overhang to serve in lieu of the bowsprit for setting proper headsails. This type of schooner became very popular but, as the cost of a schooner was based on overall length and not the waterline length, the newer knockabouts had very short bow overhangs, curved in profile. When the schooner fleet began to be converted to auxiliaries by the installation of gasoline engines, the knockabout almost entirely supplanted the bowsprit vessels in new construction. The end of schooner design in the New

England fishing fleet may be said to have been 1912; after that date the sail area declined rapidly and the emphasis was on engine operation. A number of sailing schooners were designed by prominent yacht designers to race against Canadian schooners, but these were designed primarily for racing and were, as fishermen, a decadent type.

Steam Trawlers

The first attempts to introduce steam into the New England fisheries occurred in the menhaden fisheries about 1871 at Boothbay, Maine. Steamers were well suited to this operation where runs were short and quick trips necessary, and where moderate weather was required. By 1888 there were 55 steamers, rang-

172

GLOUCESTER FISHING SCHOONER *Clara M. Littlefield*, built at Gloucester, Massachusetts, in 1892. Her register dimensions were 71'8'' x 20'5'' x 9'0'', 60 net tons. (*Smithsonian photo 43817–e.*)

←

CREW MEMBERS OF FISHING SCHOONER *Gertie E. Foster*, 1890, at Gloucester, Massachusetts. Details of deck fittings can be seen, including jib horse, galley stack, and forecastle companionway. (*Smithsonian photo 37554–g.*)

RIGGED MODEL (USNM 298232) of the fishing schooner *Rob Roy*, built at Essex, Massachusetts, in 1900. She is one of the early fishing schooners designed with a long bow overhang and short keel. For a view abaft, see p. 231. (*Smithsonian photo 44956–a.*)

ing from 27 to 214 tons register, operating in the menhaden fishery. Steamers were also tried out in the inshore fisheries—in the Long Island Sound oyster fishery about 1876, in the Maine clam and herring fisheries in 1880, and in the Connecticut lobster fishery in 1883. In the 1880's steamers were also employed at Tampa, Florida, in the Carolina Sounds, on the Great Lakes, and on the Pacific Coast. Steamers entered the American whale fishery in 1865; the first steam whaling vessel to be built in the United States was launched at Bath, Maine, in 1879.

The adoption of steamers in the offshore fisheries of New England was delayed because at first the speed of the schooners was great enough to compete with most small steamers of the time and the cost of a steam vessel was far greater than that of a schooner of similar capacity. In 1885 Captain H. B. Joyce designed and had built at Kennebunkport, Maine, the steam mackerel-seiner *Novelty*. She operated for about 4 years and then was sold to Haitian revolutionaries. It is said she was not a very profitable vessel. Captain Collins made an effort to introduce steamers into the American fisheries and though his efforts met with some success on the Pacific Coast and in southern waters, it cannot be said he had much influence in New England. The construction of the steam schooner *Alice M. Jacobs* at Essex, Massachusetts, in 1902 was the next attempt to introduce steamers and though she was reported to be very successful as a mackerel seiner, she was a very expensive vessel to build and to operate.

In 1904–05 a group representing Boston interests obtained plans of a steel steam trawler in England and built the *Spray*, 136 feet 4 inches overall, 22 feet beam, 12 feet 10½ inches depth, 450 horsepower, and able to make 11 knots in light weather. This vessel was so successful that the owners built four more trawlers in 1910–11, and an additional four in 1912–13. During the war years 1914–18, a number of large wooden steam trawlers were built. The legal requirements as to inspection and manning of steam fishing vessels adversely affected operational costs and after the war there was an increasingly great interest in diesel engines; since these could be used in wooden as well as steel vessels. In 1928–36 a number of steel diesel-powered trawlers were built, and also a large number of small wooden trawlers, or "draggers." No steam trawlers were built after the 1914–18 war and no large diesel steel trawlers after 1945, the trend being toward wooden draggers 90 to 115 feet overall.

Whalers and Sealers

The whale fishery was very important from colonial days until about 1900, by which time petroleum and steel had replaced the fishery products oil and whalebone. American whaling suffered disasters in the war periods, particularly during the War of 1812 and the American Civil War, when whaling in the Pacific and South Atlantic were being rigorously prosecuted. In earlier times much of the whaling was in Greenland waters and alongshore, and so it had been possible to warn vessels of impending war soon enough to prevent heavy losses from enemy cruisers. In colonial times sloops were often employed, and later, schooners, brigs, and ships. Much of the shore whaling was done with large whaleboats, some as long as 40 feet, fitted to row and sail. After the Revolution there was a steady expansion in the American whaling fleet. Relatively large ships were employed, and the South Atlantic and the Pacific whaling grounds became the scene of much American activity. The Massachusetts ports of New Bedford and Nantucket became important whaling centers, as did New London, Connecticut. However, whaleships were owned and operated out of many other ports, among which were Philadelphia, New York, New Haven, Boston, and Portsmouth, New Hampshire.

Whalers in the Pacific after the War of 1812 employed ships, and after 1840 barks of moderate length, 90 to 120 feet on deck, but of great capacity. At that time the fleet included some old ships, and packets and freighters of large capacity, as well as vessels built particularly for the fishery. Most were slow-sailing, deep and full-ended, and with a moderate spread of sail.

By the 1850's the effect of the California clipper ships became felt, and the later whaling ships and barks were designed for speed and easy rolling, qualities which had been found highly desirable, particularly in Arctic whaling, to escape ice packs.

The result was a fine class of clipper-built barks and ships. These were employed in the Bering Sea, which by 1845 had been found a profitable whaling ground, and by 1852–56 vessels were being built with very raking stems to enable them to work more effectively in ice under sail; the first of these appears to have been the bark *Gayhead* built at Mattapoisett, Massachusetts, in 1852. Vessels of her type were usually about 110 to 115 feet long, about 30 feet beam, and 11 to 13 feet in the hold. They usually

GRAND BANKS FISHING SCHOONER CONVERTED TO WHALER. The picture was taken at New Bedford, Massachusetts, in 1899. The vessel was built in Essex, Massachusetts, in the 1880's. (*Smithsonian photo 37554-c.*)

had a short and rather full entrance but a very long run, a rising floor, and an easy bilge. When the clipper model became popular the entrance became sharp and the vessels somewhat deeper than previously. The Civil War almost destroyed the American whale fisheries. The Confederate commerce destroyers *Shenandoah* and *Alabama* took a very heavy toll, and schooners and small whaling brigs operating in the South Atlantic suffered as much as the ships and barks fishing in the Pacific and in Bering Sea. Recovery was very slow, for relatively few new whaling vessels were built; in 1865 the ship *Pioneer*, a government transport, was converted to a steam-auxiliary whaling bark; between 1869 and 1892 a few steam-auxiliary barks were built, but the fishery was a dying one. The last whaler to be built, in 1910, was the brigantine *Viola*, at Essex, Massachusetts, by John James & Son. The center of whaling ship construction had been in the vicinity of

New Bedford, but the small whalers, schooners, and brigs were built elsewhere. Many fishing schooners and salt bankers were converted to whalers after 1890 and some 3-masted fishing schooners ended their days whaling off the coast of Brazil.

Sealing was first undertaken by Americans off the Labrador coasts in small schooners and sloops. Unimportant in colonial times, it did not become very profitable to Americans until about 1798, when the opening of trade with China and the Far East brought about its rapid growth. In the 19th century the fishery centered around New London, Connecticut; later it was centered on the Pacific Northwest coast. In the years immediately after the War of 1812 the favorite sealing vessel was a topsail schooner of the pilot-boat model but with great beam, moderate depth and draft, and with a somewhat rising floor, a hard bilge, and tumble-home in the topside. These schooners were largely employed off Cape Horn in

175

the years 1820–55; being replaced in the 1850's by fast schooners of the fisherman type. Pacific coast sealing was carried on by old fishing schooners, ex-yachts and, as sealing finally developed into illegal poaching in Alaskan waters, any fast-sailing vessel. The South Atlantic sealing ceased with the American Civil War and Pacific-coast sealing finally died out about 1910 as a commercial fishery.

Oyster Boats

At Cape Cod, on Long Island Sound, on the New Jersey coast, and on Chesapeake Bay, a fine class of centerboard schooner was produced by the oyster fisheries. The Chesapeake Bay fishery was carried on at first with shoal-draft keel schooners known as pungies; the centerboard schooner and sloop appeared on the Chesapeake about 1825. This area had been noted since the middle of the 18th century for the construction of fast-sailing craft, at first the so-called Bermuda sloop model, and then the schooners of the Virginia, or pilot-boat model. The Chesapeake Bay schooner, which later became known as the Baltimore clipper, and the pilot-boat types were long, low hulls having a straight sheer, raking ends, a straight keel with much drag, square stern, sharp entrance, a long easy run, and a V-shaped midsection with a rising straight floor, an easy bilge, and a shallow topside with a slight tumble-home. After 1825 the amount of rise in the floor steadily decreased; in the pungy it became very moderate, and in the centerboard schooner almost flat. However, the entrance and run remained fine and well formed for speed, so that keel or centerboard, the Chesapeake Bay schooners maintained a great reputation for swift sailing throughout their existence. Chesapeake Bay schooners after 1848 became also characterized by exaggeratedly long and pointed cutwaters; this soon became a traditional finish in all the Bay sailing craft and probably influenced the design of the bow elsewhere.

The New Jersey schooners were based upon those of the Bay and it was not until after 1900 that they departed much in appearance from the Chesapeake Bay centerboard oyster schooner. In about 1910, stems round in profile came into fashion in the Jersey schooners. The Long Island Sound oyster schooners were also like the Chesapeake Bay and Jersey centerboarders and were basically on the same model, though at times the oyster schooners at the western end of Long Island Sound were much influenced by contemporary schooner yachts, particularly in the

1870's. The Cape Cod oyster schooners were usually keel fishing schooners employed in summer in the mackerel fishery. A number of centerboard schooners were employed; at first these were obtained from the Chesapeake but in the 1880's Cape owners were having them built at Essex, Massachusetts, the model being essentially that of the Long Island Sound oyster schooners.

Alongshore Fishing Craft

The shore fisheries were carried on in small craft ranging from rowboats to sloops and schooners up to about 60 feet in length. There is little in the colonial records to establish what these small craft were like in hull and rig. Apparently, however, a large number of dugout log canoes were employed all along the coast—a boat-canoe having a square stern with small heart-shaped transom, a raking curved stem, a straight keel, flat bottom, good sheer, with the midsection having flat floor, an almost angular bilge, and slightly curved and flaring sides, and the entrance and run short but easy. The last known use of the dugout boat-canoe was on the Miramachi River, New Brunswick, Canada. The craft was fitted to row or sail.

The colonial shallop has been discussed (p. 162). Probably it was the most common small boat in the colonial fisheries and was about the same as the 2-masted boat of pre-Revolutionary years. It was not until after the War of 1812, apparently, that American small fishing boats developed strong local characteristics and became individual types. This may not be true of all but appears to be true of the very large majority. The double-ended lap-strake beach boats, such as the Block Island boat and the Hampton Beach, New Hampshire, Hampton boat, may be the oldest American types. The range in types of small American fishing boats has not been determined with accuracy—it is believed there were about 200 individual types under 60 feet in length, though probably not this many were in existence at one time.

In small American fishing boats the spritsail rig was the commonest. Many of the very small boats in the rowing-sailing class carried a single spritsail; a few had jibs. Two-masted spritsail rigs were also common; in some of the larger boats a jib was carried and was commonly set flying. The foresail was larger than the mainsail. At least two types of boat had three masts and three spritsails.

Gaff-sails were probably the next most popular sail form and at times, particularly after 1850, the gaff-sail predominated. The colonial shallop rig—two gaff-

176

sails, on two masts, the mainsail the larger and the foremast in the eyes of the boat, the sails boomed or the foresail "lug" (without a boom and overlapping the main)—did not remain popular after the Chebacco boat went out of fashion; thenceforth all 2-masted rigs (unless a jib was rigged and the boat was schooner-masted) had mainsails smaller than foresails. Gaffs varied in length from short clubs to long spars; the Block Island boat had very short gaffs, while catboats, sloops, and some of the 2-masted boats on the Great Lakes had long gaffs.

The leg-of-mutton sail was very popular in some localities; on Long Island Sound near New Haven, Connecticut, it was used in the oyster sharpies; and on the Chesapeake Bay it was also very popular. It cannot be determined on existing evidence if this form of sail was in continuous use in these localities from colonial times, though it was undoubtedly employed by colonial Americans. On pictorial evidence it can be said that the New Haven sharpies had the rig from 1856, and on similar evidence it was employed on the Chesapeake from 1861. The rig is supposed to have been employed in Bermuda from about 1815 on, but may have been used there continuously from early times.

The lug sail does not appear to have been used except in the 1-mast dipping-lug-rigged New Orleans centerboard fishing boat. The lateen too was rare; perhaps in colonial times it may have been popular but in the 19th century it is known to have been used in but two types of fishing boat, a small open boat once used on the Gulf Coast near Pensacola and the so-called Italian boat, or felucca, at San Francisco. Catboat-rigged 1-mast craft were very numerous in the last half of the 19th century in Cape Cod waters, Narragansett Bay, at the western end of Long Island Sound, and in New York Bay and New Jersey; another type was employed on the Gulf Coast near Pascagoula, Mississippi, and sharpie catboats were used in Florida. The jib and mainsail sloop at times was very popular and was employed quite generally in the last quarter of the 19th century, particularly on the Maine coast, at Gloucester and Cape Ann, on Long Island Sound and in New York Bay, along the New Jersey and Maryland shores, on the Carolina Sounds, the Florida and Gulf coasts, the Great Lakes, and the Pacific coast.

A few unique rigs also were employed. At one time on the Great Lakes and on Long Island Sound a form of leg-of-mutton was used in which a batten was fitted like a gaff so that the sail looked like a gaff-headed sail and gaff topsail in one; another variation of the battened sail was a leg-of-mutton with horizontal batten parallel to the boom, about one-third the hoist being above it. On the Piscataqua River in New Hampshire a few boats sometimes employed in fishing on the river had the local gundalow rig, a leg-of-mutton laced to a mast or spar that was slung, close to its heel, to a short mast or post, the heel being weighted so the spar stood nearly upright. This sail is sometimes considered a lateen but it is not; it was designed to allow spar and sail to be quickly lowered when passing under bridges.

There were many and various individual hull types. The center-board hull predominated from 1850 on, and the flat-bottom sharpie and the V-bottom hull spread rapidly along the coast from Cape Cod to Florida in the 1870's and 1880's; the former was found on the Great Lakes, on the Gulf coast of Florida, on Lake Champlain, and in at least one locality on the Pacific coast. The sharpies varied much in rig, for they ranged from small catboats and sloops to quite large schooners nearly 60 feet long. The sloops were usually called flatties; some were flat-bottomed forward of amidships and V-bottomed aft.

The skipjack, a very popular American type of boat, appears to have first attracted attention at Martha's Vineyard and in Narragansett Bay about 1860; from there it was introduced on the Gulf Coast and on the Chesapeake. Like the sharpie, the skipjack employed a variety of rig, from catboat to schooner.

Scows were also used in the fisheries; a centerboard sloop-rigged scow was employed at Portland, Maine, in the 1880's, and small scows, called garvies, with one or two spritsails and leeboards or centerboards, were popular in southern New Jersey.

Some stock boats appeared in the fisheries; these were boats, like the dory, that a boat shop could build in numbers on speculation. Fishermen bought such craft—the Connecticut dragboat and the related Whitehall boat, various types of sailing and rowing dories, sailing and rowing sharpie-skiffs, and whale and seine boats.

Live wells for keeping their catch alive, or to preserve bait, appeared in boats from the size of the sharpie-skiff to sloops and schooners of 60 feet or more. Maine built many small well smacks for the lobster fishery. Noank, Connecticut, won fame as a smack-building town, first large sloops, and after the Civil War fine schooners, and in the 1870's the Noank schooner-smack was considered the finest of the type.

Captain Collins became interested in an improved sloop-smack and tried to introduce such a boat on the Pacific coast in 1893–94 but was apparently unsuccessful. On the Florida and Gulf coasts the smack, as would be expected, was very popular.

The small sailing craft used in the fisheries were often crude. They were built to meet the pocketbook of the owner and some fisheries were not very profitable; but on the whole, they were well designed and soundly built for the fishery they were employed in. Generally, the hull forms had been carefully developed and many of the boats were graceful and handsome as well as efficient. Boats that worked in exposed waters—as in the case of the Maine Friendship sloop or the Quoddy boat, the Block Island boat of Massachusetts and Rhode Island, the Mackinaw boat of the Great Lakes, and the double-ended sloops of the Pacific Northwest—were carefully designed and fitted to produce seaworthy and safe craft.

Steam had little part in the American small-boat fishery. A few steam launches were employed in the 1890's on the Carolina Sounds and on the Great Lakes, but generally the boats were much too expensive to be employed profitably in the small-boat fisheries. This was also true of the naptha launch. But with the introduction of the small gasoline engine, the increase in the number of motorboats in the fisheries became very marked, and after about 1906 the launch began to drive the sailing boat from the field. The first fishing launches were a modification of the dory into a double-ended, flat-bottom motorboat, or a double-ended caravel-planked hull much like a Maine peapod was used. The engines were commonly single-cylinder motors of 2 to 12 horsepower, the most popular class of engine being in the 5 to 10 horsepower range. Fantail launches like the old steam launches were also used, and motors were fitted to some sailing hulls successfully; the Maine Hampton boat and some sharpies were so altered. A racing launch was the model of the V-bottom fishing launches built on the Chesapeake. By 1914 the sailing fishing boat was obsolete and fishing launches of great power and high speed were being built, usually following pleasure boats in model and powering. Gradually the boats became more powerful, and when automobile engines could be cheaply purchased from wrecked cars or as rebuilt motors, the marine gasoline engine was largely replaced by automobile and truck engines in most fishing centers.

The types of fishing launches are far less in number than were sailing types, and fisheries experts believe that many modern motor fishing boats are ill-suited to their local conditions. Seaworthiness has also decreased and the trend toward inefficient hulls and unseaworthy design is as obvious abroad as it is in the United States. The recognition of this will perhaps lead in time to their improvement.

Catalog of the Collection—Fishing Craft

FISHING SCHOONER, late 18th century
RIGGED MODEL, USNM 76243

This model was reconstructed with the intention of representing an American fishing schooner of the 18th century and was apparently based on paintings, dating from the last quarter of that century, found at Marblehead, Massachusetts. While the model is approximately correct as to spar proportion and rigging, deck arrangement, and general above-waterline appearance, profile, the hull form is too full and tubby to represent a fishing schooner of the troubled years 1740–1815, when swiftness under sail was necessary. Contemporary references to Marblehead fishing schooners of this period indicate that speed was a common characteristic of the type and is often inferred by their employment. The *Boston Gazette* for January 1, 1770, advertises:

The Hull or Body of a Fishing Schooner, a prime sailor with a half-Deck, about seven years old, Burthen about 58 Tons, together with her Masts, Booms and Bowsprit, Cables, Anchors, Boat, Sails and Rigging, with all Appurtenances thereunto belonging, as she now lays in the Harbour of Gloucester.

That others were "prime sailors" is indicated by Washington's use of Marblehead fishing schooners as sea raiders early in the Revolution.

Some Marblehead schooners of the last half of the 18th century had a very low bulwark on the main deck and only the quarterdeck was used as a fishing deck, it having high protective bulwarks; but most of

178

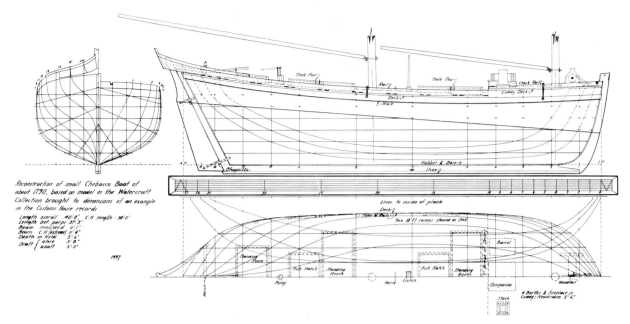

Reconstruction of small Chebacco Boat of
about 1790, based on model in the Watercraft
Collection brought to dimensions of an example
in the Customs House records

Length overall   40'0"   C.H. length   38'0"
Length bet. perps 37'3"
Beam moulded   11'1"
Beam C.H. (extreme) 11'4"
Depth in hold   5'6"
Draft ⎰ afore   3'8"
      ⎱ abaft   5'11"

1937

these schooners had high main-deck bulwarks, often
with ports cut in them to allow arming with cannon.

The model represents a keel schooner having strong
sheer, a rather upright stem with gammon-knee
head, square stern much raked and with lower
transom and round tuck, high and rather short
quarterdeck with high bulwarks, low bulwarks on
main deck, wooden windlass at heel of bowsprit, and
wooden pump barrels.

Rigged with a long pole bowsprit and raking masts,
main with a long fidded topmast and a short stump
fidded to the foremast head and carrying a windvane
only. These vessels usually carried a single large
jib, a gaff-foresail, usually fitted with a boom, a gaff-
mainsail, and a main-topmast staysail.

Scale of model is one-half inch to the foot, representing a vessel about 52 feet over the rails, 15 feet
beam, and 7½ feet depth, with bowsprit 19 feet
outside the knightheads and 25 feet in total length,
foremast 33 feet deck to cap, mainmast 34 feet deck to
cap, main-topmast 22 feet, main boom 32 feet, main
gaff 16½ feet, fore boom 22 feet, and fore gaff 16 feet
long.

Given by U. S. Bureau of Fisheries.

CHEBACCO BOAT, about 1790
Rigged Model, usnm 39198

Lion

This appears to be a very old fisherman-built model
of the type of small fishing boat first employed at
Cape Ann and known as the "Chebacco boat" or, as
it was sometimes spelled "Jebacco boat." Chebacco

Reconstruction Drawing of a Small Chebacco
Boat of about 1790, showing typical deck arrangement. Drawing is based on rigged model USNM
39198 brought to the dimensions of an example in
Customhouse records.

was the old name for what is now the village of Essex,
Massachusetts, where the type was extensively built.
As far as now can be determined, this type of boat
was a developement of the old colonial "double
shallop" early employed in the coastal fisheries of
New England. After the American Revolution and
into the first two decades of the 19th century the
Chebacco boat and her companion type, the dogbody
Chebacco, were very popular with New England
fishermen. It appears that the popularity of the
type increased at the end of the Revolution, when the
Massachusetts fishermen, impoverished by wartime
losses of their large fishing schooners and beset by local
economic and manning difficulties, were forced to
employ small and relatively inexpensive fishing craft
in lieu of building new schooners and sloops.

The Chebacco boat developed in two models: the
sharp-stern hull with a pink, always called Chebacco,
or Jebacco, boat and the square-stern variant called
dogbody Chebacco or just dogbody. In the 1790's
the popular size of Chebacco and dogbody was about
36 to 38 feet long on deck, 11 to 12 feet beam, and
about 5 feet depth of hold. After 1800 the boats
increased in size somewhat and the average length on
deck was 39 to 42 feet, with a beam of 11½ to 12½ feet

and a depth in the hold of 5½ to 6 feet 6 inches. The smaller Chebaccos had low bulwarks, but the large boats had bulwarks like the pinky and were usually rather burdensome compared to the early craft. The small boats had hatches, or "standing rooms," in which the helmsman and fishermen stood while working, but the 40-foot boats were often completely decked and without such structures. As a general rule the square-sterned dogbody Chebacco was smaller than the pink-sterned boats, as the square stern gave the same deck area in a smaller boat. The dogbody was apparently replaced by small schooners in the first decade of the 19th century, at least at Gloucester, but the pink-sterned boats were built for some years after 1800 in Massachusetts and much later than the War of 1812 in Maine and in the Maritime Provinces.

A pink-sterned Chebacco named *Lion* was built at Ipswich (Essex), Massachusetts, in 1804. She was 37 feet 9 inches between perpendiculars, 11 feet 2 inches beam, 5 feet 10 inches depth of hold, and $22\frac{47}{95}$ tons.

The sizes of the two models, based on boats built in 1804 and recorded in the customhouse records, are compared thus: *Liberty*, Chebacco boat 41 feet between perpendiculars, 11 feet 10 inches beam, 5 feet 11 inches depth of hold. *Alert*, dogbody, 38 feet 3 inches between perpendiculars, 11 feet beam, and 5 feet 11 inches depth of hold. Chebacco boats were employed in a few instances as privateers in the War of 1812 and the Royal Navy carried one on the Navy List at Halifax, Nova Scotia, as a fisheries patrol vessel or guard as late as 1815.

The model is crude in workmanship and not to scale, but indicates clearly the general arrangement and form of a pink-stern Chebacco of the late 1790's. Study of the model and comparison of measurements and proportions indicate that it represented a boat of about 38 feet on deck, 11 feet 4 inches beam, and 5 feet 6 inches depth in the hold, using specific customhouse measurements as guides. Such a Chebacco would draw about 5 feet 8 inches at post and 3 feet 6 inches forward. A scale of ½ inch to the foot applied to the model would produce dimensions of 32, 9½, and 4½ feet, respectively, too small for the type of deck fittings shown in the model.

Using this model and others as guides, and the customhouse records as references, the Chebacco boat may accurately be described as follows: The entrance was sharp but quite short, the run was long and often well formed with after sections taking a marked Y-shape. The extreme forward sections were almost V-shaped. The stem was slightly curved and raked, and the sternpost raked sharply. The boats had rather long, straight sides at deck, fore-and-aft, and the keel was straight, with marked drag. The sheer was strong and graceful. The midsection showed a rising straight floor, a rather high and hard bilge, and a nearly upright or slightly flaring topsides. The last-built Chebaccos, launched during or just before the War of 1812 had very sharp lines, a marked rise in the floor, and a rather easy bilge; the stem was rounded in profile so that the forefoot was somewhat cut away; one such boat was described as "like a pilot-boat schooner" by her British captor.

The model shows a standing-room boat with low bulwarks and the raised deck forward, the "cuddy deck," brought to the level of the bulwarks. A bow chock rail is fitted to the raised deck. The stem head stands high above the deck; it is chamfered and fitted with a pin to serve as a mooring bitt. The foremast stands right in the eyes, and in the model there is just barely room for a small handspike windlass between stem and foremast; other models show the windlass abaft the foremast. At the break in the raised deck, scaling about 5 feet abaft the foremast, is a companionway hatch and a wooden chimney. On a full-size boat the chimney would have been bricked or plastered inside, and under the cuddy deck would be found a brick fireplace and berths for the crew (two men and a boy for a boat of this size). Abaft the break and on the maindeck is a standing-room hatch scaling 8 feet wide athwartships and 2½ feet long fore-and-aft. Right abaft this is a fish hatch scaling 2½ feet long and 4 feet wide. The foreboom crotch and mainmast are next abaft and then another standing room and fish hatch like the first. Abaft these is a wooden pump and at the stern a small helmsman's standing room scaling 2½ feet long and about 5 feet wide. In the pink stern is the wooden mainsheet horse and there is no seat of ease abaft it in this model, though there is in other models. The boat is steered with a tiller that passes under the mainsheet horse.

The sail plan consists of two gaff-sails only, the mainsail somewhat larger in area than the foresail. No topsail, staysail, or jib are fitted. The sails were fitted with booms as a rule though some Chebaccos had "lug," or loose-footed, overlapping foresails. It is not known when it became practice to lace the sails to their booms but this was done soon after the War of 1812, at any rate, in the Chebaccos.

A 40-foot boat would have a foremast standing about 28 feet above deck and a mainmast standing

180

about 30 or 31 feet. The main boom would be about 22 to 24 feet long, the fore boom about 15 feet or a little less, the main gaff about 14 or 15 feet long, and the fore gaff 12 to 14 feet long; the gaffs had only moderate peak.

No forestay or shrouds were employed. The rigging of the model appears approximately correct, though the fore boom topping lift, it is thought, is of too late a form for this model and may be a later addition.

Many of the features of the Chebacco boat can still be seen in the boats used at the northern end of the Gaspé Peninsula, where the old Chebacco was introduced by Loyalists after the American Revolution. In some New England references to the Chebacco they were called "Ram's Head Boats," which suggest that the stem head of some fell inboard above deck, as in the old gundalow barges of the Piscataqua River, New Hampshire.

The Chebaccos were usually painted green above the waterline with the prominent stemhead and any adjoining chocks painted bright red. The Chebaccos had a reputation for fast sailing and seaworthiness; the large Chebaccos and dogbodies made voyages to the West Indies and fishing trips to the Gulf of St. Lawrence, to Cape Breton Island, and to Anticosti Island and the Gaspé Peninsula.

Model given by Stephen J. Martin.

DOGBODY CHEBACCO BOAT, about 1800
RIGGED MODEL, USNM 57587

This model is of a square-sterned Chebacco boat or "dogbody" of about 1790–1806. Two examples of the type from Customhouse records are the *Raven*, built in 1795, 35 feet 9 inches between perpendiculars, 11 feet 9 inches beam, 5 feet 8 inches depth in hold, and $20\frac{11}{95}$ tons; and the *Nabby*, built 1793, 36 feet 2 inches between perpendiculars, 11 feet 11 inches beam, 5 feet 10 inches depth in hold, and $21\frac{2}{95}$ tons. Since this model shows bulwarks rather than the low rail of the small Chebaccos, it may represent a larger boat than these, such as the *Patriot*, built 1795, 40 feet between perpendiculars, 12 feet 6 inches beam, 5 feet 5 inches depth in hold, and $23\frac{15}{95}$ tons; or the *Friendship*, built 1805, 39 feet between perpendiculars, 11 feet 2 inches beam, 5 feet 9 inches depth in hold, and $22\frac{1}{95}$ tons. The model, if to a scale of $\frac{1}{2}$ inch to the foot, would measure about 36 feet at rail, 11 feet 6 inches beam, and about 20 tons measurement.

The model represents a standing-room boat,

SQUARE-STERNED, CHEBACCO BOAT, or dogbody, of the first decade of the 19th century. Rigged model USNM 57587. (*Smithsonian photo 44957–c.*)

having a short and rather full entrance, short and full run, long dead flat amidships, and moderate sheer. The keel is straight and with drag, the stem curved and raking, and the post raking, with what appears to be a square tuck. It has a small-boat Y-shaped lower transom, an overhanging middle transom, and a raking flat upper transom (some of the dogbodies are stated to have had round tucks with the old upper and lower transoms of this form of stern). The midsection shows a slightly rising floor, a low, full bilge, and upright topside. In general, this model appears too full ended and burdensome for her period.

The deck arrangement is that of the pink-sterned Chebacco with cuddy-deck forward, whereas in the square-sterned boat the windlass is abaft the foremast, which was probably the usual position in the small boats, at least.

The rig, too, is like that of the pink-sterned Chebacco; in the model the foremast stands 28 feet above deck and the mainmast 30 feet. The main boom is 20 feet long, fore boom 16 feet, main gaff 13 feet, fore gaff 14 feet. The model shows a mainsheet horse; some of these boats had instead the double sheet of the large schooners.

Some of the dogbodies were clipper built, with fine lines and much dead rise, and at least one dogbody was a privateer in the early part of the War of 1812. It seems apparent that many of the larger dogbodies were converted to schooner rig and that the square-sterned boat did not survive in the Massachusetts Bay fisheries as long as did the pink-sterned Chebaccos. Nevertheless, in river boats the rig and hull combination lasted well into the last half of the 19th century, as the dogbody's rig and the square-sterned hull can be seen in prints of Hudson River towns, though the hulls may have had centerboards. It is known that such craft were employed on Maine rivers well into the last half of the 19th century, and the St. John River wood boat of New Brunswick, Canada, lasted into the early years of the present century. It may be well to note that the St. John boat had a stem with tumble-home in some cases like the old ram's head boat, and to the last of the type retained the high stem, square stern, and general model of the dogbody Chebacco. It is probable that all were descendants of the old square-sterned shallop of colonial times, though the form of the Canadian boat possibly was brought into New Brunswick by the Loyalists from Massachusetts.

Given by U. S. Fish Commission.

TYPICAL MASSACHUSETTS FISHING PINKY *Essex*, built at Essex, Massachusetts, 1821. Redrawn from incomplete plans, apparently made from the half-model, in the Watercraft Collection.

OLD-STYLE NEW ENGLAND FISHING SCHOONER, about 1820
RIGGED MODEL, USNM 57585

The model, intended to represent a Marblehead fishing schooner of about 1820 employed in the Grand Banks codfishery, shows a schooner with a high quarterdeck that is, in general form at least, intermediate between the early Marblehead schooner with a short, high quarterdeck and the New England fishing schooner of the 1830's with a short, low quarterdeck. She has an unusually long quarterdeck for her time and this must have been intended for handline fishing, employing the quarterdeck only. The vessel is identified as the *Open Sea* but this schooner has not been found in the Customhouse records.

The model shows a "full" schooner, having a short, full entrance and a short, full run with a long dead flat between. The sheer is strong, the keel straight and with some drag, the stem rabbet curved, and a gammon knee is shown. The post rakes slightly. The midsection shows a slightly rising floor, a low, full, round bilge, and a nearly vertical topside. The round-tuck stern has square upper and lower transoms, and the quarters are rather heavy.

Deck of the model shows a handspike windlass, fore-boom crutch, wooden pump barrels, a yawl boat on wooden stern davits, steps to the quarterdeck, and the usual hatches and companions of the period.

At ½ inch to the foot the model scales 65 feet over rails, 18 feet beam, and 8 feet draft at post; the bowsprit extends outboard 15½ feet, foremast stands 43½ feet above deck, and mainmast stands 45½ feet;

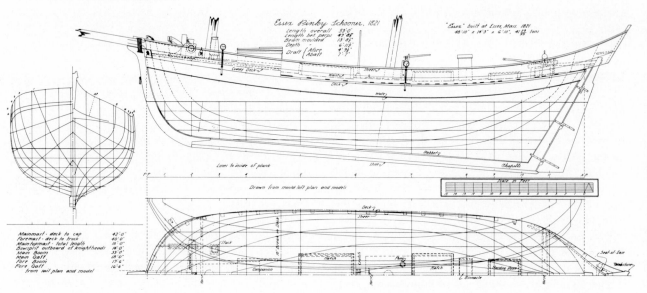

NEW ENGLAND PINKY from Friendship, Maine, showing a typical vessel of the type. (*Smithsonian photo 34911–g.*)

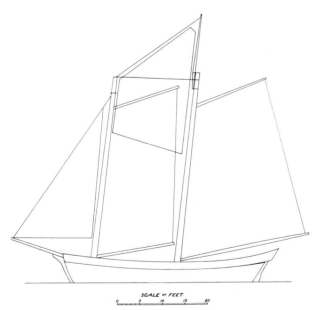

SAIL PLAN FOR A PINKY, 1840. From a copy of a sailmaker's plan in the Watercraft Collection.

the main topmast is 21½ feet in total length, fore boom 22 feet, fore gaff 21 feet, main boom 38 feet, and main gaff 24 feet. Model appears accurate but masts have somewhat too much rake. This style of schooner was sometimes called a "heeltapper," as were the earlier Marblehead schooners.

Given by U. S. Fish Commission.

PINKY FISHING SCHOONER, 1821
RIGGED MODEL, USNM 76242

This model was made to represent the New England pinky schooner *Tiger*, but the plans employed were not those of the *Tiger*. The *Tiger* was of interest because this pinky had been involved in a series of incidents with Canadian fishery patrols; under the command of Captain James Patillo she was once chased by a British brig-of-war patrolling the Canadian banks and later resisted seizure by local authorities when she was suddenly frozen in at Fortune Bay, Newfoundland. In addition, the *Tiger* had a local reputation at Gloucester for swift sailing.

183

The *Tiger* was built at Essex, Massachusetts, in 1830 and was 53 feet 6 inches between perpendiculars, 16 feet extreme beam, 7 feet depth of hold, and 51^{73}⁄$_{95}$ tons. The model, built to a scale of ½ inch to the foot, is for a pinky 53 feet overall, 48 feet 9 inches between perpendiculars, 13 feet 8½ inches moulded beam, 14 feet 1½ inches extreme beam, and 6 feet 7 inches depth of hold, drawing 7 feet 7 inches at post and 4 feet 10 inches forward. The plans used for this model appear to be those of the Pinky *Essex*, of 41^{29}⁄$_{95}$ tons, built at Essex, Massachusetts, in 1821.

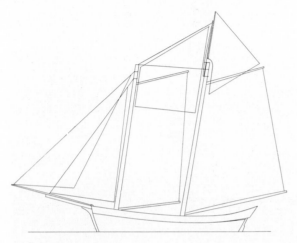

Typical Pinky Sail Plan, for the Period 1824–45, of the *Lorenzo D. Story*, of about 1842.

The model shows a pinky of the half-clipper type having a short, moderately full entrance, short but well formed run, long straight body amidships, strong sheer, particularly at rail aft, a straight keel with much drag, a curved and somewhat raking stem rabbet and gammon-knee head, a raking sternpost finished off with the pink stern of the type. The midsection shows a straight rising floor and a well rounded bilge, the fore sections being rather V-shaped and the aftermost Y-shaped. The beam is narrow, as in many Essex-built pinkies.

The spar dimensions are: bowsprit 14 feet outboard of knightheads, foremast 40 feet above deck, fore boom 17 feet 6 inches, fore gaff 16 feet 6 inches, mainmast 42 feet above deck, topmast 18 feet total length, main-boom 33 feet, main gaff 18 feet. The model shows the usual rig of a pinky: single large jib, fore and main gaff-sails boomed, and main-topmast staysail.

The invention of the mackerel jig in New England about 1815 made this fishery profitable. The mackerel move to windward, and a vessel in this fishery therefore had to be very weatherly. The pinkies, with their deep draft and relatively easy lines had this quality and were employed extensively in the mackerel fishery all along the New England and Canadian coasts from 1815 to about 1840. As a result, the pinky received the nickname of "jigger" in this period. Old fishermen stated, in 1872, that some of the large Chebaccos were fitted with bowsprits and became jiggers; from this writers assumed that the pinky then developed from the Chebacco, but old records show this was not the case and that pink-sterned schooners existed before the American Revolution.

Given by U. S. Bureau of Fisheries.

PINKY FISHING SCHOONER, 1843
Rigged Model, usnm 57586

This model is catalogued as the *Porpoise*, built at Gloucester, Massachusetts, in 1843, but this is not substantiated by the Customhouse records. This type of sharp-sterned New England fishing schooner is thought to have appeared as early as 1740 but reached its greatest popularity between 1815 and 1840. The pinky schooner was also built in Maine and in the Canadian Maritime Provinces, and was to be seen as late as 1906 in the fisheries. Some of the early and many of the later pinkies were clipper built and the type was generally very swift and weatherly, particularly in blowing weather. Though the pinky resembles the Chebacco boat and was formerly thought to have developed from that type, it now appears that the pinky schooner was merely a continuation of the old pink hull of Europe and of the American colonies schooner-rigged and fitted for the American fisheries. The pinky was employed in all fisheries on the American coasts of New England and of the Maritime Provinces, except the Grand Banks. During most of the first half of the 19th century the pinky was much used by the American fishermen operating in the Gulf of St. Lawrence and on the Labrador coast.

Pinkies usually had a short, rather full entrance, unless clipper built. The run was commonly rather fine and the after sections nearly Y–shaped. The model represents a full pinky with a short entrance, a rather short but well formed run, a rounded stem profile with gammon-knee head, and a raking stern-post surmounted with the pink stern of the type. The sheer is great, particularly aft at rail height, where the rail runs up sharply toward the typical tombstone-like transom. The midsection shows a rising floor, a full and round bilge, and a nearly upright topside.

The model bears the typical pinky rig of the period 1815–40; a large single jib hanked to a stay set up on a long pole bowsprit, a rather large foresail with gaff and boom set on a short raking mast, a large mainsail having gaff and boom, and a fidded topmast on the mainmast. A main-topmast staysail was set on the topmast but no gaff-topsail was usually fitted; the model does not show rigging for the staysail.

The deck arrangement shows a low, raised cuddy deck forward, handspike windlass, wooden pump

a jib boom fitted and set a flying jib for the mackerel fishery where weatherliness and speed were necessary; during this period, fast pinkies are reported to have outsailed the clipper sharpshooters in strong winds and gales, particularly on the wind.

Given by U. S. Bureau of Fisheries.

PINKY FISHING SCHOONER, 1832–35
BUILDER'S HALF-MODEL, USNM 54453

This half-model represents the last type of Massachusetts-built pinky clipper. Pinkies were built in

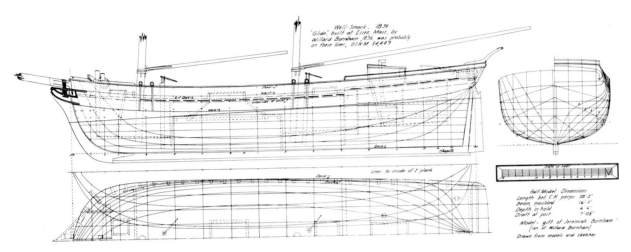

GLOUCESTER WELL-SMACK, BUILT IN 1836, AT ESSEX, Massachusetts. Lines taken off the builder's half-model (USNM 54449) of the *Glide*.

barrels, wooden chimney plastered inside or bricked, tiller steering, and other characteristics usual on the pinky type of the period.

Scale of model is ½ inch to the foot. The model is for a vessel 45 feet between perpendiculars, 14 feet beam, 6 feet 6 inches depth of hold, 8 feet 6 inches draft at post; bowsprit outboard of knightheads 14 feet, foremast stands 34 feet above deck, mainmast stands 38 feet above deck, main-topmast 13½ feet total length, main boom 30 feet, fore boom 19 feet, fore gaff 17 feet, main gaff 20 feet.

The pinkies built at Essex, Massachusetts, were usually built of very fine white oak and on good models. They lasted well and were regarded as superior sailers; many authorities considered the pinky the most seaworthy type of fishing vessel built. In the 1840's and 1850's, large pinkies sometimes had

Maine and Nova Scotia as late as 1875 for the inshore fisheries. It was formerly identified as the *July* or *July 4th*, built at Essex, Massachusetts, in 1835 by Parker Burnham. The scale of the model is ½ inch to the foot, producing a hull about 54 feet 4 inches overall, 51 feet 3 inches between perpendiculars, and 15 feet 6 inches moulded beam; whereas the *July* was 55 feet 9 inches between perpendiculars, 15 feet 8 inches extreme beam, 7 feet 1 inch depth in hold, and 54 $\frac{9}{95}$ tons. The pinky *Splendid*, built at Essex in 1832, was 53 feet 10 inches between perpendiculars, 15 feet 9½ inches extreme beam, 6 feet 7½ inches depth of hold, and 48 $\frac{9}{95}$ tons. The pinky *Meridian*, built at Essex in 1834, was 53 feet 3 inches between perpendiculars, 15 feet 6 inches extreme beam, 6 feet 11 inches depth of hold, and 50 $\frac{9}{95}$ tons. Because of the rough method then used to take tonnage measurements, precise identification of vessels by this means alone is impossible. It appears that these three pinkies all may have been built from this model, the added length of the *July* being gained by placing additional frames amidships or by spacing out the frames, common practices in the Essex yards.

The half-model represents a pinky having less sheer than was usual and an uncommonly short overhang to the pink stern. The entrance is rather full but well formed; the run is short but also well formed. The floor rises sharply, with a rather marked turn of the bilge amidships. There is a strong drag in the keel, the model showing a draft of about 8 feet at the sternpost and 4 feet 9 inches at the bow.

Given by the U. S. Fish Commission.

FISHING SCHOONER, 1836
BUILDER'S HALF-MODEL, USNM 54449

This old half-model of a fishing schooner built at Essex, Massachusetts has the name *Mount Vernon* painted on the stern. A schooner by this name, built at Essex in 1834, had registered dimensions of 59 feet between perpendiculars, 16 feet 7 inches beam, 8 feet depth of hold, and 68$\frac{41}{95}$ tons. At a scale of $\frac{1}{2}$ inch to the foot, the half-model measures 58 feet 2 inches between perpendiculars, 16 feet 3 inches moulded beam, and about 6$\frac{1}{2}$ feet depth of hold, drawing about 7 feet 10$\frac{1}{2}$ inches at post and 6 feet forward. The schooner smack *Glide*, built by the father of the donor at Essex in 1836, had about these dimensions. It is believed the half-model was used to build this schooner rather than the *Mount Vernon*, which was built by a member of another Essex family.

The model shows a full-ended and burdensome schooner of moderate sheer, having a slightly rising

floor, a slack and well rounded bilge, and an upright topside. The stem rabbet is curved and the stem fitted with a very short and heavy head, the stern is wide and square, with slightly raking sternpost, the run ends in a round tuck, with an upper and lower transom, and the entrance is short and full, as is the run. The vessel had a short, low quarterdeck.

According to Museum records, this model was stated by the donor to be one of the very early half-models made at Essex with lifts; formerly hawks' nest models were employed. Smacks had been introduced into the New England fishing fleet in colonial times but did not become numerous until after the construction of railways at Boston in 1836, and at Gloucester, about 10 years later made it possible to transport fish quickly over land from pier to market.

Given by Jeremiah Burnham, shipbuilder, Essex, Massachusetts.

FISHING SCHOONER, 1834–40
RIGGED MODEL, USNM 76245

Mount Vernon

This model was reconstructed for exhibition purposes to represent a typical New England codfishing schooner of 1835–45. Apparently the rigged model was based upon the builder's half-model USNM 54449 and both were given the name *Mount Vernon;* their dimensions were quite close to those of that schooner; her registry describes her as having a square stern and billet head, and of measuring 59 feet between perpendiculars, 16 feet 7 inches beam, 8 feet depth of hold, and 68$\frac{41}{95}$ tons. The rigged model at $\frac{1}{2}$ inch to the foot, scales about 60 feet 3 inches over the rail, 16 feet 6 inches beam, and indicates a draft of about 8 feet 6 inches at post.

The model shows a burdensome schooner having a short, low quarterdeck, a short and very full entrance and run, some drag in the keel, a short and heavy head, a square stern, and a round tuck with upper and lower transoms.

These schooners, from fore to aft, had a wooden windlass and a wooden jib-sheet horse extending from rail to rail forward of the foremast, a companionway slide hatch, fish hatch, mainmast, wooden pumps, an after fish hatch, and a break to the quarterdeck, on

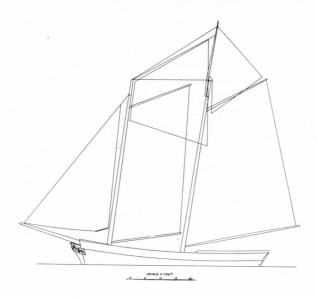

SCALE IN FEET.

SAIL PLAN of the fishing schooner *Congress*, about 1845. From a copy of the sailmaker's plan in the Watercraft Collection.

which was a companionway slide hatch to the cabin. These schooners were usually steered with a tiller, and a yawl boat was carried on wooden stern davits.

Given by the U. S. Bureau of Fisheries.

FISHING SCHOONER, 1835–46
BUILDER'S HALF-MODEL, USNM 54457

This half-model of a fishing schooner has been identified as the *Susan Center*, built at Essex, Massachusetts, in 1846. Register dimensions of the *Center* were 65 feet 3 inches in length between perpendiculars, 7 feet 1 inch extreme beam, 7 feet 1 inch depth in hold, and 74^{15}/$_{95}$ tons. At ½ inch to the foot, the half-model scales only 58 feet 4 inches between perpendiculars, but the other dimensions are within an inch of those of the *Center*. While it is possible that the vessel was built by spacing out the frames lifted from the loft, as laid down from the model, or that additional frames were added amidships, the model appears to have been made much earlier than 1846 and may represent a schooner built in the period 1835–40 for the Grand Banks fishery.

The model shows a full-ended hull with rather straight sides in deck plan, a short full entrance, a rather long and easy run, and a wide round-tuck stern with upper and lower transoms. The midsection shows a short and slightly rising floor and a full, round, and slack bilge.

A short, low quarterdeck is shown on this model and the short, heavy cutwater and head that marked many Essex-built schooners in the 1830's and 1840's. This model is much finer aft than builder's half-model 54449, above. Vessels of this general hull design were long favored for the Banks fishery as they were easy rollers, burdensome, and seaworthy.

Given by Captain J. W. Collins.

PINKY FISHING SCHOONER, 1840
BUILDER'S HALF-MODEL, USNM 76296

Trenton

The pinky schooner *Trenton* was built from this model for the Gulf of Maine codfishery at Trenton, Maine, about 1840. This model, which represents the final development of the New England pinky in the codfishery, shows the heavy displacement and moderate beam of the type, which, being very heavily ballasted and of deep draft, was notable for its seaworthiness and weatherliness, particularly in heavy seas.

The *Trenton* shows the sharp stern and the projecting pink formed by the after bulwarks being carried to a point abaft the rudderhead and clear of the plank-sheer, ending with the small transom, the shape of which caused it to be called the "tombstone." The rail sheered up sharply at the stern so that the tombstone could be made high enough for its notched top to serve as a boom crotch. Often there was also a seat of ease in the overhang of the pink, abaft the rudderhead.

The half-model shows the deep, full, double-ended form of the pinky. The keel is straight and with heavy drag, the sternpost rakes strongly, the stem rabbet curves and rakes, and the bow has a small gammon knee. The entrance is short and rather full, and the run is short and well formed, the after sections presenting a marked Y-form. The midsection shows a rising straight floor, a well rounded, easy bilge, and a rather upright topside. The sheer is strong and the hull shows a rather marked straight side in deck plan. Foreward is a low, raised cuddy deck, but the rail sheer there is unbroken. About 36 feet from the bow the bulwarks are reduced a little in height, by omitting the rail cap and reducing the stanchion height to the top of the waist plank. The top of this plank is about 4 inches below the rail cap, leaving an open space between, and the deck scuppers are similarly formed, a 1½ inch open space being left at the bottom of the bulwark plank, or waist, from the cuddy-deck break aft.

The *Trenton* was about 54 feet 5 inches long at rail, 48 feet 6 inches between perpendiculars, 13 feet 7 inches moulded beam, and 6 feet 8 inches depth of hold; she drew about 7 feet 9 inches at post and 5 feet 6 inches forward. Scale is ½ inch to the foot. The model shows the moulded lines of the hull with bulwarks built up, but the latter are now damaged, with parts missing.

Given by Gillman Hodgkins, Lamoine, Maine.

FISHING SCHOONER, 1835–45
BUILDER'S HALF-MODEL, USNM 54427

A Grand Banks codfishing schooner was built from this half-model sometime between 1835 and 1845 for Beverly Massachusetts owners at Essex, Massachusetts. These schooners, popular with Beverly fishermen, were intended to ride comfortably at anchor on the Banks and though excellent sea boats were slow sailers.

The half-model represents a full-ended, burdensome fishing schooner of moderate sheer, having a straight keel with some drag, a slightly raking sternpost, a round tuck with wide and flat upper and

GEORGES BANK HALIBUT SCHOONER OF 1840–50 HAND-LINING UNDER RIDING SAIL.   Drawn by H. Elliott under the direction of Capt. J. W. Collins.   From G. Brown Goode, *The fisheries and fishery industries of the United States*, Washington, Government Printing Office, 1884–87.

lower transoms, a raking, curved stem rabbet with a short, heavy head, and the greatest beam well forward of midlength.   The midsection shows a slightly rising straight floor, short in length and fairing into a full, round bilge, with some tumble-home in the topside.   The body is carried well fore-and-aft, and the entrance and run are both short and quite full.

There is a short quarterdeck, and the depth of bulwarks, 32 inches, is unusually great for a fishing schooner, suggesting that this vessel was intended to work in the coasting trade as well as in the fishery.

The vessel was about 64 feet 6 inches moulded length at rail, 16 feet 6 inches moulded beam, about 7 feet moulded depth, and probably drew about 8 feet 6 inches at post.   Scale of model is ½ inch to the foot.

Given by Captain Joseph W. Collins.

FISHING SCHOONER, about 1840–45
BUILDER'S HALF-MODEL, USNM 54421

This half-model represents a large New England-built fishing schooner of before 1845.   Obtained at Essex, Massachusetts, it was formerly thought to be that of the small smack *Storm King*, whose rigged model is in the Watercraft Collection bearing the date 1880, but examination of the models shows this to be incorrect.   The registry of the *Storm King* has not been found.   The model is to a scale of ½ inch to the foot, producing a vessel measuring about 77 feet on the rails, 23 feet moulded beam, and 7 feet 6 inches moulded depth, an unusually large schooner for the fisheries at the estimated date; it is probably for a schooner to be employed in the Newfoundland Grand Banks fishery.

The half-model shows a very full-bowed codfishing schooner having a long but full run, a straight raking stem with short, deep head, a nearly upright post, a wide square stern having upper and lower transoms and a round tuck, strong sheer, a straight keel with some drag, and a straight side fore-and-aft.   The midsection shows a slightly rising straight floor, a low, round bilge, and an upright topside.

Purchased November 17, 1882, from William Story of Essex and given by the U. S. Fish Commission.

188

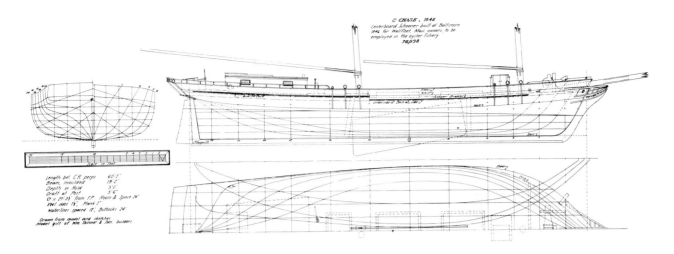

C. CHASE, 1846
Centerboard Schooner built at Baltimore
1846 for Wellfleet, Mass owners, to be
employed in the oyster fishery
76,098

Length bet. C.H perps . . . 60'7"
Beam, moulded . . . 19'2"
Depth in Hold . . . 5'0"
Draft at Post . . . 5'6"
O ll cc 33 from F.P Room & Space 24"
Keel sides 13" Plank 2"
Waterlines spaced 12" Buttocks 24"

Drawn from model and sketches
Model gift of Wm Skinner & Son, builders

CENTERBOARD FISHING SCHOONER, about 1846
BUILDER'S HALF-MODEL, USNM 76098

C. Chase

The shoal-draft centerboard fishing schooner *C. Chase* was built from this half-model at Baltimore, Maryland, about 1846 by William Skinner & Sons for Wellfleet, Massachusetts, owners but does not appear to have been registered in the Barnstable district. It represents a type much favored in the Chesapeake oyster fishery. In the decade 1845–55 New England fishermen who were seeking faster vessels obtained a considerable number of Chesapeake Bay built schooners, particularly for the oyster business at Wellfleet. These were employed in the summer in the mackerel fishery and in the winter to transport oysters from the Chesapeake to Cape Cod. Some were shoal-draft keel vessels of the pungy type, others were centerboarders like the *C. Chase*, but all had sharp lines and were designed for speed. The Chesapeake schooners proved fast in light and moderate weather and were liked in the mackerel fishery, but in blowing weather they were wet and uncomfortable. Eventually they were replaced by New England built schooners, but the centerboard type shown in the *C. Chase* was employed in the Cape Cod and Long Island Sound oyster fisheries as long as schooners were used there.

The model shows a schooner having very slight dead rise and a rather marked bilge, shallow-bodied and low-sided. The entrance is rather sharp and short; the run is very long and fine; the raking stem is fitted with a short heavy head; the transom is in two parts, both curved athwartships, the upper one curved the most; and the stern is wide. The scale of the half-model is ½ inch to the foot producing a vessel

Chesapeake Bay Centerboard Fishing Schooner *C. Chase*, built at Baltimore, Maryland, about 1846, for Cape Cod owners. Lines taken off builders' half-model USNM 76098.

60 feet 7 inches between perpendiculars, 19 feet 2 inches moulded beam, about 5 feet depth of hold, and about 5 feet 6 inches draft.

The Chesapeake schooners of this date usually had an open rail to the quarterdeck, supported by turned stanchions. Their centerboards, and the mast as well, were usually off the center line of the hull to bring the board far enough aft to give proper balance to the rig used. They carried large sail areas and lofty masts. At about the time this schooner was built, the longhead began to replace the "naval head" in the Chesapeake.

Given by William Skinner & Sons, shipbuilders, Baltimore, Maryland.

FISHING SCHOONER, 1848
BUILDER'S HALF-MODEL, USNM 76295

David R. Proctor

The codfishing schooner *David R. Proctor* was built from this model at Lamoine (now Trenton) Maine, by Louis King in 1848, for the Labrador fishery, in which she was employed for a number of years. She was a typical Banker of her period, though slightly smaller than the average Massachusetts-built Banks schooner. Vessels of this type were employed in the Labrador codfishery until it was given up by the Americans.

The model is of a burdensome fishing schooner having moderate sheer, straight keel with some drag, curved and raking stem rabbet, slightly raking post, upper-and-lower transom with round tuck, full round entrance, and a short, full run. Midsection formed with some rise in the straight floor, a low and full round bilge, and slight tumble-home in the topside.

Mounted with short, heavy cutwater, head, keel, post, and rudder.

The model shows a vessel about 58 feet moulded length at rail, 16 feet 6 inches beam, and about 7 feet moulded depth. Scale of model ½ inch to the foot.

Given by Louis King, shipbuilder, Lamoine, Maine.

FISHING SCHOONER, 1848
Rigged Model, usnm 76248

David R. Proctor

This model is of the *David R. Proctor*, also represented by the builder's half-model USNM 76295. The vessel is shown with sails furled in harbor stow and with splitting table and dressing tubs in position on deck, as she might appear when at anchor in a Labrador harbor. The standard deck arrangement of a codfishing schooner of the 1840's is shown, with the wooden stern davits for a yawl boat and other characteristic fittings.

The vessel, like nearly all of her type at the time, carried no jib boom or fore-topmast and set a large jib, boomed fore and main gaff-sails and a main-topmast staysail. When engaged in winter codfishing on Georges Bank, no topmast was carried. However, if a codfishing schooner were fitted for the summer mackerel fishery, she would be rigged with a jib boom and fore and main topmasts, carrying gaff-topsails and jib topsail in addition to her codfishing rig.

The *Proctor* was a vessel about 58 feet long at rail; her bowsprit extended 20 feet outside the stem rabbet or knightheads, the foremast stood 50 feet 6 inches above deck, and the mainmast was 51 feet long. The main-topmast was 26 feet total length, the main boom was 38 feet long, fore boom 19 feet 6 inches, main gaff 21 feet 6 inches and the fore gaff 19 feet. Scale of model is ½ inch to the foot.

Given by U. S. Bureau of Fisheries.

FISHING SCHOONER, 1845–50
Builder's Half-Model, usnm 54450

This half-model of an early sharpshooter market-boat bears the name *Elisha Holmes* on the stern. A rigged model of the *Holmes* (USNM 76247), in the Watercraft Collection, is described below. The *Elisha Holmes* was built at Essex, Massachusetts, in 1849 by Jeremiah Burnham. Her

registry dimensions were 67 feet 5 inches between perpendiculars, 18 feet 8½ inches beam, 7 feet 4 inches depth of hold, and 81¹⁴⁄₉₅ tons. The half-model, on a scale of ½ inch to the foot would produce a vessel 63 feet 9 inches between perpendiculars, 18 feet 6 inches moulded beam, and about 6 feet 9 inches depth of hold. The bulwarks indicated by the top lift of the model are unusually deep, so that they would be 30 inches high instead of the usual 26 inches. By reducing their height to 26 inches and raising the deck 4 inches, the dimensions of the model would be nearly those of the *Elisha Holmes*, so that if the half-model is not for this schooner, it is for one of the same form and period.

The schooner represented by the model would have a straight keel of marked drag; a curved, raking, and flaring stem rabbet fitted with a rather long and pointed head; a raking sternpost with a round tuck and upper and lower transoms, both flat athwartships, the upper raking and the lower curved in profile; rather straight sheer and the indicated quarterdeck low and long; a short and sharp entrance; and a long, easy run. The midsection is formed with a rising straight floor of short length, an easy bilge gradually hardening outboard, and a nearly upright topside with only a slight tumble-home. The flare forward is very marked and the rail is very round in plan; the stern is wide in proportion to the beam. The model represents an early design of sharpshooter and was intended to produce a fast sailer.

Given by U. S. Fish Commission.

FISHING SCHOONER, 1849–50
Rigged Model, usnm 76247

Elisha Holmes

This rigged model of an early sharpshooter fishing schooner was reconstructed, using the half-model usnm 54450, above, for hull lines and a sailmaker's drawing of the sails of the *Elisha Holmes*. The identification of the half-model is doubtful but that model and the rigged one do represent a typical sharpshooter of the date. The *Holmes* was built at Essex, Massachusetts, in 1849 by Jeremiah Burnham and her register dimensions were 67 feet 5 inches between perpendiculars, 18 feet 8½ inches beam, 7 feet 4 inches depth in hold, and 81¹⁴⁄₉₅ tons.

The scale of the model is ½ inch to the foot. This would produce a vessel having a length on rail of 67 feet, beam 18 feet, depth in hold 7½ feet, and draft at post of about 8 feet 3 inches. At this scale the bowsprit length overall is 32 feet, the foremast stands above deck 60 feet, the mainmast 61 feet, the fore boom is 21 feet long, fore gaff 20 feet, main boom 44 feet, main gaff 21 feet, main-topmast 28 feet 6 inches, and mainmast head 6 feet.

The model shows wooden stern davits with a yawl boat, and from foreward aft a wooden windlass, wooden jib horse, foremast, slide companionway and chimney, fish hatch, a break to the quarterdeck, bitts, mainmast, wooden pumps, fish hatch, cabin trunk, and wheelbox.

Schooners of this style and form were employed in the mackerel fishery, for which they were especially built.

Given by U. S. Bureau of Fisheries.

FISHING SCHOONER, about 1849
BUILDER'S HALF-MODEL, USNM 54455

An unidentified schooner was built from this model in 1849 at Essex, Massachusetts, for the cod and mackerel fisheries. Her design was considered at the time to be clipper built, but later fishermen referred to such schooners, which were of good capacity for their length, as half-clippers, or half-sharp. They were, however, considered fast enough for the mackerel fishery, being modeled with rather sharp ends.

The model is for a schooner having a moderately rising floor and a low, hard bilge; a rather short but well formed run, with the entrance rather full; a wide, square stern with upper and lower transoms slightly curved athwartships; a short and somewhat pointed head and heavy cutwater; and a raking stem and an almost upright post.

Scale of the model is ½ inch to the foot, producing a vessel having a length between perpendiculars of 61 feet, moulded beam of 17 feet 8 inches, moulded depth about 7 feet 1 inch, and draft at post about 8 feet 4 inches. A multicolor stripe is painted along the waist of the model.

Given by the U. S. Fish Commission.

FISHING SCHOONER, 1850
BUILDER'S HALF-MODEL, USNM 54426
LINES PLAN, USNM 160252

A cod-fishing schooner was built from this model at Essex, Massachusetts, for Beverly owners about 1850. The design is the one that succeeded the old full-ended Bankers, and the half-model shows what might be termed a full sharpshooter, being fuller and more burdensome than the sharpshooter market-

boats but, like them, designed to sail swiftly. Rather full entrances were retained in the sharp Bankers; it was thought unsafe to sharpen the entrance much or to reduce the flare forward, as it was believed that a sharp-bowed schooner would dive when at anchor on the Banks in blowing weather or when sailing on the wind heavily loaded. Schooners of this general design proved quite fast and very seaworthy. By 1850 the sharpshooter model was well established in practically all classes of Massachusetts-built fishing schooners, and remained in favor for some years.

The half-model shows a schooner having a sharp but quite short entrance, with heavy flare in the foremost sections and the greatest beam well forward, the run very long and easy, the sheer moderate, and the keel straight but with much drag. The bow rakes and flares outward at the rabbet, the post has much rake and the transom is wide and curved athwartships. In the model upper and lower transoms seem to have been intended. The head is longer, more pointed and, more graceful than the earlier models. The masts are raked sharply.

At ½ inch to the foot the model scales about 68 feet long over the rail, 18 feet moulded beam, and 7 feet 3 inches moulded depth.

Given by Captain J. W. Collins.

FISHING SCHOONER, about 1855
BUILDER'S HALF-MODEL, USNM 54422

An unidentified fishing schooner was built from this model in New England about 1855 for the Grand Banks codfishery. The model represents the transition from the early full-ended lines to the later clipper form that was beginning to find favor, in this period, in the Banker class of fishing schooner.

This half-model is for a schooner having a moderately sharp entrance and well formed run. The midsection shows a short, straight, and moderately rising floor, a low and rounded bilge, and a nearly upright topside. The sheer is marked and the keel is straight, with some drag. The bow rabbet rakes and flares forward, with a rather short and full head, the sternpost rakes slightly, the stern is wide and has a short counter and transom.

Scale of the model is ½ inch to the foot, producing a vessel about 69 feet at rail, 18 feet moulded beam, and drawing about 8 feet 9 inches at the stern.

Model purchased from W. H. Story of Essex, Massachusetts, in 1882 and given by U. S. Fish Commission.

TYPICAL SHARPSHOOTER SCHOONER AT THE TIME THE SHARPSHOOTER WAS MERGING INTO THE CLIPPER MODEL. The *Dauntless*, built at Essex, Massachusetts, in 1855. Rigged model USNM 76244. Wooden stern davits for a yawl boat, and the standard deck arrangement of the period, can be seen. (*Smithsonian photo 44695–a.*)

FISHING SCHOONER, 1855
RIGGED MODEL, USNM 76244

Dauntless

The fishing schooner *Dauntless* was built at Essex, Massachusetts, about 1855, and was lost at sea with all hands, 12 men, in 1870 while making a passage to the Gulf St. Lawrence from Gloucester.

The model represents a vessel having sharpshooter-clipper lines. The bow is full and round at the rail but sharp at the waterline, the run long and fine. The midsection is formed with a rising straight floor, a hard turn of bilge, and a slight tumble-home in the topside. The keel has much drag, the sheer is rather straight, the stem rabbet is raking and flaring with the head long and pointed, the post rakes slightly, and the counter is short and is finished with a wide, raking transom.

The masts rake strongly, and the usual long, low quarterdeck is shown. The riding sails are stowed on stern davits and the dories are lashed bottom up on deck to represent the vessel when ready to make a passage, to or from the Banks, when dory-trawling. All sails are set—jib, flying jib, fore and main gaff-sails, main gaff-topsail, and main-topmast staysail.

Scale of model is ½ inch to the foot, producing a vessel about 70 feet overall, 66 feet on the waterline,

17 feet 6 inches beam, bowsprit 30 feet total length, flying jib boom 32 feet total length, foremast 54 feet above deck, mainmast 56 feet above deck, fore boom 24 feet total length, fore gaff 22 feet, main boom 42 feet, main gaff 22 feet, main-topmast 29 feet.

Given by U. S. Bureau of Fisheries.

CENTERBOARD OYSTER SCHOONER, 1855
BUILDER'S HALF-MODEL, USNM 76096

Sunny South

The centerboard schooner *Sunny South* was built from this model at Baltimore, Maryland, in 1855 by William Skinner & Sons for the oyster fishery. She was also intended to serve as a freighting schooner. Vessels of this size and type were used for dredging oysters, transporting farm produce on the Chesapeake, freighting, and for the Florida and Bahama fruit trade.

The half-model shows a centerboard schooner with a moderately sharp, convex entrance, the greatest beam well forward of midlength, and a long, lean, and rather flat run. The hull has good sheer, a straight keel with some drag, a rather upright but flaring stem rabbet with a long, pointed, and graceful head, and a raking post with round tuck and upper and lower transoms both very wide and thin, the lower transom almost fair with the end of the run and

192

the upper well curved athwartships. Midsection has a slightly rising floor carried well out in a straight line, a quick, low bilge, and slightly rounded topsides.

The vessels had a long and low quarterdeck with open rail and trunk cabin well aft, raking masts, with the mainmast to port of the hull's centerline and the centerboard slot to starboard, with centerboard lanyard to block at mainmast hounds and thence to deck belay.

Scale of half-model is ½ inch to the foot, producing a vessel 74 feet 9 inches at the rail, 71 feet between perpendiculars, 22 feet moulded beam, 5 feet 3 inches depth of hold, and draft 6 feet 6 inches at post and 4 feet 4 inches forward.

Given by William Skinner & Sons, Shipbuilders, Baltimore, Maryland.

low, hard bilge, and a slight tumble-home in the topside. The vessel sat low in the water and her masts had much rake, her centerboard was large and passed through the garboard on one side of the keel.

Scale of the model is one-half inch to the foot, producing a schooner about 63 feet 6 inches long at rail, about 61 feet between perpendiculars, 19 feet 4 inches moulded beam, about 5 feet 6 inches moulded depth, and drawing 6 feet at post and 5 feet forward.

Given by William Skinner & Sons, shipbuilders, Baltimore, Maryland.

CHESAPEAKE BAY FISHING PUNGY, about 1885
Builder's Half-Model, usnm 312331

An unidentified pungy was built from this half-model in Dorchester County, Maryland, about 1885 by Joseph T. Spicer for the oyster fishery and general

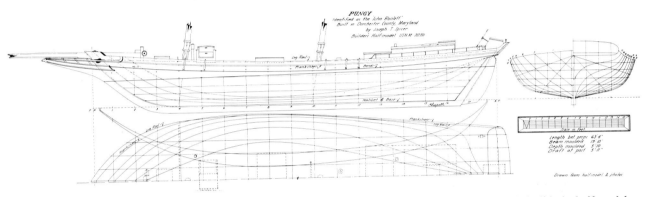

Lines of a Typical Chesapeake Bay Pungy Schooner of About 1885. Taken off builder's half-model USNM 312331.

CHESAPEAKE BAY OYSTER SCHOONER, 1855
Builder's Half-Model, usnm 76097

Breeze

The centerboard schooner *Breeze* was built from this half-model at Baltimore, Maryland, in 1855 by William Skinner & Sons for the oyster fishery. She was intended to serve as a smart-sailing oyster "buy boat" for transporting the catch to market, and to be a swift, weatherly vessel.

The model shows a shoal-draft centerboard schooner, having a straight keel with slight drag, an upright post and round-tuck stern with upper and lower transoms, stem upright at rabbet and adorned with a long, pointed head, the sheer moderate, entrance short but fairly sharp, with the greatest beam well forward, and the run long and very easy. The midsection shows a slightly rising straight floor carried well outward to a

freighting. The donor thought it to be the *John Ronlett*, but the partially illegible name "*Elizabeth J. . . . son*" appears on the stern.

The half-model is of a typical pungy, designed for swift sailing, of the Baltimore clipper type. It represents the moulded lines, to underside of deck, of a rather wide and shallow-draft keel schooner hull having moderate sheer, a straight keel with some drag, strongly raking curved stem rabbet, moderately raking post and a wide and thin square stern. Since the model is to the deck only, it does not show the typical double-transom of the pungy construction but this would be utilized, as also would the long head of her type. The entrance is sharp but rather short, the greatest beam being well forward of midlength, and the run is long and fine, ending in the usual round tuck of the pungy. The midsection shows a slightly rising straight floor, a well rounded bilge, and a remarkably

193

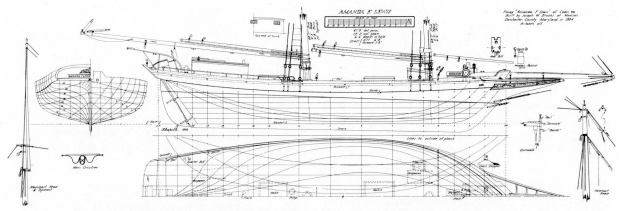

LINES AND DETAILS OF A CHESAPEAKE BAY PUNGY SCHOONER, the *Amanda F. Lewis*, built in 1884, one of the last of this now extinct type under sail. As taken off the vessel by the Historic American Merchant Marine Survey.

flaring topside. The quarters are very thin. The vessel would have the low log rail and the long and rather light masts usual in this type of schooner.

Scale of the half-model is ½ inch to the foot, producing a vessel about 63 feet 4 inches moulded length on deck, 19 feet 10 inches moulded beam, 5 feet 10 inches moulded depth, and drawing about 6 feet at post and 5 feet forward.

Given by James K. Spicer, Taylor's Island, Maryland.

FISHING SCHOONER, 1850–56
BUILDER'S HALF-MODEL, USNM 54466
LINES PLAN, USNM 160204

An unidentified schooner was built from this model at Essex, Massachusetts, sometime between 1850 and 1856 for the fresh-fish market business. These schooners, built to be swift sailers and called market-boats, were designed for short trips and brought in their catch iced. They were usually rather small carriers, about 60 feet on deck, quite sharp, and heavily sparred. Often referred to as sharpshooters in the late 1840's and 1850's, their model and general design were considered to have been inspired by the Chesapeake Bay pungy schooners brought to New England in that period.

The half-model shows a hull having sharply rising floors carried well out and straight amidships and ending in a high and very hard bilge. This form was known as "file-bottom" at Essex because of its likeness in cross-section to a triangular file. The sheer is moderate, the keel straight and with a great deal of drag. The bow rakes somewhat, the sternpost rather markedly, and the transom, which is rounded athwartships, rakes sharply. The entrance is not

very long but is quite sharp and the greatest beam is forward of the midlength; the run is long and easy. The stern is quite broad and rather shallow, with a very short counter.

Scale of the half-model is ½ inch to the foot, producing a vessel approximately 62 feet between perpendiculars, 18 feet moulded beam, and drawing about 7 feet 9 inches at the post and about 4 feet 6 inches forward.

These vessels had a long, low quarterdeck and their masts were usually sharply raked.

Given by Captain J. W. Collins.

FISHING SCHOONER, 1856
BUILDER'S HALF-MODEL, USNM 76297

J. Coolidge

The Banks schooner *J. Coolidge* was built from this half-model at Jordans Island, Gouldsboro, Maine by Hamen Cousens in 1856. She was intended for the codfishery in the Gulf of Maine and Bay of Fundy and also for the Grand Banks fishery. Over a period of nine years she made the run each winter to the Magdalen Islands in the Gulf of St. Lawrence, bringing back herring to Maine ports.

The half-model is a good example of a small Banker of her period, of the half-clipper type, having a short but rather sharp entrance, a short but well formed run, a slightly rising floor, and a full, low, and easy bilge. The stern is wide and shallow, with a very short counter. The post is rather upright, the stem rabbet moderately raking and flaring, and the head and cutwater somewhat light and graceful. The sheer is moderate and the keel straight, with some drag.

194

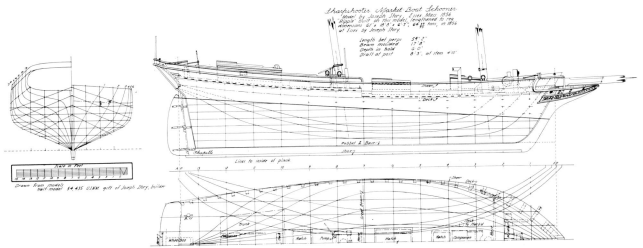

NEW ENGLAND SHARPSHOOTER MARKET-BOAT SCHOONER OF 1856. Taken off builder's half-model USNM 54435.

Scale of the model is ⅜ inch to the foot. This would produce a vessel about 63 feet 6 inches between perpendiculars, 18 feet 6 inches moulded beam, and about 8 feet 6 inches draft at post. The *J. Coolidge* measured 65 feet between perpendiculars, 19 feet 6 inches extreme beam, 7 feet depth in hold, and 52.75 tons register.

Given by Newell B. Coolidge, 1894.

FISHING SCHOONER, 1856
BUILDER'S HALF-MODEL, USNM 54435

Ripple

The market boat *Ripple* was reputedly built from this model, lengthened 6 feet, at Essex, Massachusetts, by Joseph Story in 1856. The *Ripple* was a notable sailer and she is said to have been the first schooner built at Essex with the elliptical transom which subsequently became standard. Her lines were copied by other builders with such alterations as were thought to be improvements; it may be said, however, that this model represents the sharpshooter, or file-bottom, market-boat at its highest state of development. The *Ripple* was burned at sea in 1863 by the Confederate States cruiser *Tacony*.

The half-model represents a clipper schooner having a short but sharp entrance and a very long and fine run, the greatest beam being somewhat forward of midlength, a raking post and short counter with an elliptical transom having a strong curve athwartships, a stem with a long and pointed head, marked sheer, and a straight keel having a strong drag. The midsection shows a sharply rising straight floor carried well outboard, a high and markedly hard bilge, and a

slight tumble-home in the topside. The fore sections show heavy flare.

Scale of model is ½ inch to the foot, producing a schooner 54 feet 2 inches between perpendiculars, 17 feet 8 inches moulded beam, and about 6 feet depth of hold. The register dimensions of the *Ripple* were 61 feet between perpendiculars, 18 feet 8 inches beam, 6 feet 7 inches depth of hold, and 64 ³⁸⁄₉₅ tons. Custom House records show a billethead, square stern, and no galleries.

Given by Joseph Story, shipbuilder, Essex, Massachusetts, 1882.

FISHING SCHOONERS, 1857
BUILDER'S HALF-MODEL, USNM 54448

George Fogg, Etta G. Fogg

The clipper fishing schooners *George Fogg* and *Etta G. Fogg* were built from this half-model at Essex, Massachusetts, by Charles O. Story in 1857. They were built for Wellfleet owners and were intended for the mackerel fishery in summer and for freighting oysters from the Chesapeake to that port in winter, trades that required smart, fast sailers, and the sister-schooners were considered good designs and large for their time and business. Because of the shoal-water operations of the oyster business, they were of relatively shallow draft for keel vessels. This model appears to have been one of the earliest designs of the shoal, clipper type of New England fishing schooner.

The half-model shows an extreme clipper fishing schooner of the date of build, having slight sheer, a straight keel with moderate drag, stem rabbet flaring, raking, and with small rounded forefoot, nearly up-

195

right post, and a short counter ending in a wide, elliptical, raking transom much curved athwartships. The entrance is sharp and hollow; the run long, easy, and flat. The midsection is formed with a rising straight floor, hard turn of bilge, and a slight tumble-home in the topside.

The model is mounted with a long, pointed head, cutwater, rather deep keel, post, and rudder, the marked depth of keel being intended to prevent leeway in windward sailing and necessitated by the shallow body.

Scale of model is ½ inch to the foot, producing a vessel measuring 94 feet 9 inches moulded length at rail, 89 feet between perpendiculars, 23 feet 8 inches moulded beam, 24 feet extreme beam, 8 feet 8 inches

depth in hold, and draft 10 feet 4 inches at post and 6 feet 10 inches forward.

Given by Charles O. Story, shipbuilder, Essex, Massachusetts.

FISHING SCHOONER, 1857
RIGGED MODEL, USNM 76254

Etta G. Fogg

The clipper fishing schooner *Etta G. Fogg*, built at Essex, Massachusetts, in 1857, and represented by the builder's half-model USNM 54448, is shown in this rigged model. The rig and deck arrangement of schooners built for the mackerel fishery and for oyster freighting in the late 1850's and early 1860's are shown.

The model is of a heavily sparred and canvassed schooner. The *Etta G. Fogg* was registered as 88.7 feet between perpendiculars, 24.7 feet beam, 8.3 feet

NEW ENGLAND CLIPPER FISHING SCHOONER Built in 1857 at Essex, Massachusetts, the *Etta G. Fogg*. (*Smithsonian photo 45605-c*).

196

depth of hold, and 107.25 tons burthen. She was about 94 feet 9 inches long at rail, bowsprit 36 feet extreme length, jib boom outside cap 17 feet, fore-mast above deck 67 feet 6 inches, fore-topmast total length 37 feet, fore boom 30 feet, fore gaff 29 feet, main boom 58 feet and main gaff 33 feet. The rigging details of this model show the methods used on large fishing and coasting schooners of the 1850's. Scale of model ½ inch to the foot.

The shallow, broad hull of this type of fishing schooner, combined with the very large rig, made a dangerous vessel and many of this type were lost at sea. However, these schooners were popular until as late as 1886, by which time the heavy losses had focused attention on the dangerous proportions of the extreme clipper schooner.

Given by Charles O. Story, shipbuilder, Essex, Massachusetts.

FISHING SCHOONER, 1855–60
RIGGED MODEL, USNM 25371

This model represents a fishing schooner of 1855–60, a period when the sharpshooter lines of the market boat had been applied to the more burdensome Georgesmen and Grand Bankers.

The model is of a somewhat burdensome clipper fishing schooner having a rather short and sharp entrance, moderately full at deck level and fine below, a long and easy run, good sheer, a raking stem rabbet with a long head, and a rather upright post with a short counter and a raking elliptical transom. The midsection is formed with a moderately rising floor, round full bilge, and a slight tumble-home in the topside. The keel is straight with some drag.

The vessel is shown under the usual sail of a Georgesman of her period, no fore-topmast and carrying foresail, mainsail, jumbo, jib topsail, main gaff-topsail, and fisherman's staysail.

Scale of model is ⅜ inch to the foot, producing a vessel 66 feet 4 inches at rail, 21 feet 6 inches beam, the bowsprit extending outboard the knightheads 16 feet 8 inches, jib boom extending 13 feet 4 inches outside the cap, foremast 62 feet above deck and mainmast 63 feet, main-topmast 31 feet total length, and main boom 46 feet long.

Given by Captain H. C. Chester.

CHESAPEAKE BAY FISHING SCHOONER, 1857–58
BUILDER'S HALF-MODEL, USNM 76101

A keel fishing schooner was built from this model at Baltimore, Maryland, in 1857 or 1858 by William

Skinner & Sons. It is of the type, designed for fast sailing, that was employed in the New England fisheries 1845–55, when a number of Chesapeake Bay built keel and centerboard schooners were used in the mackerel fisheries and the oyster trade.

Among the Maryland-built schooners in the Gloucester fleet were the *Garland*, built at Baltimore in 1850 (82' x 21'–4'' x 7'–3''), *Leading Star*, built at Baltimore in 1851 (69'–11'' x 20' x 6'), *John*, built in Dorchester County in 1847 (73'–9'' x 22'–6'' x 6'–6''), *Mary Jones*, built at Baltimore in 1851 (64'–4'' x 21' x 5'–8''), *Bloomfield*, built in Talbot County in 1850 (75'–4'' x 20'–7'' x 5'–1''), and *Iowa*, built in Dorchester County in 1854 (76'–9'' x 23' x 6'–7''). It is probable that the *Mary Jones* and the *Bloomfield* were centerboarders, judging by their depth.

The half-model represents a pungy schooner with bulwarks and a flush deck but with false quarterdeck rail made of a cap supported by turned stanchions, low freeboard, somewhat raking and flaring stem rabbet, slightly raking post, rather straight sheer, straight keel with moderate drag, rising floor with a high and well-rounded bilge, sharp and slightly hollow entrance, and a very long and fine run. The greatest beam occurs somewhat forward of mid-length.

The scale of the model is ½ inch to the foot, producing a schooner about 61 feet 6 inches on the rails, 57 feet 9½ inches between perpendiculars, 18 feet 1 inch moulded beam, 18 feet 6 inches extreme beam, 6 feet 6 inches depth of hold, and 7 feet 5 inches draft at post, 5 feet 9 inches forward.

These schooners had a long, pointed head and cut-water, the upper and lower transoms were curved athwartships and sharply raking, and the rather lightly rigged raking masts were lofty and light.

Given by William Skinner & Sons, shipbuilders, Baltimore, Maryland.

FISHING SCHOONER, 1857
BUILDER'S HALF-MODEL, USNM 54470
LINES PLAN, USNM 160222

Flying Fish

The clipper schooner *Flying Fish* was built from this model at Essex, Massachusetts, by Jeremiah Burnham in 1857 for the mackerel fishery. After being employed for some years as a hook-and-line fisherman out of Gloucester she was sold to New London, Connecticut, out of which port she was engaged in the Antarctic seal and sea-elephant fisheries. The *Flying Fish*, one of the fastest fishing schooners of her period, owing to her sharp lines and very large rig, is a good example of the shallow-bodied clipper schooner that came into fashion in the New England fisheries in the late 1850's and represents the transition from the older "sharpshooter" type to the extreme clipper of the end of the decade.

The model shows a vessel having moderate sheer, straight keel with drag, slightly raking and flaring stem rabbet, small round forefoot, raking post, and a short counter ending in a wide, raking, elliptical transom. The entrance is of moderate length and quite sharp, the run long, flat and fine. Midsection is formed with rising, straight floor, a hard turn of the bilge and some tumble-home in the topside. The greatest beam is a little forward of amidships.

Model is mounted with a rather long and pointed head, cutwater, rather deep keel, post, and rudder. A long quarter-deck is indicated.

Scale of model is ½ inch to the foot, producing a vessel about 74 feet over the rails, 70 feet 6 inches between perpendiculars, 21 feet moulded beam, and drawing about 9 feet 9 inches at post and 5 feet 8 inches forward.

Given by Jeremiah Burnham, shipbuilder, Essex, Massachusetts.

FISHING SCHOONER, 1857
RIGGED MODEL, USNM 160411

Flying Fish

This rigged model of the clipper fishing schooner *Flying Fish* of 1857, was made in the Museum from the builder's half-model (USNM 54470) and a sailmaker's plan. The New England fishing schooners were characterized by an almost exact similarity of deck arrangement for periods of about twenty years, for each class and size, and the deck arrangement is a standard one for this type of schooner at the date of building.

The model shows the rig of a typical mackerel-fishing schooner of the period; she carries a very large jib fitted with a bonnet.

Scale of model ½ inch to the foot. The register dimensions of the *Flying Fish* are 75 feet between perpendiculars, 22.5 feet beam, 6.5 feet depth in hood, and 94⁶⁶/₉₅ tons burthen.

Model made in the Museum.

FISHING SCHOONER, 1857
BUILDER'S HALF-MODEL, USNM 54473
LINES PLAN, USNM 160251

Lookout

The Georges Bank fishing schooner *Lookout* was built from this model at Essex, Massachusetts, in 1857 by Charles O. Story. This vessel proved very satisfactory; during the next seven years twenty or more schooners were built on the moulds of the *Lookout*, whose lines were considered excellent for this fishery until about 1868. Among these were the *Fish Hawk*, *Arizona*, *Laughing Water*, and *E. K. Kane*. The *Laughing Water* and *Arizona* were still in the Georges fleet as late as 1882.

The half-model shows a full-bodied and burdensome hull having slight sheer, a straight keel with much drag, a rather sharp and well formed entrance, a long easy run, the greatest beam slightly before the midlength, a moderately rising floor with a low round bilge rather hard amidships, a flaring bow and stem rabbet with longhead, a raking post, and a shallow elliptical transom with a rather short counter.

Scale of model is ½ inch to the foot, producing a vessel about 68 feet at the rail, 19 feet moulded beam, and drawing about 9 feet at the post and nearly 6 feet forward.

Given by Charles O. Story, shipbuilder, Essex, Massachusetts.

FISHING SCHOONER, 1858
BUILDER'S HALF-MODEL, USNM 76475

May Queen, Juno, Olive Hayward

The Grand Banks fishing schooner *May Queen* was built from this model at Orland, Maine, in 1858. She was of a burdensome type utilized not only in the Grand Banks codfishery but also in coastwise trade. The schooners *Juno* and *Olive Hayward* were also built on this model. After a few years in the Grand Banks fishery the *Juno* was sold and went into the South American trade. The *Olive Hayward*, after being in the codfishery for several seasons, was placed in the coastal trade. Reputed a fast sailer, this vessel once made the run from Boston to Orland in 16 hours, and is said to have escaped a Confederate cruiser.

The half-model represents a full-bodied vessel with rather straight sheer, a short, rather full entrance, a relatively long and fine run, the greatest beam being well forward. The keel is straight and with some drag, the post is upright and the stem slightly raking and flaring outward. The floor, carried well fore and aft, is short and has little rise, and the bilge is well-rounded.

Scale of the model is ½ inch to the foot, producing a vessel 72 feet 7 inches between perpendiculars, 21 feet beam, and 7 feet 1 inch depth of hold. The schooner's registered net tonnage was 67.28.

These Maine schooners usually had a rather short quarterdeck but otherwise resembled the Massachusetts-built schooners of their period.

Given by H. H. Buck.

FISHING SCHOONER, 1858
BUILDER'S HALF-MODEL, USNM 54471

We're Here

A fishing schooner modeled particularly for the mackerel fishery was built from this model at Essex, Massachusetts by Daniel A. and Willard R. Burnham in 1858 and named the *We're Here*. A fast-sailing vessel, she was employed in the mackerel fishery in summer and in the New Orleans and Gulf of Mexico fruit trade in winter. She was captured at New Orleans at the outbreak of the Civil War and is said to have been used as a blockade runner.

Model is painted in the fashion of the time—dark green; along the waist a multicolored stripe of white, yellow, red, white; trailboards with gilded and painted carvings; billet head gilded; bottom red copper paint.

The half-model shows a clipper fishing schooner of moderate sheer, having a straight keel with much drag, a sharp entrance, and a long, easy run, the greatest beam being slightly forward of midlength. The bow rakes and flares forward at rabbet, the post rakes, and the counter is moderately long, ending with a raking elliptical transom much curved athwartships and quite wide. The rising straight floors are brought well out and the bilge is high and hard.

The Register dimensions of the *We're Here* were 67 feet length between perpendiculars, 20 feet beam, 7 feet 5 inches depth of hold, 83 $^{99}/_{95}$ tons, square stern, billet head. The half-model is to a scale of ½ inch to the foot, and produces a vessel measuring 66½ feet between perpendiculars, 20 feet 6 inches moulded beam, about 6 feet 10 inches depth of hold, and drawing about 8 feet 10 inches at post and about 6 feet 10 inches forward.

Given by Willard R. Burnham, shipbuilder, Essex, Massachusetts.

CHESAPEAKE BAY PUNGY SCHOONER, 1858
BUILDER'S HALF-MODEL, USNM 160120

Mary and Ellen

The pungy schooner *Mary and Ellen* was built from this model at Baltimore, Maryland, in 1858, by William Skinner and Son for the oyster fishery and freighting on the Chesapeake. The pungy schooner

had the general form of the old Baltimore clipper or pilot boat that had developed on the Chesapeake in colonial times. The pungy was a shallow-draught keel schooner, with rising floor amidships, strongly raked ends, and fine lines, designed for swift sailing. Schooners of this type were used on the Chesapeake in the oyster fishery as dredgers and to transport the catch; they were also employed in general freighting, carrying goods and farm products on the Chesapeake, fruit in the Baltimore-Bahamas trade, and oysters to New England. It is thought that the pungy, which is now extinct on the Chesapeake, introduced the sharp-model schooner into the New England fishing fleet.

The half-model represents a schooner having rather straight sheer, straight keel with marked drag, strongly raking sternpost and raking, curved stem rabbet. The transom is of the old style round-tuck form, with upper and lower transoms joining at an angle. The bottom of the lower transom is straight across the top of the sternpost, forming a cross seam at right angles to the post. This T-shape was characteristic of the pungy throughout the existence of the type. The lower transom is not plainly shown in this model, however, and judging by the form it must have stood at more of an angle than in later pungy schooners. Usually, in this type, the lower transom was almost parallel to the load waterline. The greatest beam is forward of amidships and the entrance is long and sharp; the run quite fine. The midsection shows straight, rising floors carried well out and a somewhat high, round bilge, the rounding carried almost to deck level. The stern is wide and shallow; the quarters being rather thin. The stern overhang is very short. The stem is formed with a long and pointed head a little less exaggerated in the model than in the later pungy schooners. It is not known when the long-head replaced the short and deep head that first marked the Chesapeake Bay schooners, but apparently this occurred in the 1840's and the fashion spread to New England.

Scale of the model is ½ inch to the foot, and the vessel measured about 64 feet 10 inches over the rail, about 20 feet moulded beam, and drew 7 feet at the post and 3 feet 6 inches forward.

The pungy schooner type is represented by two rigged models in the Watercraft Collection. Lines plan of the *Mary and Ellen* is Survey no. 5–56 in *The Historic American Merchant Marine Survey*.

Given by William Skinner & Son, shipbuilders. Baltimore, Maryland.

FISHING SCHOONER, 1857–60
BUILDER'S HALF-MODEL, USNM 54459

This half-model was supposed to be that of the Grand Banker *Break O'Day* built and modeled by Jeremiah Burnham at Essex, Massachusetts, in 1859.

Her registry dimensions were 69 feet between perpendiculars, 21 feet 2 inches beam, 7 feet 6 inches depth of hold, 94$^{75}\!/_{95}$ tons. The half-model on a scale of $\frac{1}{2}$ inch to the foot, would produce a schooner measuring about 65 feet 6 inches between perpendiculars, 18 feet 6 inches moulded beam, and 7 feet 4 inches depth in hold. Thus it is evident that the identification is incorrect. It is now believed to be a good example of an "improved" Grand Banks schooner of the period 1857–60.

The model shows a schooner having a straight keel with moderate drag, small sheer, raking sternpost, very short counter with raking elliptical transom strongly curved athwartships, curved and raking stem rabbet, pointed and moderately long head, full entrance, rather short but well formed run, long low quarterdeck, moderately rising short straight floor, low well-rounded bilge, and nearly upright topsides. The bow at rail is full, with much flare in the forward sections. The stern is wide.

Model given by Willard R. Burnham, shipbuilder, Essex, Massachusetts.

FISHING SCHOONER, 1860
BUILDER'S HALF-MODEL, USNM 76476

Sarah Hill

The fishing schooner *Sarah Hill* was built from this model in 40 days at Orland, Maine, in 1860. The vessel was intended for the local mackerel fishery but was for many years employed in the Banks codfishery, going into the coastal trade when she became old.

The half-model shows a schooner having a sharp but short entrance, the beam being well forward, and a long and easy run. The sheer is rather straight, the keel straight with moderate drag, post upright, and stem rabbet raking slightly and flaring forward. The floors rise slightly and the bilge is low and round. The stern is wide and shallow, and the counter very short. The bow is fitted with a long and somewhat pointed head and cutwater. The vessel had a long, low quarterdeck.

The scale is $\frac{1}{2}$ inch to the foot, representing a vessel about 63 feet 10 inches between perpendiculars, 18 feet 6 inches moulded beam, and about 7 feet 6 inches depth of hold. Register dimensions of the vessel were

64 feet 1 inch between perpendiculars, 18 feet 8$\frac{1}{2}$ inches beam, 7 feet 9$\frac{1}{2}$ inches depth of hold, and 48.36 tons.

Given by H. H. Buck.

FISHING SCHOONER, 1862
BUILDER'S HALF-MODEL, USNM 160113

Laura Roberts

The New England fishing schooner *Laura Roberts* was built from this model during 1862 at Frankfort, Maine, for the Gulf of Maine codfishery. It is a good example of the fisherman-coaster schooner popular in Maine before 1880.

The half-model represents a schooner with a full, rather short entrance, full run, small rise in the floor and a full, round bilge, a wide elliptical transom, a rather raking stem and almost upright post, some drag to the keel, little sheer, and a long, low quarter-deck.

Scale of model is $\frac{1}{2}$ inch to the foot, giving a vessel about 72 feet over the rails, 20 feet beam, 6 feet depth in hold, and drawing about 7 feet 9 inches at the post.

Given by Captain J. W. Collins.

FISHING SCHOONERS, 1862
BUILDER'S HALF-MODEL, USNM 54474

Galena, Prince of Wales

The mackerel fisherman *Galena* was built for Gloucester owners from this half-model, with two frames (or 4 feet) added, in 1862 at Essex, Massachusetts, and in the next year the *Prince of Wales* was built on the same moulds, but with five more frames added to make her 10 feet longer than *Galena*. For some years these two schooners were the largest in the New England fleet. The *Galena* was finally sold to California and the *Prince of Wales* to Surinam, South America, as a trader.

The model shows a clipper hull of the period, having a moderately long entrance, long easy run, wide stern, shallow transom on a short counter, raking post, raking and flaring bow, longhead, moderate sheer, straight keel with some drag, and rising floors with a hard low bilge.

Scale is $\frac{1}{2}$ inch to the foot, giving a vessel about 84 feet between perpendiculars, 22 feet 6 inches moulded beam, about 8 feet 6 inches depth of hold, and drawing about 10 feet 6 inches at post. The *Galena's* register dimensions were 88 feet 6 inches between perpendiculars, 23 feet 9 inches beam, 8 feet 9 inches

200

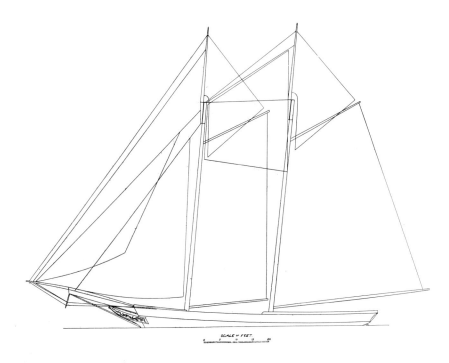

SAIL PLAN FOR A GRAND BANKER
BUILT AT ESSEX, MASSACHUSETTS,
IN 1859, the *Break O'Day*. From a
copy of the sailmaker's plan in the
Watercraft Collection.

depth of hold, and 157⁷⁷⁄₉₅ tons; the *Prince of Wales'* dimensions were 99 feet 4 inches between perpendiculars, 24 feet 2 inches beam, 9 feet depth of hold, and 180⁴⁰⁄₉₅ tons.

These dimensions show that departures from the model were made in lofting to give additional length amidships, causing an increase in beam. This practice of adding frames amidships, common at Essex in building fishermen, required the forebody and afterbody to be faired into the added sections and not only affected length and breadth but also depth.

Given by U. S. Fish Commission.

FISHING SCHOONER, about 1864
BUILDER'S HALF-MODEL, USNM 54440

A fishing schooner on this model was built at Essex, Massachusetts, about 1864 by Joseph Story as a market boat for the fresh fishery.

The half-model represents a late form of the clipper-sharpshooter class, having sharply rising floors, high hard bilge, sharp and rather long entrance, and a long fine run, the greatest beam being about at mid-length. The sheer is moderate and the keel straight and with some drag. The post is upright and the stem rabbet rakes and flares slightly. The short counter ends in a wide, shallow, elliptical transom curved athwartships and sharply raking. The bow is ornamented with a graceful cutwater and a long and rather pointed head with billet.

Scale is ½ inch to the foot, for a schooner measuring about 68 feet on the rail, 63 feet 6 inches between perpendiculars, 19 feet moulded beam, 6 feet depth of hold, and drawing about 7 feet 9 inches at post. The form and dimensions of the model indicate a powerful schooner of greater depth than usual in this period and capable of carrying a large sail area.

Model given by Joseph Story, shipbuilder, Essex, Massachusetts.

FISHING SCHOONER, 1865
BUILDER'S HALF-MODEL, USNM 76036

Sylph

The fishing schooner *Sylph* of Boston was built from this half-model at East Boston, Massachusetts, by Dennison J. Lawlor in 1865. She was first fitted out by her owners, fishermen of Irish origin, as a beam trawler, the first vessel to experiment with this gear in the New England fisheries. The gear proved unsuccessful economically and the *Sylph* then engaged in market fishing, for which she was well suited in size and model. This schooner gained a notable reputation for speed. She foundered on Georges Bank with all hands in the great gale of November 9, 1883, believed to have sunk after a collision with another schooner.

The half-model shows a schooner having rather marked sheer, straight keel with heavy drag, upright stem rabbet and post, and a short counter ending in

a raking elliptical transom curved athwartships. The entrance is long and sharp, with much hollow at forefoot, and the run is rather long and very fine. The midsection is rather heart-shaped, with a sharply rising and somewhat hollow floor, a high and rather hard bilge, and marked tumble-home in the topside.

Mounted with a pointed head, cutwater, keel, post, and rudder.

Scale of the model is ½ inch to the foot, giving a vessel about 55 feet 8½ inches between perpendiculars, 59 feet 10 inches moulded length at rail, 17 feet moulded beam, 6 feet 4 inches depth in hold, 9 feet 8 inches draft at post and 6 feet 4 inches forward.

Given by Dennison J. Lawlor, naval architect, and shipbuilder, Chelsea, Massachusetts.

FISHING SCHOONER, 1865
RIGGED MODEL, USNM 76241

Sylph

This model of the fishing schooner *Sylph* of 1865, showing her as a market fisherman, is the same vessel represented by builder's half-model USNM 76036. Considered an advanced design at her date of building she was much deeper than the average in proportion to her length and beam. Her designer and builder, Dennison J. Lawlor, was the pioneer in the development of safer fishing schooners in this period, designing a number of schooners of more than average depth and dead rise in the years 1865–85.

The model shows the deck arrangement of a market fisherman of 1860–80, with a wooden windlass right forward, iron jib-sheet horse running across the deck, foremast, slide companionway with supply hatch attached, chimney, fish hatch covered with a slide booby hatch, a break to quarterdeck, mast bitts, mainmast, wooden pumps, trunk cabin with chimney and slide hatch, wheelbox and quarter bitts, and mainsheet horse at extreme stern.

The topsides are forest green, white band below waist line of bulwarks, white boot top, red copper bottom, rail caps black, carving gilded. The masts rake strongly; the schooner has gaff mainsail and foresail, large jib, main gaff-topsail and main-topmast staysail.

Scale of the model is ½ inch to the foot.

This schooner, nearly 60 feet long at rail, had a mainmast 54 feet deck to cap, foremast 52 feet deck to truck, bowsprit 27 feet total length, 17 feet knight-heads to shoulder of pole. The fore boom was 19 feet long, fore gaff 18 feet, main boom 47 feet, main gaff 23 feet, and main-topmast 27 feet total length. She had iron ballast inside and carried sail well.

Given by U. S. Bureau of Fisheries.

202

CHESAPEAKE BAY PUNGY SCHOONER, 1865
RIGGED MODEL, USNM 76262

W. F. McKewen

The Chesapeake Bay pungy *W. F. McKewen*, an example of a type long popular on the Bay, was built in 1865 for Crisfield, Maryland, owners for the oyster fishery, being employed in oyster dredging and transporting and in general freighting in the off-season. At one time there were a large number of pungies on the Chesapeake but they were gradually replaced with centerboard schooners and bugeyes, and are now an extinct type of vessel on the Bay.

The *McKewen* is a shoal-draught schooner having a straight keel with some drag, a raking and strongly curved stem rabbet, a long, heavy, and pointed head, raking sternpost, round tuck, upper and lower transoms, and moderate sheer. The entrance is sharp and rather short, the run long and fine. The midsection shows a moderately rising straight floor, a round, easy bilge, and slightly flaring topside; the greatest beam is forward of midlength.

The model shows the typical pungy rig: sharply raking masts, the fore without a topmast, a large jib with a small club at its foot, foresail, mainsail, main gaff-topsail, and fisherman staysail. A yawl boat is carried on iron stern davits; also shown are a trunk cabin with a hatch at its fore end, wooden pumps, manual oyster-dredge winches, or "winders," rollers at rail, hatch and rail-to-rail jib-horse, and an iron windlass and heel bitt.

These schooners usually had only a low log rail made up of edge-bolted timber without stanchions; aft there was sometimes a cap-and-turned-stanchion monkey rail, occasionally carried well forward to the fore rigging or knightheads. The knightheads and hawse-timbers stood well above the log rail and were very prominent. The pungy was a modified Baltimore clipper, of privateering and slaver fame, in which the dead rise of the floors was decreased. The pungy hull form is well illustrated by the half-model of the *Mary and Ellen* (p. 199) and by half-model USNM 312331 (p. 193). The pungies were often employed in the summer fruit trade between the Bahamas and the Chesapeake and in general were noted for their sailing qualities. Their draft eventually caused their replacement with centerboard craft as the harbors and creeks along the Chesapeake silted up.

The *McKewen* was 68 feet at rail, 20 feet 9 inches beam, 7 feet depth. Scale of model is ½ inch to the foot.

Given by U.S. Bureau of Fisheries.

FISHING SCHOONER, 1866
BUILDER'S HALF-MODEL, USNM 74041

Thomas E. Evans

The market boat *Thomas E. Evans*, built at East Boston in 1866 by Dennison J. Lawlor, was employed

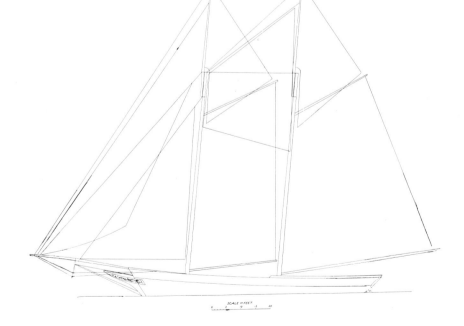

SAIL PLAN for the *Lizzie F. Choate*, a fishing schooner built at Ipswich, Massachusetts, 1866. From a copy of the sailmaker's plan in the Watercraft Collection. The vessel is also represented in the collection by builder's half-model USNM 160112.

203

in the New England fisheries for only a short time and was then sold and was operated as a packet in the Bay of Honduras. The schooner was noted for her speed.

This model resembles that of the schooner *Sylph*, whose half and rigged models (USNM 76036 and 76241) in the Watercraft Collection indicate that Lawlor had developed some rather deep fishing schooners before the efforts of Captain Joseph Collins began to show results in the New England fleets.

The half-model represents an extreme clipper fishing schooner for her date, and deeper in draft than was then common. Her entrance is long and very sharp, with some hollow near the stem; the greatest beam is abaft midlength. The run is long and flat, showing the almost constant deadrise, carried aft, characteristic of most Lawlor designs. The sheer is great and there is a long, low quarterdeck. The keel is straight with a very great drag. The stem rabbet is nearly straight and upright; the stem is fitted with a pointed and rather long head. The sternpost is vertical, the counter short, and the raking elliptical transom has much curve athwartships. The mid-section shows a sharply rising floor with hollow at the garboard carried all the way forward to the stem, hard high bilges, and tumble-home in the topside.

The scale of the model is ½ inch to the foot, giving a vessel 56 feet 4 inches between perpendiculars, 17 feet 8 inches moulded beam, 6 feet 3 inches depth of hold, and a draught of 8 feet 11 inches at post and 4 feet 6 inches at stem.

Given by Dennison J. Lawlor, naval architect and shipbuilder, Chelsea, Massachusetts.

FISHING SCHOONER, 1866
BUILDER'S HALF-MODEL, USNM 160112

Lizzie F. Choate

The clipper fishing schooner *Lizzie F. Choate* was built from this model at Ipswich, Massachusetts, in 1866 as a mackerel fisherman. A variation of the popular clipper model of her period, being more box-like in appearance than most of her class, she was considered at the time to be one of the largest and finest fishermen in New England. She engaged in the mackerel fishery in 1866–67 under the command of Captain Joseph W. Collins and in that winter she freighted oysters from the Chesapeake, to Boston. The next winter, on February 7th, 1868, she foundered at sea with the loss of several hands, while on a passage from New York to the West Indies, having entered

the fruit trade. Three of the crew were rescued from the waterlogged wreck by the brigantine *J. S. Wright*.

The half-model shows a schooner having a very straight sheer, straight keel rabbet with moderate drag but with the outside keel somewhat deeper aft than forward, a raking and flaring stem rabbet with a light, pointed head, an upright post, and short counter with a wide and rather shallow elliptical transom having much rake and a very strong curve athwartships. The entrance is long and sharp, the greatest beam in the model is about at midlength, and the run is long and very fine. The midsection shows a moderately rising floor carried well outward in a straight line, bilges low and hard, and the topsides quite straight and wall sided.

The *Choate* was about 90 feet between perpendiculars, 24¼ feet beam, and about 8 feet depth of hold as scaled from model, which is on the unusual scale for fishing schooner half-models of ⅛ inch to the foot; the vessel drew about 10 feet 9 inches at post and about 6 feet 6 inches forward.

Given by A. Choate.

FISHING SCHOONER, 1866
BUILDER'S HALF-MODEL, USNM 76478

Sarah H. Cressy

The extreme clipper schooner *Sarah H. Cressy* was built from this half-model at Essex, Massachusetts, in 1866; the design being by Dennison J. Lawlor of Chelsea, Massachusetts. This notable schooner had a reputation for speed and beauty, and was very heavily canvassed. She fished out of Gloucester and foundered with all hands in one of the furious gales of February 1875.

The model is for a schooner having a long, fine entrance and a very long, flat run, the entrance being hollow near the stem. The counter is short and finishes with an elliptical transom curved athwart-ships and set at a sharp rake. The stem rabbet flares outward but is generally rather upright; the post is vertical. The sheer is strong, the keel straight, with much drag. The head is quite long and beaked. The midsection shows a rising and slightly hollow floor, a hard bilge, and some tumble-home in the topside. The draught of this schooner was shallower than is usual in Lawlor's designs of both earlier and later date.

Model is painted forest green with the multicolored stripe (red and white) popular in New England fishing schooners when the *Cressy* was built.

Scale of the model is ½ inch to the foot, producing a vessel 71 feet between perpendiculars, 21 feet 2 inches moulded beam, and about 7 feet depth in hold.

The *Cressy* measured 72 feet between perpendiculars, 21.5 feet beam, 7.4 feet depth in hold, and 73.3 tons, square stern, billethead.

Given by Dennison J. Lawlor, naval architect and shipbuilder, Chelsea, Massachusetts.

CHESAPEAKE BAY CENTERBOARD FISHING SCHOONER, 1868
BUILDER'S HALF-MODEL, USNM 312330

A large centerboard schooner for the oyster fishery and for general freighting was built from this half-model in Dorchester County, Maryland, before 1870, by Joseph T. Spicer. The model is believed by the donor to be that of the *Travers Spicer*. These schooners had a large centerboard to one side of the keel and the after end of the board came at, or abaft the mainmast. They were intended for dredging oysters in winter and for carrying freight in summer, particularly lumber and farm produce. They had longheads and above the water resembled a pungy, but had bulwarks instead of the pungy's low log rail.

The half-model shows, to the deck only, a shoal-draught centerboard schooner having a moderate sheer, straight keel with some drag, raking post, and a curved and raking stem rabbet. The greatest beam is well forward, the entrance is moderately sharp and short, and the run is long and fine. The stern is broad and square; apparently the vessel had a pungy stern, as a round tuck is indicated, but the model shows only the line of the cross-seam; the stern is not otherwise indicated. The midsection shows a rising straight floor, well-rounded bilge, and a slightly flaring topside.

Scale of the model is ½ inch to the foot, which would produce a schooner about 73 feet moulded length on deck, 75 feet tonnage length, 20 feet 6 inches moulded beam, and 6 feet moulded depth.

Given by James K. Spicer, Taylor's Island, Maryland.

FISHING SCHOONER, 1870
BUILDER'S HALF-MODEL, USNM 76477

Alice G. Wonson

The clipper fishing schooner *Alice G. Wonson* was built from this model at Gloucester, Massachusetts, in 1870. Several other schooners were built from her

moulds. The *Wonson* was employed in the summer mackerel and winter halibut fisheries under the command of Captain Joseph W. Collins. She was considered to be an exceptionally swift sailer when built and especially fast to windward. Captain Collins considered her one of the best of the shoal-draught clipper-type schooners of her time. She was eventually lost at sea.

The half-model represents a schooner having a long and very sharp bow with some hollow near the stem, a very long, flat, and easy run, a wide elliptical transom on a short counter, heavy quarters, long pointed head, graceful sheer, straight keel with some drag, raking stem rabbet, and rather upright post. The midsection shows a rising floor with a quick, hard turn at the bilge.

The *Wonson* measured 76.6 feet between perpendiculars, 20.6 feet beam, 6.9 feet depth of hold, and 64.18 tons net, square stern, billethead. Scale of the model is ½ inch to the foot.

Given by the U. S. Fish Commission.

FISHING SCHOONER, 1870
BUILDER'S HALF-MODEL, USNM 76299

M. E. Torry

The clipper fishing schooner *M. E. Torry* was built from this model at Sargentville, Maine, in 1870 for the mackerel fishery and general work. In 1887 she was in the Banks codfishery, and was lost in the autumn of that year.

The half-model of the *Torry*, which resembles that of the Essex-built shallow-draught clipper fishermen of the 1870's, represents a wide and shallow hull with heavy quarters, an elliptical transom on a short counter, a long sharp entrance, a long flat run, moderate dead rise, hard bilges, moderate sheer and drag, an upright post, a somewhat flaring bow rabbet, and a long head.

Scale of the model is ½ inch to the foot, for a vessel 71 feet 9½ inches length between perpendiculars, 21 feet 6 inches beam, and 7 feet 2½ inches depth of hold.

Given by Robert Dority in 1897.

FISHING SCHOONER, 1870
BUILDER'S HALF-MODEL, USNM 76287

Harvest Home

The codfishing schooner *Harvest Home* was built from this model at Lamoine (now Trenton), Maine, in 1870.

The half-model shows a clipper Banker of the date, much like the Massachusetts vessels of the same class, having a sharp entrance, long easy run, short counter, elliptical transom, long head, rising floors, hard bilge, and rather heavy quarters.

Scale of the model is ½ inch to the foot. The *Harvest Home* registered 78 feet between perpendiculars, 22 feet 7 inches beam, 7 feet 7 inches depth in hold, and 78.28 gross tons.

Given by Newall B. Coolidge & Bros.

FISHING SCHOONER, 1872
BUILDER'S HALF-MODEL, USNM 57052

Nimbus

The clipper fishing schooner *Nimbus* was built by John and Hugh Bishop from this half-model at Gloucester, Massachusetts, in 1872 for the market fishery. Except in size, the *Nimbus* was similar to schooners built in the same yard for the mackerel fishery at this period, and represented a very advanced design, having the reputation of being fast and handy. She was lost by running ashore in December 1878 trying to enter the harbor at Cape Negro, Nova Scotia, during a gale. Two of her crew were lost in a dory trying to reach shore.

The half-model shows an extreme clipper fishing schooner of the period, having a long, sharp entrance with the greatest beam about at midlength, a rather short but easy run, a raking post, and a short and rather light counter ending in a wide, raking, elliptical transom. The stem rabbet rakes and flares slightly, the stem has a long graceful head, the sheer is marked, and there is a long, low quarterdeck. The keel is straight with some drag. The midsection shows a rising hollow floor carried all the way forward as well as aft, an unusually easy bilge for this date and type of schooner, and a slight tumble-home in the rounded topside. The forward sections are rounded in the topsides, rather than having the usual flare.

Mounted with head, bowsprit, and head rigging, as well as mast deadeyes at rail.

The rig of the market schooner until about 1885 was usually without jib boom and fore-topmast.

Scale of half-model is ½ inch to the foot, giving a vessel 70 feet 1 inch between perpendiculars, 75 feet 4 inches total length, 20 feet 4 inches moulded beam, 7 feet depth of hold, and drawing about 8 feet 2 inches at post and 7 feet forward; this is an unusually small amount of drag in a fishing schooner of this date and length.

Given by U.S. Fish Commission.

CHESAPEAKE BAY PUNGY SCHOONER, 1872
RIGGED MODEL, USNM 26536

J. L. Carroll

The *J. L. Carroll* was a Chesapeake Bay pungy of the small class, built on the Eastern Shore of Maryland and owned in Baltimore in 1874. These small schooners, ranging from about 42 to 50 feet at rail and drawing 4 to 6 feet at sternpost, were once numerous in the Chesapeake oyster fishery and, though too small for general freighting, were often used in summer to transport farm products to market between ports on the Bay and Baltimore, Annapolis, and Washington, or to Virginia ports such as Norfolk, Newport News, and the river towns.

The early pungies of 1840–55 were apparently deeper and with more rise of floor than the later vessels. Many were loftily sparred. Building of the pungy ceased on the Chesapeake about 1885. The last pungy afloat as a sailing vessel was the *Wave*, built in Accomack County, Virginia, in 1863; she was 57 feet 6 inches at rail, 23 feet beam, and 7 feet 9 inches depth. However at least one pungy hull was in use as a power vessel on the Bay in 1955.

The model shows a shoal-draught schooner having a straight keel with drag, curved and raking stem rabbet with a long pointed head, raking post, round tuck, upper and lower transoms, moderate sheer, short sharp entrance, long easy run, midsection with moderate deadrise, easy bilge and slightly flaring topside. The greatest beam is forward of midlength.

Scale of model is 1 inch to the foot. The *Carroll* was 47 feet 3 inches at rail, 15 feet beam, and 4 feet depth of hold.

The pungy carries the rig of her type. The *Carroll's* bowsprit outboard of knightheads was 16 feet, foremast above deck 44 feet 6 inches, mainmast 45 feet above deck, main-topmast 18 feet total length, main boom 26 feet, fore boom 17 feet, fore gaff 13 feet 6 inches, and main gaff 14 feet.

Given by T. B. Ferguson.

FISHING SCHOONER, 1871
BUILDER'S HALF-MODEL, USNM 76046

Helen M. Foster

The extreme clipper fishing schooner *Helen M. Foster* was built from this model at Scituate, Massachusetts, in 1871, the model having been made by Dennison J. Lawlor of Chelsea, Massachusetts. This schooner, intended for the market fishery out of Boston, was of somewhat shallower draught, than was usual in the Lawlor-designed schooners, being generally similar to the extreme clipper fishing schooners of the 1870's. Notable for her swift sailing and ability to carry sail, the *Foster* was a most successful vessel.

The half-model represents a schooner having a long, fine and somewhat hollow entrance, and a very long easy run, the greatest beam being abaft midlength. The rise of floor is moderate and the hollow in the garboards is carried forward as well as aft of this section. The bilges are rather low and hard, the sheer is great, the keel straight and with much drag, the post upright and the stem rabbet nearly so, the counter is short, finishing with a shallow, elliptical transom, and the head is rather long and beaked. The model shows a characteristic that marked many

men in her period; being shallow, wide, very sharp-ended, and heavily canvassed and sparred. Vessels of this design were popular for many years in the New England fishery because they carried a large rig and were stiff and very fast; however they had small ability to right themselves when knocked down, and this weakness resulted in great loss of vessel property and lives from 1865 to 1885.

The half-model shows a very long, sharp entrance with the greatest beam well aft; a long, flat, and very fine run ending in a short counter of great width and having low quarters; and a transom wide and curved athwartships, strongly raked, and elliptical in shape. The post is rather upright, the stem rabbet rakes and flares, and the head is long and graceful. The keel is straight and with some drag, the sheer is handsome.

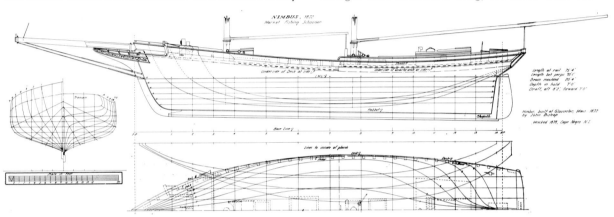

LINES OF EXTREME CLIPPER TYPE New England Fishing Schooner, the *Nimbus*, built at Gloucester, Massachusetts, in 1872. Taken off builder's half-model USNM 57052.

of the Lawlor designs, maintaining the same dead rise throughout the afterbody from midsection to the counter.

Scale of model is ½ inch to the foot, and the scaled dimensions are length over the rail 77 feet, and between perpendiculars 70 feet 6 inches, moulded beam 20 feet 8 inches, and depth in hold about 6 feet 9 inches.

Given by Dennison J. Lawlor, naval architect and shipbuilder, Chelsea, Massachusetts.

FISHING SCHOONER, 1872
BUILDER'S HALF-MODEL, USNM 160111

David F. Low

The extreme clipper fishing schooner *David F. Low* was built from this model at Gloucester for local owners in 1872, for the market and mackerel fisheries. The *Low* was representative of the design of fast fisher-

The midsection shows a rising floor, a slightly hollow and very hard bilge, and some tumble-home in the topsides. The beam is carried well aft. The shoal hull is made weatherly by use of a very deep keel outside the rabbet; in fact, the model resembles that of a centerboard-hull with a fixed straight keel substituted for the centerboard.

Scale of the half-model is ½ inch to the foot, representing a schooner approximately 79 feet 6 inches long on the rail, 74 feet between perpendiculars, 21 feet beam, 7 feet depth of hold, 57.73 net tons.

Given by Captain E. L. Rowe, Gloucester.

FISHING SCHOONER, 1872
RIGGED MODEL, USNM 39337

Mary O'Dell

The *Mary O'Dell* was built in 1872 at Bath, Maine, for the New England market fishery. Schooners of

207

her type were relatively small, ranging from 35 to 60 gross tons, and the *O'Dell* was a large vessel of her class and date. Owned at Gloucester, Massachusetts, for which port a number of fishing schooners had been built in Maine, the *O'Dell* was eventually sold to Savannah, Georgia, and operated in the southern fisheries for some years.

The model shows a schooner having a long, sharp entrance, long and very fine run, strong sheer, low quarterdeck, straight keel with drag, raking stem rabbet with a long and pointed head, nearly upright post, and a short counter with wide and rather heavy raking elliptical transom. The midsection shows a rising and slightly hollow floor, a hard bilge, and a slight tumble-home in the topside.

Shown with sails set: mainsail, foresail, jumbo or jib, flying jib or jib topsail, main gaff-topsail and main-topmast staysail.

Scale of model is ⅝ inch to the foot, producing a vessel about 71 feet between perpendiculars, 20 feet beam, 7 feet depth in hold, and 46.05 net tons. Length of bowsprit outboard the rabbet 18 feet 9 inches, jib boom outside cap 12 feet 6 inches, foremast above deck 65 feet, mainmast 66 feet, main-topmast 31 feet 10 inches total, fore boom 24 feet 4 inches, fore gaff 23 feet, main boom 58 feet 9 inches, and main gaff 28 feet 6 inches.

Given by U. S. Fish Commission.

FISHING SCHOONER, 1874
BUILDER'S HALF-MODEL, USNM 54456
LINES PLAN, USNM 160206

Howard

This half-model of a moderately sharp fishing schooner for use in the cod and halibut fisheries, but which might also be used in the mackerel hook fishery, was the work of Willard A. Burnham, who built from it the schooner *Howard* in 1874 at Essex, Massachusetts. Her design was very popular, as it combined capacity with speed to an unusual degree, and about thirty schooners were later built on her moulds, among them the *Cunard, Carrie Louise, Aberdeen, Edward Grover,* and the *Nathaniel Webster.*

The model represents a relatively full-bodied schooner having moderate rise of floor with some hollow, low and rather hard bilges, and wall-sided above. The entrance is long and sharp with some hollow near the stem; the run is long, easy, and well-formed. The greatest beam is about at midlength. The post rakes somewhat; the counter is short, finishing with a wide, shallow, elliptical transom and

marked quarters; the bow rabbet rakes and flares forward, the bow sections having moderate flare; the keel is straight, with much drag; and the sheer is average.

Scale of model is ½ inch to the foot, producing a vessel 72 feet long on the rails, 20 feet 6 inches moulded beam, 7 feet 3 inches depth in hold, and drawing about 9 feet 3 inches at post and 6 feet 6 inches forward. The *Howard* was 77 feet between perpendiculars, 21.5 feet beam, 7.6 feet depth of hold, and 78.8 tons register.

Model given by Willard A. Burnham, shipbuilder, Essex, Massachusetts.

CHESAPEAKE BAY OYSTER SCHOONER, 1875–85
BUILDER'S HALF-MODEL, USNM 76294

G. W. Garrison

The centerboard schooner *G. W. Garrison* was built from this half-model by the Brusstar Shipbuilding Company, at Baltimore, Maryland, probably for the oyster fishery. However, as she was unusually sharp forward for her type and date, and was designed for fast sailing, she may have been designed for a pilot boat, but no record of the vessel has been found.

The half-model represents a fast-sailing centerboard schooner having a sharp and slightly hollow entrance, with the greatest beam slightly forward of midlength and a long and very fine run. The keel is straight with some drag, the stem rabbet curved and raking, flaring as the rail is approached, and the stem is formed with a long head. The post rakes moderately, the counter is short and finished with a raking elliptical transom curved athwartships, and the sheer is strong. Midsection formed with slightly rising floor, a firm round bilge, and a slight tumble-home in the topside. The flare in the forward sections is very marked.

The vessel was flush-decked, and the model shows a low log rail, pungy-fashion, with prominent knight-heads.

Scale of model is ½ inch to the foot, and the vessel shown would be 76 feet moulded length at rail, about 71 feet 9 inches between perpendiculars, 21 feet moulded beam, about 6 feet 8 inches moulded depth and drawing about 5 feet 9 inches at post and 5 feet 4 inches forward. This vessel was unusually sharp forward for her type and date.

Given by Brusstar Shipbuilding Company, Baltimore, Maryland.

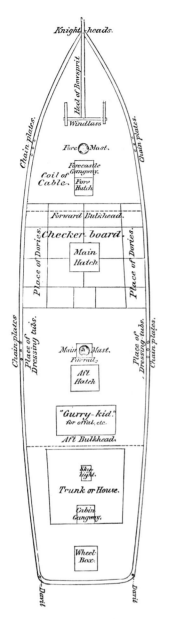

Knight heads.

Heel of Bowsprit.

Chain plates.

Windlass.

Fore Mast.

Forecastle Gangway.

Coil of Cable.

Fore Hatch.

Chain plates.

Forward Bulkhead.

Checker-board.

Place of Dories.

Main Hatch.

Place of Dories.

Chain plates.

Place of Dressing tubs.

Main Mast.

Fiferail.

Aft Hatch.

Place of Dressing tubs.

Chain plates.

"Gurry-kid." for offal, etc.

Aft Bulkhead.

Sky-light.

Trunk or House.

Cabin Gangway.

Wheel-Box.

Davit

Davit

Sketch of the
Deck of
COD SCHOONER
Centennial,
Cap.t B.A.Williams,
Gloucester, Mass.

Scale 1 inch=15 feet.

Tonnage, 115,96 tons.
Bowsprit 21 ft. beyond the Knight-heads.
Jib-boom, 15 ."
Fore-Mast, 76½ : + no top mast.
Fore boom 32 :
Main-Mast, 78" : Main top-mast, 40 ·118 ft.
Main boom, 62 :
6 dories.

DECK PLAN OF COD-FISHING
Schooner *Centennial,* 1876.
From G. Brown Goode, *The fisheries and fishery industries of the United States,* Washington, Government Printing Office, 1884–87.

FISHERY POLICE SCHOONER, 1874
BUILDER'S HALF-MODEL, USNM 160119

Folly, Frolic

The centerboard schooners *Folly* and *Frolic* were built from this half-model at Baltimore in 1874 by the Brusstar Shipbuilding Company for the Maryland State Fishery Police or "Oyster Navy," which was formed in 1868. These small swift-sailing schooners, of shoal draft, were employed in the enforcement of state fishery and conservation laws on Chesapeake Bay. The *Frolic,* in particular, became well known,

and during her long service was rebuilt or altered a number of times.

The half-model shows a sharp-ended centerboard schooner having marked sheer, a straight keel with some drag, nearly upright sternpost, short counter, raking and heart-shaped transom, raking and flaring stem rabbet much curved at forefoot, and cutwater formed with a long head. The entrance is long, sharp, and somewhat hollow in the forefoot; the run long and very fine; the forward sections moderately flared; and the midsection formed with rising straight floor, rather high hard bilge, and some tumble-home in the topside.

These schooners had a long trunk cabin amidships between the masts and a small one abaft the mainmast. A boat was carried in stern davits and occasionally a small cannon was mounted but usually the armament was a few rifles.

The schooner was gaff-rigged, carried a large jib, fore and main gaff-sails, main gaff-topsail, main-topmast staysail and usually a small jib topsail. There was no foretopmast. The centerboard passed through the garboard to one side of the keel.

Scale of half-model is ½ inch to the foot. The schooners measured 48 feet over the rail, 43 feet 6 inches between perpendiculars, 14 feet moulded beam, 4 feet 9 inches moulded depth, and drew 3 feet 6 inches with the centerboard raised.

Given by Brusstar Shipbuilding Company, Baltimore, Maryland, in 1895.

SCHOONER SMACK, 1875
RIGGED MODEL, USNM 26584

Storm King

The clipper schooner smack *Storm King* was built at Essex, Massachusetts, by William Story in 1875 for Boston owners and was employed in carrying lobsters

→

LINES OF FISHING SCHOONER *Mary Fernald*, taken off the builder's half model in the Peabody Museum, Salem, Massachusetts.

←

FISHING SCHOONER *Mary Fernald* built at Gloucester, Massachusetts, in 1875 by Poland and Woodbury. She was designed by Daniel Poland, Jr. Rigged model USNM 76246. (*Smithsonian photo 44693–k.*)

to market. These schooners were sharp and fast sailers, ranging from about 20 to 50 gross tons, and the *Storm King*, a fast sailer, was long considered an excellent vessel of her type. Similar smacks were built in Maine for the lobster fishery, and some sloop smacks were also employed in this fishery in Massachusetts and Maine.

The *Storm King* was a clipper-built keel schooner having a long and sharp entrance, long and fine run, marked sheer, straight keel with drag, rather upright stem rabbet with long head, and nearly upright post with short counter and elliptical raking transom. The midsection was formed with a strongly rising floor, high and rather hard bilge, and some tumble-home in the topside. The deck was flush, with a small trunk cabin aft, and a large fish well was built about amidships, its bottom perforated to allow circulation of salt water.

Scale of model is ¾ inch to the foot. The *Storm King* was 53 feet 4 inches at rail, 15 feet 8 inches beam, 7 feet 4 inches depth of hold, and drew about 7 feet 6 inches at post.

The bowsprit extended 14 feet 8 inches outside the rabbet, the foremast stood 47 feet 6 inches above the deck and the mainmast 48 feet 3 inches (including 4 feet of head), and the main topmast was 16 feet in total length. The main boom was 38 feet 9 inches, the fore boom 14 feet 8 inches, the fore gaff 13 feet 4 inches,

and the main gaff 17 feet 4 inches. These schooners usually carried a single large jib having a short club at foot, fore and main gaff-sails, gaff-topsail on the main, and a fisherman staysail. They were, as a rule, very heavily canvassed for smacks and usually were very stiff under sail.

Given by Johnson and Young.

SCHOONER SMACK, 1875
RIGGED MODEL, USNM 76257

Emma W. Lowe

The schooner-rigged smack *Emma W. Lowe* was built at Key West, Florida, in 1875 to engage in the market fishery out of that port, supplying the Cuban market at Havana. This was a very profitable business until the Spanish government raised the tariff at Havana, after which the fishery ceased. The Noank schooner smack was introduced at Key West by New England fishermen, and the schooners built there of native timber for the fishery were on the same model. The *Emma W. Lowe* is of similar form to the schooner smack *City of Havana* built at Key West in 1877 on the half-model USNM 76084, though the latter was slightly the smaller of the two.

The model shows a keel schooner having a long and sharp entrance, a long and fine run, moderate sheer, straight keel with some drag, raking stem rabbet

210

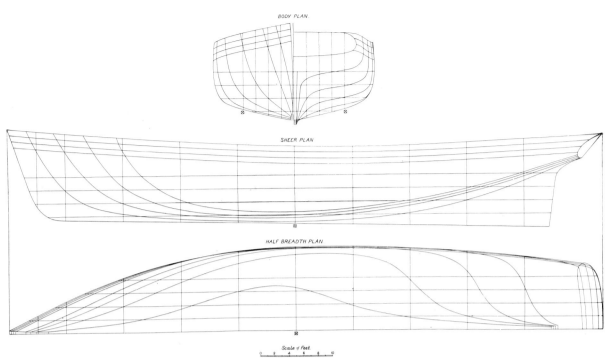

BODY PLAN.

SHEER PLAN

HALF BREADTH PLAN

Scale of Feet
0   2   4   6   8   10

PLANS OF FISHING SCHOONER "MARY FERNALD."

with long head, raking post with V-transom, and flush deck. The midsection is formed with a rising floor, easy bilge, and tumble-home in the topside.

The deck arrangement shows a wheelbox right aft, forward of this a short trunk cabin, then two wooden pumps each well outboard from the centerline, the mainmast, a hatch, well-grating, hatch, two wooden pumps, foremast, wooden rail-to-rail, jib-sheet horse, windlass, and heel bitt. The model omits the headrail of the long head employed. There are 2 shrouds on each side of each lower mast.

Scale of model is ½ inch to the foot. The smack was about 68 feet at rail, 19 feet beam, and 6 feet 9 inches depth in hold.

The rig is that of a small fore-and-main-topsail schooner having a bowsprit without cap. The vessel carries a single large jib with a short club on the foot, jib topsail, foresail and fore gaff-topsail, mainsail and main gaff-topsail, and fisherman's staysail.

Given by U. S. Bureau of Fisheries.

FISHING SCHOONER, 1875
Rigged Model, usnm 76246

Mary Fernald

The *Mary Fernald*, clipper fishing schooner, was built by Poland & Woodbury at Gloucester for local owners in 1875. She was intended for the summer mackerel fishery (purse-seining) and for the winter

frozen-herring trade to the Maritime Provinces. The model shows her ready for mackerel fishing, all sail set, with a seine boat on the port side and a seine stowed in it, and a dory astern. The *Fernald* is an excellent example of an extreme clipper fishing schooner of her date, having the relatively shoal body, marked beam, and huge rig that combined to make this class of schooner the cause of such losses during its years of popularity in the New England fisheries. She was wrecked near Whitehead, Nova Scotia, in 1895 without loss of life.

The model shows a long sharp entrance, long and very fine run, raking stem with long head, nearly upright post, short counter with wide, raking, elliptical transom, good sheer, and straight keel with drag. The midsection has a moderately rising floor, hard bilge, and a slight tumble-home in the topside, a description that fits practically all extreme clipper fishing schooners of her date.

Scale of model is ½ inch to the foot. The schooner was 78 feet between perpendiculars, and about the same at rail, 22.8 feet beam, 7.9 feet depth in hold, and 80.29 gross tons. Bowsprit extends 20 feet 6 inches outboard of rabbet, jib boom 14 feet 6 inches outside the bowsprit cap, foremast 62 feet 6 inches and mainmast 64 feet above deck, fore-topmast 36 feet and main-topmast 36 feet total length, fore boom 26 feet, fore gaff 26 feet, main boom 56 feet 6 inches,

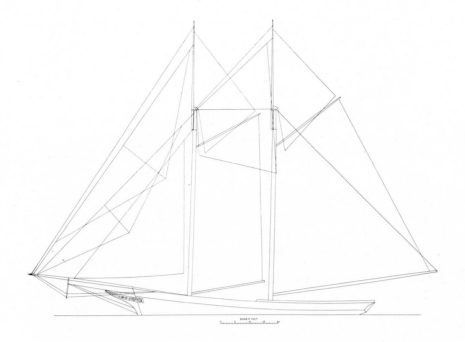

→

LINES OF A KEY WEST SCHOONER SMACK OF THE NOANK MODEL, the *City of Havana*, built at Key West, Florida, in 1877. Taken off builder's half-model USNM 76084.

←

SAIL PLAN of the fishing schooner *Mary Fernald*, from a copy of the sailmaker's plans in the Watercraft Collection.

and main gaff 28 feet 6 inches. The seine boat is 36 feet 6 inches overall and 8 feet 6 inches beam.

Given by U. S. Bureau of Fisheries.

FISHING SCHOONER, 1875
BUILDER'S HALF-MODEL, USNM 160121

Lizzie W. Matheson

The 3-masted fishing schooner *Lizzie W. Matheson* of Provincetown, Massachusetts, was built from this model at Essex by John James & Company in 1875. Burdensome but capable of sailing very well, she was intended for the hand-line codfishery on the Grand Banks, where she was employed during each summer; during the winter she ran to the West Indies or went coastwise, freighting. The *Matheson* is considered to be the first schooner of her rig regularly employed in the New England fishery. A 3-masted pinky schooner, the *Spy*, had been built at Essex in 1823 (she measured 70 feet between perpendiculars, 17 feet beam, 8 feet 6 inches depth of hold, and 91^{6}⅟₉₅ tons, pink stern, three masts, no galleries, no head) and was intended for the Banks fishery, but it does not appear she was ever so employed. The *Matheson* proved successful and was followed by a number of 3-masters, among them the *Willie A. McKay*, 1880, *Henry S. Woodruff*, 1886, *Arthur V. S. Woodruff*, 1888, and *Cora S. McKay*, 1888, all built by James at Essex. Later still, others were built, though the 3-master was never very popular in the fisheries. When the salt fishery became unprofitable, some of these 3-masters

went into other fisheries. The *Woodruff*, for example, became a whaler. The *Matheson* was lost in the West Indies in 1895.

The half-model shows a rather shallow, broad hull of the coaster type, rather sharp in the entrance and with a short but fine run. The midsection shows a slightly rising floor, low hard bilge, and slight tumble-home above. The sheer is strong, the keel is straight and with a slight drag, the stem rakes, and the post is nearly vertical. The vessel had a long, low quarter-deck carried a little forward of the mainmast. She had a graceful longhead and a short counter having a broad elliptical transom.

Scale of model is ½ inch to the foot. The *Matheson* was 106 feet 8 inches over the rail, 99 feet 5 inches between perpendiculars, 24 feet 6 inches moulded beam, 10 feet 6 inches depth of hold, and drew 11 feet at the post and 9 feet 6 inches forward.

Her rig was that of a 3-masted coaster of the time, but with the bowsprit less stived and with more sail area. A rigged model of a 3-masted fishing schooner is in the Watercraft Collection (USMN 160211, see p. 220).

Given by H. & S. Cook, Provincetown, Massachusetts.

FISHING SCHOONER, 1876
BUILDER'S HALF-MODEL, USNM 54447

Webster Sanborn

The Banker *Webster Sanborn* was built from this half-model at Essex, Massachusetts, in 1876 by David

212

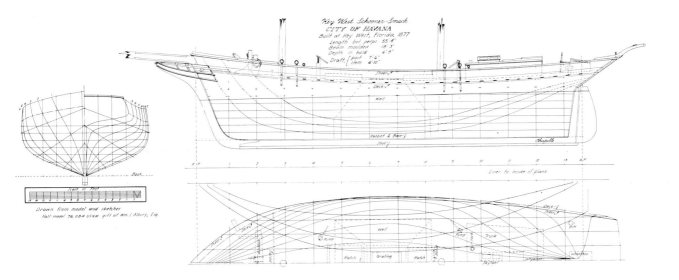

Burnham, particularly for the Grand Banks cod and halibut fisheries out of Gloucester. The vessels designed for these fisheries were much more burdensome than the market boats and Georgesmen, or than the mackerel seiners, and the model is a good example of the "full" clipper Banker of the period. In designing her an effort was made to produce a vessel with an excellent turn of speed and good capacity that would ride easily at anchor on the Banks, as well as be dry, steady, and stiff under sail. The *Sanborn* was lost at Newfoundland in the summer of 1882.

The half-model is for a schooner rather full above the load waterline and having a moderately sharp bow, straight keel with drag, raking post, fine run of medium length, raking and somewhat flaring stem rabbet, long head, and a short counter with wide elliptical transom at a sharp rake and curved athwartships. There is considerable sheer.

Scale of half-model is ½ inch to the foot, giving a vessel about 81 feet on the rails, 24 feet beam, 8 feet depth of hold, and drawing about 10 feet 9 inches at the post.

Given by David Burnham, shipbuilder, Essex, Massachusetts.

SCHOONER SMACK, 1877
BUILDER'S HALF-MODEL, USNM 76084

City of Havana

The well-smack fishing schooner *City of Havana* was built in 1877 from this model at Key West, Florida, to fish out of that port, particularly in the red snapper fishery, the market being Havana, Cuba. These smacks were designed to sail fast and all were on a deep-draft clipper model.

The half-model shows a flush-decked clipper fishing schooner having a strong sheer, straight keel, raking post with a deep V-transom set at a very sharp rake and flat athwartships, the stem rabbet raking and flaring outward and adorned with a long, pointed head. The midsection is about at midlength, with steeply rising straight floor, a high, easy bilge, and a slight tumble-home in the topside. The entrance is long and sharp and the run fine and long. The well was amidships, entered by a hatch on deck.

The rig was usually that of a pilot-boat schooner. a single large jib, boomed foresail, mainsail, and a large main-topmast staysail set on a fidded main-topmast. No gaff topsails were usually carried. This model is similar in all respects to the smack schooners built at Noank, Connecticut, 1860–80.

Scale of half-model is ½ inch to the foot, giving a vessel about 61 feet over the rails, 55 feet 4 inches between perpendiculars, 18 feet 3 inches moulded beam, about 6 feet 9 inches depth of hold, and drawing about 7 feet 6 inches at the post and 6 feet 10 inches forward.

Given by William J. Albury, Key West, Florida, 1884.

FISHING SCHOONER, 1877
RIGGED MODEL, USNM 39487

William M. Gaffney

The clipper fishing schooner *William M. Gaffney* was built at Gloucester, Massachusetts, in 1877, by John

SCHOONER CREW baiting trawls at
T-wharf, Boston, Massachusetts,
in the 1880's. Details of rigging can
be seen. (*Smithsonian photo 44790.*)

214

NOTE SIZE OF THE FORESTAYSAIL, CALLED THE "JUMBO," ON THIS MACKEREL SEINER, the *Mabel Dilloway*, photographed in 1882. (*Smithsonian photo 44792-f.*)

and Hugh Bishop for the purse-seine mackerel fishery and the winter frozen herring trade to the Province of New Brunswick.

The model represents an extreme clipper fishing schooner of the date, but with rather less flare forward than was usual, with a long, sharp entrance and a long and very fine run, raking stem rabbet with long head, straight keel with drag, nearly upright sternpost, and a short counter finishing with a raking elliptical transom curved athwartships. The sheer is strong. Midsection shows a strongly rising, slightly hollow floor, a moderately easy bilge, and a slight tumble-home in the topside. There is a long, low quarter-deck.

The model is shown with all sail set: mainsail, foresail, jumbo, jib, and jib topsail, fore and main gaff-topsails and main-topmast staysail.

Scale of model is ½ inch to the foot. The vessel measured 80 feet at rail, 22 feet beam, 7 feet depth of hold, and 74.65 gross tons.

The bowsprit extended 18 feet from rabbet, jib boom outside cap 12 feet, main boom 56 feet, fore-topmast truck 84 feet, and main-topmast truck 85 feet above deck. This model gives a good idea of the quantity of sail carried in this class of fishing schooner. Headrails are missing and appear not to have been made, although the vessel actually had these supports to her long head. Otherwise, the model is very complete.

From John Bishop, shipbuilder, Gloucester, Massachusetts.

FISHING SCHOONER, 1879
BUILDER'S HALF-MODEL, USNM 54444

Ivanhoe

The extreme clipper fishing schooner *Ivanhoe* was built from this model at Gloucester, Massachusetts, by Poland and Woodbury in 1879 for local owners. Her model, made by Daniel Poland, is the very shallow, wide, sharp-ended type that predominated in the New England fisheries at the time. These schooners depended largely upon initial stability, to withstand a knockdown, as they usually could carry little ballast (commonly stone), but they were often very fast and for this reason remained popular until later designs produced deeper, narrower, and equally fast vessels, showing that speed and safety could exist together in a fishing schooner. The builders of the *Ivanhoe* produced a large number of vessels much like her in model, and Poland was one of the leading designers of the shoal, clipper fishing schooners.

The half-model shows a shoal schooner having a straight keel with moderate drag, graceful sheer, raking stem and longhead, a short counter ending in a broad and shallow elliptical transom well-curved athwartships, with much rake and heavy quarters, a long, somewhat hollow and very sharp entrance, and a long, flat and fine run. The midsection shows a slightly hollow rising floor, hard bilge, and some tumble-home in the topside. Scale of half-model is ½ inch to the foot, producing a schooner about 87 feet on the rails, 22 feet moulded beam, and 7 feet 9 inches depth of hold. The model shows the deep outside keel of her type.

Given by Daniel Poland, Jr., shipbuilder, Gloucester, Massachusetts.

FISHING SCHOONER, 1880
BUILDER's HALF-MODEL, USNM 54454

John M. Smart Emma S. Osier

The inshore fisheries market boats *John M. Smart* of Portsmouth, New Hampshire, and the *Emma S. Osier* of Gloucester, Massachusetts, were built from this model by John Bishop at Gloucester in 1880. Swift sailing was a highly prized quality among vessels of this class of fresh fishermen making trips to the inshore grounds. Usually called "schooner boats," they were commonly under 60 feet in overall length, and due to the prevailing winds it was highly desirable that they be weatherly and carry sail well.

The half-model shows an extreme clipper schooner

with a long and sharp entrance, with some hollow near the stem, the greatest beam about amidships, and a long, easy run ending in a rather short counter and a wide elliptical transom with rather heavy quarters. The stem rabbet rakes smartly and flares forward; the head is long, beaked, and handsome; the post rakes slightly; and the keel is straight and has some drag. The sheer is lively and graceful; the model represents a strikingly handsome small schooner of the period. The midsection shows a steeply rising floor with a very slight hollow, a quick turn of bilge, and a slight tumble-home in the topside. As usual, in vessels from this builder's yard, the flare forward is slight; the sections near the bow are rounded rather than hollow and flaring.

Scale of half-model is ½ inch to the foot, giving a vessel that measures about 56 feet over the rails, about 49 feet 9 inches between perpendiculars, 15 feet 4 inches moulded beam, about 5 feet depth of hold, and drawing 6 feet 3 inches at the post and 3 feet 9 inches forward. These schooners had the market-boat rig; they were large for their class and date.

Given by John Bishop, shipbuilder, Gloucester, Massachusetts.

FISHING SCHOONER, 1880
BUILDER's HALF-MODEL, USNM 54419

This model is an early design for a large mackerel-seining schooner by George M. ("Mel") McLain of Rockport, Massachusetts, who later designed a large number of fishing schooners. His models were distinguished by grace and beauty and the vessels built from them were commonly swift and successful. This style of schooner was usually employed in fishing only during the summer. In winter the vessels either carried freight coastwise, if capacity permitted, or transported oysters or fruit to New England from southern ports.

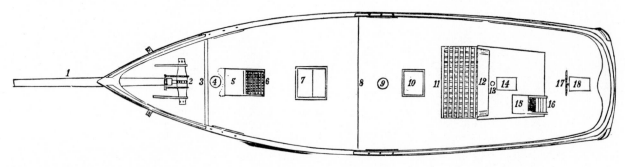

DECK PLAN OF MACKEREL SEINING SCHOONER of about 1885. From G. Brown Goode, *The fisheries and fishery industries of the United States*, Washington, Government Printing Office, 1884–87.

216

TARR AND JAMES SHIPYARD AT ESSEX, MASSACHUSETTS, ABOUT 1885, with one vessel in the water and another behind it on the ways. A new river steamer is in the background and other yards are beyond, with three ships on the ways. Center of village is to left, in background. Sheers and hoisting tackle are rigged to step the mainmast of the schooner in the foreground. The mast is alongside on the wharf. (*Smithsonian photo 44793-h.*)

No vessel was built from this half-model, which shows the popular extreme, shoal clipper of the period, with a long, sharp and flaring bow, raking stem rabbet with longhead, a long, lean and rather flat run, and ending with a wide shallow elliptical transom on a short counter, with heavy quarters. The midsection shows sharply rising floors with some hollow, a hard bilge, and tumble-home above. Model had marked drag and a handsome sheer.

Scale of half-model is ½ inch to the foot, giving a vessel that measures about 106 feet over the rail, 24 feet beam, about 7 feet depth of hold, and draws about 10 feet at the post.

Given by Captain George M. McLain, Rockport, Massachusetts.

CHESAPEAKE BAY CENTERBOARD FISHING SCHOONER, about 1880

BUILDER'S HALF-MODEL, USNM 312332

An unidentified centerboard schooner was built

from this half-model in Dorchester County, Maryland, about 1880, by Joseph T. Spicer for the Chesapeake Bay oyster fishery and for general freighting.

The half-model, which is to the deck only, represents a shoal-draught centerboard schooner having a straight keel, raking sternpost, a raking curved stem rabbet, moderate sheer, and a wide, square round-tuck pungy stern with upper and lower transoms (the model shows cross-seam and round tuck only). The stem is intended to have a long pointed head. Entrance is short and full, the greatest beam being well forward. The run is long and fine. The midsection shows a slightly rising straight floor carried well out, a full and round bilge carried well up toward the deck, and the topsides nearly vertical and shallow. Model marked on back with mast positions and centerboard size and location.

Scale of the model is ½ inch to the foot, producing a vessel that measures about 65 feet moulded deck

length, 66 feet tonnage length, 20 feet 6 inches moulded beam, 5 feet 4 inches moulded depth, and draws about 4 feet 9 inches with centerboard raised. Masts rake sharply. Foremast is 12 feet, mainmast 36 feet 9 inches, aft of stem rabbet at deck; fore end of centerboard case is 23 feet 6 inches and after end (which is abaft mainmast), 37 feet 8 inches aft of stem rabbet, making centerboard about 13 feet 8 inches long. It would be alongside the keel, with the slot in the garboard, and the mainmast would be slightly off the hull centerline, on the opposite side.

Given by James K. Spicer, Taylor's Island, Maryland.

The donor identified it as being of the *American Eagle*.

FISHING SCHOONER, 1881
RIGGED MODEL, USNM 56938

James A. Garfield

The clipper fishing schooner *James A. Garfield* was built at Bath, Maine, in 1881 for Gloucester, Massachusetts, owners. She was employed in the Georges Bank fishery hand-lining for cod.

The model represents a clipper fishing schooner of the date, having a straight keel with some drag, a curved and raking stem rabbet, longhead, nearly upright post, short counter with wide elliptical transom, good sheer, long sharp entrance, and a long and rather flat run. The midsection shows a moderate

rise of floor, a hard bilge, and a slight tumble-home in the topside.

Scale of model is ½ inch to the foot. The schooner was about 74 feet between perpendiculars, 22 feet beam, 8 feet depth of hold, and 69.90 net tons. The bowsprit was 19 feet outside the rabbet, foremast 60 feet and mainmast 60 feet 6 inches above deck, main-topmast 33 feet total length, main boom 60 feet, fore boom 23 feet 6 inches, main gaff 26 feet 6 inches, and fore gaff 23 feet.

The model represents the vessel fitted with pen-boards, stern dory, softwood fishing rails, gurry-box, etc.

All sail is set; mainsail, foresail, large jib, main top-mast staysail and main gaff-topsail. This was the usual rig of the Georgesman, though in winter many vessels struck the main-topmast and carried only the three lower sails. When at anchor on the Georges Banks these vessels usually set a triangular riding sail on the mainmast bent with adjustable hoops; the sail was stowed on the davit plank at the stern.

Given by U. S. Bureau of Fisheries.

FISHING SCHOONER, 1882
RIGGED MODEL, USNM 56939

Spencer F. Baird

The fishing schooner *Spencer F. Baird*, named in honor of the founder and first head of the U.S. Fish Commission and Secretary of the Smithsonian Insti-

218

tution (1878–87), was built at Essex in 1882 for Gloucester, Massachusetts owners by Arthur Dana Story. She was designed for the general deep-sea fisheries but particularly for the Grand Banks cod-fishery.

The model shows a clipper fishing schooner in general hull design, but of somewhat greater capacity than the extreme clipper design of her time, having a straight keel with drag, raking stem rabbet, a long-head, nearly upright post, and a short and rather heavy counter with a wide, raking, and curved ellip-

←

GLOUCESTER HARBOR IN THE 1880's, showing typical fishing schooners and a salt-carrying bark. A 2-masted lobster boat is in the right foreground. (*Smithsonian photo 43816–e.*)

MEDIUM-SIZED GLOUCESTER FISHING SCHOONER, the *Laura Sayward*, 1882, showing stern davits for a yawl boat. (*Smithsonian photo 43817–d.*)

tical transom. The quarters are heavy as in most of her type and period. The sheer is marked, the entrance long and sharp, and the run long and fine. The midsection is formed with a rising straight floor, hard bilge, and a slight tumble-home in the topside.

The *Baird* measured 78.6 feet between perpendiculars, 22 feet beam, 8 feet depth of hold, and 78.04 gross tons. She was about 86 feet at rail. Her bowsprit was 19 feet outboard from rabbet, jib-boom 12 feet 8 inches outside of bowsprit cap, foremast 64 feet and mainmast 65 feet above deck, main-topmast 36 feet total length, main boom 62 feet, fore-boom 25 feet, fore gaff 25 feet, main gaff 27 feet 6 inches.

Model shows vessel without a fore-topmast, with all sail set, and with dories stowed upside down on deck and lashed to represent the vessel ready for a passage to or from the Grand Banks. This model is a good example of a clipper-built Grand Banks schooner of 1880–85. Scale is ½ inch to the foot.

Purchased from John Bishop, shipbuilder, Gloucester, Massachusetts.

GLOUCESTER HARBOR IN 1882. The fleet contains pinkies, sloop-boats, and a variety of fishing schooner types. (*Smithsonian photo 44790–a.*)

THREE-MASTED FISHING SCHOONER, 1882
RIGGED MODEL, USNM 160211

This model represents an ideal design for a 3-masted fishing schooner, made by Thomas A. Irving, shipbuilder, of Gloucester, Massachusetts, in 1882. At the International Fisheries Exposition at London in 1883 the model was awarded a gold medal for excellence in design. Bearing the name *Lizzie W. Matheson*, it shows the rig and deck arrangement of that vessel, but the hull of the model is sharper ended than that of the half-model of the *Matheson* (USNM 160121, p. 212), and there is also more rise in the floor.

A number of 3-masted fishing schooners were built between 1875 and 1888, the majority around 1883–84. Among these were the *Grace F. Littleton*, 1883, and the *Grace E. Littleton*, 1884, both built at Bath, Maine, by Thomas E. Hagan. Some of the others were the *Lizzie W. Matheson* built 1875 at Essex, Massachusetts, and the *Willie A. McKay*, 1880; *Henry S. Woodruff*, 1886; *Arthur V. S. Woodruff*, 1888; and the *Cora S. McKay*, 1888.

The model represents a vessel 109 feet at rail, 26 feet beam, 10 feet depth in hold, and drawing about 11 feet at post. The bowsprit extends outboard of the knightheads 22 feet 6 inches, the jib boom 19 feet beyond the cap, the foremast stands 70 feet 3 inches above the deck, the mainmast 72 feet, the mizzenmast 73 feet 3 inches. All three topmasts are 40 feet heel to truck. The fore and main booms are each 23 feet 8 inches, the fore and main gaffs are 23 feet 6 inches, the mizzen boom is 53 feet 3 inches, and the mizzen gaff 29 feet 9 inches. The stern boat is 17 feet 6 inches long, 5 feet in beam, and about 3 feet in depth. Scale of the model is ½ inch to the foot.

These 3-masted fishing schooners differed from coasters of this rig and approximate size; the fishermen were usually sharper, had less freeboard, a larger rig, more rise in the floor, a long and low quarterdeck carried to just forward of the mainmast, and their deck arrangements were, of course, those of a fishing vessel. The model is somewhat more of a clipper than most if not all the 3-masted fishing schooners uilt in the period 1875–88, the majority of which were Grand Bankers, though at least one was for a time employed in the mackerel fishery as a purse-seiner. Never numerous, they were apparently successful in their business but were usually considered too large for the general fisheries. A few were built in Massachusetts and Nova Scotia during World War I.

Given by Thomas A. Irving, shipbuilder, Gloucester, Massachusetts.

WELL-SMACK FISHING SCHOONER, 1883
BUILDER'S HALF MODEL, USNM 160115

Captain Joseph W. Collins, after entering the employ of the U.S. Fish Commission, about 1880, began to agitate in newspapers and elsewhere for safer fishing vessels. He had obtained the advice of competent designers, such as Lawlor, who had impressed upon him the need in New England fishing schooners for greater depth and heavier ballast as a necessary measure to achieve safety without making them otherwise undesirable vessels. Before 1883, the Commission had begun to consider the construction of a well-smack for use as a fisheries research vessel and this gave Captain Collins a chance to propose a specific design for a "model fishing schooner."

The half-model shows a vessel having the entrance long, sharp, and somewhat hollow at the stem, with greatest beam about at midlength; the run lean and long, ending in a short counter having rather heavy quarters and a wide elliptical transom, at the bottom of which is a slight V-shaped rise from the center line.

A FAMOUS RACING FISHERMAN, NOTED FOR HER FINE SAILING QUALITIES, the *Nannie C. Bohlin*, built in 1890 at Gloucester, Massachusetts, by John Bishop. Register dimensions were 110.2′ x 23.5′ x 11.2′, 96 net tons. Her captain was Tommy Bohlin. (*Smithsonian photo 38807.*)

FISHING SCHOONER ON MARINE RAILWAY IN THE 1880's at Rocky Neck, Gloucester, showing the typical head work of an Essex-built fisherman of the period. (*Smithsonian photo 44791.*)

The keel is straight, with drag; the sheer is strong and graceful; and the midsection shows a rising floor with very hollow garboards, a hard bilge, and some tumble-home in the topside. The post is nearly vertical, and the stem is curved and raking and fitted with a long-head.

Scale of the half-model is ½ inch to the foot, producing a schooner about 78 feet over the rails, 18 feet moulded beam, about 8 feet depth of hold, and drawing about 10 feet 6 inches at the post and 6 feet 6 inches forward.

This half-model appears to be Captain Collins' first, very cautious attempt to put his ideas into force. It is basically the shoal clipper schooner of 1880 with about a foot more depth than was usual for a vessel of this class and length in 1883, to allow better for better ballasting and some dead rise in the counter, together with some reduction in width, compared with other schooners of this size. However, no vessel was ever built from the model, and it is doubtful that sufficient depth had been added to give a markedly greater stability than the older vessels possessed.

Given by U. S. Fish Commission.

WELL-SMACK FISHING SCHOONER, 1883
BUILDER'S HALF-MODEL, USNM 160116

This half-model represents one of the designs for a well-smack schooner for fisheries research prepared by Captain Joseph W. Collins in 1883. No vessel was built from this model. It appears to have been an alternate proposal to half-model USNM 160115, and was for a smaller vessel. The improvements incorporated in this model appear to be an increase in depth and a decrease in beam as compared with contemporary clipper fishing schooners of this length, somewhat lighter quarters, and the use of dead rise in the counter.

The half-model shows a keel schooner having a long, sharp, and rather hollow entrance; the greatest beam about midlength; a long, flat run with marked quarters, ending in a short counter having some dead rise; and a nearly elliptical transom, sharply raked and, because of its dead rise, somewhat V-shaped. The post is nearly upright, the stem rabbet is curved and raking, and there is a long graceful head. The floors rise rather sharply, with a slight hollow, and the bilge amidships is hard.

Scale of half-model is ½ inch to the foot, producing a vessel about 65 feet on the rail, 15 feet 6 inches beam, and about 7 feet 9 inches depth of hold.

Given by U. S. Fish Commission.

222

WELL-SMACK FISHING SCHOONER, 1883
BUILDER'S HALF-MODEL, USNM 160114
LINES PLAN, USNM 160233

This proposal for a well-smack schooner was made in 1883 for a U. S. Fish Commission fisheries research vessel, but not built. The design was prepared by U. S. Naval Constructor Samuel H. Pook, noted designer of clipper ships. The model is said to have been based on Captain Collins' design of 1883 (half-model USNM 160115) at least as to dimensions, but is far superior. It is an advanced design for the period and also strongly resembles some of the later fishing schooners.

The half-model shows a schooner having a long, sharp entrance with much hollow just abaft the stem, a long, easy run ending in a longer counter than was then common in fishing schooners, and finished with a handsome elliptical transom at a sharp rake. The midsection, which is well abaft midlength, has a very hollow, rising floor, a hard bilge, and much tumble-home above; the section is strongly S-shaped. The flare forward is slight and the foremost sections are without the usual hollow flare. The stem rabbet rakes a good deal and flares out slightly; the post rakes moderately. The model has a handsome sheer and the keel is straight with much drag. The vessel was to have a longhead. Scale of half-model is ½ inch to the foot, producing a vessel about 78 feet over the rail, 18 feet moulded beam, 8 feet depth of hold, and drawing about 10 feet at post and 8 feet forward.

Given by U. S. Fish Commission.

FISHING SCHOONER, 1883
BUILDER'S HALF-MODEL, USNM 76289

Nellie Coleman

The fishing schooner *Nellie Coleman* was built from this model at Lamoine, Maine, in 1883 for the Grand Banks fishery. However, she was first employed in the local coasting trade and did not enter the fishing business until 1889.

The half-model is of a typical clipper Banker of her date, having a rather full bow, long run, rising floor, round rather full bilge, short counter with elliptical transom, long head, moderate rake in the ends and some drag to the keel. She had much sheer and, in general, was a good example of her class.

Scale of half-model is ½ inch to the foot. The dimensions of the *Coleman* were 97 feet between perpendiculars, 25 feet 8 inches extreme beam, 9 feet 6 inches depth in hold, and 152.5 net tons.

Given by D. D. Hodgkins, 1889.

CHESAPEAKE BAY CENTERBOARD FISHING SCHOONER, about 1884
BUILDER'S HALF-MODEL, USNM 312333

An unidentified oyster schooner was built from this half-model in Dorchester County, Maryland, about 1884, by Joseph T. Spicer.

The half-model shows a shoal-draft centerboard schooner having a short, full entrance, with the greatest beam well forward, and a long easy run. The midsection shows a rising straight floor, full round bilge, and shallow upright topsides. The model is to the deck only; the stern is square and only the round tuck and cross-seam are shown, indicating a pungy-stern with upper-and-lower transoms; the stem is curved and somewhat raking on the rabbet, and the vessel had a long and pointed head; the post rakes. The lower lift of the model is missing.

Scale of the model is ½ inch to the foot. A vessel built from this model would measure about 61 feet 3 inches moulded length on deck, about 62 feet tonnage length, 20 feet 4 inches moulded beam, 5 feet moulded depth, and would draw about 4 feet 9 inches with centerboard raised.

Vessels of this type had low bulwarks, flush decks, false quarterdeck rails usually formed of a cap and turned stanchions, a trunk cabin aft, a forecastle companionway just abaft foremast, and two cargo hatches. Mainmast and centerboard case were off the hull centerline, with the centerboard passing through one garboard and the mainmast step over the opposite garboard. These schooners were swift sailers and good sail carriers, making excellent oyster dredgers. The masts were long and light and the sail area was large. They usually carried jib booms and fore and main topmasts when making long passages.

Given by James K. Spicer, Taylor's Island, Maryland.

CENTERBOARD SPONGE-FISHING SCHOONER, 1884
RIGGED MODEL, USNM 76261

City of Key West

The centerboard schooner *City of Key West* was built for the sponge fishery on the Florida Reef at Key West, Florida, in 1884. She was typical of the shoal-draft schooners employed in this business, and by the Florida wreckers from 1875 to 1900. Some sharpie schooners were also employed in this fishery.

The model shows a shoal-draft centerboard schooner having a long, sharp entrance, rather long and fine run, good sheer, straight keel, raking stem rabbet with long head, upright post, round stern, and a flush deck. The midsection is formed with a slightly rising straight floor, low and rather hard bilge, and a slight tumble-home in the topside. The rig is the usual one of such a schooner, a single large jib, fore and main sails, and main-topmast staysail.

Scale of the model is ½ inch to the foot. Custom-house measurements of the vessel were: length between perpendiculars 41.3 feet, beam 14.3 feet, depth 3.5 feet, and 12.86 net tons. The sponging schooners ranged from about 36 to about 50 feet.

Given by U. S. Bureau of Fisheries.

FISHING SCHOONER, 1884
BUILDER'S HALF-MODEL, USNM 76034

Roulette

The fishing schooner *Roulette* was built on specula-tion, in 1884, from this model at East Boston, Massa-chusetts, by Dennison J. Lawlor. The *Roulette* was the first schooner built for the New England fisheries as an improvement on the old, shoal, wide clipper fishermen of this date. She expressed the ideas of a seaworthy, swift schooner that Lawlor had developed much earlier in small market-boat fishermen and in pilot-boat schooners. It is believed that the *Roulette* was built as a result of the agitation for deeper and safer vessel initiated by Captain Joseph W. Collins, in which he had the support of Lawlor and others. After her launching, a lawsuit arose and the builder lost the vessel to a Philadelphia man, who employed her in the New England fisheries, where she attracted much attention because of her speed, weatherliness, and seaworthiness.

The half-model shows a schooner having great sheer, a very long, lean entrance with some hollow just abaft the stem, the greatest beam brought well aft, and the run moderate in length but very fine, with almost constant rise of floor throughout. The stern is a short, deep counter ending in a very sharply raked elliptical transom curved athwartships. The stem is much cut away at the forefoot and the rabbet above is plumb, as in pilot schooners of the time, but the *Roulette* had a long and pointed head. The keel is straight for much of its length, but rounding into the forefoot, beginning a little abaft the foremast. The midsection shows a sharply rising and somewhat hollow floor, with the hollow carried right forward as well as aft. The bilge is very quick and hard, and there is some tumble-home above. The post is up-right. When built, this schooner had a bowsprit

and jib boom, but soon afterwards was fitted with a spike bowsprit.

Scale of the model is ½ inch to the foot. The *Roulette* was 93 feet 2 inches over the rail, 83 feet 7 inches between perpendiculars, 23 feet 4 inches moulded beam, 9 feet 9 inches depth in hold, and drew 11 feet at post. Because of the rocker forward she drew relatively little forward, though the drag to her straight keel was very moderate.

The improvements incorporated in the *Roulette* were chiefly her greater depth—she was about 24 inches deeper than any fishing schooner of her length at the time she was built—and the narrowing of the stern to ease the quarters. As a result of her depth she carried more ballast lower than was formerly possible, her beam and powerful bilges made her as stiff under canvas as any of her contemporaries, and her fine lines made her very fast on all points of sailing. The success of this vessel led owners to accept the deeper, narrower, and more heavily bal-lasted schooners recommended by Captain Collins and others.

Given by Dennison J. Lawlor, naval architect and shipbuilder, Chelsea, Massachusetts.

FISHERIES RESEARCH SCHOONER, 1886
RIGGED MODEL, USNM 298232

Grampus

The *Grampus* was a well-smack schooner designed by Captain Joseph W. Collins of the U. S. Fish Commis-sion and built at Noank, Connecticut, in 1886. She was designed to illustrate Captain Collin's ideas of what a safe and fast fishing schooner ought to be, and was fitted to serve as a fisheries research vessel, having a suitable laboratory and apparatus aboard.

Publicized at the time of her launching as a de-parture from existing types of fishing schooners, she strongly resembled in model some of the fishing schooners designed in 1884–85 by Dennison J. Lawlor of Chelsea and East Boston, Massachusetts; indeed, it is said that Lawlor aided Collins in design-ing the *Grampus*.

This schooner was between 18 and 24 inches deeper in the hold than the average fishing schooner of her size and date, as well as some 6 to 10 inches less in beam, and the stern is much narrower. She had the straight, upright stem of a pilot-boat schooner of her date; this stem had been introduced into the New Eng-land fishing fleet by D. J. Lawlor through his designs for the schooners *John H. McManus* and *Arthur D. Story*, built in 1885, and the smaller *A. S. & R. Ham-*

mond, also built in that year, and later used by many fishing schooners famous for their sailing qualities. Successful as a research vessel, the *Grampus* does not appear to have made any reputation for speed, and the effects of her design were not great, owing to the earlier appearance of Lawlor-designed vessels having similar characteristics.

The model shows a well-smack schooner having a straight keel with much drag, stem straight and upright above the waterline, forefoot below well rounded. Post nearly upright, counter short and finished with an elliptical transom at a sharp rake and strongly curved athwartships. Sheer is great and the vessel has a long, low quarterdeck. The entrance is long, sharp, and slightly hollow; the run is long, easy and moderately flat in the buttocks. The midsection shows a rising floor having some hollow in the garboard, a hard bilge, and tumble-home in the topside; the lines of this vessel somewhat resemble those of the *Roulette* (see half-model USNM 76034), built in 1884.

The original rig of the *Grampus* included bowsprit and jib boom, but the rigged model shows a spike bowsprit that was fitted shortly after her launching, the spike bowsprit having been introduced by the *Carrie E. Phillips*, in 1887.

Scale of the model is ½ inch to the foot.

The *Grampus* was 90 feet at rail, 81 feet 6 inches between perpendiculars, 22 feet 3 inches beam, 10 feet depth of hold, and 83.30 tons register. Her draft was 11 feet 6 inches.

She carried topmasts with fore and main gaff-topsails; mainsail, foresail, main-topmast staysail, fore staysail, jib, and jib topsail; in her original rig she had a jib, forestaysail, flying jib, and jib topsail.

Given by U. S. Bureau of Fisheries.

FISHING SCHOONER, 1889
RIGGED MODEL, USNM 76253

Fredonia, Nellie Dixon

This rigged model represents the fishing schooner *Fredonia*, designed by Edward Burgess and built at Essex in 1889 by Moses Adams, who in the same year built the *Nellie Dixon* from the same plans in

SCHOONER UNDER CONSTRUCTION AT ESSEX, MASSACHUSETTS, IN WILLARD A. BURNHAM'S YARD, 1882, the *Belle Franklin*. Her register dimensions were 78.6′ x 22.2′ x 8.1′, 76 net tons. An excellent example of the "clipper" type, she was owned by John F. Wonson and Co., of Gloucester, Massachusetts. (*Smithsonian photo 34911-c.*)

FISHING SCHOONER *Fredonia*, rigged model USNM 160211. This vessel, designed by Edward Burgess and built in 1889, influenced the design of New England fishing schooners for about fifteen years. (*Smithsonian photos: Top, 44956–b; and bottom, 44956–c.*)

East Boston, Massachusetts. Burgess was the first yacht-designing specialist to design a fishing schooner (Dennison J. Lawlor had designed yachts in his long career but had not specialized in them), and this design was the second made by Burgess for a fishing schooner, the first being for the *Carrie E. Phillips*, a straight-stemmed schooner built by Arthur Dana Story at Essex in 1887, which attracted much attention by her sailing and appearance and was the first New England fishing schooner to have iron wire standing rigging. The *Fredonia* was somewhat more yacht-like, and this vessel, though built to fisherman specifications, was actually employed as a yacht for a season and was then refitted for a fisherman. Hence the less publicized *Nellie Dixon* was the first to sail as a fisherman.

The *Dixon*, less ornately finished than the *Fredonia*, which had carved trailboards, was lengthened slightly

by the stern, and the shape of the shoe, or outside keel, was altered slightly from that of the *Fredonia*, the alterations being made by the designer. Both vessels sailed well and attracted favorable attention, resulting in the introduction of the so-called "Fredonia model," having a clipper bow with strongly flaring and raking stem rabbet, adorned with a small gammon-knee head on which was carved an eagle's head. Headrails and rail knees were omitted, being replaced by iron-rod braces and cross straps. The *Phillips* had introduced the spike bowsprit, and the *Fredonia* employed it, but all vessels built on the Fredonia model did not give up the old jib boom rig until about four years had passed. The Fredonia model was also marked by a shallow forefoot, more or less rockered keel, light and relatively narrow counter, and very sharp lines at bow and stern. The midsection was formed with strongly rising and often hollow floor,

226

high and moderately hard bilge, and tumble-home in the topsides.

The rigged model of the *Fredonia* shows a sharp schooner having a straight keel rabbet with much drag and fairing into the stem rabbet just forward of the heel of the foremast, with the stem rabbet raked and flared forward. The sternpost has much rake and the counter rises steeply and fairs into a small V-shaped elliptical transom; in profile there is no break at the transom heel, the transom raking in line with the profile of the counter. The stern is narrow and light. The sheer is strong, the entrance is very long and sharp, with hollow at the forefoot; the run is relatively short and easy, the buttocks showing a slight curve as they rise aft; the midsection is formed with strongly rising floor having a slight hollow, a high and rather hard bilge, and tumble-home in the topside. The vessels had a long, low quarterdeck. A marked characteristic of this design and that of the *Carrie E. Phillips* is a very deep keel outside the keel-rabbet and a marked curve in the shoe profile.

The hull design of the *Fredonia*, a development of that of the earlier *Carrie E. Phillips*, had sharper

ends, a harder bilge, and greater capacity. The *Phillips* was 104 feet 5 inches at rail, 95 feet between perpendiculars, 24 feet 6 inches beam, and 11 feet depth. The *Fredonia* was 111 feet 6 inches at rail, 99.6 feet between perpendiculars, 23.6 feet beam, and 10.3 feet depth of hold, her actual moulded beam was 23 feet 9 inches. The *Dixon* was 114 feet 9 inches at rail, 101.9 feet between perpendiculars, 23.4 feet beam, and 9.1 feet depth of hold, the mould-loft measurements being 101 feet 2 inches between perpendiculars, 23 feet 9 inches extreme beam, 10 feet 2 inches depth of hold. The differences represent the average error in Customhouse measurements. All three schooners were trimmed well below their designed load waterline, the *Dixon* drawing 14 feet, compared with the designed draft of 12 feet indicated in the designer's plans.

Scale of model is ½ inch to the foot. It is shown with all sails set: mainsail, foresail, forestaysail, jib, jib topsail, fore and main gaff-topsails, main-topmast, or fisherman's, staysail. The vessel has dories stowed upside-down on deck and lashed, as when making a passage.

The rigged model shows the designed spar plan of the two vessels: bowsprit 36 feet 9 inches outside the rabbet at deck, foremast 60 feet 9 inches above deck,

Lines of the Fishing Schooner *Fredonia*, built in 1889, from a copy probably made from the plan of the designer Edward Burgess.

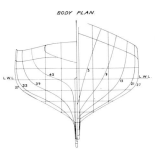

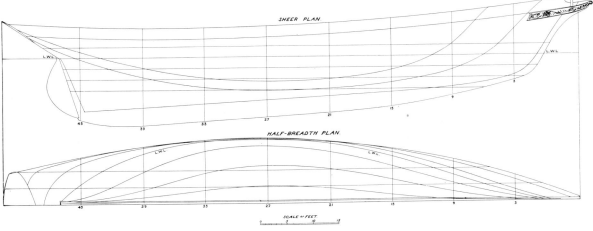

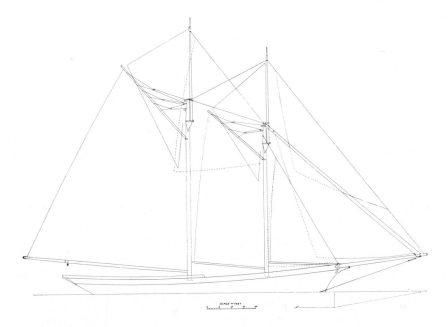

SAIL PLAN of the fishing schooner *Fredonia*, built in 1889, showing the spike bowsprit and small foresail then popular. From a probable copy of the plan of the designer Edward Burgess.

fore-topmast 34 feet in total length, mainmast 70 feet 3 inches above deck, the main-topmast 41 feet total length, main boom 68 feet 6 inches long, main gaff 38 feet, fore boom 29 feet, and fore gaff 28 feet 6 inches.

Given by U. S. Bureau of Fisheries.

WELL-SMACK FISHING SCHOONER, 1890
BUILDER'S HALF-MODEL, USNM 57051

A proposal for an improved well-smack fishing schooner made by Captain Joseph W. Collins of the U. S. Fish Commission in 1890, and one of the series of designs proposed by him from 1883 to 1892, this model was the first referred to as the *New Era;* no vessel was built to the design.

The half-model shows a schooner having a long, sharp entrance with some hollow abaft the stem, a long flat run, straight keel with some drag, raking and curved stem rabbet decorated with a longhead, an upright sternpost, moderate length of counter, a raking, V-shaped, and elliptical transom, handsome sheer, long quarterdeck, the greatest beam abaft mid-length, and the midsection showing a rising hollow floor, a high hard bilge and tumble-home in the top-side. The model shows somewhat more dead rise and depth than most schooners built in the 1880's. The design was intended to be built as a well-smack and was peculiar in that the mainmast was to be stepped on the after wall of the well, which gave that mast a very short bury below the quarterdeck.

The scale of the half-model is ½ inch to the foot.

The vessel would have been about 86 feet on the rail, 22 feet 6 inches moulded beam, 8 feet 3 inches depth of hold, and would draw about 10 feet 6 inches at post. She would have registered between 80 and 85 tons.

Given by U. S. Fish Commission.

FISHING KETCH TRAWLER, 1891
BUILDER'S HALF-MODEL, USNM 76288

Resolute

The ketch-rigged beam trawler *Resolute* of Glouces-ter was built from this half-model by Arthur Dana Story at Essex, Massachusetts, in 1891 as an experi-ment in beam-trawling in the New England fisheries. She was designed by her builder as a copy of the English ketch trawlers then in use, and was the first modern ketch-rigged fisherman to be built in New England. The *Resolute* caught large quantities of bottom fish in her trawl but their very low market prices and the frequent loss or damage to the trawl-gear caused her owners to abandon this method of fishing, as in the earlier experiment at Boston with the schooner *Sylph*. One of two unsuccessful attempts to introduce the ketch rig into the New England offshore fisheries while sail was employed, her ketch rig did not produce a fast enough sailer, so she was resparred and rigged as a schooner and employed as a dory fisher-man.

The half-model shows a flush-decked vessel having a rather straight sheer, straight keel with drag, a straight, upright stem rabbet with a small round at forefoot, raking post with a short counter and ending

228

in an elliptical, raking transom. There is dead rise in the bottom, the entrance is sharp, the run easy, and the midsection is formed with straight rising floor, hard turn of bilge, and a slight tumble-home in the topside.

Scale of model is ½ inch to the foot, producing a vessel having a moulded length at rail 90 feet 11 inches, length between perpendiculars 82 feet 1 inch, moulded beam 20 feet 10 inches, depth in hold 9 feet 6 inches, and drawing 10 feet at post and 7 feet forward.

Given by Arthur Dana Story, shipbuilder, Essex, Massachusetts.

FISHING KETCH TRAWLER, 1891
RIGGED MODEL, USNM 76263

Resolute

This rigged model of the fishing ketch *Resolute* is of the vessel represented by the builder's half-model USNM 76288. Her deck arrangement and much of her rig were copied from English trawlers, but her bowsprit was fixed instead of "reefing" (i. e., capable of being hauled inboard) as in the English boats. There were also departures from English practices in the reeving of the running rigging and in rigging fittings.

The *Resolute* was about 91 feet long at the rail; her bowsprit extended 39 feet outside the knightheads, the mainmast was 66 feet above deck to cap, main-topmast was 39 feet 6 inches long overall, main boom 41 feet 6 inches, main gaff 39 feet, mizzenmast 52 feet deck to pole head, mizzen boom 30 feet, mizzen gaff 22 feet, main-topsail yard 13 feet 6 inches, mizzen-topsail yard 10 feet 6 inches (the gaff-topsails were lug headed). Scale of model is ½ inch to the foot.

When fitted as a schooner the original deck arrangement was entirely altered. The *Resolute* was never a very fast sailer.

Given by U. S. Bureau of Fisheries.

FISHING SCHOONER, 1892
BUILDER'S HALF-MODEL, USNM 76279

New Era (No. 2)

This model was a proposed design for a market fishing schooner based upon the most advanced ideas of the time, 1892. The design shows the influence of the Fredonia model, and was made by Captain Joseph W. Collins of the U. S. Fish Commission. No vessel was built to this design; had there been the designer would probably have been disappointed, as her run was too full to allow high speed under sail in strong winds. This was the second of two proposals

for fishing schooners given this name by Captain Collins, the earlier one being for a smack-schooner.

The half-model shows a schooner having a marked and graceful sheer, keel heavily rockered, sweeping up to a much cut away forefoot. The stern rabbet rakes sharply and is finished with a small cutwater and gammon-knee head, the post rakes a great deal. The counter is of moderate length, very high and light, ending with a small and extremely raking elliptical transom, somewhat V-shaped at the bottom. The entrance is long and sharp, the run rather short and full, with buttocks too round for high speed. The greatest beam is well abaft midlength and the section there is formed with slightly hollow garboard, rising floor, high and rather hard turn of bilge, and slight tumble-home in topside.

Scale of model ½ inch to the foot; the vessel would measure 85 feet at rail, 20 feet 3 inches moulded beam, and would draw about 10 feet 6 inches or 11 feet. This model was exhibited at the International Fishery Exposition, at Bergen, Norway, in 1898.

Given by U. S. Fish Commission.

FISHING SCHOONER
RIGGED MODEL, USNM 76252

New Era (No. 2)

This rigged model of the proposal for a market fishing schooner in 1892, by Captain Joseph W. Collins, represented by builder's half-model USNM 76279, was made for exhibition purposes. The model is representative in rig, deck arrangement, and general appearance of the Fredonia-model schooners of her class and date.

Scale of the model is ½ inch to the foot. Had the schooner been built she would have been about 85 feet over the rail and her bowsprit would extend 24 feet outboard the stem rabbet, foremast 50 feet deck to cap, fore-topmast 30 feet total length, fore boom 20 feet, fore gaff 22 feet, mainmast 58 feet deck to cap, main-topmast 34 feet total length, main boom 55 feet, main gaff 38 feet 6 inches, fore crosstrees 11 feet, and main crosstrees 13 feet.

The model is under all sail—mainsail, foresail, fore-staysail, jib, jib topsail, fore and main gaff-topsails and "fishermen" or main-topmast staysail and shows the very short foremasts and very narrow fore gaff-sails which the Fredonia-model schooners often had, following the then yachting fashion. This model was exhibited at the International Fisheries Exposition at Bergen, Norway, in 1898.

Given by U. S. Fish Commission.

FISHING SCHOONER, 1892
EXHIBITION HALF-MODEL, USNM 310887

James S Steele, Richard C. Steele

An exhibition half-model was made from plans of the first fishing schooners designed by Thomas F. McManus of Boston, Massachusetts. These were built at Essex, Massachusetts, in 1892. Their design was an extreme one for the date, as the vessels were very yacht-like in form. The two schooners, both flush decked, built to this design were the *James S. Steele* and the *Richard C. Steele*. The vessels were considered fast but lacking in ability to carry sail and so the design was not again used. The schooners were employed as market boats and in the mackerel fishery. The *James S. Steele* is said to have rolled over on her side on one occasion, spilling her crew and deck load of fish into the water, but as boats were towing astern the crew managed to save themselves.

The half-model shows a schooner having a strongly rockered keel and rabbet, without any straight portion in the shoe. The post rakes sharply and the counter is unusually long and narrow for the date,

ending with a very small V-shaped transom. The bow at rabbet and cutwater fairs gradually into the keel, giving a marked forward overhang. The stem has a small gammon-knee. The sheer is marked. The entrance is long, sharp, and slightly convex; and the run is very fine, with straight buttocks. The midsection shows a sharply rising floor with much hollow at the garboard, a slack, easy bilge, and tumble-home in the topside.

The *James S. Steele* registered 78.46 gross tons, and was 88 feet between perpendiculars, 23 feet beam, and 10.4 feet in the hold. Scale of the model is ¼ inch to the foot, producing a vessel 98 feet 6 inches over the rail, 21 feet 6 inches moulded beam, and 13 feet 6 inches draft at greatest depth of shoe.

Given by Thomas F. McManus, naval architect, Boston, Massachusetts.

FISHING SCHOONER, 1899
RIGGED MODEL, USNM 285030

John J. Flaherty

The fishing schooner *John J. Flaherty* of Gloucester built at Essex, Massachusetts, in 1899 for the Grand

COD FISHING SCHOONER *John J. Flaherty*, 1899, an excellent example of the last clipper-bowed schooners built for the fisheries. Rigged model USNM 285030. (*Smithsonian photo 44693.*)

230

FISHING SCHOONER *Rob Roy* built at Essex, Massachusetts, in 1900, one of the early fishing schooners designed with a long bow overhang and short keel. For a view afore, see p. 173. Rigged model USNM 298232. (*Smithsonian photo 44956.*)

Banks codfishery and for the winter frozen-herring trade, represents an adaption of the Fredonia model to produce a large Banker combining speed with capacity. The model shows the schooner under full sail, ready for a passage to or from the Banks. She was reported to be able to carry 600,000 pounds of cod or 2200 barrels of herring. She was designed by Captain George M. McLain of Rockport, Massachusetts.

The *Flaherty* was a keel schooner having a sharp, long entrance and a moderately long and fine run, a straight keel with much drag and a shallow forefoot, raking stem rabbet with small gammon-knee head, and a raking post with short, high counter, narrow in width and ending in a sharply raking V-transom. Her sheer was great and the midsection showed a sharp floor, a high and rather hard bilge, and a slight tumble-home in the topside.

Scale of model is ½ inch to the foot. The vessel was 122 feet at rail, 102 feet at designed waterline, 25 feet 6 inches beam, 12 feet 6 inches depth in hold, and 166.35 gross tons. Her bowsprit extended out 36 feet from rabbet, foremast (including 10 feet of head) 64 feet above deck, fore-topmast 39 feet total length, fore boom 30 feet 6 inches, fore gaff 30 feet, mainmast (including 10 feet of head) 76 feet above deck, main-topmast 44 feet total length, main boom 70 feet, main gaff 39 feet 6 inches, and jumbo boom, or club, 28 feet.

Given by U. S. Bureau of Fisheries.

FISHING SCHOONER, 1900
RIGGED MODEL, USNM 285031

Senator Gardner

The fishing schooner *Senator Gardner*, designed by Captain George M. McLain, was built at Essex,

Massachusetts, in 1900 for Gloucester owners for the summer mackerel fishery and the winter frozen-herring trade between the Maritime Provinces and New England. However, she was also designed to serve in all branches of the New England fisheries if occasion demanded. The model, representing a type popular in these fisheries between 1893 and 1906, shows this schooner ready for a mackerel fishery cruise, seine boat on deck and seine stowed ready to be taken into the boat.

The *Gardner* was a schooner of the Fredonia model with some modifications, having the keel straight with much drag; the stem rabbet raking, curved, and slightly flaring; the cutwater adorned with a small gammon-knee head; the posts raking; and the counter rather narrow and with sharply raking transom; the sheer marked; and the midsection formed with a sharply rising floor, moderately hard bilge, and a slight tumble-home in the topside. The keel shoe was more curved than the rabbet and the deadwood outside the keel rabbet deeper than in schooners of 20 years earlier in design.

Scale of model is ½ inch to the foot, at which scale the length of the *Senator Gardner* was 114 feet at rail and about 92 feet at designed waterline, beam 25 feet, depth in hold 11 feet 6 inches, and her tonnage 135 gross. The bowsprit outboard of rabbet was 30 feet, foremast above deck 65 feet, fore-topmast 42 feet total length, mainmast 70 feet above deck, main-topmast 44 feet total length, main boom 67 feet, main gaff 37 feet, fore boom 31 feet, fore gaff 32 feet, and jumbo boom 27 feet. Seine boat was 40 feet long and 8 feet 6 inches beam, its greatest beam to a noticeable degree forward of midlength.

Given by U. S. Bureau of Fisheries.

FISHING SCHOONER, 1900
RIGGED MODEL, USNM 298232

Rob Roy

The fishing schooner *Rob Roy* was built at Essex in 1900 for Gloucester, Massachusetts, owners from a design by B. B. Crowninshield of Boston, a well known yacht designer. The *Rob Roy* received much publicity and introduced the long-overhang bow into the New England fishing fleet. Her hull was extremely yacht-like and combined the long bow overhang with an absence of forefoot; the keel rabbet and shoe were straight from post to about half-way between the fore and main masts, and there was a heavy drag. This underwater profile proved practical, as it permitted a cutaway forefoot yet retained enough straight keel to

allow the vessel to rest securely on a marine railway when she was hauled out. The older, curved keel shoe of the Fredonia model, and some early McManus-designed fishing schooners, caused much trouble and some accidents; vessels on occasion "fell down" on the marine railway by rolling forward on their rockered keel and forcing the shores out of place. The new form was so popular after 1900 that it became known as the "fisherman profile." The short keel and cut-away forefoot were supposed to make a vessel very quick turning and handy compared to older schooners.

Considered a very fine market schooner, the *Rob Roy* is a good example of a great many of the last sailing schooners built as fishermen at Essex and other New England shipyard towns. Her designer followed her with the *Harmony*, *Tartar*, *Stranger*, and a number of other successful schooners of the same type, which remained in use until motor vessels replaced the sailing schooner. The only departure of importance from the *Rob Roy* model was McManus' knockabout designs beginning with the *Helen B. Thomas* (half-model USNM 310888), built in 1901, in which the spike bowsprit was omitted. Few clipper-bow fishermen of the Fredonia model were built after the appearance of the *Rob Roy* in 1900.

The *Rob Roy* was a sharp schooner having a short, straight keel and shoe with much drag, knuckling into a long rising forepiece that gradually faired in profile into the slightly curved stem forming a long forward overhang. Aft, the post raked and there was a long and rather narrow counter ending in a small elliptical transom with dead rise in its bottom. The sheer was moderate, and she had the fisherman's standard low, long quarterdeck. The entrance was convex and sharp, the run long and easy. The midsection showed a sharply rising and slightly hollow floor, high and rather hard bilge, and a slight tumble-home in the topside.

Scale of model is ½ inch to the foot. The vessel was about 110 feet at rail, 88 feet at load waterline, 23 feet 6 inches beam and 11 feet depth. The spike bowsprit extended 26 feet outside the rabbet, the foremast stood 58 feet above the deck, fore-topmast 37 feet in total length, the fore boom 28 feet, and fore gaff 27 feet. The mainmast stood 71 feet above deck, main-topmast 41 feet in total length, main boom 66 feet long, main gaff 36 feet. Model shows the vessel with all sail set, including mainsail, foresail, forestaysail, jib, jib topsails, fore and main gaff-topsails, fisherman staysail.

Given by U. S. Bureau of Fisheries.

KNOCKABOUT FISHING SCHOONER, 1902
EXHIBITION HALF-MODEL, USNM 310888

Helen B. Thomas

This half-model was made to exhibit a proposed design for a fishing schooner without a bowsprit. The design was prepared in 1901 by Thomas F. McManus, of Boston, Massachusetts, who had then been designing fishing schooners for about ten years and had adapted the idea which had previously been employed only in small sailing yachts, the inboard-rigged "knockabout" sloops. McManus thought the new design would prevent the loss of fishermen by being washed off the bowsprit while handling head sails in heavy weather, a then too common accident.

For nearly a year this model was exhibited by McManus on Atlantic Ave., in Boston, in an effort to attract someone who would build a vessel to the design. The owner who finally made the experiment was Captain William Thomas of Portland, Maine, who had the *Helen B. Thomas* built at Essex, Massachusetts, by Oxner & Story and the schooner was launched in 1902. She proved to be a very fast sailer, and was long considered one of the fastest of her rig; she was also a fine sea boat, and a successful fisherman. It is said she could tack full-to-full in 20 to 25 seconds.

The half-model shows a yacht-like hull having a short, straight keel with heavy drag, a long, pointed bow and long fore overhang, with a hollow profile below the load waterline like a racing yacht. The post raked sharply and the counter was very long, ending with a sharply raked elliptical transom. The sheer was great, particularly forward, and the

THE SHIPYARD OF OXNER AND STORY at Essex, Massachusetts, in 1902. The schooner *Helen B. Thomas*, the first knockabout fisherman, is on the ways second from the left, ready to launch. (*Smithsonian photo 45785–d.*)

bow was high and light. The entrance was long and easy and the run very fine. The midsection showed a small, quick hollow at the garboards, a rising straight floor, and a hard bilge fairing into a slightly tumble-home topside.

The rig of this vessel was that of contemporary schooners as to sails; she carried foresail, mainsail, forestaysail, and jib, fore and main topsails and main-topmast staysail, and a jib topsail. She differed from her sisters, however, in having her forestay and jib stay, as well as fore-topmast stay, all inside or on the stemhead.

Scale of model is ¼ inch to the foot. The *Helen B. Thomas* was 106 feet 7 inches overall, 21 feet 6 inches moulded beam, and she drew about 13 feet ready for sea. Her register dimensions were 94.2 feet in length, 21 feet 6 inches beam, 9.2 feet depth in hold, and 76.99 gross tons. Her foremast was 40 feet 6 inches abaft the stemhead. She had 15 berths in the long forecastle and 4 in the trunk cabin aft.

The *Helen B. Thomas* was not duplicated, as later designs, because of the cost had a shorter bow overhang; but many knockabout fishermen were built, and when auxiliary power came into use, practically all the new schooners were knockabouts. The introduction of this design and, later, of auxiliary engines, were the final, basic changes in the design of the New England fishing schooner.

Given by Thomas F. McManus, naval architect, Boston, Massachusetts.

NEW JERSEY OYSTER SCHOONER, 1904
BUILDER'S HALF-MODEL, USNM 311089
LINES PLAN, HAMMS 4–19.

Anna M. Frome

The schooner *Anna M. Frome* was built from this model at Greenwich Piers, New Jersey, in 1904 by William Parsons for the oyster fishery. This schooner

was a shoal draft, centerboard vessel of a model and size that was popular in the oyster fishery on the southern coast of New Jersey.

The half-model shows a hull having moderate sheer, straight keel with slight drag, curved and very raking stem rabbet, and slightly raking sternpost, with a rather long counter ending in a deep, raking, elliptical transom curved athwartships. The model also shows a short, low, raised quaterdeck. The midsection shows a moderately rising straight floor carried well out, and a full, round bilge, with vertical topside above. The dead rise is constant toward the stern, the entrance is sharp and without hollow, and the run is formed with very straight buttocks. The stem has a longhead somewhat like that employed in Chesapeake Bay schooners, but proportionately shorter.

These large centerboard schooners employed as coasters and fishermen commonly had the long centerboard passing through the garboard on one side of the keel; the mainmast, abreast the after part of the case, was stepped off-center on the opposite side. The centerboard was lifted with an iron rod which was shackled into the top of the board and carried well aloft alongside the mainmast, ending in an eye into which a tackle block was hooked, with the upper tackle block in the hounds, and the fall brought to deck.

Scale of the model is $\frac{1}{2}$ inch to the foot, to represent a vessel 77 feet moulded length at rail, about 65 feet 3 inches between perpendiculars, 20 feet 2 inches moulded beam, and 6 feet 4 inches moulded depth, and drawing 6 feet at the post and 5 feet 5 inches forward.

Given by George Shillingsburg.

NEW JERSEY OYSTER SCHOONER, 1926
Builder's Half-Model, usnm 311090
Lines Plans, hamms 4–42

Nordic

The New Jersey oyster dredge *Nordic* was built from this half-model at Greenwich, New Jersey, in 1926 by William Parsons. A large centerboard auxiliary schooner with "baldheaded" rig, without topmasts or light sails, she was one of the largest schooners in the New Jersey fishery. The model is a good representation of the type of oyster schooner in this area during the last years in which sailing craft were built.

The model shows a long centerboard schooner having a straight keel fairing up into a curved stem of slight overhang, some drag, a slightly raking post, a short heavy counter, elliptical and raking transom, moderate sheer, and a flush deck with a low, false quarterdeck rail. The midsection shows a straight rising floor, a high hard bilge, and an upright topsides. The dead rise amidships is carried aft at a nearly constant angle, and the bottom of the transom has dead rise. The entrance is sharp and convex, the run long, straight, and easy. The centerboard is alongside the keel to port.

Scale of model is $\frac{1}{2}$ inch to the foot. The *Nordic* was 101 feet over the rails, 23 feet 2 inches moulded beam, 23 feet 7 inches extreme beam, about 81 feet 6 inches on the waterline, and drew about 8 feet with the centerboard raised.

Given by George Shillingsburg.

BILOXI FISHING and FREIGHTING SCHOONER, about 1885
Builder's Half-Model, usnm 311251

This half-model represents a type of schooner employed on the Gulf Coast for both freighting and fishing, as schooners were employed on the Chesapeake. It is believed that this model was used to build a centerboard schooner of this class at Biloxi, Mississippi, about 1885.

The model shows a shoal centerboard schooner hull having a skeg aft and with a straight keel rabbet forward, but swept up aft to the bottom of the transom. The shoe of the keel would therefore be straight and have some drag. The stem rabbet is straight and raking, and to it was attached a long head. The transom is wide, flat, and raking; the sheer is great. The entrance is sharp but not long, and the run is short and quite full; and the midsection shows slightly rising straight floor, a hard round bilge, and a nearly vertical topside.

Scale of the half-model is estimated as $\frac{1}{2}$ inch to the foot, to measure 74 feet moulded length at rail, 21 feet 6 inches moulded beam, and about 4 feet 6 inches moulded depth to deck.

Given by Henry Brasher, shipbuilder, Biloxi, Mississippi.

FISHING SCHOONER, about 1900
Builder's Half-Model, usnm 311257

A centerboard fishing schooner for South Florida was built from this model by Samuel Johnson at Apalachicola, Florida, about 1900. The vessel was intended for shrimp fishing and for freighting, and was

234

built on what might be termed a coaster's model, a type once common on the Florida coast.

The half-model shows a vessel having rising straight floor, a rather hard bilge and a slight tumble-home above. The keel is straight, with an upright sternpost having a raking V-shaped transom; the stem rabbet is straight and nearly upright; the sheer is great, and the entrance is long and quite sharp, and the run is rather short and full in the buttocks.

Scale of the half-model is supposed to be ¾ of an inch to the foot, to represent a schooner 52 feet 3 inches moulded length at rail, 18 feet moulded beam, and about 4 feet 6 inches depth of hold.

Given by Samuel Johnson.

BILOXI FISHING SCHOONER, 1901–1902
BUILDER'S HALF-MODEL, USNM 311254

This half-model of a centerboard schooner of the type once employed in the oyster fishery near Biloxi, Mississippi, was made by Martin Fontain, Sr., of Biloxi. It is not stated that a vessel was built from this half-model, which represents a typical schooner of the Biloxi type.

The half-model represents a shoal centerboard schooner having a skeg aft and the keel rabbet straight forward but sweeping up aft to the bottom of the transom; the keel shoe is thus straight, with some drag, and the rudderpost is at the end of the skeg and well inboard, so a counter is formed aft. The transom is deep and strongly raking as well as wide. The stem rabbet flares forward clipper fashion. The sheer is moderate. The entrance is sharp and slightly hollow at the forefoot, and the run is long and the buttocks quite flat.

Scale of half-model is ½ inch to the foot, to measure about 63 feet moulded length at rail, 18 feet 3 inches beam, and about 4 feet draft at post.

Given by Martin Fontain, shipbuilder, Biloxi, Mississippi.

BILOXI FISHING SCHOONER, 1910–11
BUILDER'S HALF-MODEL, USNM 311232

A fishing schooner was built from this model at Biloxi, Mississippi, in 1910–1911 by Henry Brasher for the local shrimp fishery. It represents the last type of sailing schooner built at Biloxi before auxiliary gasoline engines came into use.

The half-model shows a centerboard schooner having a small skeg aft, a straight rabbet to the keel forward but sweeping up aft to the bottom of the tran-

som, a curved and overhanging stem rabbet, a rather long counter ending in a wide and raking flat transom; moderate sheer; and a sharp convex entrance and a long, rather flat run. The midsection has a rising, straight floor; a rather hard bilge, and an almost upright topside.

Scale of half-model is ½ inch to the foot, the schooner built to the model measured 65 feet 6 inches moulded length at rail, 19 feet 6 inches moulded beam, and about 4 feet 3 inches depth of hold. These schooners had large centerboards, most often on the hull centerline between the fore and main masts, and almost reached from mast to mast.

Given by Henry Brasher, shipbuilder, Biloxi, Mississippi.

BILOXI FISHING SCHOONERS, 1917–21
BUILDER'S HALF-MODEL, USNM 311226

H. E. Gumbel, I. Heidenheim, H. Golman, Anna Eve

This small half-model was used to build at least four centerboard schooners for the shrimp fishery at Biloxi, Mississippi, between 1917 and 1921: the *H. E. Gumbel*, the *I. Heidenheim*, *H. Golman*, and the *Anna Eve*. The hull-form of the Biloxi schooner resembles that of some centerboard schooner yachts of the early 20th century. The schooner was a swift sailer, and the four built from this model won many races.

The model appears to be to a scale of ⅛ inch to the foot, and represents a hull 53 feet 6 inches moulded length on deck, 17 feet 6 inches moulded beam, and 4 feet 6 inches moulded depth.

The schooners had centerboard, shoal-draft hulls having moderate sheer, a rockered rabbet on the keel, with a skeg aft, the bottom of keel outside the rabbet straight and with moderate drag, and the stem rabbet curved from keel to deck in a long sweep, the post of the skeg being rather upright and the stern ending in a rather long counter finished with a flat, raking transom. The midsection is formed with a straight, slightly rising floor carried well out and the bilges well rounded, with the rounding carried almost to the deck. The dead rise is nearly constant in the run. The entrance is rather full and the run rather flat.

The half-model does not show the bulwarks and is to deck only, the keel, skeg, post and head are not shown.

Given by Jack Covacovich, shipbuilder, Back Bay, Biloxi, Mississippi.

BILOXI FISHING SCHOONER, 1929
BUILDER'S HALF-MODEL, USNM 311255

F. B. Walker, James Velich, L. L. Colle

The Biloxi fishing schooners *F. B. Walker*, *James Velich*, and *L. L. Colle* were built from this half-model; the first two in 1929–30 at Biloxi, Mississippi. They were clipper-bow, centerboard, shoal-draft schooners with auxiliary gasoline engines.

The half-model shows a hull having a skeg aft, with straight keel rabbet forward, but sweeping up aft to the bottom of the transom, which is raking and wide. The stem rabbet is curved and flaring, and rakes forward in the usual clipper style. The sheer is very marked. The entrance is sharp and the run easy. The midsection shows a slightly rising straight floor, a hard low bilge, and a nearly upright topside. Scale is ½ inch to the foot, to produce a schooner about 63 feet 6 inches over the rails, 20 feet moulded beam, and about 4 feet moulded depth, drawing about 4 feet 6 inches at post loaded.

Given by F. B. Walker, shipbuilder, Biloxi, Mississippi.

GULF COAST FISHING SCHOONER, 1929
BUILDER'S HALF-MODEL, USNM 311247

Baby Ann

The auxiliary fishing schooner *Baby Ann* was built from this half-model by Sideon Krebs & Son in 1929 at Pascagoula, Mississippi, for the shrimp fishery. Such schooners were fast sailers and were very stiff, carrying a heavy press of canvas. They were capable of being employed both as fishing and freighting vessels and were somewhat similar to the New Jersey oyster schooners.

The half-model shows a rather yacht-like centerboard schooner of strong sheer, having a rounded stem rabbet, a long thin counter ending in a small and sharply raking transom, an upright sternpost, and a straight keel fairing into the stem rabbet and stem. The midsection shows a rising straight floor, an easy bilge, and an upright topside. The entrance is sharp and the run is easy and rather flat in the buttocks.

Scale of the half-model is ½ inch to the foot, to measure about 74 feet moulded length at rail, 18 feet moulded beam, and drawing about 6 feet fully loaded, with centerboard raised.

Given by Sideon Krebs & Son, shipbuilders, Pascagoula, Mississippi.

V-BOTTOM FISHING SCHOONER, about 1906
BUILDER'S HALF-MODEL, USNM 311265

This model represents a V-bottom schooner built by Samuel Johnson about 1906 at Apalachicola, Florida, for the Gulf Coast fisheries. Schooners with this type of hull were used extensively, from 1900 to 1915, on the Atlantic Coast from the Chesapeake to Florida in various fisheries and for off-season freighting. They usually had longheads, a trunk cabin aft, and large centerboards. They sailed well.

The half-model shows a chine-built hull, to be fitted with centerboard and skeg, with rockered keel rabbet sweeping up aft to the bottom of the raking, wide, flat transom. The stem rabbet is curved, with little rake, and the sheer is strong. The chine in profile has marked camber; the midsection shows a very moderate rise of straight floor to the angle of the chine, and the topsides above are straight and flare out a little. The run is rather short and the entrance moderately sharp.

Scale of the half-model is supposed to be ¾ inch to the foot, indicating a schooner of about 46 feet 9 inches length on deck, 13 feet 6 inches moulded beam, and drawing about 4 feet at the skeg.

Given by Samuel Johnson, shipbuilder, Apalachicola, Florida.

GREAT LAKES GILL-NET STEAMER, 1880
RIGGED MODEL, USNM 55812

This model was made to represent an early type of small fishing steamer employed in the gill-net fisheries of the Great Lakes in the last quarter of the 19th century; the type was sometimes referred to as "fishing tugs" because of their similarity to a tug in form and often in general appearance. They varied from 10 to 40 tons register and were single-screw vessels usually carrying a simple rig and moderate sail-power for steadying purposes. The nets were worked over the stern and bow; the fish were stowed in the fore hold; and a deckhouse and pilothouse were located about amidships.

The model shows a tug hull having straight keel with drag; a curved upright stem; an upright post with round tug-stern; strong sheer; a midsection with rising floor, firm bilge, and upright topside; and a sharp, long entrance and easy run. The typical deckhouse, rig, and gear are shown. These vessels in 1880–85 had one mast, well forward in the eyes of the hull, and a gaff used for handling fish or to set a sail to steady the vessel.

236

Scale of the model is ½ inch to the foot; the vessel represented would be 61 feet at rail, 11 feet 6 inches beam, and would draw about 5 feet 6 inches. The mast was 34 feet above deck, the gaff was 15 feet 6 inches long, the smoke-stack stood 12 feet above the rail, and the vessel had a screw 4 feet 6 inches in diameter.

Given by U. S. Fish Commission.

BILOXI FISHING SCHOONER UNDER SAIL. A builder's half-model (USNM 311226) of this vessel, the *I. Heidenheim*, is in the Watercraft Collection. (*Smithsonian photo 33463.*)

MENHADEN FISHING STEAMER, 1883
RIGGED MODEL, USNM 76012

Jemima Boomer

The model is of the menhaden fishing steamer *Jemima Boomer* of Tiverton, Rhode Island, designed especially for this fishery by Dennison J. Lawlor in 1882 and launched the following year. She was considered a good example of her type, carrying a large cargo and having a speed of 9 to 10 knots loaded. These steamers worked near the land and fished only in good weather.

The model shows a single-screw wooden steamer of narrow beam having a straight keel with some drag, an upright and nearly straight stem, vertical post with

237

PADDLE-WHEEL FISHING STEAMER BUILT IN 1885 FOR SERVICE ON THE NORTH CAROLINA SOUNDS, the *Camille*. A model of this steamer, USNM 76236, is in the Watercraft Collection. (*Smithsonian photo 34648–a.*)

round, overhanging stern, moderate sheer, a sharp and long entrance, and an easy run. The midsection shows a slightly rising straight floor, low and full bilge, and rather upright topside.

The deck arrangement and gear common in this class of vessel at the date of building are shown. A deckhouse, forward, contains a pilothouse and captain quarters. A large main fish hatch is amidships and the engine house with stack is aft. Two seine boats are carried in davits at quarters. The model is sloop rigged with a loose-footed gaff mainsail and a jib tacked to stemhead; the rig was only adequate for steadying the vessel.

Scale of model is ½ inch to the foot, to represent a vessel 110 feet at rail, 17 feet beam, 7 feet 6 inches depth, and drawing 7 feet 6 inches at post and 3 feet forward. The mast was 54 feet above deck and 38 feet abaft the stem; the gaff was 21 feet long.

Given by U. S. Fish Commission.

STEAM SEINE BOAT, 1885
BUILDER'S HALF-MODEL, USNM 76022

This half-model was a proposed design for a small shoal-draft side-wheel steamer, to be named *Canvasback*, prepared in 1885 by Past Assistant Engineer George W. Baird U.S.N. The steamer was intended to operate a drag seine for the U. S. Bureau of Fisheries station at Havre de Grace, Maryland, and to work in the shallow waters of the upper Chesapeake Bay. The boat was not built.

The design as shown by the half-model called for a hull having slight sheer, a very long and sharp entrance, a very short and full run, a straight keel, an upright straight stem, raking post, and an upright rectangular transom that is wide and very shallow. The greatest beam is at the side wheels and well abaft midlength. The midsection is formed with a nearly flat floor, a low, hard, and round bilge, and a slightly flaring topside. The hull is double ended at the waterline, and forward it is rather wall sided; close to the stern, in the quarters, the flare is great.

Scale of the half-model is ½ inch to the foot, the steamer was to measure 66 feet between perpendiculars, 12 feet 6 inches moulded beam, and to displace 20¾ tons. She was to have a Herreshoff patent boiler, two independent-cylinder engines, 10 x 20 inches, of 62 indicated horsepower, and 9-foot-diameter sidewheels.

The model shows the side-wheel housing and wheel, deckhouse, and mast positions. It is painted and decorated.

Given by U. S. Fish Commission.

PADDLE-WHEEL FISHING STEAMER, 1885
RIGGED MODEL, USNM 76236

Camille

The model of the paddle-wheel steamer *Camille* represents a type of shoal-draft steamer used on Croatan Sound, North Carolina, during the last quarter of the 19th century, for working immense drag seines and the transportation of the catch to market. The *Camille* built at Manteo, North Carolina, in 1885 and owned at Edenton, was considered one of the best for her work on North Carolina waters.

The model shows a side-wheel steamer of very light draft having a very flat floor, quick bilge, and upright topside; the entrance is sharp, the run long and easy, the keel straight, and stem upright. The post is upright and there is a round overhang stern. The vessel was fitted with wide guards and had a large deckhouse. In general design these steamers were small side-wheel tugs.

Scale of model is ½ inch to the foot; the vessel was 53 feet long, 17 feet 6 inches beam over guards, and 5 feet depth of hull. The deckhouse was 24 feet long and 7 feet high; the stack stood 14 feet above the house roof.

Given by U. S. Bureau of Fisheries.

NEW HAVEN OYSTER DREDGE, 1885
RIGGED MODEL, USNM 76239

Jeremiah Smith

The oyster dredge steamer *Jeremiah Smith* was built at West Haven, Connecticut, for the oyster fishery at New Haven in 1885 and was one of the largest and finest of her type when built. She was designed for dredging oysters on Long Island Sound and for oyster cultivation on the leased oyster beds. Steam had been employed in this fishery as early as 1874 when a boiler and engine were placed in the sloop *Early Bird*

to operate dredge-winches, and in 1875 or 1876 a screw was fitted to this vessel. After that date a number of steamers were designed and built especially for oyster dredging at New Haven; they ranged from 20 to 63 tons register, from 50 to 83 feet on deck, and from 12 to 18 feet beam. Steam oyster dredges were later replaced with gasoline-engined and finally with diesel-powered vessels. However, sailing sloops, schooners, and sharpies continued to be employed in this fishery until well into the 20th century.

The *Jeremiah Smith* was a wide and rather shallow single-screw steamer having a moderately sharp entrance, a short and full run, straight keel, upright curved stem, straight above forefoot, slight sheer, upright post, and a round overhanging stern. These boats, as in the model, were marked by large deckhouse which gave protection to men and gear when working on the oyster beds in cold weather. They were not fast, 7 to 8 knots was considered sufficient speed. The dredge gear is shown to scale.

Scale of model is ½ inch to the foot; the vessel was 72 feet long, 24 feet beam, 6 feet draft, 113.38 gross tons, and 66.68 net tons.

Given by U. S. Bureau of Fisheries.

FISHING STEAMER, 1885
BUILDER'S HALF-MODEL, USNM 76286

Novelty

The schooner-rigged steam fishing vessel *Novelty* was built from this half-model at Kennebunkport, Maine,

STEAM SCHOONER *Novelty*, built for the mackerel fishery at Kennebunkport, Maine, in 1885. In 1889 she was sold as a gunboat to Haiti, and was sunk in a collision in 1891. She is represented in the Watercraft Collection by builder's half-model USNM 76286. (*Smithsonian photo 43817-g.*)

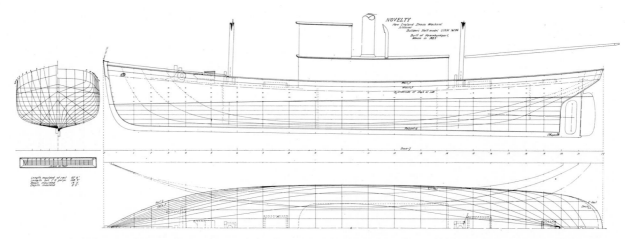

LINES OF THE STEAM MACKEREL SCHOONER *Novelty*, drawn from mould-loft drawing and checked with builder's half-model USNM 76286. In building, the foremast was placed 5 feet forward and the deckhouse was shortened, with the fore end and the stack 4 feet farther aft than shown.

in 1885 from a design by Captain H. B. Joyce. The first steam vessel in the New England offshore fisheries, she was designed for mackerel purse-seine fishing, using a "double-gang" of 40 men equipped with two purse-seines and four seine-boats. The *Novelty* was employed in fishing until December 1889, when she was sold to Haitian revolutionists, and was said to have become an important factor in their success because of her speed, being then known as the *Jacmel*. After the revolution she was taken to Philadelphia, refitted, and, after returning again to Haiti, was sunk in a collision with the Haitian naval ship *Dessalines* in 1891.

This steamer had a long sharp entrance, a long easy run, straight keel with moderate drag, rather upright and curved stem, upright post, round tugboat stern, strong sheer, and a flush rail fore-and-aft. The midsection was formed with a rising straight floor, a full and round bilge, and nearly upright topsides. In general, the lines of this vessel were those of a sharp tugboat lengthened out.

The *Novelty* was rigged as a two-masted "bald-headed" schooner without a bowsprit; the sails carried were a boom-and-gaff mainsail, a loose-footed gaff-foresail, and a single large jib. Her mainmast was well aft; forward of it was the stack with a rather long deckhouse having the pilothouse on the forward end.

Scale of half-model is ½ inch to the foot. The *Novelty* was 112 feet 6 inches moulded length at rail, 19 feet 3 inches moulded beam. She drew nearly 9 feet at post.

Given by Captain H. B. Joyce.

WELLED STEAM LAUNCH, 1890
EXHIBITION HALF-MODEL, USNM 160103

This half-model was made from plans by the designer, J. W. Water, naval architect, New York, for a fishing launch proposed to the U. S. Bureau of Fisheries in 1890. It was intended to have a well placed forward in the hull. No launch was built.

The boat was to be a caravel-planked hull having strong sheer, a straight keel with some drag, curved and rather upright stem, upright sternpost, and a round fantail stern. The entrance and run were long and fine. The midsection was formed with a rising straight floor, well rounded and rather slack bilge, and a somewhat flaring topside.

The model is mounted with keel, stem, and stern deadwoods, and propeller and rudder; the deck is strongly crowned; a large oval cockpit, or standing room, in which was to be the well, is forward; a small one is abaft the funnel; and another large one is aft. A stub funnel is shown.

Scale of the half-model is 1 inch to the foot; the launch was to be 38 feet 6 inches long, 9 feet 3 inches moulded beam, 3 feet 6 inches moulded depth, and was to draw about 3 feet 9 inches at post and 2 feet 10 inches forward.

Given by J. W. Waters, naval architect, New York, New York.

PACIFIC STEAM FISHING SCHOONER, 1891
RIGGED MODEL, USNM 76238

Royal

This model represents the steam schooner *Royal* built at Benicia, California, by M. Turner in 1891

RIGGED MODEL (USNM 76238) of the Alaskan salmon fishery steam schooner *Royal* built at Benicia, California, in 1891. She was employed chiefly in transporting fish to market and to the canneries. (*Smithsonian photo 44693-b.*)

for the Alaskan salmon fishery. She was intended primarily for transporting fish to market or to the canneries. A number of these auxiliary schooners, of which this model is characteristic, were built after 1890. They were pole-masted vessels having leg-of-mutton mainsails; the rig was that of the sailing schooners then fishing in Alaskan waters but with less sail area and without light sails.

The model shows a sharp auxiliary schooner having strong sheer, a straight keel with marked drag, a sharp entrance and fine run, a strongly curved and raking stem, an upright post, and an overhanging round stern. The midsection is formed with a rising straight floor, easy bilge, and a slight tumble-home in the topside. The vessel had a quarterdeck flush with the top of the bulwarks for about one-third the vessel's length; on it was a rail made of iron stanchions and wire. Also shown are a deckhouse with a pilothouse at its fore end, a fish hatch, a slide companionway to the forecastle, and a boat in davits amidships on the starboard side.

The rig was large enough to permit good sailing, and the screw was therefore two-bladed so that it could be brought in line with the sternpost under sail to reduce its drag.

Scale of model is ½ inch to the foot; the vessel was 81 feet at rail, 20.6 feet beam, 8.2 feet depth, and 29.54 net tons. The mainmast stood 56 feet above deck, foremast 56 feet, bowsprit outboard of rabbet

13 feet, main boom 44 feet long, and fore gaff 16 feet. Given by U. S. Bureau of Fisheries.

FISHING STEAMER, 1891
RIGGED MODEL, USNM 76240

Golden Gate

The screw fishing steamer *Golden Gate* was built at San Francisco in 1891 for the local market fishery. The model represents a type of small sloop-rigged steamer, of which several had been built after 1889 for the California coastal fishery, employing the "parenzella," a large net towed over the bottom, the Mediterranean equivalent of the otter-trawl. These steamers were the result of the efforts of Captain Joseph W. Collins to introduce steamers in the American fisheries; his paper "Suggestions for the Employment of Improved Types of Vessels in the Market Fisheries, etc.," published in 1888, attracted much attention among fishermen and resulted in a number of experiments with steamers in New England, California, and elsewhere.

The model shows a wooden, keel vessel having marked sheer, a sharp entrance of medium length, a long easy run, straight keel with some drag, stem curved at forefoot but straight above the waterline, upright post, and a round, overhanging stern. The midsection shows a moderate rise of floor, hard bilge, and a slight tumble-home in the topside. The model has a long deckhouse with the pilothouse at the fore

241

end. It is rigged with one mast and a loose-footed gaff-mainsail, with a single jib tacked to the stem-head. The steamer was single screw, and the hull generally resembled that of a contemporary tugboat.

Scale of model is ½ inch to the foot; the *Golden Gate* was 80 feet overall, 18 feet beam, 7 feet depth; length of the mast from deck to truck was 60 feet and of the gaff 20 feet; the foot of the mainsail measured 62 feet, luff 36 feet, head 18½ feet, leach 59 feet; the foot of the jib measured 15 feet, leach 45 feet, luff 47 feet. The sails were thus large enough to make this steamer an auxiliary.

Given by U. S. Bureau of Fisheries.

GREAT LAKES FISHING STEAMER, 1894
RIGGED MODEL, USNM 298233

Margaret McCann

The *Margaret McCann* was built at Grand Haven, Michigan in 1894. "Fish-tugs" of this type were very popular in the Great Lakes fisheries after 1885.

The model shows a small wooden steamer, in appearance like a small harbor tug, having a straight keel with drag, a curved and rather upright stem, rounded forefoot, round stern with flaring bulwarks, vertical post, sharp entrance; and a long, easy run. The midsection is formed with a rising straight floor, firm bilge, and upright topside. The sheer is moderate.

The pilothouse, at the fore end of the deckhouse, is slightly raised, and the whole deck structure is about one-third the length of the vessel. The model carries a small stack, boat stowed upside down on the deckhouse roof, a tall jack-staff at the bow, and an ensign and signal staff at the after end of the deckhouse. There is a net gurdy on the port side of the foredeck, a fish hatch forward of the pilothouse, and a tugboat-type iron windlass at the bow. Fish boxes are on the afterdeck.

Scale of the model is ¾ inch to the foot. The *Margaret McCann* was 69 feet between perpendiculars,

RIGGED MODEL (USNM 285032) OF THE STEAM MACKEREL SCHOONER *Alice M. Jacobs*, built at Essex, Massachusetts, in 1902. Her register dimensions were 133' x 24.8' x 12', 221 gross tons, 400 horsepower. (*Smithsonian photos: bottom, 44956–e; top, 44956–d.*)

15.2 feet beam, 6.6 feet depth, draft about 6 feet 9 inches, and 35.57 gross, 22.03 net tons.

Given by U. S. Bureau of Fisheries.

STEAM MACKEREL-SEINING SCHOONER, 1902
Rigged Model, usnm 285032

Alice M. Jacobs

The mackerel-seining steamer *Alice M. Jacobs* was built at Essex, Massachusetts, in 1902 for Gloucester owners and was the largest and finest vessel of her type that had been built in New England. At the time of her launching she was much admired and received much publicity, but her type was not immediately copied; the sailing schooner, and conversions of this class of vessel to auxiliary gasoline-engine powered schooners, continued to predominate in the fishery for many years.

The model shows a schooner-rigged screw steamer, narrow and deep, having strong sheer, a long sharp entrance and long easy run, a straight keel with much drag, a curved and raking stem that is almost straight above the waterline, and an upright post with a round, overhanging tugboat stern. The midsection is formed with a sharply rising floor, high easy bilge, and tumble-home in the topside.

The model shows a small deckhouse and pilothouse well forward, a long, low quarterdeck with funnel just forward of the mainmast, and a seine boat in davits amidships on the port side. She is schooner rigged, with single large jib tacked to stemhead, a loose-footed gaff-foresail, and a gaff-mainsail with boom. A 2-bladed screw is shown. This vessel was not intended to sail well; the rig was mainly for steadying the vessel.

Scale of the model is ½ inch to the foot; the vessel was 142 feet at rail, 24 feet beam, and 14 feet depth; the mainmast was 88 feet long, the foremast 82 feet, main boom 48 feet, and main and fore gaffs 24 feet.

The *Alice M. Jacobs* could steam at 10 knots, loaded, in seagoing trim. She was not a very successful fishing vessel economically and was a very costly one to build.

Given by Captain H. B. Joyce.

DIESEL TRAWLER, 1928
Plating Half-Model, usnm 310972

Shawmut, Trimount, William J. O'Brien

From this plating half-model of a steel diesel-powered trawler design three trawlers, the *Shawmut*, *Trimount*, and *William J. O'Brien* (hull nos. 1419–21), were built in 1928 at Quincy, Massachusetts, by the Bethlehem Shipbuilding Corporation, Ltd. Plating strakes are marked on the model, which was prepared in the shipyard as part of the drafting operation in making plans. These vessels were of the rather full-ended trawler hull model once popular but now replaced by sharper and faster vessels of far greater power and size.

Rigged Model (USNM 312017) of Diesel Steel Trawler *Storm*, built at Bath, Maine, in 1936, by the Bath Iron Works. Her register dimensions were 131.2′ x 25.1′ x 12.1′, 309 gross tons. (*Smithsonian photo 36710–a.*)

The half-model shows a straight keel with small drag; a well rounded forefoot and raking straight stem, round stern, upright post, long deadflat, short sharp entrance, short fine run, and rather straight sheer. A short, raised forecastle deck is shown forward. The midsection is formed with a slightly rising straight floor, a low, hard, round bilge, and a nearly upright topside.

Scale of the half-model is ½ inch to the foot; the vessels measured 122 feet 4 inches overall, 23 feet moulded beam, and 12 feet 6 inches moulded depth.

Given by Bethlehem Shipbuilding Corporation, Ltd., Quincy, Massachusetts.

DIESEL TRAWLER, 1929–1934
PLATING HALF-MODEL, USNM 310973

Dorchester, Quincy, Winthrop, Dartmouth, Amherst, Cornell, Thomas Whalen, Atlantic, Plymouth

From this plating half-model nine diesel-powered, steel trawlers were built at Quincy, Massachusetts, between 1929 and 1934 by the Bethlehem Shipbuilding Corporation, Ltd. The hulls, nos. 1427–29, 1433–35, and 1455–57, were named *Dorchester*, *Quincy*, *Winthrop*, *Dartmouth*, *Amherst*, *Cornell*, *Thomas Whalen*, *Atlantic*, and *Plymouth*. This model represents a class of small trawlers that today would be called "dragers" in the New England fisheries.

The model shows a piece inserted amidships to extend the hull beyond the original design length. It represents a steel trawler hull having a straight keel with a little drag, straight and slightly raking stem, cutaway forefoot, round stern with an upright sternpost, strong sheer, short and rather sharp entrance, long deadflat, and a short but well-formed run. The midsection shows a slightly rising straight floor, a low, hard bilge, and an upright topside.

Scale of half-model is ½ inch to the foot. The trawlers were 110 feet long overall, 22 feet beam and 11 feet 6 inches moulded depth.

Given by Bethlehem Shipbuilding Corporation, Ltd., Quincy, Massachusetts.

DIESEL TRAWLER, 1936
RIGGED MODEL, USNM 312017

Storm

This model is of the diesel-powered steel trawler *Storm*, built at Bath, Maine, in 1936 by the Bath Iron Works for the General Seafoods Corporation.

The model shows a modern steel trawler having a short and rather full entrance and a fine run of medium length; the keel is straight with slight drag, the stem curved and raking, and a cruiser stern brought up almost round, in plan, at rail. The midsection has a slightly rising floor, a low and rather hard bilge, and an almost upright topside.

The main deck is flush. A short raised foredeck breaks the sheer right forward; on it is a steel breakwater. At the break and on the maindeck is a steel companionway, or booby hatch; abaft this are the mast and three fish hatches, then the trawl winch, and a long deckhouse carried to the stern. At the fore end of the deckhouse roof is the pilothouse; abaft this is a stack, a short mast, and two lifeboats. A pair of trawling gallows are on each side.

The model, made by Carrol Ray Sawyer of Manchester, New Hampshire, is built of steel from shipyard plans and is shown complete with trawl wires rove off and a trawl net alongside to port. Except for relatively minor details it represents the general design of the more recent New England steel trawlers.

Scale of model is ⅜ inch to the foot. The *Storm* was 131.2 feet long, 25.1 feet beam, and 12.1 feet moulded depth.

Given by General Seafoods Corporation.

NEW ENGLAND WOODEN DIESEL DRAGGER, 1951
RIGGED MODEL USNM 316743

Albatross

The wooden dragger *Albatross* was designed by naval architect Geerd N. Hendel in 1946, and a number of vessels were built on the moulds; among them, between 1946 and 1952, were the *Albatross*, *Wild Duck*, *Pocahontas*, and *Clipper*. The *Albatross*, built by Harvey Gamage, of South Bristol, Maine, was rammed and sunk by a tanker while yet new. These craft were approximately 132 tons gross, 89 tons net, 79.1 feet tonnage length, 21.9 feet beam, and 11.8 feet depth in hold. Diesel powered, they were intended for the New England trawl fisheries. The *Albatross* was used in red-fish trawling.

The model shows the *Albatross* as built, on a scale of ⅜ inch to the foot. The vessel's length overall was 90 feet, her extreme beam 21 feet 6 inches, and her draft 10 feet 6 inches. The hull of the model has marked sheer, a straight keel with much drag, a well rounded forefoot, curved and raking stem, nearly vertical sternpost, and a round stern. The entrance is long and sharp, the run short and rather full. The

244

hull may be said to be fairly typical of the class, as is the deck arrangement, consisting of a turtleback and raised deck forward, a house well aft, and a fish hold amidships.

The vessel was schooner masted, but many of the type are sparred ketch fashion. They are powered with 300–400 horsepower diesel engines and have a service speed of a little over 8 knots.

Built for the Museum by Jay Hanna, Rockport Maine, from the builder's plans and from measurements of the vessel.

WHALING SHIP, 1851
Builder's Half-Model, usnm 160126

Cornelius Howland

The New Bedford whaling ship *Cornelius Howland* was built from this half-model at New Bedford, Massachusetts, in 1851. She was designed for whaling and sailed on her last voyage August 4, 1874, being nipped in the ice north of Bering Strait in 1876 and wrecked.

The *Howland* was a clipper-model whaler of slight sheer, having moderately rising floors, easy bilges, a rather sharp but short entrance and a long, easy run, a short heavy round-tuck stern with upper and lower transoms, straight keel, upright sternpost, and rather raking stem, with the bow flaring forward.

Scale of the model is ½ inch to the foot; producing a vessel approximately 128 feet long at rail and 27 feet 2 inches moulded beam, to inside of plank. The register dimensions of the *Howland* were 123 feet length between perpendiculars, 27 feet 9 inches breadth, 13 feet 10½ inches depth in hold, and 431³⁄₉₅ tons; billet head, no galleries, square stern.

Given by New Bedford, Massachusetts, Board of Trade.

WHALING SHIP, 1851
Builder's Half-Model, usnm 76324

Nautilus

The whaling ship *Nautilus* of New Bedford was built from this half-model at Fairhaven, Massachusetts, in 1851. Reputed a smart sailer, she was re-rigged as a bark in 1859 and was sold foreign in 1881.

The *Nautilus* was a clipper-model whaler having a short and moderately sharp entrance; long, fine run; a heavy, square round-tuck stern with rather upright sternpost and upper and lower transoms; slightly raking stem; rising floors with well rounded bilges; straight keel with slight drag; and slight sheer. Her capacity was 2400 barrels of oil, each of 31½ American gallons.

The model scales approximately 114 feet on rail and 27 feet moulded beam; the scale is ½ inch to the foot. Register dimensions of the *Nautilus* were length between perpendiculars 110 feet 9 inches, breadth 27 feet 5½ inches, depth in hold 13 feet 8¾ inches, 374 ¹⁹⁄₉₅ tons; billet head, no galleries.

Given by Gideon Allen.

WHALING SHIP, 1853
Builder's Half-Model, usnm 160124

Reindeer

The ship *Reindeer* of New Bedford was built from this half-model in Rochester Township, Massachusetts, in the year 1853. This vessel was designed for whaling and represents the superior class of ships and barks in this fishery. A "sharp bottom" was required in these vessels to make them "easy" on their spars, rigging, and hull-structure, when a whale being stripped of blubber alongside was kept afloat by a strain on the "cutting-in" tackles. If a whaling vessel had great initial stability, any roll caused by a sea would make her lift the carcass and thus cause massive strains. At the time the *Reindeer* was designed, speed under sail was deemed desirable and an effort was made to combine speed with capacity. This ship was considered one of the swiftest and finest whalers afloat in her time; she was employed largely in the Bering Sea whale fishery, for which she was especially designed. In 1862 her crew were attacked by Eskimos or Indians, and she was abandoned and crushed in the ice off the north shore of Alaska during September 1871. She was ship rigged throughout her career.

The half-model shows a wooden clipper-hulled ship having much rise in the floor and an easy turn of bilge, the bow moderately sharp and without hollow, the entrance rather short, the run fine and relatively long. Above the load waterline the bow flares out a good deal; the stem also flares forward on the rabbet and the cutwater and head are long and graceful. The stern is wide and square, with a very short overhang, upper-and-lower transoms, round tuck, and little rake in the sternpost. The sheer is slight, in the fashion of the time. The keel is straight; the vessel sailed with a slight drag.

Scale of the model is ½ inch to the foot, giving a vessel 129 feet over the rails, 120 feet 10 inches Customhouse length, 27 feet 6 inches moulded beam, and 18 feet 2 inches moulded depth to inside of plank. Customhouse dimensions were 123 feet 6 inches between perpendiculars, 28 feet 4 inches beam,

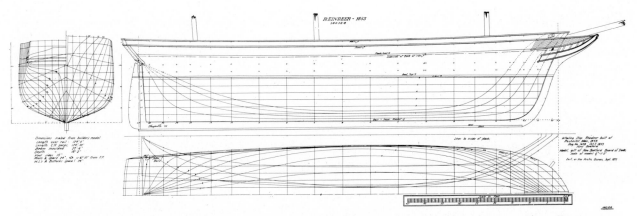

LINES OF WHALING SHIP BUILT AT ROCHESTER, MASSACHUSETTS, IN 1853. The *Reindeer* is an excellent example of the clipper-model whalers built for the Bering Sea whale fishery in the 1850's. Lines taken off builder's half-model USNM 160124.

14 feet 2 inches depth in hold, 449⁹⁹⁄₉₅ tons, register; billet head, no galleries.

Given by New Bedford Board of Trade.

WHALING SHIP, 1853
BUILDER'S HALF-MODEL, USNM 76323

Jireh Swift

The whaling ship *Jireh Swift* was built from this half-model at Dartmouth, Massachusetts, in 1853. This ship, one of the superior class of American whaling vessels of her time, was noted for her speed and was a good carrier. She was rerigged as a bark in 1857, but on her third voyage was captured and burned by the Confederate States cruiser *Shenandoah* in the Arctic Ocean near Bering Strait, June 22, 1865. It is claimed that the *Jireh Swift* would have outrun the steam cruiser had not the wind failed her. Fast-sailing was required in Bering Sea whaling if a vessel were to escape being trapped by ice floes after a sudden shift of wind.

The half-model shows a wooden, clipper-hulled ship having rising floors and a slack bilge, a sharp but rather short entrance and a long, fine run. The sheer is rather straight and the keel is straight fore-and-aft; the vessel sailed with moderate drag to the keel. The stem rakes forward rather markedly; the sections in the bow show strong outward flare; the sternpost is nearly upright, and the stern is wide and square, having upper-and-lower transoms with round tuck below.

The model scales 125 feet over the rails for length, 119 feet Customhouse length, 27 feet moulded beam, and 18 feet moulded depth. Scale of half-model is ½ inch to the foot. Customhouse dimensions of the

Jireh Swift were 122 feet 9 inches length between perpendiculars, 28 feet 7 inches beam, 14 feet 3½ inches depth in hold, and 454⁷⁄₉₅ tons register; billet head, no galleries.

Model is painted, with white band and painted ports.

Given by White & Allen, New Bedford, Massachusetts, 1895.

WHALING SHIP, 1854
BUILDER'S HALF-MODEL, USNM 160125

Onward

The whaling ship *Onward* was built from this half-model in Rochester Township, Massachusetts, for New Bedford owners in 1854. The *Onward* belonged to the clipper-model class of whaling vessels, built after 1851, designed to have moderate initial stability and sharp ends. A good sailer, the ship was very successful. She sailed on her last voyage June 25, 1872, and in 1876 was one of a fleet of whalers nipped in the ice north of Bering Strait; there she was abandoned by her crew before she was crushed.

The half-model shows a wooden, clipper whaling ship combining sharp lines with great capacity and having a rising floor, an easy bilge, a short but sharp entrance, a long and easy run, flaring bow sections and stem rabbet, a rather upright stern post, a short overhang in the upper-and-lower square transom stern, round tuck, slight sheer, and straight keel with a slight drag. The vessel had a long graceful cutwater with billet head.

Approximate dimensions to inside of plank, scaled from the half-model, are length over rails about 133 feet and beam 27 feet 6 inches. Scale of the model is

½ inch to the foot. The vessel was ship rigged throughout her career, according to the Register, and her Customhosue dimensions were length between perpendiculars 124 feet 2½ inches, breadth 28 feet 7 inches, depth in hold 14 feet 3½ inches, and 460³⁄₉₅ tons.

Given by New Bedford Board of Trade.

WHALING SHIP, 1850–75
RIGGED MODEL, USNM 25726

This model represents an ideal design for a large sailing whaler, ship-rigged. The name *U. S. Grant*, on the model, which was obtained for exhibition purposes, is fictional; no vessel of this name appears among the whaling fleet.

The model is of a clipper whaler having a sharp and short entrance, a long and easy run, a straight keel with some drag, a rather upright stem rabbet, and a simplified longhead with eagle figurehead and single trail knee but no trailboards. The post is upright, with a short counter and raking elliptical transom. Midsection is formed with slightly rising floor, low and full bilge, and a slight tumble-home in the topsides. The bottom is copper sheathed.

Model represents a full-rigged ship under topsails, spanker and jib, with cutting-in stage hoisted out and boats in davits, to show the vessel cruising for whales; and it has the typical sailing whaler's deck arrangement: topgallant forecastle with catheads on it, large wooden windlass on main deck, forecastle companionway slide, foremast, tryworks, main hatch, mainmast, pumps, after hatch, scuttle, mizzenmast, box skylight, binnacle, and wheel. Three whaleboats are on davits on the starboard side, one whaleboat and cutting-in stage are to port, and two whaleboats are upside down on gallows between the main and mizzenmasts.

Scale of model is supposed to be ⅜ inch to the foot, for a vessel about 134 feet between perpendiculars and 31 feet 6 inches beam, about the size of some of the auxiliary steam whalers of the 1870's and 1880's.

Purchased from C. H. Shute & Son, Edgartown, Massachusetts, 1875.

WHALING STEAMER, 1882
RIGGED MODEL, USNM 76237

Orca

This large model represents the bark-rigged auxiliary steamer *Orca* built at San Francisco, California, in 1882 for the Pacific and Arctic whaling out of that port. The largest of her type in the United States when built, the *Orca* was one of a number of this type built in this country during the last quarter of the 19th century, and resembles the steam whalers built in Maine about the same time, among which are the *Mary and Helen*, 1879, which became the exploring vessel U. S. S. *Rogers;* the *Belvidere*, 1880; the second *Mary and Helen*, 1882; and the *Navarch*, 1892; all built at Bath. The first steam whaler under the American flag on the Pacific was the *Pioneer*, fitted in 1865, a former government transport rebuilt and strengthened. These American steam whalers resembled the vessels employed under the British flag and usually Scotch built; notable vessels of this class were the *Bear* and *Thetis*, long part of the Arctic patrol of the U. S. Coast Guard, and the exploration ship *Alert* of the U. S. Navy.

These American-built whaling steamers, similar in size, model, and rig to the sealing steamers employed on the Canadian Atlantic seaboard, differed from most of their foreign counterparts in being quite sharp (clipper-built), with a very sharp entrance and fine run combined with marked rise of floor. The Scotch-built ships were usually rather flat floored; the last ship of this class was the Antarctic exploring ship *Discovery*, 1904.

The *Orca* was designed and built as the most complete vessel of her type; she had a steam digester for drying out oil and other apparatus considered new at the time of her building. Like many of her sisters, she carried full sail power and was fast under sail or steam because of her clipper lines.

The *Orca* was one of a fleet of vessels nipped in the ice pack in 1897, off Point Barrow, Alaska, where she was abandoned. A government expedition was sent during the winter of 1897–98 to rescue the crews.

The model represents a wooden, keel, clipper-model steam bark having a straight keel with slight drag, raking stem with longhead, upright posts with round stern of moderate overhang, and medium sheer. The entrance is sharp and the run fine. The midsection is formed with slightly rising straight floor, a low full bilge, and a slight tumble-home in the topside. This vessel had a much flatter floor than had most American steam whalers; her form resembles that of the first *Mary and Helen*, whose lines probably guided the designers of the *Orca*. The model has a deckhouse and a steam windlass forward, pilothouse just forward of stack at break of high quarterdeck, wheelhouse at stern, quarterdeck flush with rail and with stanchioned rail around it; she carried seven boats on wooden cranes, or davits and two boats on fore deckhouse.

Scale of the model is ½ inch to the foot. The *Orca* was 177 feet between perpendiculars, 32 feet 6 inches beam, and 18 feet 11 inches depth; her net tonnage was 462.39 and her nominal horsepower 280. Bowsprit outside knightheads was 28 feet long. Foremast above deck 51 feet, fore topmast 40 feet, topgallant mast and royal in one 42 feet, fore yard 59 feet 9 inches, lower topsail yard 51 feet 6 inches, upper topsail yard 49 feet 9 inches, topgallant yard 40 feet, royal yard 31 feet. Mainmast above deck 52 feet 3 inches, main topmast 40 feet, topgallant and royal masts in one 42 feet, main yard 62 feet, lower topsail yard 51 feet 9 inches, upper topsail yard 50 feet 6 inches, topgallant yard 41 feet, royal yard 31 feet 6 inches. Mizzenmast above deck 47 feet, mizzen topmast 48 feet 9 inches, spanker boom 38 feet, spanker gaff 27 feet. Stack was between main and mizzen masts and stood 16 feet 6 inches above its housing.

The *Orca*, at 177 feet between perpendiculars, can be compared with the first *Mary and Helen*, which was 134 feet between perpendiculars, 30 feet 9 inches beam, 16 feet 10 inches depth of hold, displaced 496 tons light, 1002½ tons at full load, and drew 16½ feet at post. A design prepared for a whaler built at Bath, Maine, in 1880 showed dimensions of 142 feet 9 inches in length between perpendiculars, 27 feet 6 inches moulded beam, 16 feet 6 inches depth of hold, draught of about 17 feet 6 inches at post with full load and nominal horsepower was 250.

In most of these American whalers the propeller could be hoisted into a well in the counter when under sail, and also to protect it when in the ice pack. In the *Orca* the screw was 2-bladed, so as to be turned in line with the stern and rudder posts when the vessel was under sail or in the ice, but in general the lifting screw was favored in this class of vessel.

These steam whalers were heavily planked and ceiled and were sheathed outside from keel to well above the waterline with oak or greenheart, well metalled, particularly forward. Internally they were crossbraced in the hold and well kneed; and at bow and stern the timbering was particularly heavy. The *Orca* shows the very raking stem of the ice-working whalers; this was first introduced in sailing Arctic whalers about 1850 to improve their ice-working ability. This stem allowed the vessel to slide up and out on the edge of the ice enough to bring its weight into play to break ice.

Given by U. S. Fish Commission.

FISHERIES RESEARCH STEAMER, 1880
Rigged Model, usnm 39422

Fish Hawk

The *Fish Hawk* was the first fisheries research steamer built in the United States; she was designed by Charles W. Copeland, consulting engineer of the U. S. Lighthouse Board and was built by Pusey & Jones Co., Wilmington, Delaware, for the U. S. Fish Commission, being commissioned in 1880. Designed primarily for coastal fisheries research in relatively shoal water, and not for offshore, deep-sea work, she was considered a very fine research vessel when built.

Whaling Steamer *Orca*, built at San Francisco, California, in 1882. The largest of her type when built, and most completely fitted, her register dimensions were 177' x 32'6'' x 18'11'', 462.39 net tons, 280 horsepower. Abandoned off Point Barrow, Alaska in 1889. Rigged model USNM 76237. (*Smithsonian photo 26758–h.*)

248

U.S. Fish Commission Iron Twin-Screw Steamer *Albatross*, the second vessel built for fisheries research. Rigged model USNM 160414. (*Smithsonian photo 2451*.)

The model shows an iron, twin-screw, fore-and-aft schooner-rigged steamer, wood-sheathed to the main-deck and coppered. She had slight rise of floor, a low and rather hard bilge, and an upright topside; her entrance is long and sharp and the run is of medium length and easy; straight keel, upright post and round stern, straight stem, and raking and flaring bow.

Above the maindeck the *Fish Hawk's* structure was entirely of wood. She had a hurricane deck extending the full length of the hull; on it were located the pilothouse, captain's quarters, and laboratory. She had four watertight bulkheads and one nonwatertight, and a portion of her main deck was fitted for hatching, with tanks and apparatus particularly designed for this purpose. She was also fitted for dredging and the exploration of oyster beds.

Scale of model is ½ inch to the foot. The vessel was 156 feet 6 inches overall, 146 feet 6 inches on the 7-foot (load) waterline, 27 feet moulded beam, 10 feet 9 inches depth of hold, and 6 feet 5½ inches mean draft.

Given by Pusey & Jones Company Wilmington, Delaware, shipbuilders.

FISHERIES RESEARCH STEAMER, 1882
Rigged Model, usnm 160414

Albatross

The iron twin-screw steamer *Albatross* was designed by Charles W. Copeland and built by Pusey & Jones Co. at Wilmington, Delaware, in 1882 for the U. S. Fish Commission. The second and largest vessel then built in the United States for fisheries research, she was equipped with all appliances known for this work; she was fitted for sounding and dredging, and in every way was especially designed for her employment.

She was an iron, brigantine-rigged, twin-screw steamer having medium sheer, a sharp entrance, moderately long and well formed run, straight keel, upright post, round stern, and raking and flaring stem. Her midsection was formed with a slightly rising straight floor, a low easy bilge, and an upright topside. She had six watertight bulkheads, a poop cabin extending 30 feet forward of the sternpost, a deckhouse 83 feet in length and 13 feet 6 inches wide, with pilothouse and stack on it, and a topgallant forecastle 44 feet long.

Scale of the model is ½ inch to the foot. The *Albatross* was 324 feet long overall, 200 feet on the 12-foot (load) waterline, 27 feet 6 inches moulded beam, and 16 feet 9 inches depth inside. Her displacement tonnage on 12-foot draft was 1,000 tons, and her register tonnage 400 net tons.

Given by U. S. Bureau of Fisheries.

TANCOOK WHALER, about 1910
Builder's Half-Model, usnm 311598

This half-model was made by O. B. Hamm, Mahone Bay, Lunenburg County, Nova Scotia, to represent a "Tancook whaler" of about 1910.

The model represents a double-ended clipper-bow centerboard schooner, 37 feet long, of the type built at Tancook Island in Mahone Bay on the southeast coast of Nova Scotia from about 1890 to about 1910. Three boats are supposed to have been built from this model. The whalers ranged from about 26 to 45 feet in length and were noted for their speed and seaworthiness, being used in the shore fisheries at Mahone Bay and its vicinity. Now extinct as a type, they were replaced about 1910–12 by boats modeled on the fishing schooners. Though early boats of this type were lapstrake planked, the half-model represents a caravel, or "set work," planked hull, having a straight plank keel wider in the middle than at the ends, with much drag, a very raking sternpost, raking clipper bow with small gammon-knee head, strong sheer, and sharp stern. The entrance and run are both hollow and very sharp, the run sharper than the entrance. The midsection shows very hollow garboards, a rising floor, and a high and moderately hard bilge with slightly flaring topsides.

These boats were half-decked; a cuddy was under the foredeck. They had an iron centerboard and were rigged with two pole masts, schooner fashion. They set a single jib to a stay on a short bowsprit, and had a loose-footed gaff-foresail, the clew of which overlapped the mainsail, a gaff-mainsail and a main-topmast or "fisherman's" staysail set to the mainmast pole head.

Scale of the model is ½ inch to the foot; 37 feet moulded length at gunwale, 9 feet beam, 4 feet draft at post, and 2 feet 3 inches forward.

Given by George Stadel, Jr., naval architect, Stamford, Connecticut.

QUODDY BOAT, 1880
Builder's Half-Model, usnm 54478

This half-model represents a large fishing boat from Passamaquoddy Bay, Maine, of a type sometimes

Sardine Carrier of the smaller size in use at Eastport, Maine, in the 1880's. This type was known as a quoddy boat, after Passamaquoddy Bay, Maine. Rigged model USNM 12099. (*Smithsonian photo 45605–j.*)

called "Quoddy boat" but more generally called "pinky" locally, though it does not have the pink stern usually associated with the pinky schooner in North America. These boats were employed in the local herring fishery for attending the weirs and carrying fish to the factories. The boats were double-enders and varied in length from about 20 to 40 feet on deck. Boats from 20 to 28 feet in length usually had one mast and a single gaff-sail. These, as late as 1890, were clench built, as a rule. They sometimes had a small bowsprit, built to unship, on which was set a small flying jib. The larger boats were caravel built; they were sloop rigged and had a standing bowsprit, gaff mainsail, and one large jib hanked on a stay. They always had a cuddy in a small trunk cabin forward, a

QUODDY BOAT *Yankee Hero*, 1889. Rigged model USNM 76266. An average size boat of her type, she was built to carry sardines from the weirs to the canneries. The builder's half-model of this boat is USNM 76293. (*Smithsonian photo 44696–g.*)

large fish hatch amidships, and a standing well, or small hatch, right aft for the helmsman.

The Quoddy boat was noted for its seaworthiness, and this half-model represents one of the larger class. It shows finer lines than were usual in this type, but represents a typical boat from the builder's yard, and the boats built from it were said to be among the swiftest of the type.

The model shows a double-ended, keel hull having strong sheer, a raking and somewhat curved stem, a raking straight post, the keel straight and with much drag, the greatest beam slightly forward of mid-length, a sharp entrance, and a long, well formed run. The midsection has a straight, rising floor ending in a hard turn of bilge and rather vertical sides. There is hollow in the sections fore and aft, with the most marked hollow in the after sections, near the post, which are strongly S-shaped.

Scale of the model is ½ inch to the foot, giving a boat about 37 feet 3 inches on deck, 12 feet 9 inches moulded beam, 5 feet 8 inches moulded depth, and drawing about 5 feet 3 inches at post and 3 feet forward. These boats were usually ballasted with iron ore obtained locally.

Model made at Eastport, Maine, about 1880 and given by Albert Hallet, boatbuilder, Eastport, 1882.

QUODDY BOAT, 1880
RIGGED MODEL, USNM 12099

This model represents the smaller class of Quoddy boat, as built by the donor, Albert Hallet of Eastport, Maine, about 1880. These boats, which ranged from 20 to 28 feet in length, were cat-rigged with a single gaff-sail. Most were lapstrake planked but in later years caravel planking became favored in all sizes of the Quoddy boat.

The model is cataloged as being on a scale of ½ inch to the foot, and this produces a large boat for the rig, 35 feet at gunwale and 12 feet beam, with the length of mast 39 feet 6 inches. On a scale of ¾ inch to the foot, the boat would be 23 feet 5 inches at gunwale and 8 feet beam, with the length of mast 26 feet 4 inches. It is probable that the model was on the latter scale.

The model shows a caravel-planked, keel, half-decked, sailing boat having a straight keel with much drag, sharply raking straight sternpost, curved and raking stem, much sheer, sharp entrance, and sharper run. The midsection is formed with a rising straight floor, firm round bilge, and slightly flaring topside. The mast stands well forward, with heel over the fore end of the straight keel; it has marked rake. The gaff is rather short and has a single halyard. Deck arrangement shows a forward cuddy deck entered through a slide hatch just abaft the mast, and abaft this the boat is open, with the washboards along the sides having low coamings. The open portion is fitted with pen boards and hatch boards forward to form standing and fish rooms. Chock rails are located near the bow and stern. In summer weather some of these single-sail boats set a flying jib on a plank bowsprit that could be readily unshipped.

Given by Albert Hallet, boatbuilder, Eastport, Maine.

QUODDY BOAT, 1889
BUILDER'S HALF-MODEL, USNM 76293 *Yankee Hero*

The Quoddy boat *Yankee Hero* was built from this half-model by J. Brown in 1889 at Lubec, Maine, for

251

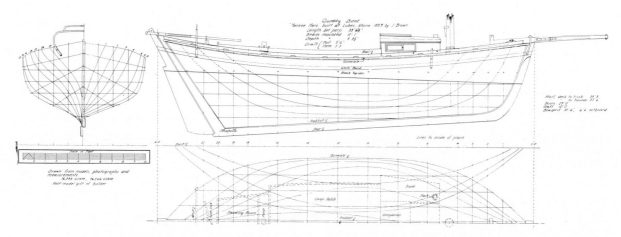

QUODDY BOAT *Yankee Hero* built at Lubec, Maine, in 1889, jib-and-mainsail rig. Lines taken off builder's half-model USNM 76293. Deck arrangement and spar dimensions are from rigged model USNM 76266.

use as a sardine carrier, to attend a weir and carry the catch to a cannery. The model is for an average size boat of the type. The *Yankee Hero* is represented by a rigged model (USNM 76266) in the Watercraft Collection.

Boats of this type were very popular in the shore fisheries of eastern Maine, from the Penobscot to the Canadian border and beyond, on the western shore of the Bay of Fundy, in New Brunswick. Some were smacks having live wells, and on occasion were employed in the lobster fisheries.

The half-model represents a caravel-planked, keel, double-ended, decked sloop having strong sheer, straight keel with heavy drag, straight and raking post, slightly curved and raking stem. The midsection formed with sharply rising straight floor, hard bilge, and rather upright topside. The bow sections flare; the after sections are somewhat Y-shaped near post. Greatest beam is at midlength; the entrance is sharp, long, and somewhat convex; the run is long, easy, and quite hollow.

Scale of the model is ¾ inch to the foot, producing a vessel 33 feet 6½ inches overall, 32 feet 3 inches on deck, 11 feet 1 inch moulded beam, 5 feet 3½ inches moulded depth, and drawing about 5 feet 6 inches aft and 3 feet 3 inches forward.

Given by J. Brown, boatbuilder, Lubec, Maine, 1894.

QUODDY BOAT, 1889
RIGGED MODEL, USNM 76266

Yankee Hero

This sloop-rigged model is of the Quoddy boat *Yankee Hero*, represented by the builder's half-model USNM 76293, shows the rig and deck arrangement

common in this type of sardine carrier once employed in the vicinity of Passamaquoddy Bay, Maine. Boats of this type and size usually referred to locally as pinkies, were decked and fitted, with a small cuddy abaft the mast, a large fish hatch amidships and a small standing room for the helmsman well aft. Noted for seaworthiness, the type was swift and handy under sail.

Scale of model is 1 inch to the foot, representing a boat 32 feet 3 inches in length. The mast stands 39 feet 3 inches above deck, bowsprit 6 feet 6 inches outboard of stem rabbet at deck, boom 29 feet and gaff 10 feet long. The rudder is hung outboard and the boat is steered with a tiller.

Given by the U. S. Bureau of Fisheries.

SURFBOAT, 1875
RIGGED MODEL, USNM 24999

This model represents a class of boats used rather extensively by the old Lighthouse Board and to a lesser extent by the old Life Saving Service in Maine coastal areas before 1876. The boat was somewhat similar to some of the double-ended Hampton whalers built at Hampton Beach, New Hampshire, for the fisheries, except that the surfboat had no sails. Boats of this form and size were very seaworthy and could be easily worked under oars or sails. The model somewhat resembles also the Labrador whaler once built in Nova Scotia, Canada, for the Labrador fisheries.

The model shows a double-ended, open, lapstrake rowing boat having a straight keel, upright curved stem, raking post with rudder hung outboard, strong sheer, sharp entrance and run, and midsection with rising floor, moderately hard bilge, and flaring side.

Fitted with five thwarts and a horseshoe-shaped stern seat with backboard. It is fitted to steer with a tiller; but is not fitted for sail.

Scale of model is 2 inches to the foot, for a boat 22 feet at gunwale, 6 feet 3 inches beam, about 3 feet keel to gunwale amidships, with oars 14 feet 6 inches long.

Given by Cragin & Sheldon, boatbuilders, Boston, Massachusetts.

MAINE PEAPOD, 1883
RIGGED MODEL, USNM 56864

The Maine peapod was a double-ended rowing-sailing boat developed about 1870 at North Haven, Maine, for use in the lobster fishery. The building of this type of boat finally centered at Jonesport, Maine, and it became well-known on the Maine coast as a safe and handy small rowing boat. The type was built lapstrake, caravel, or strip planked; and there was much variation in the model; but the boats were commonly around 15 feet long, though a few were as long as 18 feet. This model is of a type also employed by lighthouse tenders on the Maine coast. Many peapods, though primarily a rowing type, were fitted to sail.

The model shows a double-ended, lapstrake-planked, keel, open rowing-sailing boat having a strong sheer, straight keel with some drag, a curved and upright stem and stern, with rudder mounted on post, and a sharp entrance and run. The midsection is formed with a rising straight floor, firm round bilge, and flaring topside. Cat-rigged with a single gaff-sail having a single halyard from an iron crane at masthead. The boat has two thwarts widely spaced so that the amidships is left clear to handle lobster pots. These boats were often rowed standing, and for this long-shanked iron oarlocks were fitted.

Scale of the model is 1 inch to the foot, for a boat 15 feet at gunwale, 4 feet 6 inches beam, 1 foot 6 inches depth, fitted with a 14-foot mast 14-foot boom and 6-foot gaff.

Given by U. S. Fish Commission.

JONESPORT PEAPOD, 1885
RIGGED MODEL, USNM 57561

This model represents a type of peapod once popular at Jonesport, Maine, and employed in the alongshore lobster fishery, working among the ledges where a large boat would be in danger. A burdensome boat, with fine ends, the type is said to have been swift, having been modeled particularly for sailing, but it was also capable of being rowed easily. The model

shows a double-ended, keel, lapstrake, open boat having strong sheer; a sharp entrance and run, the latter the finer of the two; a straight keel with much wood outside the rabbet and some drag; a straight raking sternpost with rudder hung on it; a curved and rather upright stem; and the midsection with slightly rising straight floor, low round bilge, and flaring topside. The two thwarts are widely spaced to make room amidships for lobster pots. The mast thwart is well forward. Rigged with the single loose-footed spritsail common to the type.

Scale of model is 1 inch to the foot, for a boat measuring 15 feet over gunwales, 4 feet 9 inches beam, and 1 foot 10 inches depth, mast 13 feet long and 11 feet 6 inches above its thwart, and spritsail 12 feet 6 inches long. Fitted with thole-pins and one pair of oars.

Model given by U. S. Fish Commission.

MUSCONGUS BAY SLOOP, 1880
RIGGED MODEL, USNM 55795

This model represents a class of centerboard sloops once employed in the vicinity of Muscongus Bay, Maine, in the shore and lobster fisheries. With clipper bow and counter stern, they were originally built at Friendship, Bristol, and Bremen, Maine, but the building of the type spread along the coast in the 1880's and 1890's. These sloops were the forerunners of the better known Friendship sloops, which they resembled in rig and above-water appearance. The Muscongus Bay sloops were built with either caravel or lapstrake planking on the same model, and this rigged model, though finished caravel, was evidently intended to represent a lapstrake boat, judging by the model builder's use of a lower moulding on the sheer strake. These boats, which had a fine reputation for speed and seaworthiness, ranged in size from 16 to about 26 feet length at gunwale and carried a jib-and-mainsail rig.

The model shows a rather deep centerboard sloop having a straight keel with some drag, raking post and short counter stern ending in a raking V–shaped transom (sometimes this was elliptical), and a raking stem with a simple longhead supported by trail knees. The midsection has a sharply rising straight floor, an easy round bilge, and an upright or slightly flaring topsides. The entrance is long and sharp, the run well formed and of moderate length, and the sheer very strong. Small boats had an oval cockpit; the larger boats, as shown in the model, had a trunk cabin. These boats usually had live wells on each side of the centerboard case, and the stone ballast was floored over in the cockpit.

Scale of model is 1 inch to the foot, producing a boat 26 feet at gunwale, 8 feet beam, mast 25 feet 6 inches above deck, bowsprit 6 feet outside rabbet, main boom 25 feet 9 inches, and gaff 15 feet. The model represents a large boat of the type.

Model by U. S. Fish Commission. Restored by Merritt Edson, 1958.

MAINE HAMPTON BOAT, 1879
BUILDER'S HALF-MODEL, USNM 54484

This model represents a small, lapstrake, 2-masted centerboard Hampton boat, a type once popular among fishermen on Casco Bay and along the coast to Muscongus Bay. The half-model, one of the earliest of this type that has been found, is of a boat built some time prior to 1879 at Phippsburg, on the lower Kennebec River, and intended for the inshore fisheries at the mouth of that river. These boats had a great reputation, in the period when sail was used in small fishing craft, for being swift, close-winded, and seaworthy. They received their name from the old

double-ended boats of the type originated at Hampton Beach, New Hampshire; they do not, however, resemble the old double-ender, being an entirely different form of boat. As fishing craft they had long wash boards and, except for a very short stern deck, were rarely otherwise decked, but when built for pleasure craft they had an oval cockpit and a long forward deck. The planking was usually lapstrake, but caravel planking was sometimes employed, and by 1890 was replacing clench work. Typically they had two thwarts with the centerboard case between, oval coamings, a platform over stone ballast, standing rooms formed by pen boards, a fish room amidships, and were fitted with oars and locks or tholes. When gasoline motors first came into use, many Hampton boats, because of their peculiar form could readily be converted from sailing craft to launches. They carried two spritsails, the foresail the larger. The foremast was stepped close to the bow and the foresail had no boom, overlapping the mainsail slightly and sometimes with a short club at the clew; the shorter of the two masts, the mainmast, was stepped close abaft the centerboard case; the mainsail had a boom.

MUSCONGUS BAY SLOOP, 1880. A type of centerboard boat used on the Maine coast in the vicinity of Muscongus Bay. It was a forerunner of the later and better known Friendship sloop. Rigged model USNM 55795. (*Smithsonian photo 45606–c.*)

Both masts were supported by the thwarts, and the sprits were relatively long, so the sails as a rule had peak. Some boats carried a short plank bowsprit that unshipped; on this a small jib was set flying in light winds. There were variations in the rig of Hampton boats on the Maine coast, but the one described was by far the most common.

The half-model is of an open, centerboard boat, lap-strake planked, the plank keel is wide alongside the centerboard and tapered toward bow and stern; it is straight in profile and extends only a little outside the rabbet. The keel has much drag; the stem is slightly rounded and raking; the sternpost is raking, with a flat, raking transom and the rudder hung outboard; the sheer is strong, the midsection shows a hollow, rising floor, a high and hard bilge, and a nearly upright topside; the entrance is long and very sharp; and the run is rather short but very well formed.

Model has been repaired and a lift added below the plank keel by error, it being supposed that the wide, moulded plank keel was the top of a missing lift.

MAINE HAMPTON BOAT, 1880
RIGGED MODEL, USNM 57032

This model represents a variation in the Maine Hampton boat type once employed at Matinicus Island, Maine, in the shore and lobster fisheries. Unlike most boats of the type, the Matinicus Island boats had a single mast. Swift sailers and good sea boats, they were usually lapstrake planked. They were fitted to row, and some towed a small skiff when lobstering.

The model shows a Maine Hampton boat hull having a centerboard, side decks, strong sheer, straight plank keel with some drag, nearly straight and up-right stem, raking post, short counter ending with a raking elliptical transom, long and very sharp entrance, and a long and very fine run. The midsection shows a rising floor with hollow at the garboard, a firm round bilge, and a slight tumble-home in the topside. The model appears unusual in having a counter; most contemporary descriptions and some half-models show that these boats commonly had a

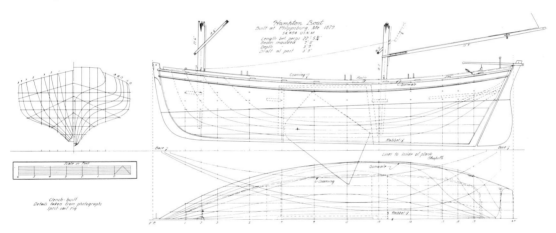

PLAN OF A MAINE HAMPTON BOAT OF 1879, BUILT AT PHIPPSBURG, MAINE. Lines taken off builder's half-model USNM 54484, the oldest of the type yet found.

This model is less sharp at deck forward and not so wall sided forward as later boats of this type whose half-models are in the Watercraft Collection.

Scale of model 1 inch to the foot, for a boat measuring, to inside of plank, about 21 feet 10 inches at gunwale moulded length, 7 feet 11 inches moulded beam, 3 feet 9 inches moulded depth, rabbet to gunwale, 22 feet 5 inches overall length, and 3 feet 9 inches draft at post.

Given by Charles H. McIntire, Phippsburg, Maine, 1879.

flat, raking, and rather heart-shaped transom with the rudder hung outboard. The rigged model somewhat resembles the builder's half-model (USNM 311150, p. 257) of the *Egretta*, which has a counter.

The model shows a U-shaped seat at the stern, ballast platformed over, and a fish-room made with pen-boards amidships. The rig is that of a spritsail jib-and-mainsail boat, with a large rather square-headed spritsail having no boom but a short club at the clew, and a jib set up on a bowsprit.

Scale of the model is 1 inch to the foot; for a boat 21 feet at gunwale, 6 feet 3 inches beam, 3 feet 6

MAINE HAMPTON BOAT UNDER SAIL, about 1890.
(*Photo courtesy Albert Barnes and the Mariners' Museum,
Newport News, Virginia.*)

inches depth, 3 feet draft with board raised, bowsprit
outboard of stem 5 feet 6 inches, mast 20 feet 6 inches,
sprit 16 feet, and club 2 feet 6 inches.

Given by U. S. Fish Commission.

MAINE HAMPTON BOAT, 1883
RIGGED MODEL, USNM 57031

This model represents a variation of the Maine
Hampton boat from Monhegan Island. It differs
from boats of this class in other areas of its range
in having the counter stern and elliptical transom
seen in half-model USNM 57032 instead of the usual
hull profile shown in half-models USNM 54484 and
311151; probably the counter was employed most
commonly when these boats were built as pleasure
craft.

The model shows a vessel with a sharp entrance,
the greatest beam on deck well abaft midlength and
the run long and fine. The sheer is marked, the
keel is made of plank tapering each way from amidships, where it is widest, and straight in profile with
strong drag. The post is raked and there is a counter
of moderate length finished with a raking elliptical
transom like that of a contemporary fishing schooner
(usually, these boats had a raking flat heart-shaped
transom, with the rudder hung outboard). The
stem is upright and bold. The midsection shows a
rising floor, very hollow at garboard, a high and
hard bilge, and an upright topside, the forward
sections near the bow markedly wall sided, while
aft the sections are strongly Y-shaped.

The rig shown consists of two spritsails, the foresail
the largest and loose-footed. The mainsail is boomed.
Many boats, as in the model, were fitted with a light
bowsprit that could be unshipped; on it was set
a jib in fine weather.

Scale of the model is 1 inch to the foot. The boat
represented is about average in size for her date—
20 feet 6 inches at gunwale, 6 feet beam, 2 feet 9
inches draft with centerboard raised, mainmast
above thwart 13 feet 6 inches, foremast above thwart
19 feet, bowsprit outside rabbet 5 feet, main boom
9 feet. The boat shows the typical arrangement
described under half-model USNM 54484.

This model was obtained at Friendship Maine, 1883, from Franklin Thompson, and was given by U. S. Fish Commission. Restored by Merritt Edson, 1958.

MAINE HAMPTON BOAT, about 1900
BUILDER'S HALF-MODEL, USNM 311150

Egretta

The Hampton boat *Egretta* was built from this model by Frank Johnson at Bailey's Island, Maine, about 1900, and another boat was later built from her moulds.

The model, which represents a somewhat larger Hampton boat than was usual in Casco Bay, is made to a scale of ¾ inch to the foot, giving a vessel 27 feet 2¾ inches overall, 8 feet 6½ inches moulded beam and 8 feet 7¼ inches extreme beam, and drawing about 2 feet 9 inches with centerboard raised. The *Egretta* carried the usual Hampton boat 2-mast sprit-sail rig without jib. The boats from this model were clench-built.

The half-model shows the overhanging counter which some Hamptons had as early as 1882; it represents moulded lines and shows the exaggerated sharpness of the bow at plank-sheer that usually characterized the Casco Bay Hampton boat. The entrance is long and sharp with rather wall-sided sections well forward and the greatest beam at the gunwale well abaft midlength, but moving forward at each level line in the model as the rabbet is approached; the total shift of greatest beam between the lowest lift, or level line, in the model and the greatest beam at gunwale being 4 feet 6 inches toward the stern. The run is long and very fine, beginning well forward of amidships. The stem profile is rounded and the sternpost and transom both rake, the transom, which has the greater rake, is somewhat U-shaped and flat across. These boats had foredecks 8 feet long and after decks 4 feet long; the side decks were about 12 inches, with the cockpit thus formed having a low oval coaming. The rudder post came up through the counter in the after deck. This model shows the last developments in the Casco Bay sailing Hampton boats.

Given by Frank Johnson, Bailey's Island, Maine, 1936.

MAINE HAMPTON BOAT, 1900–01
BUILDER'S HALF-MODEL, USNM 311151

This half-model represents two boats, said to have been smart sailers, built at Orr's Island, Maine, for the Casco Bay fishery. They were modeled by Herbert Wilson and built by Dennis Wilson, it is believed in 1900–01.

This half-model represents the common type of fishing Hampton boat of Casco Bay, having a straight, rather upright stem, and a raking post and flat transom with the rudder hung outboard. The sheer is lively and the keel is a plank on the flat, wide amidships and tapered toward each end. The centerboard is slightly forward of midlength. The midsection has hollow floors and a firm bilge, the forward sections being rather U-shaped; the run is long and extraordinarily fine, beginning well forward of amidships. The greatest beam at gunwale is well abaft midlength, but moves progressively forward as the lifts, or level lines, approach the rabbet; this is an exaggerated shift, the distance from greatest beam at gunwale to that at the lowest level line being about 10 feet.

Scale of the model is ¾ inch to the foot, to represent the moulded form of a boat approximately 22 feet long, 7½ feet beam, and drawing nearly 3 feet with centerboard raised.

Given by Dennis Wilson, Orr's Island, Maine, 1936.

NEW ENGLAND BOAT, 1876
RIGGED MODEL, USNM 26585

Little Maud

This model represents a variation in the Hampton boat that was once common on the New England coast from Massachusetts to eastern Maine. This style of Hampton boat, with its caravel-planked hull, had a short vogue. The hull had much the appearance of the contemporary fishing schooner, which probably influenced the type. It reputedly sailed well and was seaworthy. Boats of this model but with flat heart-shaped transoms and rudder outboard, and with rather upright, straight stems and lapstrake hull, were once used at Rockport, Massachusetts, for the lobster fishery.

These vessels had a strong sheer, straight keel with some drag, raking straight or flaring stem, raking post, and V-shaped transom with rudder post through its heel, or a very short counter with elliptical transom. The entrance was sharp, long and often rather hollow at the forefoot. The run was long and very fine. The midsection was formed with a straight, rising floor, high and moderately high bilge, and tumble-home in the topside.

The model shows a long foredeck, oval cockpit, or standing room, short after deck; steering with a tiller. The rig is that of the Hampton boat—two spritsails, the foresail the larger and loosefooted, the main with boom.

Scale of model is 1 inch to the foot; this boat was 19 feet 2 inches at gunwale, 6 feet 6 inches beam, foremast 13 feet 6 inches above deck, mainmast 12 feet 9 inches above thwart. The bald clipper bow of the model was very popular in small New England fishing boats, between 1865 and 1885, even when no bowsprit was employed.

Given by Johnson & Young, 1876. Restored by Merritt Edson, 1958.

GLOUCESTER WATERBOAT, 1883
RIGGED MODEL, USNM 56937

Aqua Pura

Cat-rigged keel waterboats of the type illustrated by this model were used to supply the fishing schooners at Gloucester, Massachusetts. Water was carried in wooden tanks below deck amidships and some boats also carried ice in a hold abaft the tanks. Water was transferred by manually operated force-pumps placed on deck. The boats usually had no cabin or trunk, as they did not leave the harbor and usually had a

permanent station at a wharf, leaving only upon request to supply a vessel with either water or ice. The boats, which ranged in length from about 35 to 45 feet, usually carried two men and were handy craft, designed to work among the wharves and in the crowded slips and harbor. Most of the waterboats were built at Essex, Massachusetts; similar boats were also employed at Boston to supply its fishing fleet.

The model represents a waterboat having a sharp and moderately long entrance, a rather short but well formed run, straight keel of moderate drag and with a skeg and more than average deadwood outside the rabbet, flush decked and with log rail, moderate draft, good sheer, upright curved stem, and a round fantail stern like that of a tug. The midsection shows a rising straight floor carried well out, a firm, round

GLOUCESTER WATERBOAT *Aqua Pura*, built in 1883. This rigged model, USNM 56973, shows very well the typical deck arrangement and rig. (*Smithsonian photo 44693–m.*)

258

bilge, and an upright side with heavy guard at gunwale. The mast is stepped right forward. A hatch is shown on port side to the forehold, a hatchway to tanks amidship, pumps, and a cockpit for the helmsman. There are heavy mooring cavels along the deck at rail for tying the boat to vessels when supplying them.

Scale of the model is 1 inch to the foot; the vessel represented was 37 feet on deck, 12 feet beam, length of mast above deck 39 feet, boom 37 feet, and gaff 16 feet.

Given by U. S. Bureau of Fisheries.

PURSE-SEINE BOAT, about 1875
RIGGED MODEL, USNM 25826

This model is of a purse-seine boat of the form employed in the New England mackerel fishery about

The model is painted in the style of 1875, bright green bottom, white topsides, sheer strake set off with beading, red and yellow.

Scale of model is 1 inch to the foot, for a boat 36 feet long, 8 feet beam, depth amidships 2 feet 6 inches and at ends 4 feet 6 inches, length of oars 12 feet and of steering sweep 18 feet.

These boats rowed easily, turned quickly, and could be towed at speeds of 10 to 12 miles per hour with safety. Later boats were fuller forward at gunwale and more straight-sided in plan.

Given by U. S. Fish Commission.

NEW ENGLAND SAILING DORY, 1882
RIGGED MODEL, USNM 160179

This is a model of the sailing dories once employed in the shore fisheries in the vicinity of Rockport, Massa-

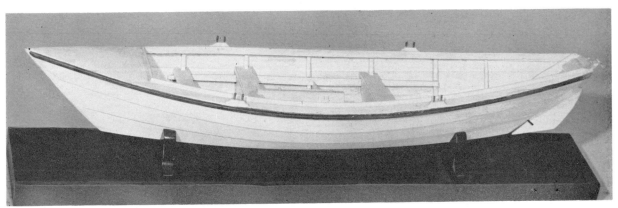

NEW ENGLAND SAILING-ROWING DORY, 1880–83, EMPLOYED IN THE SHORE FISHERIES. Rigged model USNM 160179, with centerboard case abaft the second thwart. These boats were rigged with one mast and a spritsail and jib or with two masts and leg-of-mutton sails. (*Smithsonian photo 44696–c.*)

1875–80. It is said that the boats were developed from whaleboats and were at first 28 feet long. The length was increased to 35 to 38 feet in 1875 and to 40 feet in 1882. The boats were lightly but strongly built and in general, resembled burdensome whaleboats except that the seine boat was usually wider aft, to carry the seine near the stern.

The model shows a double-ended, caravel-planked, keel, open boat having slightly rockered keel, curved stem and sternpost, strong sheer, the hull wide and full at gunwale aft and sharper forward, and an easy and sharp entrance and run, the latter the fuller. The midsection shows a slightly rising floor, easy turn of bilge, and a slightly flaring topside. Fitted with rowlocks, purse seine, pursing gear, oars, oar holders, pump, towing link, six thwarts, roller, and the usual gear of a mackerel seine boat about to leave the schooner.

chusetts. They were rigged with a sprit-mainsail and a jib tacked to the stemhead, but some of the Cape Ann dories in the 1890's used a leg-of-mutton mainsail instead of the spritsail. These boats, considered fast and seaworthy for their size, were worked by one or two fishermen for short periods, but in exposed waters.

The boat represented was of the dory type having a narrow flat bottom with some fore-and-aft camber, a raking and very slightly curved stem that is straighter than usual in this type of vessel, a raking "tombstone" transom with rudder hung outboard, strong sheer, and a sharp entrance and run. The lapstrake-planked topsides are heavily flaring and nearly straight. The model shows a centerboard amidships, washboards along the sides, a short bow deck with coamings, three thwarts with pen boards, and oars.

The mast step and clamp are not shown, and the rig is omitted.

The scale of the model is 1 inch to the foot, giving a dory 23 feet on the gunwales, 5 feet 3 inches beam, and 2 feet depth.

Given by Captain J. W. Collins.

NEW ENGLAND SAILING DORY, 1880–83
RIGGED MODEL, USNM 57573

This large rigged model represents a class of rowing-sailing dories once common in the New England shore fisheries, particularly in the vicinity of Cape Ann, Massachusetts. They had the reputation of being seaworthy and swift. The range of length was from about 17 feet to 24 feet at gunwale; the boats were fitted with centerboards and were either rigged with one mast and a loose-footed spritsail and a jib tacked to the stemhead, or with two masts and leg-of-mutton sails having high-cocked booms and moderate hoists.

The model shows an open lapstrake dory having rather narrow flat bottom slightly rockered fore-and-aft, flaring and straight topsides, a sharp entrance with a raking and slightly curved stem, a narrow V-shaped transom sharply raked and with the rudder hung on it outboard, and a strong, lively sheer.

The boat is fitted to row with two pairs of oars. There are washboards along the sides and short fore-deck, three thwarts with pen boards under and mast holes in the two forward thwarts; the after hole is for a sloop rig and the forward hole to allow the mast to be shifted forward and the jib omitted (the usual heavy weather rig). There is a centerboard amidships. The boat has three strakes to a side.

Scale of the model is 4 inches to the foot (one-third full size); the dory was 21 feet on the gunwale, 5 feet beam, 21¾ inches depth amidships, and length of mast 14 feet. The side frames in some of these boats were curved rather than straight, as in the model, which appears to represent a "stock," or standard, sailing dory from a once-noted boat builder, Higgins & Gifford, Gloucester, Massachusetts.

Given by Captain J. W. Collins.

NANTUCKET DORY, 1876
RIGGED MODEL, USNM 25657

This model represents the type of dory once used at Nantucket and nearby Cape Cod by clam diggers and alongshore fishermen. It was a dory of small size and light weight in order to allow the boat to be pulled over the flats by one man.

The model shows an open dory having a strong sheer, a narrow, flat bottom with some fore-and-aft rocker, raking stem and V-shaped transom, and flaring straight sides lapstrake planked. It was intended for rowing only.

Scale of model is 1 inch to the foot; the dory was 16 feet 6 inches overall, beam 4 feet at gunwales and 2 feet 6 inches on the bottom, and about 18 inches deep.

Given by W. H. Chase, 2nd.

FISHING DORY, 1876
RIGGED MODEL, USNM 55792

This is a model of the standard or "stock" fishing dory carried by fishing schooners in the period 1860–95, usually referred to as a "15-foot dory."

The model shows a rowing boat of the dory form having a rather narrow flat bottom with slight fore-and-aft camber, straight flaring sides planked lapstrake, strong sheer, raking and slightly curved stem, raking V-shaped transom, very narrow at the bottom, wider at the gunwale and "tombstone" shaped, and fitted with movable thwarts to allow the dory to be nested on the deck of a fishing schooner, by stowing one inside another.

These boats usually had three sets of tholes and three thwarts, in the foremost of which was a mast step. A small spritsail was sometimes rigged, and when loaded and under sail in a fresh wind, the dory skillfully handled could be worked to windward after a fashion, even though without a keel or centerboard.

Scale of model is 1 inch to the foot, providing a boat 18 feet 6 inches on the gunwale, 15 feet on the bottom, 5 feet beam, and 24 inches depth.

Given by Starling & Stevens, boatbuilders, Ferryville, Maine.

SCHOONER'S YAWL BOAT, 1880
RIGGED MODEL, USNM 25000

The yawl boat was employed on coasting schooners throughout their existence in the trade; yawls were also carried by most fishing schooners until the period 1875–85, when they were almost entirely replaced with the dory. In fishing schooners, until about 1866, the stern davits were usually wood; by 1870 iron davits were being fitted to all new schooners and also to coasters. The yawls varied in model and size to fit their work and the ideas of the individual builder. In many localities along the coast these boats were a standard production of the boat shops.

The model represents a typical yawl of a New England fishing schooner or coaster of about 1855–70. It shows a caravel-planked open boat having a straight

NEW ENGLAND SHORE FISHERY SCENE, 1862. A keel
New England 2-masted lobster boat is in the foreground. Dories and a spritsail rigged skiff are on
the beach. (*Smithsonian photo 44790–f.*)

keel with skeg, a curved raking stem, a raking flat and
heart-shaped transom, sharp entrance, easy run, and
strong sheer. The beam is great and is carried well
aft; the gunwale is full at bow to give flaring forward
sections. The midsection is formed with a rising
straight floor, rather slack bilge, and flaring topside.
There is a good deal of wood outside the keel rabbet.

The rudder is hung outboard and fitted with a steering yoke; the model has five thwarts and stern sheets.
Square tholes are shown. Boats of this type were usually fitted to sail as well as to row; the usual rig was a
loose-footed spritsail, but other rigs were employed,
particularly the boomed gaff-sail.

Scale of model is 2 inches to the foot, for a boat 20
feet on the gunwales, 6 feet beam, and 2 feet 6 inches
rabbet to gunwale. The model is of a large yawl,
the range of length being from 16 to 22 feet; 18 feet
was a common length on fishing schooners.

Given by Cragin & Sheldon, boatbuilders, Boston,
Massachusetts.

BOSTON FISHING CUTTER, 1890
RIGGED MODEL, USNM 57131

This model of an improved Irish fishing cutter such
as was used at Boston, Massachusetts, from 1857 to
about 1906, represents a more finished design than
most of the Irish cutters but shows the general features
of their design. This type of sailing fishing boat, introduced at Boston in 1857 by Patrick Gannon, a
boatbuilder from County Galway in Ireland who had
settled at Boston, was the old Galway hooker, a cutter
having a good turn of speed. The Boston boats were
variously called "Irish boats," "Boston hookers," and
"dundavoes." As the years passed, the Irish boat
changed in details from the old Galway hooker, developing a sharper entrance, a straighter and more
upright stem, and an improved rig. The Boston
boats were often swift sailers, seaworthy and weatherly,
though sometimes roughly built and finished.

A cuddy deck forward is entered through a companionway. Abaft the break, these boats were open,
with the after end partitioned off with pen-boards to
form a steering well there, with a large fish pen amidships. The stone or iron ballast was floored over in
the open part of the boat, and the fish pen was often

covered with hatch boards when making a passage. The standing room aft was often fitted with side seats or thwarts. Though the model does not have them, these boats usually had low monkey rails of plank-on-edge from the stern forward to a point abreast the mast. One characteristic of these boats was a hawse chock, often with an outward curve, bolted to the outside of the log rail forward and to one side of the stemhead; the model-builder has not shown this but has shown in its place, farther aft, a cathead never used on this craft.

The rig is that of a cutter with reefing bowsprit, carrying a gaff-mainsail laced to the boom, forestay-sail and a jib set flying on an iron traveler on the bowsprit. No topsails were commonly fitted nor were topmasts employed. The bowsprit in the model is to port of the stemhead, which stands high above rail.

The model shows very well the hull characteristics of an ideal boat of the type, having strong sheer, a straight keel with much drag, straight and rather upright stern with almost angular forefoot, raking post with rudder hung outboard, transom flat and heart-shaped, sharp entrance, long and fine run, and midsection with rising straight floor, high and rather hard bilge, tumble-home topsides. In the model the tumble-home is perhaps less marked than in some of the actual boats, though wall-sided boats may be seen in old photographs of the Boston Irish boats at T-Wharf (in the Watercraft Collection). The boats steered with a short, heavy tiller.

Scale of model is 1 inch to the foot. The boat shown would have been 36 feet at gunwale, 29 feet on the keel rabbet, 9 feet 3 inches beam, drawing 5 feet 8 inches at post and 2 feet 9 inches forward, mast 34 feet 9 inches above deck, bowsprit 10 feet 6 inches outside the stem, main boom 32 feet 6 inches, and main gaff 21 feet 3 inches.

Given by Captain J. W. Collins.

WHALEBOAT, 1883
RIGGED MODEL, USNM 57199

This is a miniature of a fully equipped New Bedford whaleboat of the old 30-foot length class employed in the Arctic whaling, 1860–85. These boats, built at New Bedford, Massachusetts, were batten-seam caravel-planked hulls having very light and strong construction. The topsides were usually lapstrake. The length varied from 28 to 30 feet at gunwale. They were noted for their good qualities under oars and sail and in all conditions.

The model shows a double-ended, open, caravel-planked, centerboard, rowing-and-sailing boat having a straight keel, raking and curved stem and stern posts, strong sheer, sharp entrance and sharper run, rising floor, round and easy bilge, and flaring topside. The boat has five thwarts, one mast, and a boomed gaff-sail and a jib tacked to the stem. A timberhead or "loggerhead" was placed aft near the stern to belay the harpoon line.

Scale of model is 2 inches to the foot; the boat was 30 feet at gunwale, 6 feet 6 inches beam, and 2 feet 3 inches depth amidships keel to gunwale. The mast was 24 feet 4½ inches in total length, main boom 19 feet 6 inches, gaff 13 feet 3 inches, oars 18 feet, and steering sweep 21 feet. These boats carried a large spread of sail, as they could use the weight of their crew when under sail to keep the boat on its feet.

Given by U. S. Bureau of Fisheries.

BLOCK ISLAND BOAT, 1875
RIGGED MODEL, USNM 25825

The old Block Island boats, known as "cowhorns," were noted for their seaworthiness. Originally built to be launched from beaches, they were small craft from about 18 to 26 feet long but, from the middle of the 19th century on, larger boats, up to about 40 feet gunwale length, were built, as these could work out of the partial harbors built at various times prior to completion of the "Government harbor" in 1873. Tradition claims that only one of these boats was lost, but the Customhouse records show that two were lost or wrecked: the *Vanderbilt* was lost in November 1871, and the mail boat *Thomas J. Lynch* was wrecked in 1889 on Peaked Rock off Point Judith. Considering the number of these boats and the exposed waters in which they worked, this record is an excellent one.

The rig of these boats was 2-masted, with the foremast stepped in the eyes of the boat; the masts were usually of nearly equal height and with some rake. The sails had short gaffs with single halyards; the foresail was boomless and overlapped the mainsail; the latter had a boom but the foot of the sail was not laced. The boats were fitted to row.

The model represents a typical Block Island boat of the small class in 1875; it illustrates a lapstrake, double-ended, open keel boat having a straight keel with marked drag, raking straight sternpost with rudder hung outboard, raking and slightly curved stem with prominent stemhead, strong sheer, upright washboards along the gunwales for about two-thirds the boat's length, and fitted with thwarts and stern sheets.

The midsection shows a sharply rising floor and very slack bilge, with sharply flaring topside—the section is an almost perfect V. The entrance is sharp, as is the run, the latter being the finer of the two.

Scale of the model is cataloged as ½ inch to the foot, which would produce a vessel measuring 33 feet at gunwale, 13 feet beam, 4 feet 6 inches depth to gunwale, and washboards 12 inches high. Spar dimensions at this scale would be foremast above gunwale 34 feet 3 inches, mainmast 22 feet 6 inches, fore gaff 5 feet, main gaff 4 feet 3 inches, and main boom 19 feet 8 inches. These spar dimensions show a much shorter mainmast and longer gaffs than appears to have been usual; a sailmaker's drawing and old photographs indicate that these dimensions in a boat of this approximate length commonly were mainmast above gunwale 32 feet 6 inches, foremast 34 feet, fore gaff and main gaff 4 feet, and main boom 20 feet. Due to

the drag of the keel the mainmast appeared shorter than it actually was, when the boats were afloat.

Details of this model, which include oyster tongs, suggest the cataloged scale is in error and the model may be to a scale of ¾ inch to the foot, making it represent a boat 22 feet 3 inches overall, 8 feet 8 inches beam, about 3 feet 3 inches depth, foremast 22 feet 6 inches above the rail cap, mainmast 18 feet (it should be 21 feet 6 inches), main boom 13 feet, and gaffs 3 feet (they should be 2 feet). Boats of this size were once common in this type.

Made and given by Captain H. C. Chester. Restored by Merritt Edson, 1958.

NO MAN'S LAND BOAT, 1882
Rigged Model, usnm 25898

The No Man's Land boat, also known as the Vineyard Sound boat, was once a common form of beaching boat on the south side of Cape Cod. It varied somewhat in model. Originally it was a light,

Eastern Catboats and Block Island Boats in harbor, about 1900. (*Smithsonian photo 46597–b, Courtesy of the late John Howard Benson.*)

lapstrake-planked, open boat with a rather deep keel outside the rabbet; by 1880 it was commonly being fitted with a centerboard placed a little forward of amidships; and the last sailing model was caravel-planked, half-decked, and unsuited for beach work. The later style, developed at Martha's Vineyard in the 1890's, was deeper and more powerful, beaching not being required. It carried two masts and small spritsails, and was fitted to work under oars.

This model shows the early keel fishing boat intended for beach work and designed to sail well in strong winds and rough water. It is a double-ended, lapstrake, open boat having a straight keel, straight raking post, slightly curved raking stem, strong sheer, sharp entrance, fine run, and the midsection formed with straight rising floor, firm round bilge, and flaring topside. The rudder is hung outboard on the post.

The rig is a 2-masted spritsail form; a tall foremast is stepped in the eyes of the boat and a short mainmast is stepped a little abaft midlength. The spritsails are rather square headed and loose footed; the foresail overlaps the main; and the latter has a short club at its clew.

Scale of model is 1½ inch to the foot; the boat would be 22 feet 8 inches at gunwale, 8 feet 10 inches beam, 4 feet 6 inches from bottom of keel to gunwale, the foremast 15 feet and the mainmast 13 feet 4 inches above thwart. This model appears to have been somewhat deeper than was average: more emphasis being placed on sailing than beaching qualities in this example.

Given by Captain William H. Cleveland.

NO MAN'S LAND BOAT, about 1885
BUILDER'S HALF-MODEL, USNM 54477

This half-model was made about 1880 and from it a number of beach-fishing boats, employed on the island of No Man's Land as well as at Nantucket and Martha's Vineyard and along the Cape Cod shore in the vicinity, were built by James Beetle at New Bedford, Massachusetts. Boats of a similar type were built at Martha's Vineyard, Fairhaven, and along the shores of Vineyard Sound.

The model represents a double-ended open boat with straight keel, strong sheer, curved stem, and a straight, raking post. The beam is carried well fore-and-aft, and the greatest beam is about at midlength. The floors are rising and the turn of the bilge is rather hard, with the topsides slightly flaring. The entrance is sharp and slightly hollow abaft the stem, and the run is easy, with a marked hollow just

forward of the post. The centerboard slot, in these boats, was usually in the garboard to prevent beach pebbles from jamming the case during beaching or launching.

The boats measured 17 feet ½ inch moulded length, 5 feet 8¾ inches moulded beam, and 2 feet 2⅜ inches moulded depth; the model is on a scale of 1 inch to the foot.

Given by James Beetle, boatbuilder, New Bedford, Massachusetts.

NO MAN'S LAND BOAT UNDER SAIL. This recently restored boat has proved to be a fast sailer. (*Photos courtesy of Robert Baker.*)

264

VINEYARD HAVEN HALF-SKIPJACK, about 1885
BUILDER'S HALF-MODEL, USNM 160122

This half-model represents several boats built at Vineyard Haven, Massachusetts, about 1885, for shore fishing. They appear to have been experimental and combined a round-bottom sloop hull forebody with the V-bottom and chine of a skipjack, or "corner boat" as the type was called at Provincetown. The V-bottom hull form seems to have appeared on Narragansett Bay and spread eastward

form was very economical to build. These vessels used a jib and mainsail rig. Some boats built on the model were lapstrake planked, or "clinker built," also called "clench built."

The half-model represents a shoal centerboard sloop having forward a round bottom of the normal form, with nearly straight and upright stem, straight keel with some drag, and skeg aft; and a V-bottom beginning slightly forward of midlength and ending in a V-shaped transom flat across and set at a sharp

FISHING CATBOAT of the type used on the Massachusetts and Rhode Island coast, 1875–80. Rigged model USNM 25026. (*Smithsonian photo 45605–h.*)

soon after the Civil War, but it also appeared in southern waters in the 1870's along the Gulf and, Florida coasts. The origin of the V-bottom model is obscure. Apparently the half-model was an attempt to secure the seaworthiness of a round bottom forward with the sail carrying power of a wide V-bottom aft, for it is doubtful that this combination of

rake, the rudder stock being inboard and entering hull just forward of the heel of the transom. The sheer is strong; the sternpost rakes; and the midsection is V-bottom with a straight, rising floor right out to the angular bilge, and above this chine the topsides are slightly convex and flaring, the flare being carried aft to the transom. The forebody is somewhat U-

265

shaped; the entrance is long and sharp, with the greatest beam abaft midlength; and the run is short and rather full.

Scale of the model is 1 inch to the foot; at this scale the vessel would be about 21 feet on deck, 7 feet 3 inches moulded beam, draft aft about 1 foot 9 inches, 1 foot 1 inch forward, and centerboard 6 feet long.

Given by U. S. Fish Commission.

EASTERN CATBOAT, 1875–80
RIGGED MODEL, USNM 25026

Catboats of the type illustrated in this model were formerly used in the Massachusetts and Rhode Island shore fisheries from Narrangansett Bay to Cape Ann, with some variation in model. The fishing cats were generally quite seaworthy and fast; their rig was smaller for their length than in the racing and pleasure-sailing catboats, and their hulls were usually better formed for rough water work. Catboats of the appearance of this model were particularly popular at Newport, Rhode Island, and in Massachusetts at Buzzard's Bay, Martha's Vineyard, Nantucket, Falmouth, and to the eastward at Plymouth, Cohasset, Hingham, and in Boston harbor. In other ports the cats often had rather upright flat transoms with the rudder hung outboard; this model of cat was particularly popular at Chatham, Cape Cod, and vicinity and became known as the "Cape cat." Usually the Chatham catboats were more powerful boats than the type shown in the model.

This model is of a wide, centerboard catboat having a long, sharp entrance, rather long and very fine run, straight keel with some drag, skeg, upright post, raking V–transom with rudder post through its heel, an upright and nearly straight stem, and strong sheer. The midsection shows a rising straight floor, a high and rather hard bilge, and an upright or slightly flaring topside. The mast is stepped close to the stem, abaft this is a trunk cabin and an oval cockpit in which are seats around the sides and after end (stone or iron ballast was stowed under the cockpit floor). The large centerboard is located amidships. Rigged without shrouds or stays and with a boomed gaff-sail.

Scale of the model is 1 inch to the foot, for a boat measuring 19 feet 9 inches on deck, 7 feet 6 inches beam, moulded depth amidships about 3 feet, mast standing above deck 19 feet 6 inches, boom 22 feet, and gaff 11 feet.

The model represents a medium-size fishing catboat

built about 1875; this type ranged in length from about 18 to 25 feet, but catboats for use in the fishing-party business in the summer season were as large as 40 feet on deck, and the Cape cats commonly ranged from 20 to 24 feet. Some of the eastern cats had counters which brought their deck length above the average, without a comparative increase in beam, depth, and waterline length. Catboats in the vicinity of Martha's Vineyard often had live wells on each side of the centerboard case and some had these covered by a deck and hatch at gunwale height, so that the cockpit was separated from the cabin trunk by a bridge deck, but the cockpit coaming usually enclosed the well hatches as well as the cockpit, which was not self-bailing though often watertight. Some cats had a plank bowsprit and forestay, often no more than a form of cathead to handle the ground-tackle, but some set a small jib on the forestay. The catboats of the 1870's and 1880's usually steered with a tiller but all large boats, and later boats above 25 feet in length, were steered with a wheel and gear.

Given by William H. Chase, Jr.

PROVIDENCE or NEWPORT BOAT, about 1875
RIGGED MODEL, USNM 29537

This rigged model of a small, rowing-sailing, fishing boat represents a type, variously named Providence River boat or Newport boat, once popular on Narragansett Bay, in Rhode Island, in the lobster and hook-and-line fisheries.

The model shows a lapstrake, keel, rowing-and-sailing boat, open and with wide gunwale caps, having a sharp entrance and short run, a live well amidships, good sheer, straight keel and skeg, curved stem, raking transom with rudder outboard, and midsection with rising floor, easy bilge, and flaring topside. It is cat-rigged with the mast stepped in a thwart and a gaff-and-boom mainsail, and is fitted to row. A bowsprit and jib were added in light weather.

Made by a prominent boatbuilder, T. D. Stoddard, of Newport, Rhode Island, it represents a boat built before 1876. Boats of this form and size, varying slightly in model and appearance, were built at Providence, Newport, Warren and Bristol; they ranged in length from about 11 feet to nearly 15 feet.

Model represents the larger of the boats; scale is 1½ inch to the foot, producing a boat 13 feet 6 inches long, 11 feet 8 inches on the straight part of the keel, and 5 feet 4 inches beam; the mast was 15 feet long.

Given by J. M. K. Southwick. Restored by Merritt Edson, 1958.

266

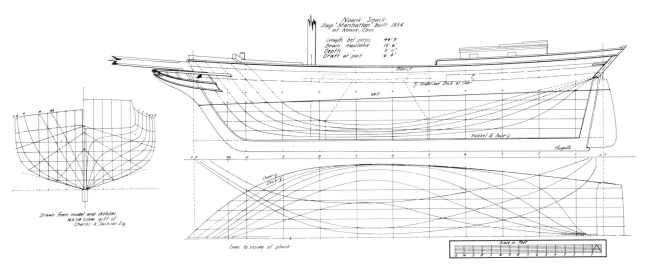

NOANK WELL-SMACK SLOOP *Manhattan*, built at Noank, Connecticut, in 1854 for the New York fisheries. Lines taken off builder's half-model USNM 160118.

NOANK WELL-SMACK SLOOP, 1854
BUILDER'S HALF-MODEL, USNM 160118

Manhattan

The sloop-rigged well-smack *Manhattan* was built from this model in 1854 at Noank, Connecticut, for local owners. Clipper built and intended as a swift sailer for use in the New York market fishery, she was similar to sloops such as the *Pronto* and *Viva*, built at New York by William H. Webb in 1842 for the Havana, Cuba, fishery. Noank shipbuilders had a great reputation for fine seagoing sloops, having built such craft for the fisheries and for whaling, sealing, and coastal trade since colonial times. The *Manhattan* was built at the time the large sloops were beginning to be replaced with schooners in the New York fisheries, and represents the final development of the Noank seagoing sloop model.

Employed as smacks, these sloops had a fish well amidships and were rigged with a large gaff-mainsail and a single large jib, with gaff-topsail and jib topsail to be set in light weather. They also had a square course and small square topsail set flying, as in the New York pilot schooners. Some had flush decks and others low quarterdecks like that of the *Manhattan;* earlier vessels had high quarterdecks like those of the North River sloops, and usually an open rail. These vessels were heavily sparred and canvassed.

The half-model shows a keel, clipper sloop with straight sheer; a straight keel with some drag; raking post and stem; a short, sharp entrance with the greatest beam well forward of midlength; and a

long, lean run. The midsection shows a rising floor, rather hard bilge, and little tumble-home above. The head is long and pointed; the transom is square and raking.

Scale of model is ½ inch to the foot, for a vessel 47 feet 9 inches moulded length at rail, about 44 feet 9 inches between perpendiculars, 15 feet 6 inches moulded beam, 5 feet 11 inches moulded depth, and drawing about 6 feet 4 inches at post and about 5 feet forward.

Given by L. D. Ashby of Noank, Connecticut.

NOANK SLOOP, 1885
RIGGED MODEL, USNM 26809

Sloops of the type and size represented by this model were employed in the lobster fishery on Long Island Sound from Saybrook to New London, Connecticut, and on Narragansett Bay, Rhode Island. The type is thought to have originated at Noank, Connecticut, and for that reason they were often called "Noank sloops" though built elsewhere. The majority of them were smacks between 18 and 30 feet long, with centerboard and on each side of the centerboard case a live well. They usually carried a jib-and-mainsail rig; a few of the larger boats carried gaff-topsails and jib topsails. Considered seaworthy, the type was noted for its speed, and boats up to about 28 feet length were usually handled by one man.

The model indicates a rather deep centerboard sloop having a straight keel with some drag, a curved and rather upright stem nearly straight above the load waterline, an upright post, and a skeg. The stern is formed with a strongly raking V-transom with the rudder stock brought up through its heel, steering with a tiller. The sheer is great. The entrance is long and sharp, with some hollow at the forefoot; the run is of moderate length, with rather flat buttocks. The midsection is formed with a rising floor, moderately hard bilge, and flaring topside, the sections near the stern over the skeg having some hollow in the garboards. The boat shown was half-decked, with live wells on each side of the centerboard case; larger boats had trunk cabins forward, usually U-shaped so that, in plan, the cabin sides and coamings formed an oval.

Scale of the model is 1 inch to the foot. The boat shown would be 24 feet 6 inches at gunwale, 10 feet 6 inches beam, 4 feet 6 inches from keel rabbet to gunwale amidships, and drew about 2 feet 6 inches with centerboard raised; bowsprit 9 feet outside the stem, mast 26 feet 6 inches above deck, main boom 26 feet, and gaff 11 feet 6 inches. Boats up to about 24 feet in length did not usually have shrouds, but the larger boats often had one or two on a side. The bowsprit was usually made of a wide plank and was hogged down outboard the stem. The type remained in use in the commercial fisheries on the Sound until about 1914–15, particularly in the oyster fishery.

Given by Captain H. C. Chester. Restored by Merritt Edson, 1958.

MENHADEN CARRY-AWAY BOAT, 1865
Builder's Half-Model, usnm 54341

This model represents the type of menhaden fishing boats used immediately after the Civil War; these were soon replaced by small sloops, which as early as 1871 began to be replaced by steamers. It was employed to build twelve boats at Greenport, Long Island, in 1865. The boats worked in "gangs" of three, with one of the three boats in the "gang" acting as seine boat, the other two as carry-away boats.

The boats were open, double-ended caravel-built hulls, with one mast well forward; they had a gaff rig, the gaff rather short and the boom long. The boats built on this model were reported very fast sailers and stiff when carrying sail in a breeze. It is said that the first boats to be employed in the menhaden fishery were the Block Island "cowhorns" and that this model represents the result of the experience with Block Island boats.

The half-model represents a wide, shoal, double-ended hull having strong sheer, a straight keel with

some drag, and a strongly rounded stem and sternpost, with a curved rudder hung outboard on the latter. The midsection is formed with a slightly rising straight floor, and a slack, well-rounded bilge, with slightly flaring topsides. The bow sections flare somewhat and the after sections near the stern flare to a greater degree. The model resembles the whaleboat, or Gloucester seine boat, in profile but is more burdensome and wider than either.

Scale of the model is 1 inch to the foot, to measure about 35 feet 10 inches at the rail, 13 feet 10 inches moulded beam, 3 feet 8 inches moulded depth, and drawing about 3 feet 3 inches aft and 2 feet 8 inches forward. In lieu of a centerboard, the keel is quite deep below the rabbet.

Given by Charles A. Jackson.

MENHADEN CARRY-AWAY SLOOP, 1875
Rigged Model, usnm 57029

This model represents the small sloops that soon after the Civil War replaced the double-ender boats (shown by builder's half-model usnm 54341) in the menhaden fishery on Long Island Sound. As with the double-enders, three such sloops made up a sailing gang, two boats usually working the purse seine and the third carrying away the catch to market or plant. By 1885 these gangs were obsolete, and the menhaden steamers were driving the sloops out of the fishery.

These sloops were shoal, yacht-like, centerboard craft having a long, sharp entrance, fine run, strong sheer, straight keel with some drag, upright post, strongly raking V-shaped transom with rudderpost passing through its heel, and a raking stem rabbet with longhead of moderate length. The midsection was formed with a slightly rising straight floor, low, round and firm bilge, and rather upright topside. Amidships was a cargo hold entered through a large hatch, aft was a small cabin trunk, and forward of the mast a windlass.

Scale of the model is ½ inch to the foot; at this scale the sloop shown would measure 43 feet 6 inches on deck, 14 feet beam, 3 feet 6 inches draught at post, hatchway amidships 14 feet long and 8 feet wide, mainmast 45 feet 6 inches above deck, bowsprit 15 feet outside rabbet at deck, topmast 22 feet 6 inches total length, main boom 44 feet, main gaff 21 feet, and sharpie skiff 11 feet 9 inches long and 4 feet beam.

The sloops carried a large gaff-mainsail, a jib-headed gaff-topsail, a large single jib, and a jib topsail.

Often fast sailers, they were very similar to the centerboard oyster sloops used on Narragansett Bay in the same period; some had the clipper bow shown in this model, others had straight and upright stems; some had the V–transom of the model, others had a short counter or fantail. The model represents a sloop steered with a tiller, but some employed steering gear and wheel. The sloops were commonly rather low-sided, the bulwarks were usually no more than log rails, and the centerboards were large. Usually each sloop could accommodate four men.

Given by U. S. Fish Commission.

LONG ISLAND FISHING SLOOP, 1869
BUILDER'S HALF-MODEL, USNM 315706

A centerboard fishing sloop, name unknown, was built on this model by John Ewing, in 1869, in the vicinity of East Moriches, Long Island, New York. Sloops of this size and type usually had a large oval cockpit-cabin trunk arrangement and much resembled contemporary sloop yachts. They were fast, weatherly and very handy craft; in experienced hands they were seaworthy enough for the oyster and other inshore fisheries in which this sloop was employed.

The half-model represents a wide, shoal, centerboard sloop having strong sheer, a straight keel with some drag, nearly vertical curved stem rabbet with rounded forefoot, raking post, and a sharply raking V-shaped transom. The entrance is long, sharp, and markedly hollow abaft the stem; the run is long, flat and fine. The greatest beam is at midlength, the model showing the "raking midsection" that permits maximum length in both run and entrance. The midsection shows a rising straight floor, a high, firm, round bilge, and a slightly flaring topside.

Scale of the model is 1 inch to the foot. The sloop had a moulded length on deck of 25 feet 9 inches, moulded beam of 9 feet 6 inches, and a moulded depth of 2 feet 7 inches. The frames were spaced 12 inches apart, the centerboard was 7 feet long, with the pivot about 7 feet 8 inches from the stem rabbet.

Rigged with a single, large jib and a gaff-mainsail; the bowsprit was of plank and long outboard; the centerboard was on the centerline of the hull, and the stem was straight and unadorned.

Gift of Mrs. Otis A. Palmer, East Moriches, Long Island, New York.

LONG ISLAND FISHING SLOOP, 1889
BUILDER'S HALF-MODEL, USNM 315696

Estelle

The centerboard fishing sloop *Estelle* was built on this model in the vicinity of Jamesport, Long Island, New York, in 1889, by M. Corwin. The model is of a

269

type of sloop then popular in Great South Bay and elsewhere on Long Island for oyster tonging and other purposes.

The half-model represents a shallow, wide, centerboard sloop having graceful sheer, a straight keel with moderate drag, raking curved stem rabbet with the forefoot rounded in a hard curve, skeg aft having a raking post and the stern formed with a raking V-shaped transom, with only a short overhang beyond the sternpost. The entrance is rather short, but sharp with some hollow in the forefoot; the run is long and rather flat; the greatest beam is a little forward of midlength; the midsection is formed with a rising straight floor, a high firm bilge, and a slightly flaring topside.

Scale of the model is 1 inch to the foot, for a sloop with a moulded length at deck 26 feet 6 inches, moulded beam 10 feet, and moulded depth 2 feet 5 inches. Model is made to deck. The sloop had low log rails, the centerboard was on the centerline of the hull, and was about 6 feet long, with the pivot about 10 feet from the forward end of the deck.

Sloops of this model usually had a plain, straight stem, but some had billet heads. They had an oval cockpit with a trunk forward; the mast was stepped well forward; and they carried a large, single jib, a gaff-mainsail and sometimes a gaff-topsail and jib topsail, both hoisted on a long pole head on the mast.

Gift of Mrs. Otis A. Palmer, East Moriches, Long Island, New York.

LONG ISLAND FISHING SLOOP, about 1890
BUILDER'S HALF-MODEL, USNM 315705

A centerboard fishing sloop, name unknown, was built on this model about 1890 near East Moriches, Long Island, New York.

The half-model is of a shoal, rather wide, centerboard sloop having moderate sheer, a straight keel with some drag and a skeg aft, stem rabbet curved and somewhat raking, with a well rounded forefoot, and a round fantail counter stern overhanging the slightly raked sternpost on the skeg. The hull is formed with a raking midsection, giving a long, sharp entrance with marked hollow in the forefoot, and a rather long and straight run. The midsection shows a rising straight floor, a rather firm round bilge, and a slight tumble-home in the topside.

Scale of the model is ¾ inch to the foot, for a moulded length at rail of 30 feet 2 inches, moulded beam 10 feet 3 inches, and a moulded depth to rail 3 feet 3 inches; the rail height is 6½ inches amidships, 5¾

inches at stern, and 7½ inches at bow. The centerboard was on the center line of the hull and was about 7 feet 6 inches long, with the fore end of the slot about 10 feet 6 inches from the stem rabbet at rail. The sloop had a clipper bow with trails. It had a cockpit and was jib-and-mainsail rigged with a single, large jib and a gaff-mainsail. This type of sloop was very popular on the shores of Long Island and in New York Bay in the 1880's and 1890's.

Gift of Mrs. Otis A. Palmer, East Moriches, Long Island, New York.

FISHING LAUNCH, 1915
BUILDER'S HALF-MODEL, USNM 315701

A small fishing and general service launch was built on this model at East Moriches, Long Island, New York, by Otis A. Palmer, in 1915. In general, this model is similar in form to USNM 315702 by the same builder.

The model shows a straight-sheered low-sided launch hull having a long, straight and flat run, the rabbet of the keel straight from the stern to a point about a third of the overall length from the stem, where the keel rabbet cambers moderately and fairs into a well rounded stem rabbet. The transom is flat, with a sharp tumble-home. The entrance is rather short and convex; the greatest beam is slightly forward of midlength. Midsection shows a slightly rising straight floor, a full round bilge, and a flaring topside.

Scale of the model is 1 inch to the foot, for a moulded length overall of 21 feet 8 inches, moulded beam 5 feet 8 inches, and moulded depth 2 feet. The boat probably had a skeg; the rudder post was inboard of the top of the transom.

Gift of Mrs. Otis A. Palmer, East Moriches, Long Island, New York.

FISHING LAUNCH, 1915–16
BUILDER'S HALF-MODEL, USNM 315702

A launch for fishing and general service was built on this model at the U.S. Coast Guard station, Smith's Point, Long Island, New York, by Otis A. Palmer, in 1915–16. The launch was powered with a 4-cylinder Mora automobile engine and a 16-inch propeller. It was fast, and a number of similar design were built by Palmer.

The model shows a long, low and rather narrow launch, much like some early racing launches, having straight sheer, a straight keel rabbet from the stern to a point about a third the length of the hull from the stem, where there is a gentle rocker to the heel of the stem. The stem rabbet is curved and raking, with a well rounded forefoot. The stern is formed by a flat transom having a marked tumble-home. The entrance is long and convex, the run is long and very flat. The greatest beam on deck is about a third the length abaft the stem, and the midsection is formed with a straight, slightly rising floor, an easy turn of bilge, and a flaring topside. The dead rise dies out as it approaches the stern.

Scale of the model is 1 inch to the foot, for a moulded length overall of 27 feet 6 inches, moulded beam 6 feet 1 inch, and a moulded depth 2 feet 1 inch. The boat had skeg and was built to 30 feet overall length by lengthening the spacing of the mould stations.

Gift of Mrs. Otis A. Palmer, East Moriches, Long Island, New York.

SHARPIE LAUNCH, 1947
BUILDER'S HALF-MODEL, USNM 315699

Sharpie launches have had periods of popularity on the shores of Long Island and Connecticut. This half-model represents a 23½-foot sharpie launch designed in 1947 by Otis A. Palmer of East Moriches, Long Island. A number of launches of this type, which is cheap and efficient and very suitable for fisheries in protected waters, have been built in this area. In 1949 Palmer built the *Sassafras*, 20 feet overall, for which a speed of 22 miles per hour was claimed; the engine was a 4-cylinder 144-cubic-inch Scripps, the propeller a 13- x 8½-inch narrow blade. Some of these boats have a trunk cabin forward.

The half-model is of a square-sterned sharpie hull having moderate sheer, a rockered flat bottom, raking and curved stem rabbet, and a flat transom set at slight rake. The entrance is long and sharp. The greatest beam on the bottom is slightly abaft midlength, the greatest beam at gunwale a little forward of midlength. The boat is somewhat like a dory in general design. The midsection is formed with a flat bottom, an angular bilge, and strongly flaring straight sides.

CENTERBOARD SLOOP used as carry-away boat in the menhaden fishery on Long Island Sound in the 1870's. Rigged model USNM 57029. (*Smithsonian photo 45605-e.*)

271

Scale of model is 1 inch to the foot, giving a moulded length at gunwale 23 feet 4 inches, moulded beam at gunwale 7 feet 2 inches and at chine 4 feet 6 inches, and moulded depth 2 feet 9 inches. Width of bottom is 3 feet 8 inches at transom.

Gift of Mrs. Otis A. Palmer, East Moriches, Long Island, New York.

CHESAPEAKE BAY LOG CANOE, about 1875
RIGGED MODEL, USNM 25003

This is a rather crude model of an early type Chesapeake Bay log canoe in which a keel was used instead of a centerboard; the model apparently represents a canoe, relatively small for the type, from the vicinity of Tilghman's Island, Maryland. These canoes, built of two or more logs hewn to shape and bolted together to form a shoal, double-ended, canoe-like hull and rigged in various fashions, were used for tonging oysters, crabbing and fishing on the lower Chesapeake Bay.

The model represents a double-ended, shoal-bodied hull having washboards along the sides, keel straight with much wood below the rabbet line, straight raking sternpost with rudder hung outboard, curved and slightly flaring stem, and a short bowsprit secured to the foredeck. Entrance and run are sharp, the run the finer of the two. Midsection formed with slightly rising straight floor, firm round bilge and slightly flaring topside. Rigged with small jib and two leg-of-mutton sails, of which the foresail is the more lofty; on sharply raking masts.

Scale of model is 1 inch to the foot; the canoe represented was 27 feet 6 inches long, 5 feet 3 inches beam, 2 feet 9 inches height of side, foremast 20 feet 3 inches above thwart, mainmast 16 feet 3 inches. Boat shown with oars 9 feet long and tongs 17 feet long, with heads 2 feet wide.

Given by T. B. Ferguson, Baltimore, Maryland.

CHESAPEAKE BAY LOG CANOE, about 1890
BUILDER'S HALF-MODEL, USNM 312328

Oyster Creek

The standing-rig canoe *Oyster Creek* was built from this half-model on Taylor's Island, Maryland, by Joseph T. Spicer about 1890. This canoe was of log construction, and the half-model is made to meet the requirements of this mode of building, in that the lifts are vertical rather than, as in normal construction, horizontal. There are three vertical lifts, indicating a "five-log canoe," with a center log and two

wing logs on each side. The *Oyster Creek* was reputed to be a fast sailer on the wind and was employed in the oyster and crab fisheries. The canoes of this class were "half-decked," having a long cockpit with narrow side decks and short end decks, and a cuddy in a small trunk forward; they were used in tonging and dredging oysters as well as for crabbing and transportation.

The half-model indicates a canoe-like hull with a large centerboard, having a moderately sharp entrance and a fine run; the midsection is slightly forward of midlength overall. The model shows a moderate sheer, straight keel, and a straight-raking post and stem. The midsection shows straight rising floors carried well out and a high and rather hard bilge. The *Oyster Creek* had a long, deep, and pointed head like a bugeye and, according to the donor's description, a small trunk cabin forward. She was rigged with two leg-of-mutton sails, the fore the larger, and a single large jib hanked to a stay set up on a short bowsprit.

Scale of the half-model is ¾ inch to the foot. The model scales 40 feet at gunwale, 8 feet 4 inches extreme beam, and 2 feet 9 inches rabbet to gunwale.

Given by James K. Spicer, Taylor's Island, Dorchester County, Maryland.

CHESAPEAKE BAY BUGEYE, SCHOONER-RIGGED, 1860–85
RIGGED MODEL, USNM 42757

This model represents an early bugeye hull with schooner, or "square rig," instead of the standard leg-of-mutton rig. Schooner-rigged bugeyes appear to have had a period of great popularity on the Chesapeake from 1870 to 1885, and were considered to be faster sailers than those with the leg-of-mutton sail plan. To carry the schooner rig the bugeye hull had to be powerful and stiff, and as the cost was the greater, the leg-of-mutton eventually replaced it, though a few bugeyes retained the square rig until recent years.

This model illustrates one of these vessels employed in the oyster fishery, complete with winches, or "winders," and with all sails set: large jib, foresail, mainsail, main gaff-topsail, and main-topmast staysail. It shows a double-ended hull having marked sheer, straight keel with some drag, raking post and stem, and longhead. Midsection with slight rise of floor, low and well-rounded bilge, and nearly upright topside. The bow is sharp and the run fine, the latter a little longer and sharper than the entrance. The model appears to be intended to represent a centerboard boat, though some early bugeyes, like the log canoes, had keels instead of centerboards. This model is of the period where a keel might have been employed.

Scale of the model is 1 inch to the foot; the vessel would measure 48 feet at rail, 12 feet beam, and 4 feet in depth; bowsprit 13 feet 6 inches long outside knightheads, foremast 38 feet and mainmast 38 feet 6 inches above deck, main-topmast 7 feet 6 inches total length, main boom 25 feet, main gaff 11 feet 6 inches, fore boom 16 feet 9 inches, and fore gaff 11 feet.

Like most of her class this vessel had log rails and prominent knightheads.

Given by T. B. Ferguson. Restored by Eugene Beach, 1958.

decked, is of a bugeye though the size represents that of a canoe.

The model shows a double-ended hull having a straight keel, raking sternpost with rudder hung outboard on it, raking stem with a long head, marked sheer, sharp entrance, and a long and rather easy run. The beam is greatest forward of midlength, and the midsection shows a rising floor, very easy and slack bilge, and a somewhat flaring topside. The keel outside the rabbet, is very deep (1 foot along the bottom) and takes the place of the later centerboard. The masts rake sharply; the bowsprit "hogs" down markedly at its outer end. The deck arrangement shows a short trunk cabin with a hatch built into its forward end, then the mainmast, dredge winches and rollers,

Schooner - Rigged Chesapeake Bay Bugeye, 1865–75, referred to locally as "square-rigged." Rigged model USNM 42757. (*Smithsonian photo 45605-f*.)

CHESAPEAKE BAY BUGEYE, SCHOONER-RIGGED, 1865–75

Rigged Model, usnm 55807

This model of a small schooner-rigged, or "square rigged," bugeye of about 1865–75, having a keel instead of a centerboard, represents the transition between the small log canoe of the Bay and the larger, decked bugeyes. This model, being completely

main hatch, foremast, and heel bitt. These vessels steered with a tiller. They early obtained a reputation for speed and seaworthiness.

Scale of the model is 1 inch to the foot. The vessel would have been 35 feet long at deck or log rail, 33 feet on the keel, 7 feet 6 inches beam, 3 feet depth in hold, bowsprit outboard of knightheads 9 feet 6 inches, foremast above deck 25 feet, mainmast above deck

25 feet, main-topmast 8 feet 6 inches total length (with 2 feet of doubling), fore-boom 13 feet 6 inches, foregaff 9 feet, main boom 18 feet, main gaff 10 feet, jib club 3 feet 6 inches. The spars were very light. Model is shown under full sail, with jib, foresail and mainsail, and main gaff-topsail.

There were no knightheads, in fact, in this model, but the log rail is brought up sharply near the bow to serve in their place.

Given by U. S. Fish Commission.

CHESAPEAKE BAY BUGEYE, 1885
BUILDER'S HALF-MODEL, USNM 76290

Lillie Sterling

The bugeye *Lillie Sterling* of Crisfield, Maryland, was built from this half-model at Pocomoke City, Maryland, by E. James Tull in 1885, and the design won an award for the builder at the World's Columbian Exposition in 1893. The *Sterling* was built for the Chesapeake Bay oyster fishery. The half-model represents a small vessel of her type, by later standards, but one popular in her period of build. She does not have the overhanging stern platform, or "patent stern," of the later bugeyes, nor does she have the "drake's tail" or "pink" enclosing the rudderpost head that also marked later bugeyes.

As a development of the older log canoe of this area the bugeye differed from the various classes of these canoes only in being completely decked, a characteristic that appears to have determined whether or not a vessel was a bugeye. Canoes larger than the *Sterling* were often built; these were called "brogans," "standing-rig canoes," and "coastin' canoes." When so called they had large cockpits with only short decks at the ends, a small cuddy well forward, and narrow side decks.

The *Sterling* was not log-built, but framed and planked in the conventional manner, a style of construction slowly becoming common in bugeyes when the *Sterling* was designed. However, log-bottom bugeyes, with the logs forming the whole bottom to just above the turn of the bilge, and with plank-and-frame topsides, remained popular until recent times because of the great durability of the log construction.

Small bugeyes of the class of the *Lillie Sterling*, which is also represented by a rigged model in the Watercraft Collection, had a small trunk cabin; in the *Sterling* this was well aft but in many the trunk was forward, just abaft the foremast. A large cargo hatch was placed between the masts and sometimes a small hatch was placed well forward. In the *Sterling* there is a small hatch abaft the mainmast against the fore-end of the trunk cabin. The early bugeyes steered with a tiller and the mainsheet set up to the rudder-head. Some small bugeyes had a small cockpit, or a "standing room" or hatch for the helmsman during heavy weather. A larger hatch was sometimes fitted amidships in which stood the crew operating the dredge winches; this standing room was in addition to a cargo hatch; sometimes the standing room deck, or sole, was self-bailing.

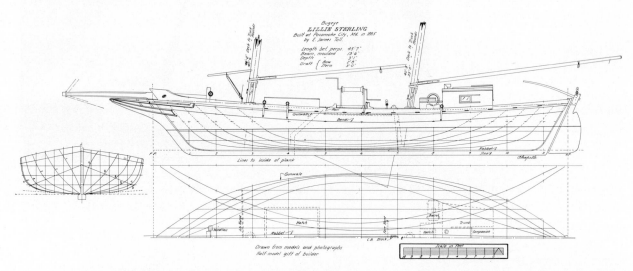

LINES OF THE SMALL CHESAPEAKE BAY BUGEYE, *Lillie Sterling*, built at Pocomoke City, Maryland, in 1885. The lines were taken off builder's half-model USNM 76290, the deck arrangement and spar dimensions are from rigged model USNM 76256.

274

The half-model represents a double-ended canoe-like vessel of shoal draft, fitted with a large center-board nearly amidships and having moderate sheer, straight keel with some drag, raking stem and stern rabbets, long pointed head, rudder hung outboard on the sternpost, a sharp, well-formed entrance and run, and midsection with slightly rising straight floor and full round bilge carried to deck, so the topsides flare somewhat. The run is longer and sharper than the entrance. Greatest beam is about at midlength.

Scale of half-model is ½ inch to the foot. The bugeye was 45 feet 7 inches on deck, 13 feet 6 inches moulded beam, 3 feet 1 inch moulded depth, and drew 3 feet at post and 2 feet 8 inches at bow; the centerboard was 11 feet long and 4 feet deep.

Given by E. James Tull, shipbuilder, Pocomoke City, Maryland.

CHESAPEAKE BAY BUGEYE, 1885
RIGGED MODEL, USNM 76256

Lillie Sterling

This rigged model represents the *Lillie Sterling*, which was built on the builder's half-model USNM 76290 at Pocomoke City, Maryland, in 1885. It shows the typical deck arrangement and rig of the bugeye of the *Sterling's* size and date of build. These two models brought an award to the builder at the World's Columbian Exposition in 1893.

The bugeye rig is more nearly related to the schooner than to the ketch rig. The foresail is slightly larger than the after or mainsail; the masts are nearly of equal length; and the distribution of sail area in the bugeye is very like that of the old pilot-boat schooner rig. The sails are jib headed, and the masts rake sharply, with two shrouds to a side on the fore-mast and one to a side on the main.

Scale of model is ½ inch to the foot, representing a bugeye 42 feet in length, in which the bowsprit extends 10 feet outboard the stem rabbet at deck, the foremast is 46 feet deck to truck, mainmast 40 feet deck to truck, jib club 5 feet long, fore boom 16 feet 3 inches, main boom 22 feet 6 inches long, and centerboard 11 feet long.

Given by U. S. Bureau of Fisheries.

CHESAPEAKE BAY BUGEYE, 1893
BUILDER'S HALF-MODEL, USNM 311015

Triumph

The large framed bugeye *Triumph* was built from this model at Tilghman's Island, Maryland, in 1893 by John B. Harrison and represents the highest development of the type. A typical large bugeye employed in the oyster fishery on the Chesapeake, with moderate sail area and graceful appearance, the *Triumph* is said to have been very swift. When built she did not have the "patent stern," and the model shows only the "drake's tail," the projecting pink-like structure at the stern enclosing the head of the rudderpost and intended to give the rudder support and protection, that has been a character-istic of the bugeye type in recent years.

The half-model shows a canoe-like double-ended centerboard hull to deck and to moulded lines, having bold sheer, straight keel with small drag, and raking stem and post, with the stem rabbet slightly rounded at forefoot. The head is very long and pointed, the rudder is hung on the post, and the midsection shows a rising straight floor, round easy bilge, and slightly rounded topside.

A low, log rail is surmounted by a low open rail made of a wooden cap supported by short, closely spaced pipe stanchions with a bolt passing through each. A small trunk cabin is aft. The masts rake about 2¼ inches to the foot.

Scale of half-model is ½ inch to the foot; the *Triumph* was about 65 feet long at deck, 18 feet 2 inches moulded beam, 5 feet 3½ inches moulded depth, and drew about 3 feet 6 inches with center-board raised.

Given by John B. Harrison, shipbuilder, Tilgh-man's Island, Maryland.

CHESAPEAKE BAY SKIPJACK, 1897
RIGGED MODEL, USNM 312828

Carrie Price

The Chesapeake Bay skipjack, or "bateau," *Carrie Price* was built at Holland's Island, Maryland, in 1897 by James H. Price for an oyster dredge.

The model shows her to have been a rather typical early type of skipjack having a long, sharp entrance and very long and flat run; the stem at rabbet is straight and raking; the transom is flat and rakes sharply. The sheer is slight. The rudder is hung outboard of the transom on a false sternpost which also supports the long skeg. The keel is straight and there is moderate drag; the centerboard is long and shallow. The midsection is formed with very slightly rising bottom, low angular chine, and straight flaring topside. The chine is low forward, being be-low the load waterline. The deadrise of the bottom increases from amidships each way to bow and stern.

The skipjack is shown with the typical longhead, headrails, and trails. The single mast is stepped well forward and has much rake. Rig is typical and includes a single large jib and a leg-of-mutton mainsail laced to a long boom. Model shows this skipjack as taken off and does not show the usual deck plan of an oyster dredge skipjack of this size. The deck arrangement shown is heel bitts right forward, iron jib horse, mast, low trunk cabin, main hatch, and after hatch.

Scale of model is ⅜ inch to the foot; the *Price* was 40 feet 6 inches over the log rail, 14 feet 3 inches beam, and drew 2 feet at post and 1 foot 5 inches at stem with centerboard raised. Her mainmast stood 56 feet 9 inches above the deck, the boom was 41 feet 3 inches long, and the bowsprit extended 14 feet 9 inches outboard of the stem rabbet at deck.

Made and given by William E. Lee.

CHESAPEAKE BAY SKIPJACK, 1903
BUILDER'S HALF-MODEL, USNM 312329

Lillie G Spicer

The Chesapeake Bay skipjack, or "bateau," *Lillie G. Spicer* was built from this model at Taylor's Island, Dorchester County, Maryland, in 1903 by Joseph T. Spicer for the oyster fishery. This model of sloop, which became popular on the Chesapeake about 1890, was an adaption of the skipjack model that appears to have come into use on Long Island Sound about 1860. The skipjack or "V-bottom," or "diamond bottom," or "corner boat" was a framed hull having sections made up of straight lines with the bottom V-form and usually planked fore-and-aft. The Chesapeake builders, however, adapted the skiff or sharpie construction and planked the bottom athwartships; to obtain the necessary twist in the bottom plank they put it on so that the seams raked aft on each side of the keel. This form of bottom plank, locally known as "herring-bone," is now used in Chesapeake Bay V-bottom motorboats.

The rig of the Chesapeake skipjacks was usually a large jib-headed mainsail and a single large jib hanked to a stay set up on a bowsprit. The mast raked sharply aft and the bowsprit was hogged down outboard. These sloops had the long head of the bugeye and most of them, like the *Spicer*, had the rudder "outdoors," hung on the sternpost outside the transom. The oyster dredge skipjacks ranged in Custom House measurement from about 35 feet to 60 feet on deck. A few were rigged like bugeyes, with two masts.

The half-model shows a V-bottom hull, wide and shoal, having a wide square stern raking slightly and the stem rabbet straight and also with a slight rake. The keel rabbet cambers fore-and-aft (the model shows the skeg); the keel was thus straight and had some drag. The entrance is rather long and sharp and the run somewhat short and full; the dead rise of the bottom is moderate and the sides flare out above the chine, or angular bilge. The sheer is moderate and the freeboard low.

These very shoal-draft craft had a long centerboard; the *Spicer's* was 13 feet 6 inches. This sloop had a trunk cabin forward, just abaft the mast, and a large cargo hatch amidships with a small standing-room hatch for the helmsman. In recent times skipjacks often have an after trunk in place of the old standing-room hatch.

Scale of the half-model is 1 inch to the foot; the *Spicer* was 40 feet 4 inches on deck, 15 feet 3 inches moulded beam, and 34 inches moulded depth (register dimensions 38.2 feet x 15.0 feet x 2.7 feet). A rigged model of a skipjack is in the Watercraft Collection (USNM 312828, on p. 275).

Given by James K. Spicer, Taylor's Island, Dorchester County, Maryland.

CHESAPEAKE BAY "CRAB SCRAPER," 1915
RIGGED MODEL, USNM 316629

Jesse Willard

Model is of a small skipjack, or "bateau," of a type once used on the Eastern Shore of Maryland in the Chesapeake Bay crab fishery, in summer. These boats were also used in wintertime oyster tonging, in some localities. The boats ranged in size from 24 to 30 feet on deck and, as a class, they were smart sailers. The sailing crabber and oyster tonger went out of fashion after the 1914–18 war, being replaced by launches.

The model represents a boat built at Dames Quarters, near Deal Island, Maryland, in 1915, named the *Jesse Willard* in honor of the boxing champion of the world at that time. The *Willard* was a typical boat of her class in rig, form, and size. These boats were V-bottomed, of the form known as "skipjack" to yachtsmen but called "bateau" on the Eastern Shore. The *Willard* was abandoned at Cambridge, Maryland, about 1950, after being converted to a motor boat.

The model shows the *Willard* as a bateau having a strong sheer, a straight keel line formed by a skeg, moderate drag, a raking straight stem rabbet, and a raking, flat transom. She has a longhead, trails, and head rails. The midsection is formed by a rising straight floor, an angular, or chine, bilge, and a straight and flaring topside. The rail is formed of a cap with pipe stanchions set on a log rail; the rudder is hung outboard on a false sternpost; the mast is stepped well forward, with some rake. The boat is "half-decked," with a large cockpit and a small portable cabin trunk, which was placed over the forward end of the cockpit in winter oyster tonging but was usually removed for the summer fishery. The entrance is rather long, sharp and convex, the run easy and quite straight. A large centerboard is housed amidships. The rig is jib and mainsail, the latter a leg-of-mutton fitted with a laced boom. Model is painted as the actual boat.

The *Jesse Willard* was 25 feet 6 inches long at the rail cap, 8 feet 8 inches extreme beam, and drew 1 foot 8¼ inches at the sternpost, with centerboard raised. Model was constructed from plans taken off

the boat and shows all important details of construction. Scale of model is ¾ inch to the foot.

Made for the museum by Merritt A. Edson, Jr.

RACING LAUNCH, 1902
BUILDER'S HALF-MODEL, USNM 311239

Fairbanks No. 2

The racing launch *Fairbanks No. 2* was built from this half-model in 1902 at Oxford, Maryland, by Charles W. Langdon. A champion racing launch in her day, she was powered with a Smalley engine, made by the Fairbanks Scale Company and rated at 12 to 15 horsepower; the boat is reputed to have reached a speed of nearly 26 statute miles per hour. This boat was used as a model for the Chesapeake Bay fishing launches, now known as "Hooper Island boats"; these, until very recent years had practically the same features of design, except that they had a little more beam and depth in proportion to their

CHESAPEAKE BAY SKIPJACK, or "crab scraper," *Jess Willard*, built near Deal Island, Maryland, in 1915. Rigged model USNM 316629. (*Smithsonian photo 45606-g.*)

length. The model has proved to be a good sea boat in the Chesapeake, and very efficient.

The half-model shows a long and very narrow V-bottom, launch, having the greatest depth of keel rabbet at the forefoot; the bow is curved and raking and the keel rabbet runs nearly in a straight line, from the forefoot up and aft, to the bottom of the stern, which is round in plan, with much tumble-home, a form once called a "torpedo stern" but now called "dove-tail" by some on the Chesapeake. The sheer is straight. On deck the greatest beam is about amidships, but at the chines it is close to the stern. The entrance is therefore very long and sharp, while the run is also long and very flat. The chine in profile is nearly coincident with the load waterline over its full length. The half breadth of the model is to the keel rabbet, not to the centerline.

Scale of the model is 1 inch to the foot; the boat was 37 feet overall, 34 feet 3 inches on deck, 4 feet 2½ inches moulded beam at deck, 3 feet 8½ inches at chines, drew about 1 foot 10½ inches at the propeller, and displaced 1890 pounds without crew.

steep, short-dangerous seas of the Chesapeake and ran steadily on their course, as required in the trotline crab fishery.

The half-model is of a long, low, and narrow V-bottom wooden launch having slight sheer; a rockered keel rabbet; a slight camber in the chine profile, with the chine almost coincident with the load line at bow and stern; a straight, raking stem rabbet with small round at forefoot; and a dove-tail, or torpedo, stern round in plan, with the sides of the hull brought around in a sharp tumble-home by vertical, tapered staving. This marked tumble-home in the stern, in profile, was the hallmark of this type of launch. The deck plan shows the beam to be carried well fore and aft; the greatest breadth at rail is slightly forward of midlength. The chine, in plan, is also carried well fore and aft with only moderate reduction in width, but at the bow the chines are brought in to form a very sharp entrance. The run is long and flat, being nearly straight in the buttocks as the stern is approached. The midsection is formed with a straight, rising floor, an angular chine-bilge, and a straight,

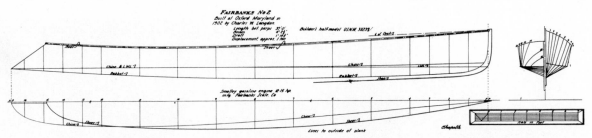

LINES OF A RACING V-BOTTOM MOTOR BOAT OF 1902, the *Fairbanks No. 2*. This model inspired the modern fishing launches of the Chesapeake Bay region. Taken off builder's half-model USNM 311239.

Given by Charles W. Langdon, boatbuilder, Oxford, Maryland.

CHESAPEAKE BAY FISHING LAUNCH, about 1912

BUILDER'S HALF-MODEL, USNM 315109

This model of a typical Chesapeake Bay Hooper Island fishing launch was employed to build a boat in Dorchester County, Maryland, at or near Cambridge about 1912, and represents the class built there between 1910 and 1925. Boats of this type were employed in the crab fishery in summer and in oyster tonging in winter. The half-model represents a fishing launch adaption of the racing launch form of the *Fairbanks No. 2*, the half-model of which (USNM 311239, p. 277) is in the Watercraft Collection. Well adapted to their work, these boats were seaworthy in the

strongly flaring topside. In the forebody the topside flare is very great, becoming hollow near the stem rabbet. Toward the stern the flare of the topsides gradually decreases and becomes tumble-home near where the stern begins to be rounded. A skeg and a shallow outside keel are fitted; the propeller and rudder are well inboard of the extreme stern; and the rudderpost, of iron, is fitted with a semibalanced wooden rudder blade. The dead rise carried to the extreme stern is an unusual feature shown in this model.

Heavily built of pine and oak, these launches have a long cockpit in which is located the engine in a box abaft midlength. The side decks are narrow and the cockpit has a low coaming its full length. Near the bow is a short forward deck and a small, low trunk cabin that usually contains two bunks and a stove;

at the extreme stern is a short deck, on which the iron tiller traverses; and steering is by steering lines or by a steering lever near the engine box. In recent years the cabin of these boats have commonly been fitted with a high hatch which serves also as a sheltered steering position, and a small steering wheel is sometimes fitted here. The fuel tank is usually under the after deck. Boats built since 1925 have more beam in proportion to length and have upright square transoms, called locally "box sterns."

This model of launch was originally developed for low power and used marine gasoline engines of 5 to 15 horsepower (most of these boats were intended for engines ranging from 7 to 10 horsepower), with which they are said to have achieved speeds of from 7 to 12 miles per hour under service conditions. Automobile engines are now employed; ratings up to 250 horsepower and speeds up to 30 miles per hour are claimed for some launches.

The model is to the inside of plank and its half-breadth is to the keel rabbet. The scale is ¾ inch to the foot; launches built to this half-model were

The half-model shows a V-bottom hull having the keel rabbet straight in the forebody but sweeping up aft to the bottom of the stern, there to be fitted with a skeg. The stern is round in plan and raking in profile and is intended to be formed by vertical staving on stern frames at chine and gunwale. The bow is straight and raking. The midsection shows a straight, rising floor carried to the angular chine and a straight, somewhat flaring topsides above the chine. The sheer is marked. In profile the chine curves slightly fore-and-aft and is low at the bow, so that it would not show there when boat was afloat.

Scale of the half-model is ½ inch to the foot, for a boat to measure 60 feet moulded length at gunwale, 18 feet moulded beam, and drawing about 4 feet at skeg.

Boats of this size and type had a pilothouse and engine trunk aft, with quarters there for the captain, a cargo hatch and hold forward of the engine room, and a forecastle in the bow. The boats usually carried one mast and a gaff-sail and jib to steady

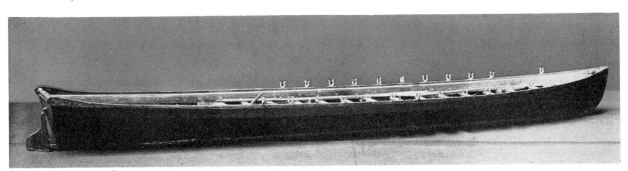

ROWING GALLEY USED FOR SHAD FISHING ON THE POTOMAC RIVER, 1880. Rigged model USNM 55877. (*Smithsonian photo 4058.*)

about 34 feet long stem rabbet to extreme stern at chine, 6 feet 4 inches extreme beam at deck, depth 3 feet 1 inch rabbet to gunwale, and draft about 2 feet 3 inches at heel of rudder post. A notation on the model indicates that the cabin was 8 feet long.

Given by James B. Richardson, boatbuilder, Cambridge, Maryland.

CHESAPEAKE BAY V-BOTTOM MOTOR VESSEL, 1929
BUILDER'S HALF-MODEL, USNM 311016

This half-model was made by John B. Harrison in 1929 for a V-bottom, motor vessel for use as a "buy boat" in transporting oysters and to haul shell as well as general freight. No boat was built from it.

the boat in heavy weather. The rudder post was inboard of the stern.

Given by John B. Harrison, shipbuilder, Tilghman's Island, Maryland.

POTOMAC RIVER SHAD DRAG-SEINE GALLEY, 1880
RIGGED MODEL, USNM 55877

This model represents a large rowing boat, or "galley," once employed in the Potomac River shad-fishery to work a drag seine. These boats carried about 1200 to 1500 fathoms of seine, made 30 feet deep at the channel, or hauling, end and 12 feet deep at the shore end. The mesh was 2½ to 3 inches. The boats rowed 2 oars single-banked and, depending

CROATAN FISHING BOAT used for shad fishing in the vicinity of Roanoke Island in the North Carolina Sounds, 1880's and 1890's. Rigged model USNM 76255. (*Smithsonian photo 45606–a.*)

on their length, 14 to 24 oars double-banked. Nets were carried in the stern and most boats had a net roller on top of the transom.

The model represents a very long, open, keel, rowing boat having a long, sharp entrance and a short, full run, with a very wide transom stern, the stem curved and raking, the post nearly upright, the sheer rather straight, and the keel straight, with some drag. The midsection had a slightly rising straight floor, an easy bilge, and a slightly flaring topside. To give longitudinal strength, the boat was braced along its centerline by a "hogrod" truss passed over some of the thwarts. The after quarter of the boat was without thwarts.

Scale of model is ½ inch to the foot, for a boat 72 feet long, 12 feet beam, and 3 feet 9 inches depth amidships.

Given by U. S. Bureau of Fisheries.

POTOMAC RIVER FISH LIGHTER, 1883
RIGGED MODEL, USNM 56950

During the latter part of the 19th-century fishermen on the lower Potomac River employed a special form of lighter, or barge, to transport fish to market. Aboard these craft, which were between 45 and 60 feet long, the daily catch was placed, and at a fixed time a number of them were picked up by a tug and towed to port. Most of them operated out of Washington and Alexandria.

The lighters represented by the model were of flatiron shape and had a flat bottom, usually rockered aft only in profile, with little flare to the straight sides and wide at the stern, a rather sharp bow, long entrance, short but easy run, rather raking stem, and the greatest beam just forward of the transom, which was rather upright.

They were steered with an outboard rudder having a tiller. Aft was a small cuddy for the crew and amidships a long hatch with covers. A strong towing bitt was placed forward. The boats were tarred instead of painted and were roughly built.

Scale of model is ⅜ inch to the foot; the boat represented was 52 feet overall, 14 feet 8 inches beam, and about 5 feet 4 inches depth. The lighers were towed quite fast, hence their unusual form.

Given by George Woltz.

ROANOKE RIVER DUGOUT CANOE, 1893
RIGGED MODEL, USNM 76275

Dugout canoes of this type were once used on the Roanoke River, in North Carolina, in the shad fishery employing dip-nets. The canoes were made by hollowing out a cypress log; they were rowed, paddled, and poled.

The type of canoe shown by the model was double-ended, having a nearly flat bottom and slightly flaring topside. It was roughly decked with plank for a short distance at each end and fitted with three seats, or thwarts. Amidships it had a deck, under which was a shallow live well, or box, in which the bottom of the canoe was perforated to allow circulation of water. Some of these canoes had a stern seat and were employed by sportsmen in fishing on the river.

Scale of model is 1 inch to the foot, for a canoe 18 feet 3 inches long, 3 feet beam, and 14 inches depth, with a well 1 foot 9 inches square on the bottom, and its hatch 6 by 9 inches.

Given by U. S. Bureau of Fisheries.

ALBERMARLE SOUND SHAD BOATS BEING BUILT AT ROANOKE ISLAND, NORTH CAROLINA, at the yard of the noted local builder, Washington Creef, in the 1890's. These boats, fitted with planked stern deadwoods, are large for their class. A good example of the simple boat shops in which these small fishing boats were built. (*Smithsonian photo 44793-f.*)

CROATAN FISHING BOAT, 1890
RIGGED MODEL, USNM 76255

Boats of this type were once employed in the shad fishery on the North Carolina Sounds in the vicinity of Roanoke Island. They were noted for sailing qualities and seaworthiness. Hulls of some of these boats, with gasoline engines installed, were to be seen at Roanoke Island in 1953.

The model is of an open, caravel-planked, centerboard boat, like a yawl boat in form and having strong sheer, a straight plank keel with some drag, a straight raking stem, a raking heart-shaped transom with rudder hung outboard, the greatest beam a little forward of midlength, a sharp entrance, and a long and fine run. There is some reverse curve in the afterbody sections, and the midsection is formed with a rising straight floor, easy bilge, and flaring topside.

Model shows narrow washboards and low coamings along the sides, a very short stern deck, six thwarts,

281

and sternsheets. The centerboard is slightly forward of midlength. The model does not have the usual skeg, the run being formed with a planked deadwood not commonly found in this type. The mast is stepped in the third thwart, at the fore end of the centerboard case, and rigged with a loose-footed sprit-mainsail; the jib is tacked to the stemhead; there is a pole topmast, with much of it overlapping the mainmast, and a jib-headed boom topsail is sheeted independently of the mainsail.

Scale of the model is 1 inch to the foot, for a boat 24 feet long, 7 feet 3 inches beam, and about 2 feet 3 inches depth, mainmast 14 feet 6 inches above thwart, sprit 20 feet 6 inches long, and topmast 21 feet 9 inches total length and standing 13 feet 11 inches above masthead. The boat is fitted to row two oars to a side; six sandbags are shown as ballast. Made and given by U.S. Fish Commission, 1893.

Restored by Merritt Edson, Jr., 1958.

SHARPIE, about 1890
RIGGED MODEL, USNM 76249

The sharpie, a flat-bottom sailing boat with the bottom planked athwartships, was employed widely in the American coastal fisheries during the last half of the 19th century. The boat type, developed sometime before 1849, first rose to prominence at New Haven, Connecticut, and by 1876 the "New Haven sharpie" had become a standardized model and rig built in two basic sizes. One, between 24 and 28 feet overall, carried about 75 to 100 bushels of oysters, and was rigged with one or two masts and leg-of-mutton sails; the other, between 34 and 36 feet, carried 150 to 175 bushels. The New Haven sharpie was low sided and rather narrow; the beam on the bottom was one-sixth to one-fifth the length; the beam of a 35-foot boat was about 6 feet at chines, 7 feet 2 inches at rail; that of a 28-foot boat was 4 feet 6 inches to 4 feet 9 inches at chine and about 6 feet beam at rail. The stem was straight and upright, the stern was either round (with a vertically staved fantail) or finished in a flat and much raked transom. The sheer was strong and the rocker of the bottom was such that the heel of the stem was brought just clear of the water. The bottom was flat athwartships and the sides straight and quite flaring. A large centerboard was fitted; its length was almost one-third that of the boat, and the sharpies were half-decked, with a large oval cockpit. The masts could be shifted so that the boat could be sailed with various combinations of sail. The rig was simple and efficient; the sails were loose-footed and spread by a sprit boom whose heel was set up by a mast tackle to give flat sails on the wind.

From this parent type many variations of sharpie were developed as the type was introduced into new localities. In general, the variations were in the direction of increased size, particularly in beam, to give greater capacity for a given length. The sharpie was introduced on Lake Champlain and on the Great Lakes, on the North Carolina Sounds, and, by 1885, on the Florida coast. It was also adapted to yachting in the years between 1857 and 1885.

The model represents a small sharpie of the type developed first on the North Carolina sounds. This was a close copy of the New Haven type except for a marked increase in the beam. The first New Haven sharpie was brought to the Carolina Sounds in 1875 and was a 34-foot boat. Soon the sharpie was being built there in lengths up to 45 feet and by 1890 the rig had become that of a gaff-schooner. In Florida the type was first a yacht, but commercial sharpies were soon being built with some modifications in rig, and as schooners up to about 60 feet of length. Generally speaking, the sharpies had the reputation of being inexpensive and swift, as well as of carrying heavy loads on light draft. This model is of an oyster sharpie of Newbern, North Carolina, built about 1889.

The model shows a flat-bottom, skiff-like hull having a large centerboard, two masts and two leg-

SHARPIE SCHOONER 28–32 feet long, a type once popular in the Middle and South Atlantic Coast fisheries. Drawing by Kunhardt, from *Forest and Stream*, 1885.

282

of-mutton sails with sprit booms, a long and sharp bow with heel raised to clear the water, a straight and upright stem, a bottom rockered fore-and-aft, a flat and raking transom, strong sheer, and flaring sides. The deck arrangement is for a half-decked boat having a large oval cockpit, a long foredeck, and a short afterdeck. The foremast is stepped in the eyes of the boat, the main at the after end of the centerboard case.

The model is on a scale of 1 inch to the foot, and is for a sharpie 35 feet on the gunwale, 10 feet 9 inches beam, 2 feet 2 inches depth, cockpit 15 feet 9 inches long, and 7 feet 9 inches wide, foremast 33 feet 6 inches above deck, mainmast 29 feet 9 inches above its thwart, fore sprit 20 feet, main sprit 14 feet 6 inches. Rail chocks are fitted at bow and stern. The model shows an unusually wide hull; 8 feet 10 inches beam would probably be the normal width of a boat of this length and date on the Carolina sounds.

Given by U. S. Bureau of Fisheries.

NORTH CAROLINA FISHING LAUNCH, 1929
BUILDER's HALF-MODEL, USNM 311244

Seabird

The gasoline-engined fishing launch *Seabird* was built from this half-model at Beaufort, North Carolina, in 1929 by Whitehurst & Rice.

The *Seabird* had a raised deck forward, under which there was a cuddy. She was caravel-planked and had a skeg, the keel rabbet cambering fore-and-aft (more sharply aft). She had a straight shoe to the keel and skeg, a raking square stern, a curved and rather upright stem rabbet. The sheer was rather straight. The midsection showed a rising floor, rather slack round bilge, and nearly plumb topside. The entrance was long and sharp, the run short and rather full.

Model is believed to be on a scale of ¾ inch to the foot, to produce a launch about 28 feet 8 inches moulded length at gunwale, 9 feet 4 inches moulded beam, and drawing about 2 feet 9 inches. The engine was in box in cockpit well aft.

Given by John Rice, shipbuilder, Beaufort, North Carolina.

MENHADEN STRIKER BOAT, about 1932
BUILDER's HALF-MODEL, USNM 311245

A rowing striker boat was built from this half-model about 1932 by Whitehurst & Rice at Beaufort, North Carolina.

The boat was a rowing dinghy in model, having a square upright transom with a slight deadrise in the bottom, rather straight upright stem rabbet, straight keel shoe with skeg, the keel rabbet rising aft, and moderate sheer. The midsection shows a rather rounded, rising floor, a slack bilge, and nearly upright topsides. Both in model and arrangement it generally resembles a yacht tender.

Scale of the model is 1 inch to the foot, for a boat 13 feet 6 inches long, 4 feet moulded beam, and about 1 foot 4 inches deep.

Given by John Rice, shipbuilder, Beaufort, North Carolina.

MENHADEN FISHING BOAT, 1934
BUILDER's HALF-MODEL, USNM 311243

A menhaden fishing boat was built from this model at Beaufort, North Carolina, in 1934 by Whitehurst & Rice.

The half-model is for a V-bottom launch, or "Hatteras boat," having a moderate rise of floor amidships, angular chine, and flaring straight topside. The stem rabbet is straight and rather upright, the stern is round, flaring and formed by vertical staving. In profile, the chine has little camber and is low forward, the foremost section just abaft the stem being almost a V-shape from gunwale to rabbet; afloat, it is not visible forward. The sheer is moderate; keel rabbet is straight forward and rises aft to the bottom of the stern; keel-shoe is straight, with some drag, and has a skeg; rudder post is inboard of the stern; forward sections have a hollow flare; entrance is sharp and has the appearance of being slightly hollow near the stem at waterline; and the run is short but easy. These boats have a reputation for seaworthiness.

Scale of model is ½ inch to the foot, for a boat 50 feet 6 inches moulded length at gunwale, 10 feet 4 inches moulded beam, and drawing about 4 feet at the skeg.

Given by John Rice, shipbuilder, Beaufort, North Carolina.

KEY WEST SPONGE SLOOP, 1880
RIGGED MODEL, USNM 76251

The sloop represented by this model was built at Key West, Florida, in 1880 for the sponge fishery on the Florida reefs and among the Keys, in shoal water. She was caravel-planked and had a skeg and straight keel with some drag, upright post, raking V-transom, upright straight stem, strong sheer, long and sharp

entrance, and a long, easy run. The midsection had a rising floor, high and rather easy bilge, and slightly flaring topside.

Scale of the model is 1 inch to the foot; the boat was 24 feet 3 inches at gunwale, 10 feet 3 inches beam, and 2 feet 6 inches moulded depth. It has a jib and mainsail rig, and the spar dimensions, which are also recorded as those of the *Terror*, are mainmast 27 feet 6 inches above deck, topmast heel to truck 11 feet 9 inches, bowsprit outside stem 12 feet, main boom 26 feet 6 inches, and main gaff 12 feet 9 inches.

The model, which shows an elliptical cockpit and trunk, appears to have been built with some reference to the half-model of the *Terror* (USNM 76083), but it does not have the cuddy and there are other departures. About 1890 sharpie sloops 24–28 feet in length became popular as small spongers at Key West. Resembling in hull and rig the small half-decked sloop yachts of 1870–80, they represent but one of the many types of small sloops employed in the Florida sponge fishery.

Given by U. S. Bureau of Fisheries.

KEY WEST SPONGE SLOOP, 1881
BUILDER'S HALF-MODEL, USNM 76083

Terror

The small centerboard sloop *Terror* was built from this model at Key West, Florida, in 1881, for the sponge fishery on the Florida reef and among the Keys, where shoal draft was desirable. She was similar, in hull, rig, and arrangement of deck to many of the small sloop yachts of 1870–80, which apparently inspired this design. The craft employed in the Key West sponge fishery were not homogeneous in type. Some were old yachts, some were centerboard schooners of small size, some were sharpie sloops, some were centerboard sloops similar to *Terror*, while others were small keel sloops of the same model and rig as the Key West smackee and Bahama sloops.

The *Terror* was a shoal centerboard sloop having a nearly plumb stem, raking and V-shaped flat transom, a long and sharp entrance, and a rather short run. The hull had a skeg and the after sections were slightly hollow at the garboard. The midsection showed a rising floor and an easy bilge. The rudder post was inboard, entering the hull at the heel of the transom.

284

KEY WEST SPONGE SLOOPS and
smackees, about 1892. (*Smithsonian
photo 44791–h.*)

⟶

KEY WEST SPONGE SLOOP. Rigged
model USNM 76251. (*Smithsonian
photo 45605–g.*)

The model shows an elliptical house and cockpit
coaming. Rig was a gaff mainsail and a single jib
hanked to a stay. The sloop had a long main boom
and bowsprit, the latter well hogged down, and a
large sail area, as spongers did not work in heavy
weather, and speed rather than seaworthiness was
much prized.

Scale of the model is ¾ inch to the foot, giving a vessel about 24 feet 3 inches on deck, 10 feet moulded
beam, 2 feet 8 inches moulded depth, and drawing
about 2 feet with centerboard raised, the latter being
about 7 feet long and 3 feet 6 inches wide, and located
in the middle third of the length.

Given by Lawrence Higgs, Key West, Florida.

KEY WEST SMACKEE, 1883
BUILDER'S HALF-MODEL, USNM 76086

Jeff Brown

The leg-of-mutton sloop *Jeff Brown* was built from
this model at Key West, Florida, in 1883. She was
a small-well smack. Sloops of this size and type,
locally known as "smackees," ranged in length from
17 to 26 feet length and were shoal, keel craft with
skegs, most with the rudder hung outboard. Some

had straight stems, others had small gammon-knee
heads and, in general, they resembled the small
fishing and sponging sloops of the Bahamas. Most
had a flat transom with post and rudder outboard
and some had clipper bows or stems rounded in
profile

The *Jeff Brown* is also represented by a rigged model
(USNM 76258) in the Watercraft Collection.

The half-model, for a fast and seaworthy small
boat, shows a shoal, keel-sloop hull having a handsome sheer, raking curved stem, sharply raking V-
or heart-shaped flat transom, with rudder stock passing through its heel, nearly vertical post, straight keel
with drag, sharp entrance, and a very long easy run.
The midsection shows a sharply rising and slightly
hollow floor; the hollow is carried right aft to the
transom but disappears forward; an almost constant
deadrise is shown in the after sections. Forward the
flare is moderate. The keel outside the rabbet is
quite deep.

Scale of the model is 1 inch to the foot, to scale
about giving a vessel 25 feet 3¼ inches overall, 24
feet 3 inches on deck, 8 feet 5½ inches moulded
beam and 2 feet 10½ inches moulded depth. The
draft at post would be about 3 feet and about 2 feet

285

2 inches forward. The well amidships was about 5 feet 6 inches square at bottom and 3 feet 6 inches at underside of deck. Most of the boats contemporary with the *Jeff Brown* were somewhat smaller than she was, but by 1895 the smackees were generally of her size.

Given by the U. S. Fish Commission.

KEY WEST SMACKEE, 1883
RIGGED MODEL, USNM 76258

Jeff Brown

The leg-of-mutton sloop *Jeff Brown* that was built at Key West, Florida, in 1883 from half-model USNM 76086 was fitted as shown in this rigged model. Most of these small smacks carried a variation of the leg-of-mutton Bermuda or Bahama rig, a jib-headed mainsail and large single jib. The model, however, shows the mainsail laced to the boom, which was not done in either of these rigs. Some had a small cabin trunk that could be fitted over one of the hatches when it was desirable to shelter the crew.

The model shows a small sloop-rigged boat having a straight keel and skeg, straight raking stem, rather upright post and V-shaped transom with rudder stock passing through its heel, sharp entrance, good run, and a midsection with rising floor slightly hollow at the garboard, firm bilge, and flaring topside.

The deck arrangement shown includes a U-shaped standing well for the helmsman, a well hatch amidships, and a small hatch to a cuddy forward.

Scale of the model is 1 inch to the foot; the boat was 25 feet 3¼ inches overall, 24 feet 3 inches at gunwale, 8 feet 3½ inches beam, about 2 feet 10 inches depth; the mast stood 28 feet 9 inches above deck, the bowsprit extended 6 feet outside the stem, and the boom was 23 feet long.

Given by U. S. Bureau of Fisheries.

BAHAMA SCHOONER SMACK, 1883
RIGGED MODEL, USNM 76010

This model represents the type of schooner smack used in the Bahama Islands; many schooners of this type worked out of Great Abaco and nearby islands, supplying fish to Nassau. In general they resembled the old pungy schooners of the Chesapeake Bay, some had overhanging sterns but many had heart-shaped raking transoms with outboard rudders and sternposts. The schooners had a reputation for speed

and weatherliness. Sloops were built on the same general model but with greater proportionate beam.

The model shows a caravel-planked, keel schooner having a straight keel with much drag, a curved and raking stem rabbet with longhead, a light square stern, moderate sheer, a long and sharp entrance, a long easy run, and the midsection formed with a sharply rising straight floor, an easy round bilge, and an upright topside. These schooners were flush decked, with low bulwarks or a log rail; they usually had aft a trunk cabin, amidships a large well entered through a hatch with grating, and just abaft the foremast a slide companionway to enter the forepeak.

This model shows a schooner having a single large jib, a loose-footed foresail, boomed loose-footed mainsail; the main topmast is fitted but the main gaff-topsail and main-topmast staysail are omitted. Model is equipped with two square-stern dinghies.

These schooners were usually metal sheathed with Muntz metal or "yellow metal" and the inside of the wells was sometimes sheathen with sheet-lead, as yellow metal was thought to poison the fish in the well. The lead also had the advantage of being easily worked around frames, keel, and in the perforations of the bottom. The marine boring worm toredo caused damage to these smacks in Bahamian waters.

Scale of the model is ½ inch to the foot, for a schooner 54 feet at rail, 14 feet 3 inches beam, 5 feet depth (the keel outside rabbet scales 21 inches deep), trunk cabin 12 feet long and 7 feet wide, bowsprit outboard of rabbet 10 feet, foremast above deck 44 feet, mainmast 44 feet, main topmast 15 feet total length, fore gaff 12 feet, main boom 30 feet, and main gaff 13 feet. In latter years these schooners often had a boomed foresail and in the late 1880's schooners resembling the Key West smacks were built in the Bahamas.

Given by Commissioners for the Bahama Islands, International Fisheries Exposition, London, 1883.

BAHAMA SPONGE-FISHING SCHOONER, 1883
RIGGED MODEL, USNM 160143

This model represents a class of Bahama schooner formerly used in the sponge fishery and in the sea-turtle fishery. The schooners were clipper built and resembled the old Baltimore clipper type, from which they are supposed to have descended.

The model shows a sharp schooner having a straight keel with much drag, strongly curved and raking stem rabbet with a longhead, raking post and heart-

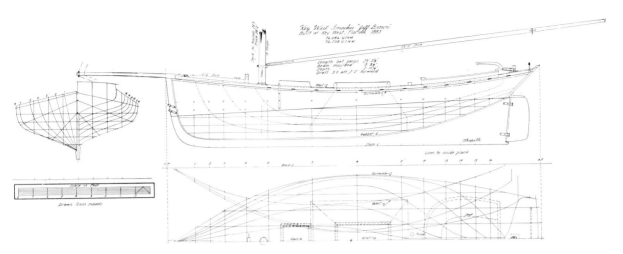

PLAN OF THE KEY WEST SMACKEE *Jeff Brown* built at Key West, Florida, 1883. Taken off the builder's half-model USNM 76086. Deck arrangement and spar dimensions from the rigged model USNM 76258.

shaped transom of marked width, sharp convex entrance, long sharp run, medium sheer, low bulwarks, and flush deck. The midsection shows a sharply rising straight floor, high easy bilge, and flaring topside. The flare forward is moderate. A large trunk cabin is placed well aft; the model shows two sponging dinghies stowed bottom up on deck. The model is schooner rigged with three lower sails; the foresail is boomless. These boats usually had a large deck box in which there was a charcoal brazier or fireplace to serve as the galley. When sponge-fishing, the schooner usually worked two dinghies only; when in the turtle fishery, only one boat was usually carried.

Scale of model is ½ inch to the foot; the schooner was 54 feet at rail, 14 feet 6 inches beam, 5 feet depth, bowsprit outside rabbet 10 feet 6 inches, foremast 43 feet 6 inches, mainmast 44 feet above deck, main topmast heel to truck 14 feet, fore gaff 12 feet, main boom 30 feet, main gaff 13 feet 6 inches, dinghies 13 feet long and 4 feet 6 inches beam, and sponge hooks shown 17 and 25 feet long.

Given by commissioners for the Bahama Islands, International Fisheries Exposition, London, 1883.

FLORIDA CAT-RIGGED SHARPIE OYSTER BOAT, about 1880
RIGGED MODEL, USNM 76272

This model represents a sharpie, or "flattie," cat-rigged boat built about 1880 for the local oyster fishery at Cedar Keys, Florida. The sharpies built at Cedar Keys were of a wide range in size; from about 18 feet to nearly 40 feet at gunwale; the smaller boats

were 1-masted and cat or sloop rigged; the larger sharpies were 2-masted sharpie rig or leg-of-mutton schooners. Generally, the sharpies built on the west coast of Florida were less well finished than those built elsewhere.

The model shows a wide, sharpie hull having strong sheer, the greatest beam unusually far forward, the bottom cambered fore and aft, straight stem with a slight tumble-home, slightly raking transom, skeg fitted aft and rudder hung outboard, and moderate flare to sides. There is a deck forward and wide washboards with coamings along the sides, one thwart amidships, and a large centerboard amidships. The boat is fitted to row. Although the sloop rig, usually with a jib and gaff-mainsail, was most common in these boats in the 1890's, it is rigged catboat fashion with single boomed gaff-sail. The model represents an unusually ugly boat of the type.

Scale of model is 1 inch to the foot, producing a sharpie 20 feet on the gunwales, 11 feet beam, 21 inches depth, mast 17 feet 4 inches above the gunwales, boom 19 feet 6 inches, gaff 10 feet, and oars 12 feet 3 inches.

Given by U. S. Bureau of Fisheries.

FLORIDA SLOOP-RIGGED FISHING SHARPIE, 1880
RIGGED MODEL, USNM 76273

This model is of one of a class of sharpies once common in the Florida Gulf Coast fisheries in the vicinity of St. Andrews and Panama City. These boats ranged in length from about 16 to 22 feet on the gunwale and were either open or half decked. They were unusual in having a fore-gripe, or bow skeg, as well as a skeg aft. As a result they were very steady on the helm. When a fisherman was taking up his gear he often had to attend this rather than the helm, so the fore-gripe proved useful in these boats.

The model shows an open skiff-like sharpie having a flat bottom and straight, flaring sides, the flare very great at stern, strong camber fore-and-aft with moderate round forward and more aft, strong sheer, large centerboard, a nearly vertical straight stem, a raking transom of marked width, the rudder hung outboard, a bow (or breast) thwart, a wide mast thwart, one thwart aft of the centerboard case, and stern sheets. There is a skeg at stern, and a smaller skeg, or fore-gripe, at stem; the bow is long and sharp with a short but rising and flat run. These boats were characterized by the marked twist in their side planks; the flare of the sides gradually increasing as the stern was approached.

The rig consists of a loose-footed sprit-mainsail and jib, the latter tacked to the stemhead. The model is fitted to row; a pair of oars and a steering sweep are stowed.

Scale of model is 1 inch to the foot, producing a boat 20 feet 9 inches on the gunwale, 5 feet 7 inches beam, 22½ inches depth, mast 14 feet 8 inches above gunwales, sprit 18 feet 6 inches, and oars 12 feet 2 inches.

Given by U. S. Bureau of Fisheries.

CEDAR KEYS SEINE SKIFF, about 1890
RIGGED MODEL, USNM 76270

This model is of a wide, shoal, sharpie skiff of the "flat iron" model that was once employed in the alongshore seine fishery at Cedar Keys, Florida. These boats were commonly fitted to row only, two oars to a side, using double thole pins at each oar.

As illustrated by the model, the skiff had its greatest beam well aft, abaft the second thwart from the stem, and carried the seine at the stern, on a net deck a few inches below the gunwale. The stem was straight and nearly upright; the sides flared, the amount increasing from bow to stern. The sheer was slight and the rocker of the bottom moderate, coming from the heel of the stem in a straight line for about a fourth the bottom length and then curving very gently amidships to well aft, where the short run was formed. The entrance was rather sharp, considering the great beam. The boat was arranged with a foredeck at thwart height, two rowing thwarts, and a net deck about 4 feet long about 3 inches below the gunwale. The bottom was cross-planked and there was a very shallow skeg, or fore-gripe, at the stem and a small skeg at the stern. The transom was wide and set at a moderate rake. Floor boards were fitted inside to protect the bottom.

Scale of the model is 1 inch to the foot, for a skiff 20 feet 7 inches long overall, 8 feet 3 inches beam, about 18 inches deep, stern 6 feet 4 inches wide at gunwale with a vertical depth of about 13 inches, foredeck reaching aft 4 feet 6 inches from face of stem, and net deck carried forward 4 feet 3 inches from top of transom. Oars shown lashed to thwarts, 12 feet long.

Given by U. S. Fish Commission.

FLORIDA GILL-NET ROWING SKIFF, 1893
RIGGED MODEL, USNM 76271

This type of rowing skiff was once used at Cedar Keys, Florida, for gill-net mullet fishing. These boats were burdensome and did not have to be rowed long distances or maneuvered quickly.

This model shows a large, open, flat-bottomed sharpie rowing skiff having strong sheer; a short,

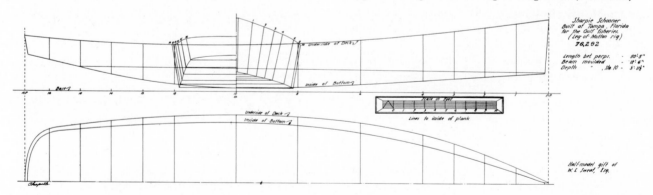

LINES OF A FLORIDA SHARPIE SCHOONER, BUILT AT TAMPA, FLORIDA, about 1891–92. Taken off builder's half-model USNM 76292.

straight, and upright stem; sharp entrance and short run; straight sides with moderate flare; a wide stern with a flat and raking transom; and the bottom much cambered fore-and-aft and fitted with bow and stern skegs, the former large. On the stern is mounted a platform for the nets. Fitted with two thwarts and tholes.

Scale of the model is 1 inch to the foot, for a boat 20 feet 6 inches at gunwale, 7 feet 9 inches beam, and 19½ inches deep amidships.

Given by U. S. Bureau of Fisheries.

FLORIDA SHARPIE SCHOONER, 1892
BUILDER'S HALF-MODEL, USNM 76292

A large schooner-rigged sharpie was built from this half-model at Tampa, Florida, in 1891–92. This vessel was to be employed in the Gulf fisheries of that port, serving as a "run boat" to carry the catch from the "fishing ranches" to the Tampa market. Similar schooners were employed on the Florida east coast, in the Spanish mackerel fishery. The type was swift and could carry heavy loads on a light draft. The bottom was planked athwartships, and many of these sharpie schooners had clipper bows and round sterns or had flat, raking transoms. They were usually lofty in rig; some had gaff-sails and others had leg-of-mutton sails. Sharpies having no headsail and only two leg-of-mutton sails, with hulls up to 45 feet length, were also employed at Tampa in the fisheries; these usually had round sterns and straight, upright stems.

The half-model is of a schooner-rigged sharpie, having marked sheer and a long, sharp forebody with the greatest beam well aft of amidships. The run is

short but easy and somewhat full near the stern. The bottom is cambered heavily fore-and-aft, the camber being greatest toward the stern, which is round and slightly flaring. The stem rabbet is straight and slightly raking. The midsection has flat floor carried straight across, an angular bilge, and a straight and slightly flaring topside. Scale of the model is ½ inch to the foot, for a vessel about 50 feet 5 inches on gunwale, 12 feet 6 inches moulded beam, and 3 feet 11½ inches moulded depth.

Somewhat similar schooners were built for the oyster fishery on the North Carolina Sounds in the period 1890 to 1910. These schooners usually had a short trunk cabin aft and a large hatch between the masts.

Given by W. S. Sweat, Tampa, Florida, 1892.

FLORIDA SPONGE SLOOP, about 1906
BUILDER'S HALF-MODEL, USNM 311525

Emily

The centerboard sponge sloop *Emily* was built from this half-model at Tarpon Springs, Florida, for the Florida sponge fishery.

The model represents a centerboard sloop having some dead flat amidships and rather straight sheer; the keel is straight and its rabbet curves up aft to the V-shaped raking transom, where a skeg is fitted; the stem rabbet is nearly upright; and the entrance is sharp but short and the run short and full. The midsection shows a rising floor, hard bilge, and vertical topsides.

Scale of the half-model is ¾ inch to the foot, producing a sloop 26 feet 8 inches moulded length at

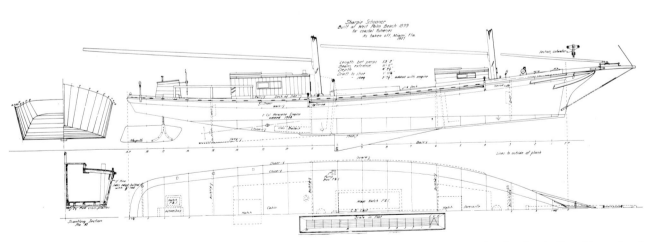

PLAN OF A SHARPIE FISHING SCHOONER BUILT AT WEST PALM BEACH, FLORIDA, in 1899 for the Spanish mackerel fishery along the Florida reef. As taken off the vessel by the author.

289

deck, 8 feet moulded beam, and about 3 feet moulded depth.

Given by E. P. Macrenaris, Tarpon Springs, Florida.

V-BOTTOM FISHING SCHOONER, about 1908
BUILDER'S HALF-MODEL, USNM 311265

This model of a fishing and freighting schooner was built by Samuel Johnson, at Apalachicola, Florida, about 1908, the half-model represents a V-bottom hull having a keel rabbet that is straight forward and rises aft to the bottom of the transom, so as to be fitted with a skeg and centerboard. The transom rakes and is flat athwartships; the stem rabbet is rather straight and upright; the entrance is short but sharp and the run short but rather straight in the buttocks. The midsection shows a gently rising straight floor carried out to the chine, which is rounded off slightly; the topside flares out a little and is straight. The sheer is marked. The model somewhat resembles that of the Chesapeake Bay V-bottom hulls.

Scale of the model is ¾ inch to the foot, for a vessel measuring 46 feet 6 inches length on deck, 13 feet 6 inches moulded beam, and about 4 feet moulded depth.

Given by Samuel Johnson, shipbuilder, Apalachicola, Florida.

FLORIDA FISHING BOAT, 1912
BUILDER'S HALF-MODEL, USNM 311261

This model is of a fishing craft stated by the donor to have been built at Apalachicola, Florida, about 1912, and fitted with sail. However, judging by its form, this model is of a launch and not of a sailing hull.

The half-model has a sharp, short entrance with the greatest beam well forward of midlength; a long, flat run; a straight keel with skeg aft, the keel rabbet rising aft to the bottom of the flat and raking transom but straight forward; a nearly straight and upright stem rabbet; and a rather straight sheer. The midsection is formed with a moderately rising floor, a hard turn of bilge, and a nearly upright topsides.

Scale of the model is 1 inch to the foot, for a boat measuring 31 feet 10½ inches moulded length at rail, 10 feet 3 inches moulded beam, and about 3 feet moulded depth.

Given by Samuel Johnson, shipbuilder, Apalachcola, Florida.

FLORIDA SPONGE BOAT, 1931
RIGGED MODEL, USNM 311882

Century of Progress

This model represents a modern "Greek sponge boat," the *Century of Progress*. Built in 1931, she was rigged as a yawl and auxiliary-powered with a gasoline engine, and was employed on the west coast of Florida in the vicinity of Tarpon Springs.

The half-model shows a caravel-planked keel sailing hull having a rather short, straight keel with some drag, a raking and strongly curved stem with the head carried high above deck, a raking sternpost; and a deep, heavy flat transom with rudder hung outboard and its blade partly cut away for the propeller aperture.

The entrance is short and convex, the run short and full; the sheer is great; and the midsection is formed with a rising floor, very slack bilge, and flaring topside.

She is rigged with a short mainmast having a gaff sail with loose foot and boom; the headstays come down to the stemhead and are capable of carrying a jib, though none is shown. The short jigger mast is stepped on the transom rail; its sail is a loose-footed leg-of-mutton sheeted to a swinging boom or outrigger, with the heel fixed on the transom.

The deck arrangement shows at the bow a short raised deck with a cathead to port and at the break of this deck a timberhead carried high above the rail to starboard. Also to starboard and abaft the timberhead is a ladder for a diver, and abaft this and on the centerline is a high mooring bitt. Next abaft is the mainmast, followed by a diver's pump in a deck box, a low trunk cabin, a short deck space, a small after trunk cabin, small hatch, tiller, and transom with the jigger stepped on it.

The model is painted white topsides, with a red copper bottom, and red and yellow moulding at and above the plank-sheer.

Scale of the model is ⅜ inch to the foot, for a boat 43 feet 5 inches long at rail, 14 feet 10 inches beam, and drawing 5 feet 3 inches at post.

Made and given by Ray F. Henry.

FLORIDA SPONGE BOAT, about 1935
BUILDER'S HALF-MODEL, USNM 311524

A yawl-rigged auxiliary-powered sponge-fishing boat was built from this half-model on the west coast of Florida near Tarpon Springs about 1935. This class of sponge boat is represented by a rigged model in the Watercraft Collection.

GREEK SPONGE BOAT from Tarpon Springs, Florida, showing typical hull at the time, about 1920, when the type was being "modernized." (*Smithsonian photo 33424.*)

The half-model represents a caravel-planked keel hull having a straight keel with some drag, a strongly curved stem rabbet and stem, a raking sternpost, flat transom with rudder hung outboard, an almost straight sheer, and the midsection formed with a straight rising floor, very slack bilge, and flaring topside. The entrance and run are unusually full and short.

The scale of the half-model is ¾ inch to the foot, for a boat measuring 37 feet moulded length at rail, 13 feet 7 inches moulded beam, and about 6 feet 6 inches moulded depth.

Given by A. Kaminis, Tarpon Springs, Florida.

FLORIDA SPONGE BOAT, 1943
BUILDER'S HALF-MODEL, USNM 312756

A yawl-rigged auxiliary-powered sponge boat was built from this half-model on the west coast of Florida at Tarpon Springs in 1943 by Leo Paskalitis. These boats were used by sponge divers of Greek descent, using diving hoods. A boat of this type is represented by a rigged model in the Watercraft Collection.

Scale of the model is ¾ inch to the foot, and represents a boat about 37 feet 9 inches moulded length, 14 feet 3 inches moulded beam, and about 6 feet 6 inches moulded depth.

The half-model is for a keel, sailing hull having a straight keel with some drag, raking post, flat and rather deep transom with rudder hung outboard, curved and raking stem rabbet, moderate sheer, short and full entrance, short but clean run, and a midsection formed with slightly rising straight floor, slack well-rounded bilge, and slightly flaring topside.

These boats were very seaworthy but not fast under sail or power. They replaced an older form of rowing and sailing double-ended boat having a single large square-headed spritsail; much sheer; a high stem and sternpost, both curved; short straight keel; and steeply rising floor and very slack bilge, with flaring topsides. They are similar in almost all particulars, to the "Sacoleve," of the Greek Archipelago.

Given by Philip A. Sawyer, St. Augustine, Florida, 1943.

MENHADEN PURSE-SEINE BOAT, 1921
BUILDER'S HALF-MODEL, USNM 311250

Purse seineboats were built from this half-model for the menhaden fishery at Millville, Florida, in 1921. The half-model represents an open, double-ended caravel-planked boat having curved and rather upright stem and stern rabbets fairing into a straight keel rabbet, moderate sheer, rather sharp and convex ends, and a midsection formed with a slightly rising straight floor, hard round bilge, and slightly flaring topside.

Scale of half-model is 1 inch to the foot, for a boat measuring 31 feet moulded length at gunwale, 8 feet moulded beam, and about 2 feet 8 inches moulded depth. These boats resembled the Gloucester seine boats in both form and arrangement, but are slightly more burdensome than those used in the mackerel fishery in New England.

Given by Alexander Ceruti, Millville, Florida.

FLORIDA SHRIMP BOAT, 1933
BUILDER'S HALF-MODEL, USNM 312757

A shrimping boat was built from this model in 1933 at Tarpon Springs, on the west coast of Florida, and 40 or 50 boats are said to have been built on it before 1943. Powered with automobile engines, and good carriers for their length, these boats usually have a small trunk cabin forward.

The half-model represents a launch-type fishing boat having a long, sharp entrance and a short full run, rather straight sheer, an upright and somewhat curved stem rabbet, a flat and slightly raking transom, and a midsection showing a rising straight floor, slack bilge, and rather upright topside.

Scale of the model is 1 inch to the foot. The boat was 34 feet 3 inches moulded length at gunwale, and 10 feet beam.

Given by Philip A. Sawyer, St. Augustine, Florida.

NEW ORLEANS LUGGER, about 1890
BUILDER'S HALF-MODEL, USNM 311218

A lugger was built from this half-model, about 1890, by Henry Frentz at Biloxi, Mississippi, to engage in the shrimp and other shore fisheries. This type of centerboard, shoal-draft boat, rigged with one mast and a large dipping lug sail, was popularly known as the "New Orleans lugger." This type is also represented by a rigged model (USNM 76267) in the Watercraft Collection. The boats had a great local reputation for speed and seaworthiness, and could sail very close to the wind.

The half-model shows a shoal, centerboard hull having a straight keel with slight drag, bold, sweeping sheer, upright and slightly curved stem, and a slightly raking post and transom, with rudder hung outboard. The stern is broad and the beam is carried well forward, so the bow at deck is rather round and full; the greatest beam at rail is forward of midlength.

The entrance is short, slightly hollow, and sharp. The run is rather long and easy. The plank keel was wide at the centerboard slot and tapered to bow and stern. The midsection shows slightly rising floors carried out straight and an easy bilge, coming plumb in the topsides. The bow sections are convex and without hollow; the run is hollow just forward of the post; and the transom is heart-shaped. The vessel is caravel planked.

Scale of the model is ¾ inch to the foot, for a vessel about 33 feet 3 inches on deck, 11 feet 4 inches moulded beam, 3 feet 2 inches moulded depth, and drawing about 2 feet 3 inches at post.

Given by George Frentz, Biloxi, Mississippi, 1936.

NEW ORLEANS LUGGER, about 1893
RIGGED MODEL, USNM 76267

This model represents the type of lug-rigged fishing boat, having a centerboard hull; once employed at and near New Orleans and commonly called the "New Orleans lugger"; it is the only known type of American fishing boat that had a dipping lug sail in the 19th century. A half-model (USNM 311218) of one of these luggers, in the Watercraft Collection, is for a smaller boat than this one. These boats were very weatherly and swift. The range of length was 18 to 45 feet long.

The rigged model is of a caravel-planked centerboard hull, partially decked and having a large oval-shaped cockpit with a cuddy under a flush deck forward, entered through a slide companionway. The cockpit is partly covered with hatch covers and partitioned with pen boards. The entrance is rather full, with the sides at deck level rather straight fore-and-aft, in plan. The run is long and easy; the keel, a wide plank, is straight with some drag; the stern is nearly upright and is finished with a wide, heart-shaped transom, with the rudder hung outboard; and the stem is nearly straight and upright. The midsection shows a rising, straight floor, firm bilge, and upright topside.

The mast stands well abaft the stem; to it a single large, loose-footed dipping lug is fitted. The tack travels on an iron horse across the bow and the sheet travels on another iron horse across the stern (by belaying the sheet and tack to windward it was not necessary to dip the lug in making short tacks in confined waters).

Scale of the model, which represents a large boat of the type, is 1 inch to the foot, for a boat 40 feet 6 inches at gunwale, 12 feet 6 inches beam, 4 feet 9 inches moulded depth, 2 feet 9 inches draft at post, mast 45 feet heel to truck, and yard 38 feet 6 inches.

Given by U. S. Bureau of Fisheries.

LOUISIANA OYSTER SLOOP, about 1900
Builder's Half-Model, usnm 311188

Spectre

This model was employed in the construction of the sloop *Spectre* at Morgan City, Louisiana, about 1900, for the oyster fishery.

The half-model shows a centerboard sloop hull having a straight, upright stem rabbet, the keel rabbet straight forward but sweeping up aft to the bottom of a V-shaped raking transom. A small skeg is shown and the shoe of the keel is straight, with some drag. The entrance is short and rather sharp; the run is short and full in the buttocks. The midsection is formed with a rising floor, a hard round bilge, and nearly upright topside. The sides amidships are nearly straight fore-and-aft and in general the hull is full-ended and burdensome. The sheer is very great.

Scale of the model is apparently ¾ inch to the foot, for a boat measuring 36 feet moulded length at gunwale, 13 feet moulded beam, and about 5 feet moulded depth. Although for a much more burdensome vessel, this half-model resembles somewhat the old New York and Long Island Sound centerboard working sloops of 1845–1900, which had a single large jib, gaff-mainsail, and a long bowsprit.

Given by R. J. Terrebonne, Morgan City, Louisiana.

BILOXI CATBOAT, about 1911
Builder's Half-Model, usnm 311225

This model represents a centerboard catboat built by Anson Holley at Biloxi, Mississippi about 1911. These boats were used in the shrimp fishery to some extent before launches were employed. They carried the single gaff-sail of the cat rig and differed from pleasure catboats only in being more burdensome and having fuller ends. They usually had a cuddy forward.

The half-model shows a 24-foot centerboard catboat having moderate sheer, a rockered keel rabbet with skeg, producing a straight keel shoe with some drag, a raking flat transom, and a rather upright curved stem rabbet. The midsection has a rising straight floor, a hard turn of bilge, and upright topsides. The entrance is short and sharp; the run is rather full and short.

Scale of the model is ½ inch to the foot, for a boat measuring 24 feet moulded length at gunwale, 9 feet moulded beam, and about 2 feet 4 inches moulded depth.

Given by Anson Holley, shipbuilder, Biloxi, Mississippi.

FISHING SLOOP, about 1912
Builder's Half-Model, usnm 311237

Annie

The fishing sloop *Annie* was built from this half-model at Corpus Christi, Texas, about 1912 for the local fisheries.

The half-model shows a keel sloop of yacht-like form having a short, straight keel with some drag, a raking post, a long counter ending in a sharply raking V-shaped transom. The stem rabbet is curved and fairs into the keel rabbet well aft, giving a marked forward overhang. The entrance is sharp but short; the run is rather long and easy. The sheer is rather straight. The midsection shows a rising straight floor and a very slack bilge, with a shallow upright topside. The greatest beam is about at midlength.

Scale of the model is ½ inch to the foot; the model scales about 35 feet 9 inches length at rail, 11 feet moulded beam, and 5 feet 9 inches moulded depth.

Given by Gustaf T. Nelson, shipbuilder, Corpus Christi, Texas.

BILOXI SCHOONER-TYPE FISHING VESSEL, about 1932
Builder's Half-Model, usnm 311224

A power fishing boat was built from this half-model, about 1932, at Biloxi, Mississippi, by Anson Holley.

The half-model is of the proportions and general form of the centerboard schooners built earlier at Biloxi, but is slightly modified at the stem; the outline of the usual clipper bow rabbet is penciled on the back of the model, indicating the extent of the change from the old schooner form. It shows a vessel having a straight keel, a curved and rather upright stem rabbet, raking flat transom, a slightly hollow, sharp entrance and long flat run, moderate sheer, a straight side fore-and-aft amidships with greatest beam forward of midlength; the midsection shows a rising straight floor, hard turn of bilge, and an almost upright topside.

Scale of the model is ½ inch to the foot, to represent a vessel measuring about 60 feet 3 inches at gunwale or rail, 14 feet 6 inches moulded beam, and about 4 feet moulded depth.

Model given by Anson Holley, shipbuilder, Biloxi, Mississippi.

BILOXI FISHING LAUNCH, about 1900
BUILDER'S HALF-MODEL, USNM 311227

A fishing launch was built from this half-model about 1900 or earlier by Willy Nels Johnson at Biloxi, Mississippi. It may be the model from which the launch *Blue Ribbon* was built about 1895.

The half-model shows a narrow launch of the old type, having a straight and upright stem, keel rabbet straight forward and swept up aft to the fantail stern. Aft there is a skeg. The sheer is moderate; the entrance is long and sharp and the run rather short but well-formed; and the midsection shows a rising floor, a slack round bilge, and an upright topside. In general the form of this model resembles that of the old steam and naphtha launches of the 1890's.

Scale of model is probably ¾ inch to the foot, to produce a boat about 27 feet 6 inches moulded length at gunwale, 7 feet 4 inches moulded beam, and about 3 feet moulded depth.

Given by Jack Covacovich, shipbuilder, Biloxi, Mississippi.

BILOXI FISHING LAUNCH, 1912–14
BUILDER'S HALF-MODEL, USNM 311223

Six fishing launches were built from this model at Biloxi, Mississippi, by Anson Holley about 1912–14. The model is of a type of Gulf coast fishing launch much used in the local shrimp fishery.

The half-model shows a skeg-fitted hull, having a keel rabbet straight forward and swept up aft to the bottom of the transom, which is raking, flat, and wide. The straight keel shoe has some drag; the stem is straight and slightly raking; the entrance is short and sharp, and the run is also short but well-formed. The hull has a rather long straight side amidships, and the midsection shows a rising floor, a hard round bilge, and a nearly upright topside. The hull of such launches as represented by this model was relatively shoal; the boats were suited only for work in protected waters.

Scale of the model is ¾ inch to the foot, and it represents a launch about 29 feet 9 inches moulded length at gunwale, 8 feet 10 inches moulded beam, and drawing about 2 feet 4 inches at skeg.

Given by Anson Holley, shipbuilder. Biloxi, Mississippi.

BILOXI SHRIMP BOAT, 1905–10
BUILDER'S HALF-MODEL, USNM 311219

A launch for the shrimp fishery was built from this half-model at Biloxi, Mississippi, about 1905–10 by Anson Holley. The half-model is much damaged but represents a launch having rather straight sheer, the keel rabbet is nearly straight forward; but curves in a long sweep aft, where a skeg was to be fitted. The greatest depth of hull is well forward, the bow is long and sharp, and the run is straight and rather flat. The stem is curved at the rabbet and is rather upright; the transom is wide, flat, and raking.

Scale of the half-model is apparently ⅜ inch to the foot, producing a vessel about 29 feet 6 inches long and perhaps 9 feet 6 inches beam.

Model given by Anson Holley, shipbuilder, Biloxi, Mississippi.

BILOXI SHRIMP BOAT, 1912–14
BUILDER'S HALF-MODEL, USNM 311221

This half-model is of a shrimp boat, built at Biloxi, Mississippi, in 1912–14 by Anson Holley. She was designed for a relatively low-powered gasoline engine.

The half-model represents a shoal launch having slight sheer, a rockered keel rabbet (there is the suggestion of a built-in skeg aft to give reverse curves in the sections in the wake of the built-in skeg), a straight keel shoe with some drag, a slightly raking and almost straight stem rabbet, and a wide and sharply raking transom. The midsection shows a moderately rising floor, a quick turn of bilge, and a rather upright topside. The entrance is long and sharp and the run is well formed.

Scale of the model is ⅜ inch to the foot, for a boat measuring 36 feet 6 inches moulded length at gunwale, 9 feet 3 inches moulded beam, and about 4 feet moulded depth.

Given by Anson Holley, shipbuilder, Biloxi, Mississippi.

BILOXI SHRIMP BOAT, about 1915
BUILDER'S HALF-MODEL, USNM 311220

Twelve launches for the shrimp fishery were built from this model at Biloxi, Mississippi, before 1920 by Anson Holley.

The half-model represents a long, shallow launch having slight sheer, a cambered keel rabbet sweeping up aft and intended to be fitted with a skeg, a wide square stern raking slightly, and a rather upright curved stem rabbet. The entrance is sharp and rather long, the run long and straight in the buttocks. The greatest depth of hull is near the bow. The midsection shows a rising floor, rather hard bilge, and an upright topside. The bow is rather high and bold.

Scale of the model is ⅜ inch to the foot, for a boat measuring about 37 feet 4 inches moulded length at gunwale, 9 feet moulded beam, and about 3 feet draft at skeg.

Given by Anson Holley, shipbuilder, Biloxi, Mississippi.

BILOXI SHRIMP BOAT, 1920–22
BUILDER'S HALF-MODEL, USNM 311233

A launch for the shrimp fishery was built from this model at Biloxi, Mississippi, in 1920–22 by Henry Brasher.

The half-model shows a round-bottomed launch with its greatest depth well forward and having a sharp entrance and rather long and flat run, a straight upright stem rabbet, a vertical square stern with a broad transom, a cambered keel rabbet, to which a skeg is intended to be fitted aft, and little sheer. The midsection shows a slightly rising floor, hard bilge, and upright topside.

Scale of the model is ¾ inch to the foot, to produce a launch about 34 feet 2 inches moulded length at gunwale, 9 feet 8 inches moulded beam, and drawing about 3 feet at skeg.

Given by Henry Brasher, shipbuilder, Biloxi, Mississippi.

PASCAGOULA SHRIMP BOAT, 1925
BUILDER'S HALF-MODEL, USNM 311248

Lucille

The shrimp boat *Lucille* was built from this model at Pascagoula, Mississippi, in 1925 by Portevin Brothers. She was a gasoline-engine powered launch, with the cuddy in a small trunk cabin.

The half-model shows a launch-type hull having a wide square stern, a long run, a short sharp entrance, an upright curved stem, and a raking flat transom. The midsection shows a rising floor with a rather slack round bilge.

Scale of the model is ¾ inch to the foot; the launch was 38 feet long, 12 feet beam, and about 4 feet moulded depth.

Given by Portevin Brothers, boatbuilders, Pascagoula, Mississippi.

TEXAS COAST FISHING LAUNCH, about 1928–30
BUILDER'S HALF-MODEL, USNM 311251

A fishing launch was to be built from this model at Palacios, Texas, by Rowland Hicks about 1928–30, but was not laid down.

The half-model shows a launch-type hull to be fitted with skeg and straight shoe with some drag; the keel rabbet is straight forward and sweeps up aft to a fantail stern, the stem is nearly straight and upright, and the sheer is quite straight. The midsection shows a rising floor, slack round bilge, and flaring topsides. The entrance is sharp and the run rather full.

The model is on the scale of ⅜ inch to the foot, to represent a launch 38 feet moulded length at gunwale, 12 feet moulded beam, and about 6 feet depth of side.

Given by Rowland Hicks, boatbuilder, Palacios, Texas.

MOTOR FISHING BOAT, 1929
BUILDER'S HALF-MODEL, USNM 311251

This model is of a design for a fishing vessel proposed by Rowland Hicks, of Palacios, Texas, but never built.

The half-model shows a very full-ended and burdensome motor vessel having a fantail stern, straight sheer, keel rabbet straight forward and curved up aft to the stern (a small skeg is shown), stem nearly straight and upright, entrance short and full, as is the run. The midsection shows a rounding and rising floor, a very slack bilge, and a flaring topside. The greatest beam is forward of midlength.

Scale of the model is ¼ inch to the foot, for a vessel about 53 feet moulded length on deck, 21 feet moulded beam, and about 7 feet moulded depth.

Given by Rowland Hicks, boatbuilder, Palacios, Texas.

BILOXI TRAWL BOAT, 1930
BUILDER'S HALF-MODEL, USNM 311229

From this model a trawl boat was built in 1930 at Biloxi, Mississippi, by Jack Covacovich. Altogether, four boats were built from it.

The half-model is for a launch having an upright stem rabbet, upright flat transom, small sheer, and the keel rabbet straight forward but rising aft to the bottom of the transom and intended to be fitted with a skeg. The entrance is short but sharp, the run long and flat, the stern is wide, the greatest beam is well forward of midlength, and the midsection is formed with a rising floor, slack rounded bilge, and an upright topside.

Scale of the model is ½ inch to the foot, for a vessel 33 feet 3 inches moulded length, 10 feet 4 inches moulded beam, and about 5 feet moulded depth.

Given by Jack Covacovich, shipbuilder, Biloxi, Mississippi.

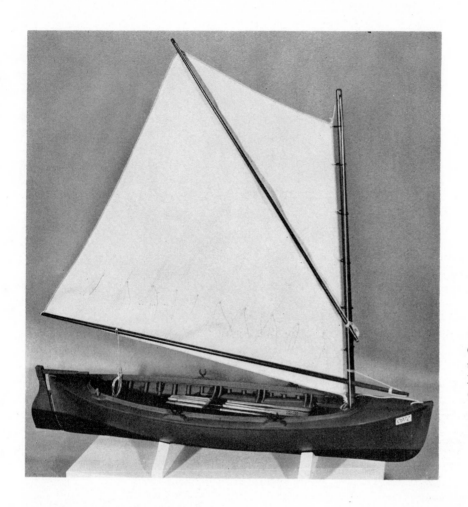

COLUMBIA RIVER SALMON BOAT of the type developed about 1885. Rigged model USNM 285033. (*Smithsonian photo 45606.*)

BILOXI FISHING LAUNCH, 1933–37
Builder's Half-Model, usnm 211230

Seacoast No. 1, Dr. Kulgis, Remma B.

A number of fishing launches were built at Biloxi, Mississippi, from this model by W. H. Bowen between 1933 and 1937. Among these were *Seacoast No. 1, Dr. Kulgis,* and *Remma B.* This class of fishing launch worked in sheltered waters.

The half-model shows a common type of fishing launch having a caravel-planked hull the keel rabbet in a long sweep, with a skeg fitted aft to give a straight keel having some drag, a raking curved stem, and a raking flat transom of marked width. The hull is rather wide and shoal; the midsection shows a rising straight floor, a hard turn of bilge, and a nearly upright topside. The entrance is short but sharp; the run is also short, with the dead rise amidships carried at a nearly constant angle to the transom. The sheer is marked.

Scale of the model is apparently ½ inch to the foot, to produce a launch 25 feet 3 inches long, 12 feet beam, and about 2 feet draft.

Given by W. H. Bowen, boatbuilder, Biloxi, Mississippi.

LOUISIANA PIROGUE, 1882
Rigged Model, usnm 55820

This type of canoe, or pirogue, was dug out of a single large cypress log and was usually rather boatlike in form.

The model represents an open log canoe having a sharp bow curved at the forefoot and nearly upright above, a sharp entrance and a short but easy run, a nearly upright heart-shaped transom, rather straight sheer and straight keel, and the midsection showing a nearly flat floor, round easy bilge, and flaring topside.

The model is fitted with two thwarts, stern sheets, and four oars. These canoes were rowed, paddled, or poled, and a few were sailed with a small spritsail; in these there was often a rather deep keel nailed to the bottom about amidships.

296

Scale of model is 2 inches to the foot, giving a length of 17 feet, beam 3 feet 1½ inches, depth inside 16 inches, and oars 6 feet 2 inches long.

Given by U. S. Bureau of Fisheries.

LOUISIANA PIROGUE, 1886
RIGGED MODEL, USNM 160353

This model, from Assumption Parish, Louisiana, is of the same type as the dugout canoe shown above. These craft were employed on the bayous, rivers, and along the protected coastal waters of Louisiana and neighboring States in the fisheries as well as for hunting and general transportation.

This model represents a vessel made from a cypress log shaped and hollowed to form a sharp-bowed open canoe having a narrow flat bottom, a round easy bilge, a flaring topside, a long, sharp, and slightly hollow entrance, an easy run, slight sheer, a straight keel, or bottom line, with the stem curved at forefoot and nearly straight and upright above, and the stern slightly raking and formed into a narrow V-shaped transom. The model, the appearance roughly that of a narrow Whitehall rowboat, is fitted with two sets of tholes on a side and a seat at each end, with risers shown for shifting the thwarts amidships.

Scale of model is 1 inch to the foot, for a vessel having a length of 17 feet 8 inches, beam 30 inches, and depth inside 11½ inches.

Given by U. S. Bureau of Fisheries.

LOUISIANA PIROGUE, 1946
FULL SIZE CRAFT, USNM 314923

A dugout (made of a single red-cypress log) of the type employed on the bayous of southern Louisiana, this craft is of the small, one-man, hunting and fishing type, and was built by Ebdon Allemand in 1946 as part of the Acadian Bicentennial Celebration. A motion picture film record was made of the construction of the canoe, showing the traditional methods employed in building pirogues.

The canoe is 12 feet long and 23 inches wide at gunwale and about 10 inches deep. It is double-ended, with rather straight sheer, bottom straight for most of its length, but rockered toward each end in the last 2½ feet. The bow and stern are curved in profile; the midsection is formed with a flat bottom, quick turn of bilge, and flaring topsides; and the entrance and run are nearly alike, sharp with slight hollow close to stem and stern. This canoe has thin sides and is light enough to be carried by one

man. It is fair and smooth and very well finished. With paddle.

From Esso Standard Oil Company, New York.

COLUMBIA RIVER SALMON BOAT, 1876
RIGGED MODEL, USNM 22216

This type of boat was introduced on the Pacific coast in 1868 for use of the gill-net fishermen at San Francisco, California. In 1869 one of these boats was sold to a fisherman for use on the lower Columbia River, and there the model was extensively copied. The early boats were 22 to 23 feet long but in the late 1880's the length reached 28 feet, which apparently became the standard. The type was also introduced into the British Columbian and Alaskan fisheries.

COLUMBIA RIVER SALMON BOATS, unrigged, about 1914. (*Smithsonian photo 46597–c.*)

The San Francisco boats usually had a leg-of-mutton sail, but elsewhere the spritsail was employed. All had centerboards and a single mast and sail.

The model shows a sharp-stern, caravel-planked, centerboard, sailing hull, having sharp entrance and run, the latter the finer of the two and both with hollow in the lower waterlines; full-ended at deck; strong sheer; straight keel; straight and rather upright sternpost; no rudder shown but one would normally be fitted to the upright curved stem; washboards along gunwales, with low coaming. The midsection shows a rising straight floor, low and rather hard bilge, and upright topside. The model is fitted to row, having three thwarts and three oars. A mast is stepped in a clamp well forward, and rigged with a single spritsail (on occasion a sprit boom was used).

Scale of model is 1 inch to the foot, giving a boat 25 feet 6 inches at gunwale, 6 feet 3 inches beam, 2

feet 3 inches deep amidships, 3 feet at ends, mast 16 feet 3 inches, spritsail 14 feet 6 inches, and oars 12 feet long. This was considered large for a boat of the type when she was built, 24 feet then being average.

Given by Livingston Stone.

COLUMBIA RIVER SALMON BOAT, 1885
RIGGED MODEL, USNM 285033

0.972

This model represents a Columbia River salmon boat of later date than that represented by USNM 22216, and shows the inboard arrangement of these boats in great detail.

The model is of a double-ended centerboard, half-decked boat rigged with one mast set in a clamp at the after end of the foredeck, a spritsail with sprit, and a sprit boom. The entrance and run are sharp and somewhat hollow, the sheer moderate, the keel straight and with slight drag, the stem and sternposts both rather upright and with heels rounded, the stem more so. The midsection is formed with a rising straight floor, rather easy turn of bilge, and flaring topside.

The boat is fitted with short bow and stern decks and a narrow washboard along each side. The coaming is carried around the boat and is rounded at bow and stern. There are three thwarts, with a "dividing board" just abaft the after thwart. The centerboard case extends from the forward to the aftermost thwart and is capped; the centerboard is raised and lowered by a jointed iron handle. On each side of the case, between the forward and middle, and middle and aftermost thwarts are fish holds with hatches at thwart level. The boat is fitted to row two pairs of oars and is steered with an outboard rudder and tiller. The painter leads through a navel hole in short foredeck; another navel hole is in the short after-deck. A fore-and-aft hole through the stem head serves as a fair leader, or hawse, for the bow painter.

Scale of model is 1 inch to the foot; the boat represented was 26 feet 5 inches overall, 7 feet 6 inches beam, 2 feet 9 inches deep amidships, 3 feet 9 inches

298

at bow, and 3 feet 10 inches at stern, centerboard about 6 feet 6 inches long, mast 22 feet 6 inches, sprit 22 feet, sprit boom 26 feet long.

The rigging shown in the model is that indicated in contemporary photographs and drawings.

Transferred from the Bureau of Fisheries. Restored by Merritt Edson, 1958.

SAN FRANCISCO ITALIAN FISHING BOAT, 1876
RIGGED MODEL, USNM 22213

This model represents a type of fishing boat employed at San Francisco by fishermen of Italian, Portuguese, and Greek extraction; the local name of the type was Dago boat but governmental reports on the boats refer to them as Feluccas. The type is now extinct. The boats were considered very fast and seaworthy and were employed for many years in the local market fishery. In confined waters they usually employed sweeps in place of sail.

The model shows a double-ended half-decked, caravel-planked sailing hull having a straight keel with slight drag, upright straight stem and sternpost, strong sheer, and sharp, hollow entrance and run, the latter the finer. The midsection shows a rising floor, hard bilge, and slightly flaring topside.

The deck is well crowned; there is a small high hatch abaft amidships and a small standing-room hatch aft for the helmsman. The boat carries a single lateen sail, and a jib rigged on a bowsprit. The mast rakes forward sharply.

Scale of model is ¾ inch to the foot representing a boat 26 feet 10 inches at gunwale, 9 feet 6 inches beam, 2 feet 6 inches depth, bowsprit 3 feet 4 inches outboard, mast 17 feet 8 inches above deck, and yard 32 feet 4 inches.

Given by Livingston Stone. Restored by Merritt Edson, 1958.

SAN FRANCISCO ITALIAN FISHING BOAT, 1876
RIGGED MODEL, USNM 22214

This is another boat of the type represented by rigged model USNM 22213. These boats ranged in size from about 18 feet to nearly 40 feet, the most common

SAN FRANCISCO FISHING BOAT of 1876, developed by local fishermen of Italian descent. Rigged model USNM 22214. (*Smithsonian photo 45606–b.*)

299

ITALIAN FISHING BOATS AT THEIR PIER IN SAN FRANCISCO, CALIFORNIA, IN THE LATE 1880's. (*Smithsonian photo 33142–b.*)

⟶

SAN FRANCISCO ITALIAN fishing boat sailing on the wind in the late 1880's. (*Smithsonian photo 33142–c.*)

size being in the range of 26 to 32 feet. The large boats went as far afield as Monterey, Drake's Bay, or the Farralone Islands. The boats were stiff and carried a press of sail; the fishermen were skilled handlers of the rig and sailed in an apparently reckless but actually safe manner.

The model represents a half-decked, double-ended, caravel-planked sailing hull having a straight keel with slight drag, upright straight post and stem, strong sheer, low bulwarks, high-crowned deck, sharp entrance with hollow at forefoot, sharp and very hollow run, and the midsection with rising straight floor, hard bilge, and rather upright topside.

The boat has a bowsprit, a long hatch amidships, and a steersman's standing-room hatch right aft. It is rigged with a single lateen sail and a small jib.

Scale of the model is ¾ inch to the foot, giving a boat 26 feet overall, 9 feet 3 inches beam, 2 feet 6 inches depth. This appears to have been an average size boat of the type.

Given by Livingston Stone. Restored by Merritt Edson, 1958.

SAN FRANCISCO ITALIAN FISHING BOAT, 1876
RIGGED MODEL, USNM 22215

This model is of a large double-ended, flush-deck boat of the same type as USNM 22213 and 22214, once employed at San Francisco.

The model shows a boat having easy sheer, straight keel, upright curved stem, upright post, sharp entrance hollow near forefoot, a fine, hollow run, and the midsection formed with a rising straight floor, high easy bilge, and slightly flaring topside.

The deck is heavily crowned, with low, flush bulwarks. Forward is a wooden horse for the fore tack of the lateen mainsail; this horse also secures the heel of the bowsprit, which is to starboard of the stem head. There is a very large hatch amidships and a small steering-room hatch right aft. The single mast is fitted with a large lateen sail. A jib is set to the bowsprit.

300

Scale of model is ¾ inch to the foot, representing a large boat of the type, about 37 feet 10 inches overall, 11 feet 6 inches beam, and 3 feet depth.

Given by Livingston Stone. Restored by Merritt Edson, 1958.

SAN FRANCISCO CHINESE SHRIMP BOAT, 1876
RIGGED MODEL, USNM 22217

This model of a boat in use in 1876, shows a type once used by Chinese fishermen on San Francisco Bay and vicinity, in California. Roughly and cheaply built, these boats were designed for easy beaching and were buoyant; they sailed well with the wind free but usually used oars to work to windward. The range in length was from 15 to 40 feet.

The boat represented by the model was a flat-bottom double-ended open sharpie with wedgelike ends, moderate flare amidships, strong fore-and-aft camber in the bottom near the ends but nearly straight amidships, and moderate sheer. There were platforms on the gunwale at each end and two thwarts. The craft was rigged with a lateen sail and one mast stepped about one-third the length from the bow. It was

steered with a sweep and was fitted to be rowed, sailed, or sculled. Some of these boats had a small keel nailed to the bottom amidships.

Scale of the model is 1⅞ inch to the foot; to measure about 39 feet overall, 7 feet beam, 3 feet depth, the model may be too narrow for the length.

Given by U. S. Bureau of Fisheries.

CHINESE DUGOUT CANOE, 1876
RIGGED MODEL, USNM 72744

This type of dugout canoe, once used by Chinese fishermen on the California and Oregon coasts in the alongshore fisheries, was intended to be poled and sculled not far from shore.

The canoes represented by this model were roughly made from a log dug out from end to end, the end transoms being nailed on. They had strong sheer and some rocker in the bottom, the latter flat athwartships for a short distance, and were round-bilged, with slightly flaring topsides. The sides, along which washboards were fitted, were straight in plan, and the bow and stern square and raking.

Scale of model is 1 inch to the foot, for a canoe 20

feet long, 3 feet 6 inches beam, and about 2 feet depth of side. The model is fitted with two sculls, single tholes with a becket, and one pole.

Given by U. S. Bureau of Fisheries.

WELL-SMACK SLOOP, 1894
RIGGED MODEL, USNM 76268

Sparrowhawk

This model was made from a design prepared in 1893–94 by Captain J. W. Collins for an improved well smack for use in the shore fisheries of the Pacific Coast. The purpose was to produce a swift and safe sloop of moderate size to bring live fish to market without the need of ice, which at the time was scarce and expensive in the fishing areas where the sloop was intended to be used. Such an improved smack, it was believed, would also prove useful in southern waters. In 1895 the sloop *Sparrowhawk* was built from this design, but without the well, by Lawrence Jensen at Gloucester, Massachusetts. Ballasted with iron inside and built for fishing, her speed attracted such attention that she was purchased and fitted as a yacht with ballast keel and additional sail. The attempt to introduce the well into small craft was not very successful in spite of the practical advantages, and relatively few American fishing boats, except in New England and on the Florida coast, have employed this fitting since 1885.

The model represents a keel sloop with strong and graceful sheer, long, sharp entrance, stem straight above the waterline and much curved below, the keel and rabbet much rockered and the outside deadwood quite deep, forefoot very shallow, raking post, high and light counter ending in a small V-shaped transom, and the run short but well formed. The greatest beam is abaft midlength. The midsection shows a steeply rising floor with slight hollow at the garboards, a very slack and easy bilge, and a flaring topside.

The well, of the usual truncated pyramid form, was amidships and there was a raised cuddy deck forward in the design (in the model the deck is flush), a companionway slide-hatch was placed just forward of the well hatch, then the well grating, hatch to hold, binnacle, and, well aft, a steersman's cockpit, or oval standing room.

The boat was steered with a tiller. The mainmast stood about one-third the overall length from the stem and the rig was that of a cutter but with fixed bowsprit, following the then fashion in American keel cutter yachts.

Scale of model is 1 inch to the foot. The smack was

34 feet 3 inches at gunwale (the design showed a log-rail forward and 1-foot bulwarks aft), load waterline was 28 feet 2½ inches, beam 10 feet 9¾ inches, depth 6 feet, extreme draft 5 feet ½ inch, fish well at bottom 8 feet long and 5 feet wide, well at deck 3 feet long and 2 feet wide. Mast from deck to hounds was 22 feet 9 inches, masthead 4 feet 6 inches, topmast heel to truck 22 feet, main boom 30 feet 6 inches, gaff 20 feet, and bowsprit outside face of stem 14 feet 6 inches.

Sails carried were gaff-mainsail with foot laced to boom, jackyard gaff-topsail with headyard 23 feet 6 inches long and foot boom 16 feet 6 inches long, forestaysail, jib, and jib topsail.

Smacks of this size would usually be manned by a crew of two, and boats of this type and model would have been very profitable in many areas.

Given by U. S. Bureau of Fisheries.

GREAT LAKES POUND-NET SHARPIE under sail, 1890. (*Smithsonian photo 44793-g.*)

LAKE ERIE POUND-NET SHARPIE, about 1876
RIGGED MODEL, USNM 26790

Sharpies of this type were once used in the pound-net fisheries on Lake Erie and later on Lake Huron. The model, developed before 1870, was employed in a variety of sizes and some variation in appearance. The boats ranged from 20 to about 42 feet on the gunwale and had the usual flat bottom and athwartships bottom-planking of the sharpie, with strong fore-and-aft rocker, flaring straight sides, long sharp entrance,

302

short but flat run, strong sheer, straight and raking stem, flat and raking transom with balanced rudder hung outboard.

The boats were open, but with a wide gunwale cap, and were fitted with two thwarts, the bow mast thwart and stern sheets usually connected to short side-seats at the fore ends of which was a pen board. The masts were in the usual sharpie position but the sails were battened at the head, so that they appeared to be gaff-sails with gaff-topsails in one, the battens being on each side of the sail and fastened through it. These sharpies were designed to carry heavy loads and had very large rigs, so were fast and powerful boats. An average boat was about 36 feet long, 10 feet beam, and 3 feet deep. The lifting of the bowl of the pounds required a very stiff boat, hence the marked beam of the pound-net sharpies generally.

The model is on a scale of 1 inch to the foot; the boat would be 24 feet 9 inches on the gunwales, 9 feet 6 inches beam, width of stern 7 feet, depth amidships about 3 feet, foremast 23 feet 3 inches, and mainmast 21 feet 6 inches. The boat represented is a sharpie built at Dover Bay, Ohio, where the sharpies were 20 to 26 feet long, 7 feet 9 inches to 9 feet 6 inches beam, and 28 inches to 36 inches deep; the model is thus somewhat wide in proportion to her length.

Given by J. W. Milner.

LAKE ERIE POUND-NET SHARPIE, about 1893
Rigged Model, usnm 76265

This model of a pound-net sharpie represents the type built at Green Bay, Ohio, in the 1880's for the local pound-net fisheries. An attempt was made, under the sponsorship of the Bureau of Fisheries, to introduce this model of sharpie into the North Carolina Sounds, but this was not very successful. Few boats of this model and rig were built there, though the model was cataloged as being from the Carolina Sounds.

The model shows a typical Lake Erie pound-net sharpie, having a flat, rockered bottom, straight raking stem, flat raking transom, flaring straight sides, strong sheer, wide stern, sharp entrance, and a short and flat run with good lift at the stern. The model is open, with thwarts and stern sheets, two masts, and pound-net boat rig.

Scale of model is 1 inch to the foot; the model scales 28 feet at gunwale, 9 feet 6 inches beam, 3 feet depth, foremast above thwart 27 feet 3 inches, and mainmast above thwart 25 feet 6 inches. The foresail is loose footed, the mainsail boomed. As a class the pound-net sharpies were very loftily rigged; the use of a boom on the foresail seems to have been a matter of individual owner preference.

Given by U. S. Bureau of Fisheries.

Maritime Materials in the Watercraft Collection of the United States National Museum

Historic American Merchant Marine Survey

A collection of ship and boat plans, photographs, and notes obtained by U. S. Works Progress Administration Project 6, in 1937. Plans are of varying quality, precision, completeness, and scale. A special catalog is obtainable from the Curator of Transportation.

Griffiths' Collection

Ship plans, some items of correspondence, half-models, patent drawings, and other material pertaining to work of the American ship-designer, John W. Griffiths, of New York. He designed a number of clipper ships, steamers, and other craft in the period 1842–70, and was senior editor of *The Monthly Nautical Magazine and Quarterly Review*, later as *United States Nautical Magazine and Naval Journal*, New York City 1854–57. No catalog of this material is at present available.

Ship Plan Files

Plans of a large number of sailing ships, American and foreign; small American sailing and power craft; steamships; and of some models in the Watercraft Collection. Includes plans from the collections of the author and of others. Plans are of varying completeness; many are suitable for model-building and for illustration.

Bibliography

ALBION, ROBERT GREENHALGH. *Square-riggers on schedule; the New York sailing packets to England, France, and the cotton ports.* Princeton University Press, 1938, pp. xii+371, illustr.

  Competent history of the New York packet trade in the North Atlantic; economic marine history illustrated by some reproductions of paintings of notable packet ships; a list of packets by Lines is given.

BOOLE, L. H. *The shipwright's handbook and draughtsman's guide.* Milwaukee, Burdick and Treyser, 1858, pp. 41, illustr.

  Description of all loft work required for merchant ships and use of the half-model. Introduction refers to the early use of the half-model at New York.

BREWINGTON, MARION V. *Chesapeake Bay log canoes.* Newport News, Virginia, The Mariner's Museum, 1937, 2 vols., illustr.

  History and study of the development of the type; illustrated with plans and photographs (vol. 2 contains plans).

————. *Chesapeake Bay bugeyes.* Newport News, Virginia, The Mariner's Museum, 1941, pp. x+117, illustr.

  A very complete study of the type, complete with photographs of these boats, with details, plans, and general history of development of the type.

BUTTS, I. R. *The merchant's and shipwright's manual and shipbuilder's and sailmaker's assistant.* Boston, I. R. Butts & Co., 1870 (ed. 4), illustr.

  Useful material on sparring of vessels, tonnage measurement and calculations.

CHAPELLE, HOWARD I. *The Baltimore clipper; its origin and development.* Salem, Massachusetts, Marine Research Society, 1930, pp. xii+192, illustr.

  History of the Baltimore clipper type, with plans of examples at various dates.

————. *The history of American sailing ships.* New York, W. W. Norton & Co., 1935, pp. xvii+400, illustr.

  Discussion of the design and development of American sailing vessels, with plans.

————. *Old American sailing craft.* New York, Kennedy Publishing Co., 1936 (ed. 2, New York, Crown Publishing Co., 1939), pp. xiii+239, illustr.

  Reprint of some articles by author that appeared in *Yachting Magazine*, 1932–35. Describes some types, with special reference to their use as yachts. Illustrated by plans.

————. *American small sailing craft, their design, development, and construction.* New York, W. W. Norton & Co., 1951, pp. xviii+363, illustr.

  Plans and descriptions of a large number of American commercial small sailing boat types under 45 feet in length, with some discussion of colonial craft and the history of the development of types of boats described.

CLARK, ARTHUR H. *The clipper ship era; an epitome of famous American and British clipper ships, their owners, builders, commanders, and crews, 1843–1869.* New York and London, G. P. Putnam's Sons, 1910, pp. xii+404, illustr.

A short history of the American clipper ship, with personal recollections and opinions.

CUTLER, CARL C. *Greyhounds of the sea; the story of the American clipper ship.* New York and London, G. P. Putnam's Sons, 1930, pp. xxvii+592, illustr.

Standard history of the American clipper ship, with some plans, a list of packets, some lines drawings, and extensive discussion of the ships, their builders, their design, and sailing records.

DAVIS, CHARLES G. *Ships of the past.* Salem, Massachusetts, The Marine Research Society, 1929, pp. xi+170, illustr.

Contains short and inaccurate history of the development of the New England fishing schooner and some useful information on individual schooners, including photographs, plans, and sketches of details. Plans of New England and Nova Scotian pinkies, New Orleans lugger, and Block Island boat.

EASTMAN, RALPH M. *Pilots and pilot boats of Boston Harbor.* Boston, Second Bank—State Street Trust Company, 1956, pp. x+89, illustr. (some in color).

Pictures of boats and a short account of Boston pilotage.

FAIRBURN, WILLIAM ARMSTRONG. *Merchant sail.* Center Lovell, Maine, Fairburn Marine Educational Foundation, Inc. (privately printed and distributed), 1954–55, 6 vols., no plans or illustr.

Deals with freighting ships, clipper ships, and down-Easters. Contains a list of packet ships and an extensive discussion of their design and records. Fairburn was naval architect for the Sewalls of Bath, Maine, at the end of the sailing ship period. He deals extensively with the little-recognized influences of economics on sailing ship design in the 19th century. Interesting and controversial evaluation of McKay and other clipper ship designers.

GOODE, GEORGE BROWN. *The fisheries and fishery industries of the United States.* Prepared through the cooperation of the commissioner of fisheries and the superintendent of the tenth Census. Washington, D. C., Government Printing Office, 1884–87, 2 vols. and atlas.

Describes various fisheries gear and boats, including many small American fishing craft, with many illustrations (the atlas contains all the plates, but few illustrations of small craft).

GRIFFITHS, JOHN W. *The shipbuilder's manual, and nautical referee.* New York, published by the author, 1853, 2 vols., illustr.

Material on design, construction, and masting.

————. *A treatise on marine and naval architecture, or theory and practice blended in shipbuilding.* London, George Philip & Son, 1857 (new ed.; ed. 1, 1851), pp. 200, illustr. (50 engravings).

Instructions on design by use of half-model; discussion of ship design and construction, steamship and sail, lines plans.

————. *The progressive ship builder.* New York, John W. Griffiths, 1875, 2 vols., illustr.

Ship design, lofting, construction and masting for steam and sail. (First issued in a limited series of pamphlets, later bound, by the Nautical Gazette Press, New York.)

HALL, HENRY. *Report on the shipbuilding industry of the United States.* In U. S. Census Office, 10th Census, 1880, census reports, vol. 8, Washington, D. C., Government Printing Office, 1884, pp. vi+276.

Usually called "Hall's Report on Shipbuilding" and bound as an independent publication, it is basically an economic report. It contains material on three- and four-masted coasters and some descriptions of smaller vessels; much interesting information of American small craft, but is poorly illustrated as far as these are concerned; lines and some sail plans of clipper ships of note; material on post-Civil-War steamers built before 1880, including some plans; records of some shipyards; and a discussion of the economics of the shipbuilding industry during the period of the down-Easters.

HOWE, OCTAVIUS T., and MATTHEWS, FREDERICK C. *American clipper ships, 1833–1858.* Salem, Massachusetts, The Marine Research Society, 1926–27, 2 vols., illustr.

Reproduction of paintings of clipper and alleged clipper ships, with short histories of the vessels.

KEMP, DIXON. *A manual of yacht and boat sailing.* London, Horace Cox, Field Office, 1884 (ed. 4), 1895 (ed. 8), illustr.

First published in 1878 and last revised in 1913 (ed. 11), the editions cited contain plans and descriptions of a Block Island boat, Bermuda sloop, and sharpies.

KUNHARDT, C. P. *Small yachts; their design and construction exemplified by the ruling types of modern practice.* New York, Forest and Stream Publishing Co., 1891 (new and enl. ed.; ed. 1, 1885), pp. v+369, illustr.

Plan of sharpie sloop and much accurate material on the New Haven sharpie, and on catboats, skiffs, and a round-stern bugeye.

LUBBOCK, BASIL. *The Western Ocean packets.* Glasgow, J. Brown & Son, Ltd., 1925, pp. xiii+155.

Reprint of magazine articles containing a popular history of some notable ships and illustrated with reproductions of paintings of some of them.

——————. *The down-Easters, American deepwater sailing ships, 1869–1929.* Glasgow, Brown, Son & Ferguson, Ltd., and Boston, C. E. Lauriat Co., 1929, pp. xv +280 (the American edition is in 2 vols.).

Profusely illustrated with photographs of down-Easters. The records of the individual ships are given.

M'KAY, L. *The practical shipbuilder: containing the best mechanical and philosophical principles for the construction of different classes of vessels, and the practical adaptation of their several parts, with the rules carefully detailed. The whole being plainly and comprehensively arranged for the instruction of the inexperienced.* New York, Collins Keese & Co., 1839, pp. 107, 7 plates.

First American book on ship design and lofting. Lines of freighting ship, brig, and schooner, and a description of design and construction in the pre-clipper period. Masting rules are given and useful information on contemporary ship-design practice.

McKAY, RICHARD C. *Some famous sailing ships and their builder, Donald McKay.* New York and London, G. P. Putnam's Sons, 1928, pp. xxviii+395, illustr.

Partisan account of Donald McKay and the ships he built.

MATTHEWS, FREDERICK C. *American merchant ships, 1850–1900.* Salem, Massachusetts, The Marine Research Society, 1930 (ser. 1), 1931 (ser. 2), 2 vols., illustr.

Contains reproductions of paintings and photographs of down-Easters, clippers, and freighting ships.

McFARLAND, RAYMOND. *A history of the New England fisheries, with maps.* Philadelphia, University of Pennsylvania, New York, D. Appleton & Co., agents, 1911, pp. v+457, 3 maps.

Emphasis on political and economic history, with a short account of the development of the vessels.

—————. *The masts of Gloucester; recollections of a fisherman.* New York, W. W. Norton & Co., Inc., 1937, pp. x+268, illustr.

Recollections of life aboard a fishing schooner at the turn of the century, with some description of individual vessels.

MORRIS, EDWARD PARMELEE. *The fore-and-aft rig in America.* New Haven, Connecticut, Yale University Press, 1927, pp. xx+215, pl.

The pioneering study of the rigs of American small commercial sailing craft and of schooner and other rigs in North America. Contains much material on colonial craft.

MORRISON, JOHN H. *History of American steam navigation.* New York, W. F. Sametz & Co., Inc., 1903, pp. iii+630, illustr.

A general history of the American steamship up to 1900. Not complete and nontechnical. Illustrated with fine sketches of notable steamers drawn from old paintings and prints.

PARKER, W. J. LEWIS, Lt., U. S. C. G. *The great coal schooners of New England, 1870–1909.* Mystic, Connecticut, The Marine Historical Association, Inc., 1948, pp. 135.

History and description of schooners in the coal trade illustrated by photographs of notable vessels and plans of a large five-masted coaster.

PIERCE, WESLEY GEORGE. *Goin' fishin'; the story of the deep-sea fisherman of New England.* Salem, Massachusetts, The Marine Research Society, 1934, pp. xiii+323, illustr.

Personal account of a fisherman, with some descriptions of vessels and an inaccurate history of their development.

Pilot lore from sail to steam and historical sketches of the various interests identified with the development of the world's greatest port. New York, The United New York and New Jersey Sandy Hook Pilots' Benevolent Society, 1922, xxiii+323, illustr.

Memorial to pilots, with some records of individual pilot boats and pilots.

PREBLE, GEORGE HENRY, R. Adm., U.S.N. *A chronological history of the origin and development of steam navigation.* Philadelphia, L. R. Hamersly & Co., 1883, pp. xix+484.

An attempt to recount the complete history of steam navigation up to 1880, but with many important omissions.

PROCTOR, GEORGE H. *The fishermen's memorial and record book.* Gloucester, Massachusetts, Procter Brothers, 1873, pp. iv+172, illustr.

A useful record of schooners lost and many recollections of old fishing vessels and events.

ROBINSON, JOHN, and DOW, GEORGE FRANCIS. *The sailing ships of New England, 1607–1907.* Salem, Massachusetts. The Marine Research Society, 1922 (ser. 1), pp. 66, illustr. (1924, ser. 2; 1928, ser. 3).

Reproductions of paintings and photographs of freighting ships.

RUSSELL, CHARLES EDWARD. *From Sandy Hook to 62°; being some account of the adventures, exploits, and services of the old New York pilotboat.* New York and London, The Century Co., 1929, pp. vi+400, illustr.

A journalist's recollections and stories of the New York pilots with a list of some of the losses of New York and New Jersey pilot schooners.

STARBUCK, ALEXANDER. *History of the American whale fishery, from its earliest inception to the year 1876.* Waltham, Massachusetts, published by the author, 1878, pp. i+768, 6 pls.

Contains material on whaling vessels.

STEVENSON, DAVID. *Sketch of the civil engineering of North America.* London, John Weale, 1838, pp. vii+320, illustr.

Lines and data on Hudson River and Long Island Sound steamers of the period.

STUART, CHARLES B. *The naval and mail steamers of the United States.* New York, Charles B. Norton, 1853 (ed. 2), pp. 216

Plan of a coastal steamer and pictures, engine, and boiler plans of notable naval and mail steamers.

TREDGOLD, THOMAS. *Tredgold on the steam engine, marine engines and boilers.* London, James S. Virtue, n.d., 2 vols., illustr.

Plans of Ohio River packet steamer, 1838.

TURNBULL, ARCHIBALD DOUGLAS. *John Stevens, an American record.* New York and London, The Century Co., 1928, pp. xvii+545, illustr.

Contains descriptions of Steven's experiments with steamboats, engines, and boilers, with much valuable detail.

UNITED STATES FISH COMMISSION. *Annual reports* and *Bulletins.* Washington, Government Printing Office, 1871–94.

Contain articles on fishing vessels and small craft.

UNITED STATES WORKS PROGRESS ADMINISTRATION, NATIONAL ARCHIVES PROJECT. *Ship registers and enrollments* (titles vary), varying places of publication, 1938–41.

Mimeographed volumes of Register enrollment information from the Customhouse records of many United States ports. Those consulted were: Portland, Maine; Portsmouth, New Hampshire; Barnstable, Boston, Dighton-Fall River, Gloucester, New Bedford, Plymouth, Massachusetts; Bristol, Newport, Providence, Rhode Island; New Orleans, Louisiana.

VARNEY, WILLIAM H. *Ship-builder's manual, or mould loft guide.* Three parts. New York, Thomas Homan, 1877, pp. viii+45, illustr. (8 pls.)

Only part 1 has been seen, and it is believed that the other parts were not published. Part 1 deals with loft-work, with details on laying down wooden steamers.

WEBB, WILLIAM HENRY. *Plans of wooden vessels selected as types from one hundred and fifty of various kinds . . . built by Wm. H. Webb, in the city of New York, from the year 1840 to the year 1869. . . .* New York, published by the author, n.d., 2 vols., illustr.

Plans of noted clipper ships built by the author, a leading American ship designer and builder of the clipper ship period.

Fore and Aft, Cleveland, Ohio (vol. 1, 1899?).

Plans and articles, small fishing craft.

Forest and Stream. New York (vols. 1–100, 1873–1930).

Plans of pleasure and hunting craft and information on small fishing boats (sail).

Marine Coast Fisherman, Camden, Maine (vol. 1, 1947).

Plans and articles, United States and Canadian fishing boats.

Nautical Research Journal, Nautical Research Guild, New York (vol. 1, 1949).

Plans and articles, American ships.

Rudder, New York (vol. 1, 1890; vols. 3–5 as *Rudder, Sail and Paddle*).

Plans and articles, small boats and pleasure craft; historical articles on the American fishing schooner.

Steamship Bill of Facts, Journal of the Steamship Historical Society of America, West Barrington, Rhode Island (vol. 1, 1944).

Material on steamship history and development.

The American Neptune, Salem, Massachusetts (vol. 1, 1941).

Marine research; articles on American small craft and ships, sail and steam.

United States Nautical Magazine and Naval Journal, New York, Griffiths and Bates (vols. 1–7, 1854–58; vols. 1–2 as *Monthly Nautical Magazine and Quarterly Review*.

Contains much technical data and some plans of clipper ships and trading vessels; material on contemporary steamers, with lines of a few vessels; articles on the form, design, and construction of coasters; plans and descriptions of a number of Great Lakes vessels; critical articles on specific ship designs.

Yachting, New York (vol. 1, 1907).

Plans of pleasure craft; articles on American small boat types; historical articles on American fishing schooners.

Index

(Italic numbers indicate illustrations.)

Bahama sponge-fishing schooner, 1883, descr. of rigged model, 286–287

Baird, George W., U.S.N. engineer, 238

Baird, Spencer Fullerton, Secretary of the Smithsonian Institution, 1878–1887, establishment of U.S. Fish Commission, 6

Baltic, Collins Line steamer, 114

Baltimore clipper, 40–47; appearance, 20; French purchases, 20–21; *Nonpareil*, 21; size, 22; brigantine, built by Flannigan and Persons, 23–*24*; changes in model, 23; *Ann McKim*, 24, 31; *United States*, 24; slavers, 25–26; *Vaquero*, 25, 26, 32; builders in France, 20–21; builders in Cuba, 26; comparison in speed with clipper ships, 32; shortcomings, 34. (*See* Baltimore clipper brig)

Baltimore clipper brig, descr. of half-model, *67–68*

Baltimore shipbuilding, 24–25

Barbadoes, American privateer ship of the Revolution, descr., 19–*20*

Barge, colonial, 16; lake cargo, 115; canal tug-barge, 148–*149*; coastal, 151

Bark, 4, *51*; *William Shroeder*, 60; *Edward Koppisch*, 61; *Saone*, 61–62; *Crusader*, 62; *Hesper*, 62; *Julia*, 62; *Albemarle*, 37, 62, *63*; *Gayhead*, 174

Barkentine, 45

Bateau, Chesapeake Bay—*See* Skipjack, Chesapeake Bay

Bath Iron Works, shipbuilder, 243

Batory, diesel-powered trans-Atlantic liner, descr. of rigged model, 143–144

Baxter, William, barge designer, 148–149

Bazaar, merchant ship, *50*

Beach, Eugene, model-builder, 273

Bear, steam whaler and sealer, U.S. Coast Guard vessel, 247

Beetle, James, boatbuilder, 264

Belle Franklin, fishing schooner, under construction, *225*

Belle of the West, clipper ship, 34

Belvidere, steam whaling ship, 247

Berbice, American privateer schooner, descr., 19

Bermuda schooners, descr., 22

Bermuda sloop, descr., 16–17; relation to Chesapeake Bay schooners, 19

Bertha Louise, 3-masted schooner, coaster, *43*

Bethlehem Steel Company, Shipbuilding Division, 148, 243–244

Biloxi catboat, descr. of half-model, 293

Biloxi fishing and freighting schooner, descr. of half-model, 234

Biloxi fishing launch, about 1900, descr. of half-model, 294

Biloxi fishing launch, 1912–14, descr. of half-model, 294

Biloxi fishing launch, 1933–37, descr. of half-model, 296; *Seacoast No. 1*, 296; *Dr. Kulgis*, 296; *Remma B.*, 296

Biloxi fishing schooner, descr. of half-models, 235; *H. E. Grumbel*, 235; *I. Heidenheim*, 235, *237*; *H. Golman*, 235; *Anna Eve*, 235; *F. B. Walker*, 236; *James Velich*, 236; *L. L. Colle*, 236

Biloxi freight boat-launch, descr. of half-model, 157–158

Biloxi schooner-type fishing vessel, about 1932, descr. of half-model, 293–294

Biloxi shrimp boat, 1905–10, descr. of half-model, 294

Biloxi shrimp boat, 1912–14, descr. of half-model, 294

Biloxi shrimp boat, about 1915, descr. of half-model, 294–295

Biloxi shrimp boat, 1920–22, descr. of half-model, 295

Biloxi trawl boat, 1930, descr. of half-model, 295

Bishop, John, shipbuilder, 215, 216, 221

Bishop, John and Hugh, shipbuilders, 206

Black Ball Line, packet service, 27

Blanchard Shipyard, Yarmouth, Maine, *39*

Block Island boat, 176; descr. of rigged model, 262–263; in harbor, *263*; *Thomas J. Lynch*, 262; *Vanderbilt*, 262

Block model, description, *11–12*; history, 11–12; age, 12; taking off, 12

Bloomer, 2-masted coasting schooner, *81*

Bloomfield, Maryland-built fishing schooner, 197

BOATBUILDERS: Adams, Edward H., 103, 105; Angelo, Stephen, 152; Beetle, James, 264; Bowen, W. H., 296; Brown, J., 251; Clasper, J. H., 102; Cornwall and Weston, 99; Corwin, M., 269; Cragin & Sheldon, 253; Cram, John, 159; Creef, Washington, 281; Ewing, John, 269; Fogarty, "Bat", 92, 94, 95, 157; Gannon, Patrick, 261; Hallet, Albert, 251; Harrison, James B., 275, 279; Hicks, Rowland, 295; Higgins and

Gifford, 260; Holley, Anson, 157, 293, 294, 295; Johnson, Frank, 257; Johnson, Samuel, 95, 151, 152, 158, 234; Johnson, John, 97, 98, 137, 236; Langdon, Charles W., 95, 157, 277; Lawley, George, & Son, 96, 156; Nash and Sons, 98; Nelson, Gustaf T., 152; Palmer, Otis, 95, 96, 158, 159, 270, 271; Paskalitis, Leo, 291; Portevin Brothers, 295; Price, James H., 275; Rushton, J. H., 100; Stoddard, T. D., 266; Tull, E. James, 274; Whitehurst & Rice, 283; Wilson, Herbert and Dennis, 257

Boatbuilding in English colonies, 14; timber in colonial, 16

Boat-canoes, colonial, descr., 15, 176

Booze, Thomas, shipbuilder, 25

Boston fishing cutter, descr. of rigged model, 261–262

"Boston Hookers," 261

"Boston model" of ship, 34

Bowen, W. H., boatbuilder, 296

Brasher, Henry, shipbuilder, 235

Break O'Day, fishing schooner, 200; sail plan, *201*

Breeze, Chesapeake Bay oyster schooner, descr. of half-model, 193

Brig, 26, 44, 48; *Spark*, 22; *Dove*, 63–64; *Powhatan*, 64–65; *Pocahontas*, 64–65; *Palos*, 65–66; *Salisbury*, 65; *Carthage*, 65; *Athens*, 65; *Corinth*, 65; *James Gray*, 65; *Nicholas*, 65; *James Caskie*, 65; *Ark*, 65; *Massachusetts*, 65; *Smith*, 65; *Tuttle*, 65; *Keying*, 65; *Chenamus*, 66–67. (*See* Baltimore clipper brig)

Brigantine, Spanish, descr., 14; Baltimore, built by Flannigan and Parsons, 23, *24*; West Indian traders, 38–39; Baltimore clipper, 40–47; coasting, 43–44; rig, 43, 44, 45; hull forms, 44; *San Blas*, 48; descr. of unnamed half-models, 64, 69; *Amethyst*, 66; *Watson*, 68; *Telula*, 68; *Iscarion*, 69; *Abby Watson*, 69; *Fredonia*, 70; *Anita Owen*, 70; *Hurricane Bird*, 70; *Alexander Kirkland*, 70–71; *George Latimer*, 70, 71; *Eva M. Johnson*, 71; *Mary E. Pennel*, 71; *Antelope*, 72; *Gazelle*, 72; *Minnie Smith*, 72; *J. W. Parker*, 72–73; fishing, 162; whaling, 175; *Viola*, 175

Briggs, Enos, shipbuilder, 8

"Brogan," 274

Brown, Adam and Noah, shipbuilders, 23

Brown, J., boatbuilder, 251

Brusstar Shipbuilding Company, ship-builders, 208–209
Bugeye—*See* Chesapeake Bay bugeye
Builder—*See* BOATBUILDERS, MODEL-BUILDERS, SHIPBUILDERS
Bulwarks, in half-models, 10
Bureau of Fisheries, U.S., 6
Burgess, Edward, naval architect, 170
Burnham, Daniel A., and Willard R., shipbuilders, 199, 208
Burnham, David, shipbuilder, 213
Burnham, Jeremiah, shipbuilder, 190, 197, 198, 200

C

C. C. Thompson, merchant ship, descr. of half-model, 59–60
C. Chase, Chesapeake Bay centerboard fishing schooner, descr. of half-model, *189*
Cactus, 3-masted coasting schooner, *87*
Calderon, screw cargo steamer, descr. of decorative half-model, 133–134
California (renamed *Uruguay*), passenger liner, descr. of rigged model, 143
Cambrai, U.S. Army transport—*See American Merchant*, 141
Camille, paddle-wheel fishing steamer, descr. of rigged model, *238*–239
Canada, ships, 46; builders, 46, 47; brigantines, schooners, 46; ship-builders, 46, 47; relation to American ships, 46; salt fish carriers, 47, *49*; clipper, last of, 47; ocean freight ship, *52*; merchant vessel, descr. of un-named half-model, 60; shipbuilder W. Powers, 60, 94; schooner-yacht, 94; chebacco boat, 165, 181; sharp-shooters, 168; racing, 172; dogbody, 182; Tancook whaler, 250
Canal tug, 119, 148; *Robert E. Stockton*, 119, 128–129; *William Baxter*, 148–*149*
Candelaria (1), 2-masted trading schooner, Puerto Rico, descr. of half-model, 83
Candelaria (2), 2-masted trading schooner, Puerto Rico, descr. of half-model, 83
Canoe, boat canoe, 15, 176; "pilot canoe," 50; *Sairey Gamp*, 100–101; *Capital*, 101; canvas-covered, 101; dugout, 176; Chesapeake Bay log canoe, 272; *Oyster Creek*, 272; Roa-

noke River, 280; Louisiana piroque, 296–297; Chinese dugout, 301–302
Canvasback, steam seine boat, 238
"Cape Cat," 266
Cape Cod oyster schooners, 176
Capital, wooden sailing-paddling cruis-ing canoe, descr. of full-sized canoe, 101
Car of Neptune, Fulton's third American steamboat, 112
Carrie E. Phillips, fishing schooner, 170, 226, 227
Carrie Louise, fishing schooner, 208
Carrie Price, Chesapeake Bay skipjack, descr. of rigged model, 275–276
Carter, C. P., and Company, ship-builders, *73*, 83, 84, 85
Carthage, brig, 65
Cat rig, 177
Cat-rigged sharpie, Florida oyster boat, 287
Catboat, *263*, *265*, 266; Biloxi, 293
Catch, descr. of colonial, 14, 15, 162; replacement, 162; rig, 162
Cedar Keys seine skiff, about 1890, descr. of rigged model, 288
Centennial, fishing schooner, 1876, deck layout, *209*
Centerboard, in coasters, 40; in fishing schooners, 176; in boat hulls, 177
Centerboard schooner, *C. Chase*, 189; *Mary Jones, Bloomfield*, 197; Chesa-peake Bay fishing schooner, 205, 217–218, 223; *G. W. Harrison*, 208; *City of Key West*, 223–224; *Anna M. Frome*, 233; *Nordic*, 234; fishing schooner, about 1900, 234; Biloxi fishing schooners, 235, 236
Centerboard sloop, descr. of half-models, 94, 95, 96; *Eclipse*, 94; *Mer-maid*, 94; *Pathfinder*, 95; *Ariel*, 96; *Minnezitka*, 96–97
Century of Progress, Florida sponge boat, 1931, descr. of rigged model, 290
Challenge, clipper ship, 7
Chancellor Livingston, side-wheel steamer, descr. of rigged model, 127–128
Chapelle, Howard I., ship plans, 303
Charmer, 2-masted packet schooner, descr. of half-model, *78*–79
Chasseur, Baltimore privateer, 22; yacht, 9, 88
Chebacco boat, ancestry, 16; origin, *164*; development, *164*; description, *164*, *165*, 166; size, 164; mooring, 164–165; arrangement, 164; dog-

body type, 164, *181*–*182*; construc-tion areas, 165; relation to pinky, 165; fare, 165–166; relation to Gaspe boats, 165; reconstruction, *179*; *Lion*, *179*–181
Chenamus, brig, descr. of half-model, 66–67
Chesapeake Bay bugeye, 55; schooner, descr. of unnamed rigged models, 272, *273*–274; *Lillie Sterling*, *274*–275; *Triumph*, 275
Chesapeake Bay bugeye schooner, 1860–85, descr. of rigged model, *272–273*
Chesapeake Bay bugeye schooner, 1865–75, descr. of rigged model, *273*–274
Chesapeake Bay centerboard fishing schooner, 1868, descr. of half-model, 205
Chesapeake Bay centerboard fishing schooner, 1880, descr. of half-model, 217–218
Chesapeake Bay centerboard fishing schooner, 1884, descr. of half-model, 223
Chesapeake Bay fishing launch, about 1912, descr. of half-model, 278–279
Chesapeake Bay fishing pungy, about 1885, descr. of half-model, 193–194
Chesapeake Bay fishing schooner, 1857–58, keel, pungy type, descr. of half-model, 197
Chesapeake Bay log canoe, about 1875, descr. of rigged model, 272; *Oyster Creek*, 272
Chesapeake Bay oyster schooners, 176
Chesapeake Bay skipjack—*See* Skip-jack, Chesapeake Bay
Chesapeake Bay V-bottom motor ves-sel, 1929, descr. of half-model, 279
Chinese-American craft, 301
Chinese dugout canoe, 1876, descr. of rigged model, 301–302
City of Ellsworth, 2-masted coasting and packet schooner, descr. of half-model, 81–82
City of Havana, schooner smack, descr. of half-model, 213; lines, *213*
City of Key West, centerboard sponge fishing schooner, descr. of rigged model, 223–224
City of Paris, trans-Atlantic liner—*See Philadelphia*, 139–140
Clara M. Littlefield, fishing schooner, *173*
Clasper, J. H., boatbuilder, 102

318

324

Stevens, John, steamboat designer, inventor, 109, 110, 112
Stevens, Robert L., model tester, 121, 123, 124, 125, 126, 127
Stevens' multitubular boiler and steam engine, descr., *123*, 124, *125*; screw propellor, descr. of replica, 124; twin-screw steamboat, descr. of rigged model, *123, 124, 125*
Stoddard, T. D., boatbuilder, 266
Storm, diesel trawler, *243;* descr. of rigged model, 244
Storm King, fishing schooner, smack, 188; schooner smack, descr. of rigged model, 209–210
Story, Arthur Dana, shipbuilder, 219
Story, Charles O., shipbuilder, 196, 197, 198
Story, Joseph, shipbuilder, 195, 201
Story, William, shipbuilder, 209
Stranger, fishing schooner, 232
Sunny South, clipper ship, 34, *35*, 37, 53; centerboard oyster schooner, descr. of half-model, 192
Surfboat, 1875, descr. of rigged model, 252–253
Surprise, clipper ship, 34
Susan Center, fishing schooner, half-model formerly identified as, 187
Susan P. Thurlow, 3-masted coasting schooner, descr. of half-model, 84
Swallowtail Packet Line, 27
Swan, Hunter, and Wigham Richardson, shipbuilders, 140
Swift, American privateer schooner of the Revolution, 19
Sylph, fishing schooner, 204; descr. of half-model, 201–202; descr. of rigged model, 202

T

Tancook whaler, descr. of half-model, 250
Tanker, standard American, Type 2–SE–A1 steamer, descr. of rigged model, 146
Tarr and James Shipyard, *217*
Tartar, fishing schooner, 232
Telula, brigantine, descr. of half-model, 68
Ten Eyck, James, professional sculler, 102; E. H., amateur sculler, 102
"Tern" schooners, 47
Terror, Key West sponge sloop, descr. of half-model, 284–285

Thetis, steam whaler and sealer, U.S. Coast Guard vessel, 247
Thomas A. Edison, stern-wheel river steamer, *136;* descr. of half-model, 137
Thomas E. Evans, fishing schooner, descr. of half-model, 203–204
Thomas E. Moran, harbor tug, descr. of rigged model, *153*
Thomas Howard, pilot schooner, descr. of half-model, 90–91
Thomas J. Lynch, Block Island boat, loss of, 262
Thomas W. Lawson, only 7-masted coasting schooner, 42
Thomas Whalen, diesel trawler, descr. of half-model, 244
Thompson, James & George, shipbuilders, 139
Three-masted coasting schooner—*See* Coasting schooner
Three-masted fishing schooner, 170; descr. of half-model, 212; descr. of rigged model, 220–221
Tiger, pinky fishing schooner, 183–184
Timber, employed in colonial shipbuilding and boatbuilding, 16
Tobey and Littlefield, shipbuilders, 130
Tools, for model building, 10; colonial ship and boat building, 16
Travers Spicer, Maryland-built centerboard schooner, 205
Trawler, introduction of steam, 172–174; *Spray*, 174; *Sylph*, 201–202; *Resolute*, 228–229; *Shawmut*, 243–244; *Trimount*, 243–244; *William J. O'Brien*, 243–244; *Dorchester*, 244; *Amherst*, 244; *Cornell*, 244; *Thomas Whalen*, 244; *Atlantic*, 244; *Plymouth*, 244; *Storm*, 243, 244; *Wild Duck*, 244; *Pocahontas*, 244; *Clipper*, 244; *Albatross*, 249–250
Trenton, pinky fishing schooner, 1840, descr. of half-model, 187
Trimount, diesel trawler, descr. of half-model, 243–244
Trio, European steam launch, descr. of rigged model, 155
Triumph, Chesapeake Bay bugeye, descr. of half-model, 275
Tug, development, 119; harbor, 119; *Robert F. Stockton*, 128–129; canal, 128–129, 148–149; *William Baxter*, 148–149; *Atlantic*, 149; seagoing, 149, 150–151, 154; *Rattler*, 150; *Conestoga*, 150–151; descr. of unnamed half-models, 151–152; *Maria*, 152; *Thomas*

E. Moran, 152; descr. of unnamed rigged model, *154*
Tull, E. James, boat and shipbuilder, 274
Turner, Matthew, shipbuilder, 240
Tuttle, brig, 65
Two-masted schooner—*See* Coasting schooner, Fishing schooner

U

Uneeda, sternwheel wooden river steamer, descr. of half-model, 137
United States, early clipper ship, 24; steamship, 114
Universe, packet ship, descr. of half-model, 57
Uruguay (ex *California*), passenger liner, descr. of rigged model, 143
U. S. Grant, 130, 247
U.S. Bureau of Fisheries, 6
U.S. Fish Commission, 3; establishment, 6; changes in name, 6; Collins, 169–170; smack, 170
U.S. Lightship 82, descr. of half-model, 138–139
U.S. Lightship 89, descr. of half-model, 139
U.S. Lightship 98, descr. of half-model, 139
U.S. Lightship 99, descr. of half-model, 139
U.S. Maritime Commission, 4
U.S. Shipping Board, Emergency Fleet Corporation, 141–142

V

V-bottom, in New Jersey motor garvey, 160; sailing-fishing boats, 177; motor fishing boats, 178; fishing schooner, descr. of half-models, 236, 290; half-skipjack, 265–266
Vaquero, Baltimore clipper schooner packet, 25–*26;* dimensions, 25; record run, 25, 32; lines, *26*
Vandalia, screw steamer, 115
Vanderbilt, "Commodore" W. K., shipowner, 114
Vanderbilt, steamer, 114, 115; Block Island boat, loss of, 262
Vesuvius, river steamboat, 116
Victory Ship, standard American cargo steamer, descr. of rigged model, 146, *147*, 148